Holt Algebra 2

Chapter Resources
Volume 1

HOLT McDOUGAL
a division of Houghton Mifflin Harcourt

Contents

Description of Contents

Family Letter

A two-page letter is provided for each chapter in both English and Spanish. The letter describes some of the math concepts covered in the chapter. A list of key vocabulary words from the chapter is included, and some worked-out examples are provided.

Practice A, B, and C

There are three practice worksheets for every lesson. All of these reinforce the content of the lesson. Practice B is shown with answers in the Teacher's Edition and is appropriate for the on-level student. It is also available as a workbook (Practice Workbook)

Practice A is easier than Practice B but still practices the content of the lesson. Practice C is more challenging than Practice B.

Reteach

The Reteach worksheet (one per lesson) provides an alternate way to teach or review the main concepts of the lesson. This worksheet is two pages long and the first page with answers is shown in the Teacher's Edition.

Challenge

The Challenge worksheet (one per lesson) enhances critical thinking skills and extends the lesson. This worksheet is shown with answers in the Teacher's Edition.

Problem Solving

The Problem Solving worksheet (one per lesson) provides practice in problem solving and opportunities for real-world applications and for interdisciplinary connections. There are both multiple choice and short response problems. This worksheet is shown in the Teacher's Edition.

Reading Strategies

The Reading Strategies worksheet (one per lesson) provides tools to help the student master math vocabulary or symbols. This worksheet is shown with answers in the Teacher's Edition.

Holt Algebra 2

Date _____

Dear Family,

In this chapter, your child will classify real numbers and use their properties, will simplify numeric expressions with squares and square roots, will simplify algebraic expressions, and will learn about functions.

Real numbers can be classified as follows.

Natural Numbers	Also called the counting numbers: 1, 2, 3, ...
Whole Numbers	The natural numbers and zero: 0, 1, 2, 3, ...
Integers	The whole numbers and their opposites: ..., −3, −2, −1, 0, 1, 2, 3, ...
Rational Numbers	The integers, and fractions and decimals whose decimal forms either terminate (2.5) or repeat (1.666...)
Irrational Numbers	Fractions and decimals whose decimal forms do not terminate or repeat, including numbers such as π and $\sqrt{7}$

The **additive identity** is 0 because any number plus 0 results in that number.

The **multiplicative identity** is 1 because any number times 1 results in that number.

An inverse yields the identity for that operation when that operation is performed.

The **additive inverse** of 6 is −6 because $6 + (-6) = 0$.

The **multiplicative inverse** of 2 is $\frac{1}{2}$ because $2 \cdot \frac{1}{2} = 1$.

Expressions can include squares and square roots. Knowing these properties will make simplifying expressions easier.

Property	Example
Product Property of Square Roots	$\sqrt{4 \cdot 3} = \sqrt{4} \cdot \sqrt{3}$
Quotient Property of Square Roots	$\sqrt{\dfrac{4}{16}} = \dfrac{\sqrt{4}}{\sqrt{16}}$
Zero Exponent Property	$12^0 = 1$
Negative Exponent Property	$\left(\dfrac{2}{3}\right)^{-2} = \left(\dfrac{3}{2}\right)^2$
Product of Powers Property	$4^3 \cdot 4^2 = 4^{3+2}$
Quotient of Powers Property	$\dfrac{3^7}{3^2} = 3^{7-2}$
Power of a Power Property	$(4^3)^2 = (4)^{3 \cdot 2}$
Power of a Product Property	$(3 \cdot 4)^2 = 3^2 \cdot 4^2$
Power of a Quotient Property	$\left(\dfrac{3}{5}\right)^2 = \dfrac{3^2}{5^2}$

Holt Algebra 2

Students will also learn about relations. A **relation** is a pairing of input and output values. The set of input values is called the **domain** and the set of output values is called the **range**. Relations can be represented as a set of ordered pairs, as a mapping diagram, or as a graph.

Ordered Pairs	**Mapping Diagram**	**Graph**
{(2, 5), (3, 6), (5, 8)}	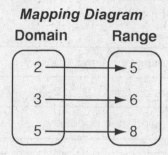	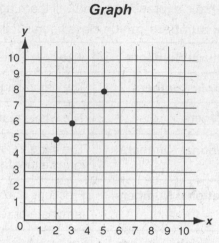

A relation is a **function** if there is only one output for each input. The relation shown above is a function. It has only 3 ordered pairs. Some functions have an infinite number of ordered pairs. These functions can be described by equations.

A function where each output value is 5 less than each input value can be written in either of the following ways.

$y = x - 5$	input: x	output: y
$f(x) = x - 5$	input: x	output: $f(x)$

The second equation is written in **function notation**. The graph of $f(x) = x - 5$ is a line.

Five function families will be explored. The following are the **parent functions**, the simplest of each type of function.

constant	linear	quadratic	cubic	square root
$f(x) = c$	$f(x) = x$	$f(x) = x^2$	$f(x) = x^3$	$f(x) = \sqrt{x}$
![constant graph]	![linear graph]	![quadratic graph]	![cubic graph]	![square root graph]

Many functions are **transformations** of these parent functions. Transformations are translations (slides), reflections (flips), stretches (pulls), and compressions (pushes).

For additional resources, visit go.hrw.com and enter the keyword MB7 Parent.

Holt Algebra 2

LESSON 1-1 Practice A
Sets of Numbers

Order the given numbers from least to greatest.

1. $-2.6,\ 2\sqrt{7}\ ,\ \dfrac{3}{4},\ 1.\overline{8}$

    a. Rewrite each number as a decimal.

        $2\sqrt{7} \approx$ _____ $\dfrac{3}{4} =$ _____

    b. Order the decimals. _____

    c. Order the original numbers. _____

Order the given numbers from least to greatest.

2. $2.8,\ \sqrt{10},\ \dfrac{2}{11},\ \dfrac{9}{7}$

    _____

3. $-\sqrt{2},\ \dfrac{1}{8},\ -5.916,\ \dfrac{-6}{11}$

    _____

4. $\dfrac{-7}{5},\ \sqrt{23},\ \dfrac{-\pi}{4},\ 3.\overline{14}$

    _____

5. $-6\dfrac{1}{8},\ 6.159,\ \pi,\ -6.5$

    _____

**Classify each number. Write all classifications that apply:
real, rational, integer, whole, natural.**

6. $4.3\overline{57}$ _____

7. $\dfrac{7}{4}$ _____

8. -6 _____

Rewrite each set using the notation indicated.

9. $(-6, -4]$; set-builder notation   _____

10. $4 \le x < 6$; words   _____

     _____

11. $\{x \mid x \ge 10\}$; interval notation   _____

12.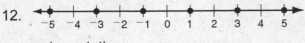

    roster notation   _____

     Holt Algebra 2

LESSON
1-1
Practice B
Sets of Numbers

Order the given numbers from least to greatest. Then classify each number by the subsets of the real numbers to which it belongs.

1. $\dfrac{2}{3}, 6.1\overline{7}, \sqrt{28}, -3\dfrac{1}{8}, -4.9$

_____

_____

2. $5\pi, -6\sqrt{3}, \dfrac{-8}{3}, 4.\overline{615}, 0$

_____

_____

Rewrite each set in the indicated notation.

3. negative multiples of 3; set-builder notation

_____

4. [–4, 0) or (10, 21); words

_____

_____

_____

_____

5.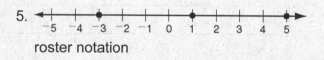

roster notation

_____

6.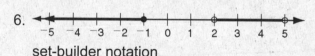

set-builder notation

_____

The length of a necktie is generally in the range [52, 58] inches. The width of a tie is in the range [2.75, 3.5] inches. Use this information for Exercises 7–8.

7. Represent the range of the length of neckties in roster notation. Assume that all neckties come in whole-inch lengths.

_____

8. Represent the range of the width of neckties in set-builder notation.

_____

LESSON 1-1

Practice C

Sets of Numbers

Use the table for Exercises 1–5.

Density of Some Minerals	
Mineral	**Density (g/cm³)**
Aluminite	1.68
Cryptohalite	$2\frac{1}{100}$
Fluorannite	$3\frac{7}{40}$
Graphite	2.16
Titanium	$4\frac{2}{5}$
Ziesite	3.86

1. Order the densities of the minerals from least to greatest.

   _____

2. Which subset of real numbers best describes the densities of these minerals?

   _____

3. Explain why the densities cannot be represented using set-builder notation.

   _____

   _____

4. Use interval notation to describe a set of numbers that contains the densities of the minerals.

   _____

5. What types of real numbers are NOT shown in the table?

   _____

Tell whether each statement is true or false. If false, give a counterexample.

6. All real numbers are rational numbers.

   _____

7. Every member of the interval (0, 8] is a natural number.

   _____

Solve.

8. Use interval notation to express the set of numbers NOT represented on the number line.

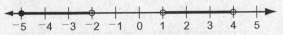

   _____

9. Identify one rational number and one irrational number that are members of the interval (−8, 8).

   _____

Holt Algebra 2

**LESSON
1-1**

Reteach

Sets of Numbers

As you move from left to right on a number line, the numbers increase.
Use a number line to help you order real numbers.

Order from least to greatest:

$$\sqrt{11},\, -2.\overline{6},\, \frac{1}{2},\, -\frac{\pi}{2},\, 2.354.$$

Use a calculator to approximate $\sqrt{11}$ and $-\dfrac{\pi}{2}$ as decimals:

$$\sqrt{11} \approx 3.32 \text{ and } -\frac{\pi}{2} \approx -1.57.$$

Plot each point on a number line.

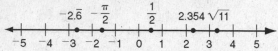

Read the numbers from left to right on the number line.

From least to greatest, the order is $-2.\overline{6},\, -\dfrac{\pi}{2}, \dfrac{1}{2},\, 2.354,\, \sqrt{11}.$

**Order the given numbers from least to greatest. Use a number line to
help you.**

1. $\pi,\, -1.\overline{9},\, 2\dfrac{2}{3},\, -0.456,$ and $\sqrt{3}$

   $\pi \approx 3.14,\ 2\dfrac{2}{3} \approx 2.67,$ and $\sqrt{3} \approx 1.73$

   _____

   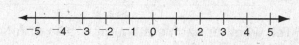

2. $-1.75,\, 1,\, \dfrac{1}{5},\, 1.55,$ and $-\sqrt{5}$

   $\dfrac{1}{5} = $ _____

   $-\sqrt{5} \approx $ _____

   _____

   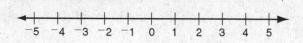

3. $\sqrt{6},\, -2.\overline{63},\, -4.36,\, 2\sqrt{3},$ and $-\dfrac{1}{6}$

   $\sqrt{6} \approx $ _____

   $2\sqrt{3} \approx $ _____

   $-\dfrac{1}{6} \approx $ _____

   _____

   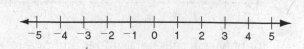

Holt Algebra 2

Reteach

Sets of Numbers (continued)

You can represent the same set in different ways.

Number line:

Words: The set of numbers greater than or equal to –2 and less than 0
OR greater than or equal to 1

> ∞ means infinity and
> –∞ means negative infinity.

Interval Notation: [–2, 0) or [1, ∞)

> Brackets [ ] include the endpoints.
> Parentheses ( ) do not include endpoints.

Set-Builder Notation: $\{x \mid -2 \le x < 0 \text{ or } x \ge 1\}$

> Read this as "*x* such that"

This set cannot be described in **roster notation** because you cannot list
the **real** numbers in the intervals shown on the number line.

The roster notation of $\mathbb{N}$, the set of natural numbers, is {1, 2, 3, ...}.

The set-builder notation of $\mathbb{N}$ is $\{x \mid x \in \mathbb{N}\}$.

Rewrite each set using the indicated notation.

4. the set of integers, or $\mathbb{Z}$; roster notation {..., –3, –2, _____}

5. {0, 4, 8, 12, 16, ...}; words   _____

6. $-5 \le x \le 12$; interval notation   [_____

7. $\{x \mid x < 0\}$; interval notation   (–∞ _____

8.
```
  ─┼──○──┼──┼──┼──┼──┼──●──┼──┼──→
  -2  -1  0  1  2  3  4  5  6  7  8
```

set-builder notation $\{x \mid$ _____

LESSON 1-1

Challenge
Sets and Subsets

The set $A = \{2, 4, 6, 8\}$ is a subset of the even natural numbers. Each element of set A is an even natural number. The set $B = \{2, 3, 4, 5, 6\}$ is not a subset of the even natural numbers. Set B contains the odd numbers 3 and 5 which are not in the set of even natural numbers.

Consider the empty set $\varnothing$ which can also be written as { }. It is the set with no elements. Is $\varnothing$ a subset of the even natural numbers as well? If yes, then every element in $\varnothing$ must be an even natural number.

If no, then there must be an element in this set that is not an even natural number. Since there are no elements in $\varnothing$ that are not even natural numbers, $\varnothing$ must be a subset of the set of even natural numbers.

For Exercises 1–4 it may help to list all the subsets.

1. How many subsets does set $E = \{5\}$ have? _____

2. How many subsets does set $F = \{5, 10\}$ have? _____

3. How many subsets does set $G = \{5, 10, 15\}$ have? _____

4. How many subsets does set $H = \{5, 10, 15, 20\}$ have? _____

5. What pattern do you see developing in the number of subsets for each set?

   _____

6. How many subsets are there for a set of 8 elements? Explain your reasoning.

   _____

7. How many subsets would there be for a set of n elements? _____

Set T has 5 elements.

8. How many subsets of set T have 5 elements? _____

9. How many subsets of set T have 4 elements? _____

10. How many subsets of set T have 3 elements? _____

11. How many subsets of set T have 2 elements? _____

12. How many subsets of set T have 1 element? _____

13. How many subsets of set T have 0 elements? _____

14. Where have you seen this sequence of numbers before?

   _____

LESSON 1-1

Problem Solving
Sets of Numbers

Ari is comparing the density of some common substances. Density measures how compact a substance is. Use the data in the table for Exercises 1–3.

Substance	Density (kg/m³)
Air	$1\frac{3}{10}$
Copper	8.9
Helium	$\frac{9}{50}$
Hydrogen	0.09
Milk	1030
Olive oil	900

1. Ari begins by ordering the densities from least to greatest. Write his ordered list.

   _____

2. Should Ari use roster, interval, or set-builder notation to represent his data? Why?

   _____

   _____

3. Which subset of the real numbers best describes the densities given in the table? Choose from $\mathbb{R}$, $\mathbb{Q}$, $\mathbb{Z}$, and $\mathbb{N}$.

   _____

   _____

Choose the letter for the best answer.

4. Jean wrote the possible readings on the speedometer of her new car in set-builder notation. Which could be what she wrote?

   A $\{x \mid 0 > x > 120\}$

   B $\{x \mid x = 10n \text{ and } n \le 12\}$

   C $\{10, 20, 30, 40, 50, \dots, 120\}$

   D $\{x \mid 0 \le x \le 120\}$

5. Members of the Booster Club are designing a calendar of the school year to sell as a fund raiser. They begin by making a roster of the possible number of days in a month. Which shows the roster?

   F $\{30, 31\}$

   G $\{x \mid 28 \le x \le 31\}$

   H $\{28, 29, 30, 31\}$

   J $\{x \mid x \ge 28 \text{ and } x \in \mathbb{N}\}$

Tell whether each statement is true or false. If false, give a counterexample.

6. Trish and Alex are comparing the populations of different cities in Texas. Alex says the population of a city is always an integer.

   _____

   _____

   _____

7. Neil and Sandy are cutting out circles as decorations. Sandy comments that the distance around a circle is always a rational number.

   _____

   _____

   _____

LESSON 1-1

Reading Strategies
Understand Symbols

There are many different ways to represent the same interval.

Representing Intervals				
Number Line	**Inequality**	**Interval Notation**	**Set-Builder Notation**	**Words**
(number line: open circle at 2, shaded right) $-5\ -4\ -3\ -2\ -1\ 0\ 1\ 2\ 3\ 4\ 5$	$x > 2$	$(2, \infty)$	$\{x \mid x > 2\}$	Numbers greater than 2
(number line: closed dot at 2, shaded left) $-5\ -4\ -3\ -2\ -1\ 0\ 1\ 2\ 3\ 4\ 5$	$x \le 2$	$(-\infty, 2]$	$\{x \mid x \le 2\}$	Numbers less than or equal to 2
(number line: open circle at 2, shaded both ways) $-5\ -4\ -3\ -2\ -1\ 0\ 1\ 2\ 3\ 4\ 5$	$x \ne 2$	$(-\infty, 2)$ OR $(2, \infty)$	$\{x \mid x \ne 2$ and $x \in \mathbb{R}\}$	All real numbers except 2
(number line: open circles at −1 and 1, shaded between; closed dots 3 to 4) $-5\ -4\ -3\ -2\ -1\ 0\ 1\ 2\ 3\ 4\ 5$	$-1 < x < 1$ OR $3 \le x \le 4$	$(-1, 1)$ OR $[3, 4]$	$\{x \mid$ $-1 < x < 1$ OR $3 \le x \le 4\}$	Numbers between −1 and 1 or from 3 to 4

Brackets [ ] include the endpoints.
Parentheses ( ) do not include endpoints.

Use words to describe each interval.

1. $\{x \mid x \ge -3\}$

_____

2. $(-6, 4)$

_____

3. $(\infty, -1]$

_____

4. $\{x \mid x \ne 0$ and $x \in \mathbb{R}\}$

_____

5. $[-10, -5]$ OR $[-2, \infty)$

_____

LESSON 1-2

Practice A

Properties of Real Numbers

Find the additive inverse of each number.

1. –5

$$-5 + \underline{\hspace{2cm}} = 0$$

2. 6.1

$$6.1 + \underline{\hspace{2cm}} = 0$$

3. $\dfrac{1}{2}$

$$\dfrac{1}{2} + \underline{\hspace{2cm}} = 0$$

Find the multiplicative inverse of each number.

4. 11

$$11 \cdot \underline{\hspace{2cm}} = 1$$

5. 3.5

$$3.5 \cdot \underline{\hspace{2cm}} = 1$$

6. $\dfrac{-2}{3}$

$$\dfrac{-2}{3} \cdot \underline{\hspace{2cm}} = 1$$

Complete each number sentence. Make each statement true.

7. $5(7 + 2) = 5(7) + 5(\underline{\hspace{2cm}})$

8. $(-4 + 6) - 3 = \underline{\hspace{2cm}} + (6 - 3)$

Identify the property demonstrated by each equation.

9. $7x = x \cdot 7$

10. $c(3 + 5) = 3c + 5c$

_____

11. $(4 + y) + 1 = 4 + (y + 1)$

12. $0 = y + (-y)$

_____

Use the table for Exercises 11–14. Use properties and mental math to help you find each cost.

The Outfit Outlet	
Jeans	$23.50
T-shirt	$9.95
Hat	$6.75

13. cost of a T-shirt and a hat _____

14. cost of 2 T-shirts and a pair of jeans _____

15. cost of a pair of jeans at a 20% discount _____

16. total cost of one of each item _____

Determine if each statement is sometimes, always, or never true. Give an example or property to support your answer.

17. $a + b + c = 3c$ _____

18. $4x \cdot 6 = 6x \cdot 4$ _____

19. $z + (-z) = 5$ _____

Practice B

Properties of Real Numbers

Find the additive and multiplicative inverse of each number.

1. -6

2. $3\frac{1}{4}$

3. -0.7

_____   _____   _____

Identify the property demonstrated by each equation.

4. $x(a - b) = ax - bx$

5. $m + (n + 6) = (n + 6) + m$

_____   _____

6. $4(gh) = (4g)h$

7. $\dfrac{-\sqrt{5}}{w} \cdot \dfrac{w}{-\sqrt{5}} = 1$

_____   _____

Use mental math to find each value.

8. 5% rebate on a $150 cell phone

9. cost of 8 items at $12.98 each

_____   _____

Classify each statement as sometimes, always, or never true. Give examples or properties to support your answer.

10. $d + (-d) = 0$

11. $a + (bc) = (a + b) \cdot (a + c)$

_____   _____

Use the table for Exercises 12–14. Write an expression to represent each total cost and then simplify it.

12. cost of 2 pens and 3 notebooks

_____

13. cost of 1 binder and 5 notebooks

_____

14. cost of 3 notebooks at 20% discount, a binder at 25% discount, and 2 pens

_____

School Supply Store	
Item	**Price**
Notebook	$1.79
Pen	$2.89
Binder	$3.19

LESSON 1-2 **Practice C**

Properties of Real Numbers

Find the missing term or terms and state the property illustrated.

1. $3x \cdot$ _____ $= 3y \cdot$ _____

_____

2. $2\pi +$ _____ $= 2\pi$

_____

3. $\dfrac{t}{4} - \dfrac{s}{4} = \dfrac{1}{4} \cdot ($ _____ $-$ _____ $)$

_____

4. $m \cdot$ _____ $= 1$

_____

Identify which properties make each statement true for all real values of *k*.

5. $\dfrac{3}{4}(k+4) = \dfrac{3k+12}{4}$

_____

6. $25 + k + (75 \cdot 1) = 100 + k$

_____

Solve.

7. Mona lives in Florida. She drives 550 miles to Texas. Her car's tank holds 15 gallons of gas and she gets an average of 25 miles per gallon of gas. If Mona fills up her gas tank before she leaves, how many more times will she have to fill up the tank to drive to Texas and back to Florida?

_____

8. Glenn bought a new shirt on sale for 30% off. The original price of the shirt was $19.49. Write an expression without subtraction to find the sale price of the shirt. Then find the sale price.

_____

9. Describe how to use mental math to find the total cost for dinner if the bill is $25.59 and you add a 15% tip.

_____

10. All merchandise at the Ski Shack is marked down 15%. Over the weekend all sales qualify for an additional 25% off. Prove that taking 40% off the original price is not the same as taking a 15% discount and then a 25% discount. Which is greater?

_____

_____

_____

Holt Algebra 2

LESSON 1-2

Reteach

Properties of Real Numbers

Properties of Addition	Examples
Additive Identity 0 is the additive identity.	$4 + 0 = 4$ $n + 0 = 0 + n = n$
Additive Inverse The sum of a number and its opposite is 0.	$8 + (-8) = 0$ $n + (-n) = 0$
Closure Property The sum of any two real numbers is a real number.	$3 + 5 = 8$ $a + b \in \mathbb{R}$
Commutative Property The order does not change the sum.	$6 + 12 = 12 + 6$ $a + b = b + a$
Associative Property The grouping does not change the sum.	$(2 + 5) + 9 = 2 + (9 + 5)$ $(a + b) + c = a + (b + c)$

> The additive inverse of 8 is –8.
> The additive inverse of –8 is 8.

Find the additive inverse of each number.

1. 20

   $20 + ($ _____ $) = 0$

2. –36

   $-36 + ($ _____ $) = 0$

3. –7.9

   $-7.9 + ($ _____ $) = 0$

4. $\dfrac{2}{3}$

5. $\sqrt{3}$

6. $-\dfrac{3}{4}$

_____   _____   _____

Identify the property of addition demonstrated by each equation.

7. $x + 0 = x$ _____

8. $(2 + m) + 5n = 2 + (m + 5n)$ _____

9. $4r + 6s = 6s + 4r$ _____

10. $\pi + (-\pi) = 0$ _____

11. $c + (-2) = -2 + c$ _____

12. $1 = 0 + 1$ _____

LESSON 1-2 Reteach
Properties of Real Numbers (continued)

Properties of Multiplication	Examples
Multiplicative Identity 1 is the multiplicative identity.	$-12 \cdot 1 = -12$ $n \cdot 1 = 1 \cdot n = n$
Multiplicative Inverse The product of a number and its reciprocal is 1.	$-\dfrac{2}{3} \cdot \left(-\dfrac{3}{2}\right) = 1$ The multiplicative inverse of $-\dfrac{2}{3}$ is $-\dfrac{3}{2}$. $n \cdot \dfrac{1}{n} = 1, n \neq 0$
Closure Property The product of any two real numbers is a real number.	$8(-0.5) = -4$ $ab \in \mathbb{R}$
Commutative Property The order does not change the product.	$3\left(\dfrac{1}{6}\right) = \dfrac{1}{6}(3)$ $ab = ba$
Associative Property The grouping does not change the product.	$(3 \cdot 7)4 = 3(7 \cdot 4)$ $(ab)c = a(bc)$
Distributive Property	$-2(4 + 7) = -2(4) + (-2)(7)$ $a(b + c) = ab + ac$

Find the multiplicative inverse of each number.

13. 25

$25 \cdot ($ _____ $) = 1$

14. $-\dfrac{3}{5}$

$-\dfrac{3}{5} \cdot ($ _____ $) = 1$

15. $-\dfrac{1}{8}$

$-\dfrac{1}{8} \cdot ($ _____ $) = 1$

16. $\dfrac{1}{3}$

17. -4

18. π

_____   _____   _____

IIdentify the property of multiplication demonstrated by each equation.

19. $6(2x + y) = 6(2x) + 6y$ _____

20. $9(4.2) = (4.2)9$ _____

21. $4(3\sqrt{10}) = (4 \cdot 3)\sqrt{10}$ _____

LESSON
1-2

Challenge
Set Relationships

Consider the subset of the whole numbers consisting only of the elements
0 and 1, the set $A = \{0, 1\}$. Now study the following tables for addition and
multiplication of these numbers.

+	0	1
0	0	1
1	1	2

×	0	1
0	0	0
1	0	1

1. Is set A closed under the operation of addition? multiplication?
   Explain how you know.

   _____

   _____

2. Does set A have an identity element for addition? multiplication?
   Explain how you know.

   _____

   _____

Consider the set $B = \{a, b, c\}$ and the operation §, which is defined in the
table below.

§	a	b	c
a	c	a	b
b	a	b	c
c	b	c	a

3. Is set B closed under the operation of §? Explain how you know.

   _____

4. Does set B have an identity element for §? If so, what is it and how

   did you decide this was the identity? _____

5. Is set B commutative for the operation of §? Explain how you know.

   _____

6. What is the inverse for each of the elements a, b, and c?

   _____

Problem Solving
Properties of Real Numbers

**Three friends eat together at a restaurant. Their bill is shown at right.
Use mental math for Exercises 1–4.**

1. Luke and Willy split one order of the Cajun boil, and they each have a glass of milk. What is Luke's cost for his food and drink?

_____

2. Laska has a bowl of gumbo and a salad. What is her share of the 8.5% sales tax?

_____

3. The group decides to leave double the sales tax as the tip and to divide that amount evenly among themselves. What is Willy's share of the tip?

_____

4. Explain how you would use mental math and the subtotal to find the amount of a 20% tip.

_____

_____

Lou's Fine Foods	
Milk (2)	$3.00
Cajun boil	$8.50
Gumbo (bowl)	$4.25
Salad	$3.75
Subtotal	$19.50
Sales tax	$1.66
TOTAL	$21.16

**A music store advertises CDs at 15% off the marked price. There is a
6% sales tax added for each purchase. Use mental math to help you
choose the letter for the best answer.**

5. Todd buys a two-disk set marked $14.95 and a single CD marked $10.95. What is the total of his bill?

   A $23.34

   B $24.90

   C $26.01

   D $27.45

6. Hedy buys 6 CDs marked "3 for $25." What is her total bill?

   F $41.60

   G $42.50

   H $45.05

   J $50.50

7. Pedro's total before tax is $66.00. How much tax does he pay?

   A $9.96

   B $6.60

   C $3.96

   D $3.36

8. Gail and Pam decide to share the cost of a three-disk set marked $35.00. What is Pam's share of the total?

   F $14.50

   G $15.77

   H $29.75*

   J $31.54

LESSON 1-2

Reading Strategies
Draw Conclusions

Examples, counterexamples, and properties of real numbers can help you classify a statement as sometimes, always, or never true. A counterexample is used to prove that the statement is false.

$\dfrac{a}{b} = \dfrac{b}{a}$ **sometimes true**

True: $\dfrac{1}{-1} = \dfrac{-1}{1}$;   **False:** $\dfrac{1}{2} = \dfrac{2}{1}$

Show a **true** example and a **false** example.

$a - (b + c) = a - b - c$
Use properties of real numbers.
By the **Distributive Property**:
$a + (-1)(b + c) = a + (-b) + (-c) = a - b - c$

$a - (b + c) = a - b - c$
always true

$a - b = a + (-b)$
Use properties of real numbers.
The **additive identity** is 0.
$a + (-b) = a$ only
when $-b = b = 0$, not when $b = 1$
Use a counterexample.

$a - b = a$ where $b = 1$
never true
Counterexample: $3 - 1 = 2$

Classify each statement as sometimes, always, or never true. Support your answer.

1. $\dfrac{1}{n} + \left(-\dfrac{1}{n}\right) = 0, n \neq 0$

_____

2. $\dfrac{a}{b} \cdot 1 = 1$

_____

3. $a \cdot b = b$ where $a = -1$

_____

4. $(a + b)\dfrac{1}{c} = 1 + \dfrac{b}{c}$

_____

Holt Algebra 2

LESSON 1-3

Practice A
Square Roots

Identify perfect squares that are closest in value to these numbers.

1. 47

    perfect square < 47 _____

    perfect square > 47 _____

2. 119

    perfect square < 119 _____

    perfect square > 119 _____

Estimate to the nearest whole number.

3. $\sqrt{55}$ 4. $\sqrt{92}$ 5. $\sqrt{135}$

_____   _____   _____

Estimate to the nearest tenth.

6. $\sqrt{42}$ 7. $\sqrt{76}$ 8. $\sqrt{90}$

_____   _____   _____

Simplify each expression. Use perfect square factors to help you.

9. $\sqrt{48}$ 10. $\sqrt{75}$ 11. $-\sqrt{576}$

_____   _____   _____

12. $\sqrt{45}$ 13. $\sqrt{72}$ 14. $\sqrt{200}$

_____   _____   _____

Simplify each expression.

15. $\sqrt{3} \cdot \sqrt{12}$ 16. $\dfrac{\sqrt{128}}{\sqrt{2}}$ 17. $\dfrac{-4\sqrt{8}}{3}$

_____   _____   _____

Add or subtract.

18. $3\sqrt{5} + 4\sqrt{5}$ 19. $2\sqrt{9} - 2\sqrt{2}$ 20. $-3\sqrt{15n} + 7\sqrt{15n}$

_____   _____   _____

LESSON 1-3 — Practice B
Square Roots

Estimate to the nearest tenth.

1. $\sqrt{78}$

2. $-\sqrt{57}$

3. $\sqrt{39}$

_____   _____   _____

Simplify each expression.

4. $\sqrt{243}$

5. $\dfrac{\sqrt{90}}{\sqrt{40}}$

6. $\sqrt{42} \cdot \sqrt{3}$

_____   _____   _____

7. $-\dfrac{4}{\sqrt{144}}$

8. $\sqrt{\dfrac{125}{5}}$

9. $-\sqrt{320}$

_____   _____   _____

Simplify by rationalizing each denominator.

10. $\dfrac{6}{\sqrt{5}}$

11. $\dfrac{-3\sqrt{15}}{\sqrt{3}}$

12. $\dfrac{\sqrt{13}}{4\sqrt{6}}$

_____   _____   _____

Add or subtract.

13. $7\sqrt{5} - 10\sqrt{5}$

14. $12\sqrt{3} + 3\sqrt{12}$

15. $-6\sqrt{50} + 4\sqrt{32}$

_____   _____   _____

Solve.

16. A building has a mural painted on an outside wall. The mural is a square with an area of 14,400 ft². What is the width of the mural?

_____

**LESSON
1-3**

Practice C
Square Roots

Each figure below is made from squares. Given the area of each figure, find its perimeter to the nearest tenth.

1.

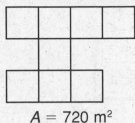

$A = 720$ m²

2.

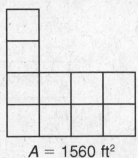

$A = 1560$ ft²

3.

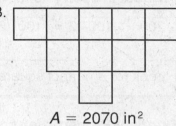

$A = 2070$ in²

_____   _____   _____

Simplify each expression. Rationalize denominators when necessary. Then estimate the value of each simplified expression to the nearest whole number.

4. $\dfrac{\sqrt{375}}{\sqrt{100}}$

5. $\dfrac{4\sqrt{8}+3\sqrt{72}}{-\sqrt{50}}$

_____   _____

6. $-3\sqrt{60} \cdot 7\sqrt{44}$

7. $\sqrt{\dfrac{99}{121}}$

_____   _____

8. $\dfrac{-9\sqrt{80}}{\sqrt{32}}$

9. $\dfrac{7\sqrt{3}-12\sqrt{3}}{\sqrt{108}}$

_____   _____

Solve.

10. Karly is building a patio using large square tiles with an area of 42.25 ft² each. She uses 9 tiles to make a square patio. What is the perimeter of her patio?

_____

Holt Algebra 2

LESSON 1-3 Reteach
Square Roots

Use properties of square roots to simplify expressions with square roots.

Product Property: for $a > 0$ and $b > 0$, $\sqrt{ab} = \sqrt{a} \cdot \sqrt{b}$

$$\sqrt{200} = \sqrt{100 \cdot 2} = \sqrt{100}\sqrt{2} = 10\sqrt{2} \qquad \sqrt{27} \cdot \sqrt{3} = \sqrt{27 \cdot 3} = \sqrt{81} = 9$$

| Look for a perfect square factor. | Multiply under the radical. |

Quotient Property: for $a > 0$ and $b > 0$, $\sqrt{\dfrac{a}{b}} = \dfrac{\sqrt{a}}{\sqrt{b}}$

$$\sqrt{\frac{25}{49}} = \frac{\sqrt{25}}{\sqrt{49}} = \frac{5}{7} \qquad\qquad \frac{\sqrt{108}}{\sqrt{3}} = \sqrt{\frac{108}{3}} = \sqrt{36} = 6$$

| Evaluate perfect square factors. | Divide under the radical. |

Simplify each expression.

1. $\sqrt{20}$

   $\sqrt{4 \cdot 5}$

   $\sqrt{4} \cdot$ _____

   _____

2. $\sqrt{63}$

   $\sqrt{9 \cdot}$ _____

   $\sqrt{9} \cdot$ _____

   _____

3. $\sqrt{80}$

   $\sqrt{16 \cdot}$ _____

   $\sqrt{16} \cdot$ _____

   _____

4. $\sqrt{3} \cdot \sqrt{12}$

   $\sqrt{\rule{1.5cm}{0.1pt}} \cdot \rule{1.5cm}{0.1pt}$

   _____

5. $\sqrt{\dfrac{64}{25}}$

   $\dfrac{\sqrt{\rule{1cm}{0.1pt}}}{\sqrt{\rule{1cm}{0.1pt}}}$

   _____

6. $\dfrac{\sqrt{200}}{\sqrt{8}}$

   $\dfrac{\sqrt{\rule{1cm}{0.1pt}}}{\sqrt{\rule{1cm}{0.1pt}}}$

   _____

7. $\sqrt{6} \cdot \sqrt{24}$

   _____

8. $\dfrac{\sqrt{448}}{\sqrt{7}}$

   _____

9. $\sqrt{\dfrac{49}{100}}$

   _____

LESSON	**Reteach**
1-3	***Square Roots*** (continued)

Rationalize the denominator to eliminate radicals from the denominator.

$$\frac{3\sqrt{5}}{\sqrt{2}} = \frac{3\sqrt{5}}{\sqrt{2}} \cdot \frac{\sqrt{2}}{\sqrt{2}} = \frac{3\sqrt{5 \cdot 2}}{2} = \frac{3\sqrt{10}}{2}$$

Multiply by 1: $\frac{\sqrt{2}}{\sqrt{2}} = 1$

Think: $\sqrt{2} \cdot \sqrt{2} = 2$

Combine like radical terms to add or subtract square roots.

$3\sqrt{2} + \sqrt{8}$

$3\sqrt{2} + \sqrt{4 \cdot 2}$ ◄—— Try to use $\sqrt{2}$ as a factor.

$3\sqrt{2} + 2\sqrt{2}$

$(3+2)\sqrt{2}$ ◄—— Both terms contain $\sqrt{2}$. Combine like terms.

$5\sqrt{2}$

Simplify by rationalizing each denominator.

10. $\dfrac{4}{\sqrt{5}}$

$\dfrac{4}{\sqrt{5}} \cdot \dfrac{\sqrt{5}}{\sqrt{5}}$

_____

11. $\dfrac{1}{\sqrt{6}}$

$\dfrac{1}{\sqrt{6}}$ _____

_____

12. $\dfrac{3\sqrt{2}}{\sqrt{8}}$

$\dfrac{3\sqrt{2}}{\sqrt{8}} \cdot$ _____

_____

Add or subtract.

13. $12\sqrt{7} - 4\sqrt{7}$

$(12-4)\sqrt{7}$

_____

14. $\sqrt{75} - \sqrt{27}$

$\sqrt{25 \cdot 3} - \sqrt{9 \cdot 3}$

_____

15. $6\sqrt{5} + \sqrt{45}$

$6\sqrt{5} +$ _____

_____

LESSON
1-3

Challenge

Koch Snowflake

Triangle *ABC* is an equilateral triangle with side length *s*. Draw a line from vertex *A* that is perpendicular to the opposite side. Label that point of intersection *D*.

1. Use the Pythagorean Theorem to find the length of $\overline{AD}$ in terms of *s*.

   _____

2. Find the area of triangle *ABC* in terms of *s*.

   _____

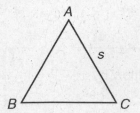

Equilateral triangle *UVW* has side length of 9 units.

3. Find the area of triangle *UVW*.

   _____

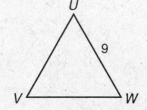

An equilateral triangle is centered on each side of triangle *UVW*. The result is a 6-point star. This star is made up of 12 separate line segments

4. Find the length of each of the 12 segments.

   _____

5. Find the area of the star.

   _____

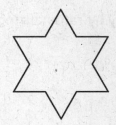

Again an equilateral triangle is centered on each side of the star. The new figure has 18 points.

6. Find the length of each segment in this figure.

   _____

7. Find the area of this figure.

   _____

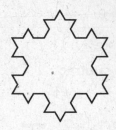

If this process were to continue forever, it would generate a figure known as the Koch Snowflake. The snowflake could be contained entirely within a circle.

8. Find the radius of the circle.

   _____

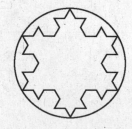

LESSON 1-3

Problem Solving
Square Roots

**A downtown public park has a design of three
square fountains. The fountains are arranged so
that they create a perspective illusion. The area
covered by the largest fountain is 144 square
yards. Use this information for Exercises 1–3.**

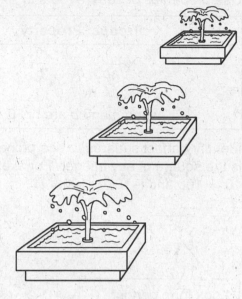

1. The area covered by the smallest fountain is
   one-fourth the area covered by the largest fountain.
   What is the side length of the smallest fountain?

   _____

2. How does the side length of the smallest fountain
   compare to the side length of the largest fountain?

   _____

   _____

3. The area covered by the middle fountain is

   $2\frac{1}{4}$ times the area covered by the smallest fountain.

   What is the side length of the middle fountain?

   _____

**There is a rectangular vacant lot between Ken's house and his
school. The dimensions of the lot are 125 ft by 35 ft. Choose the
letter for the best answer.**

4. Instead of walking along the length and
   width of the lot, Ken sometimes takes a
   shortcut and walks along the diagonal.
   What is the difference in distance
   between Ken walking along the sidewalk
   or taking a shortcut?

   A 30 ft   C 160 ft

   B 130 ft   D 190 ft

5. Ken gets a job mowing the lot. He
   charges $30 to mow a square lot 35 feet
   long. At the same rate, about what will he
   charge to mow this lot?

   F $60   H $107

   G $84   J $1050

6. The owner of the lot divides it into 3
   garden plots. Two of the plots have an
   area of 1225 square feet each. What
   could be the dimensions of the third plot?

   A 125 ft by 125 ft

   B 75 ft by 35 ft

   C 55 ft by 35 ft

   D 35 ft by 35 ft

7. Ken has a job mowing a park that is
   made up of 6 congruent square areas
   separated by paths. The total area of the
   park is 1734 square yards. What is the
   approximate length of the side of each
   square?

   F 145 yd   H 42 yd

   G 132 yd   J 17 yd

Holt Algebra 2

| LESSON 1-3 | **Reading Strategies**
Identify Relationships |

Use properties of square roots to simplify expressions with square roots.

Product Property	Quotient Property
$\sqrt{ab} = \sqrt{a} \cdot \sqrt{b}$	$\sqrt{\dfrac{a}{b}} = \dfrac{\sqrt{a}}{\sqrt{b}}$
when a and b are not 0.	when a and b are not 0.

Identify perfect squares to use properties of square roots. A perfect square is the square of any integer. For example, 100 is a perfect square because $10^2 = 100$ and $(-10)^2 = 100$.

$\sqrt{72} = \sqrt{36 \times 2} = 6\sqrt{2}$

Look for a perfect square factor of 72.

$\sqrt{\dfrac{64}{25}} = \dfrac{\sqrt{64}}{\sqrt{25}} = \dfrac{8}{5}$

Think: 64 and 25 are both perfect squares.

Make perfect squares to use properties of square roots.

$\sqrt{24} \times \sqrt{6} = \sqrt{24 \cdot 6} = \sqrt{144} = 12$

Multiply to simplify.

$\dfrac{\sqrt{125}}{\sqrt{5}} = \sqrt{\dfrac{125}{5}} = \sqrt{25} = 5$

Divide to simplify.

Answer each question.

1. List the perfect squares for the integers from 1 to 10.

_____

2. Explain how to use a perfect square to simplify $\sqrt{500}$. Then simplify.

_____

_____

3. Explain how to use a perfect square to simplify $\sqrt{75} \cdot \sqrt{3}$. Then simplify.

_____

_____

4. Explain how to use the Quotient Property of Square Roots to simplify $\dfrac{\sqrt{48}}{\sqrt{16}}$. Then simplify.

_____

Holt Algebra 2

Name _____ Date _____ Class_____

Practice A
Simplifying Algebraic Expressions

Write an algebraic expression to represent each situation.

1. 7 more than g _____

2. 10 less than twice w _____

3. the cost of 3 notebooks at m dollars each _____

Evaluate each expression for $x = 2$, $y = 1$, and $z = -3$. Simplify.

4. $3x + y$

5. $2y + z^2$

_____   _____

6. $\dfrac{2x^2}{y + z}$

7. $3xy - 2z$

_____   _____

Draw lines to connect like terms. Then simplify each expression.

8. $7 - 3y + 8 + 10y$

9. $4s + 6t - 2s + 7t$

10. $4a + ab - 6ab + 7a$

_____   _____   _____

11. $14v - 12 + 7w + (-4v)$

12. $10x - 3y + x - 3x$

13. $-9fg + 3g + (-7f) + 3f$

_____   _____   _____

Use the Distributive Property. Then simplify.

14. $3(x - 2y) + 5x$

15. $21c + 5d(1 - c) - cd$

16. $16j - 4(7k - 3j) + 25k$

_____   _____   _____

Solve.

17. Ann, Raul, and Suzanna ran the team relay in h minutes each.
    Roger and Pete ran the race in k minutes each. Write an
    expression for the total time for the team.

_____

LESSON	**Practice B**
1-4	*Simplifying Algebraic Expressions*

Write an algebraic expression to represent each situation.

1. the measure of the complement of an angle with measure w _____

2. the number of eggs in d cartons that each hold 1 dozen eggs _____

Evaluate each expression for the given values of the variables.

3. $4t - 3s^2 + s^3$ for $t = -2$ and $s = -3$

4. $\dfrac{5wp + 2w}{3wp^2}$ for $w = 4$ and $p = -1$

_____   _____

Simplify each expression.

5. $-(4r - 3t) + 6r - t$

6. $5(a + b) - 6(2a + 3b)$

_____   _____

Simplify each expression. Then evaluate the expression for the given values of the variables.

7. $-2(d - 3c) + 4d + c$
   for $d = 0$ and $c = -2$

8. $-3f(2 - 3f + 4g) + g$
   for $f = -1$ and $g = 1$

_____   _____

Solve.

9. Marco delivers newspapers on the weekend. He delivers
   s newspapers on Saturday and $4s$ newspapers on Sunday.
   He earns $0.15 for each paper he delivers.

   a. Write an expression for the total amount of money
      Marco earns each weekend.   _____

   b. Evaluate your expression for $s = 50$.   _____

   c. Write an expression for the amount of money Marco
      earns in a year if he delivers the same number of
      papers every weekend.   _____

10. A tank holds 500 gallons of water. It starts out full, then
    10 gallons are released every minute.

    a. Write an expression for the number of gallons in the
       tank after m minutes.   _____

    b. Write an expression for the number of gallons in the tank
       after m minutes if 2 gallons are *also* added every minute. _____

Holt Algebra 2

LESSON
1-4

Practice C
Simplifying Algebraic Expressions

Complete the table. Circle which expressions are equivalent for the given values of *x*.

1.

x	$(x-9)^2$	$x^2 - 81$	$x^2 - 18x + 81$
−2			
−1			
1			
2			

Write and simplify an expression for the perimeter of each figure.

2.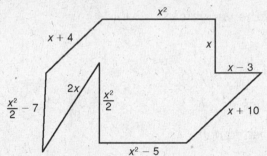

3.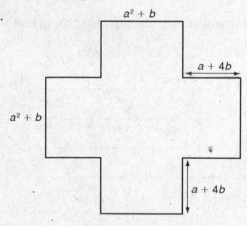

_____   _____

Solve.

4. An Internet search engine company charges fees for advertising links. There is a $5 fee to set up an account and a set charge each time someone clicks on the link.

   a. Tony set up an account with a search engine company. The set charge is $0.75 per click. Write an expression for the amount Tony will pay for setup and *c* clicks.

   _____

   b. After a month, Tony noticed he wasn't getting many buyers at his website. He chose an increased rate of $1.25 per click. Write an expression for the amount Tony will pay for setup, *c* clicks at $0.75 per click, and *d* clicks at $1.25 per click.

   _____

   c. Find Tony's cost if he got 50 clicks in the first month and 85 clicks in the second month.

   _____

Holt Algebra 2

LESSON 1-4

Reteach

Simplifying Algebraic Expressions

To evaluate an algebraic expression you substitute numbers for variables. Then follow the **order of operations**.

Here is a sentence that can help you remember the order of operations.

Please	**E**xcuse	**M**y	**D**ear	**A**unt	**S**ally
Parentheses	**E**xponents	**M**ultiply	**D**ivide	**A**dd	**S**ubtract

Evaluate $x - 2xy + y^2$ for $x = 4$ and $y = 6$.

$4 - 2(4)(6) + (6)^2$	*Substitute 4 for x and 6 for y.*
$4 - 2(4)(6) + 36$	*Evaluate exponents: $6^2 = 36$.*
$4 - 48 + 36$	*Multiply from left to right.*
-8	*Add and subtract from left to right.*

Evaluate each expression for the given values of the variables.

1. $a^2 + 2ab^2 - 3a$ for $a = 5$ and $b = 2$

   $5^2 + 2(5)(2)^2 -$ _____   *Substitute 5 for a and 2 for b.*

   $25 +$ _____   *Evaluate exponents.*

   _____   *Multiply from left to right.*

   _____   *Add and subtract from left to right.*

2. $c^2 - cd + 3d$ for $c = 7$ and $d = 6$

   _____   *Substitute for the variables.*

   _____   *Evaluate exponents.*

   _____   *Multiply from left to right.*

   _____   *Add and subtract from left to right.*

3. $\dfrac{(5m - n^3)}{3n}$ for $m = 4$ and $n = 2$

   _____   *Substitute for the variables.*

   _____   *Evaluate exponents inside parentheses.*

   _____   *Multiply inside parentheses.*

   _____   *Subtract inside parentheses.*

   _____   *Multiply from left to right.*

   _____   *Divide from left to right.*

Holt Algebra 2

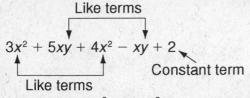

LESSON 1-4

Reteach

Simplifying Algebraic Expressions *(continued)*

Add or subtract the coefficients of like terms to simplify an algebraic expression.

Like terms

$3x^2 + 5xy + 4x^2 - xy + 2$ ← Constant term

Like terms

Like Terms: $3x^2$ and $4x^2$

$5xy$ and $-xy$

Coefficients of x^2 : 3 and 4
Coefficients of xy : 5 and -1

$3x^2 + 5xy + 4x^2 - xy + 2$

$3x^2 + 4x^2 + 5xy - xy + 2$ *Group like terms.*

$7x^2 + 4xy + 2$ *Add or subtract like terms.*

Think: $3x^2 + 4x^2 = 7x^2$
$5xy - 1xy = 4xy$

You can use the Distributive Property to simplify an algebraic expression.

$-2(a^2 - ab) + 6ab + 2a^2$

$-2a^2 + 2ab + 6ab + 2a^2$ *Distribute.*

$-2a^2 + 2a^2 + 2ab + 6ab$ *Group like terms.*

$8ab$ *Add or subtract like terms.*

$-2(a^2 - ab) = -2(a^2) - 2(-ab)$
$= -2a^2 + 2ab$

Think: $-2a^2 + 2a^2 = 0$

Simplify each expression.

4. $-6x + 3 - 2x + 4x$

_____ *Group like terms.*

_____ *Add or subtract like terms.*

5. $c(4c + d) - c^2 + cd$

_____ *Distribute.*

_____ *Group like terms.*

_____ *Add or subtract like terms.*

6. $4a^2 + 5ab - 4a^2 - 2ab - 7$ 7. $3(s - 4t) + 3s - t$

_____   _____

LESSON 1-4

Challenge

Another Way to Look at It

Combining like terms is a direct application of the Distributive Property. Here is another way to look at $5x + 9x = 14x$

$$5x + 9x = (5 + 9)x = (14)x = 14x$$

The common factor of x can be factored out of the expression and, the addition operation performed prior to the multiplication.

This process can be applied to other situations. You can apply the Distributive Property to adding fractions with a common denominator.

Factor out the common factor of $\frac{1}{15}$ and then add.

$$\frac{5}{15} + \frac{9}{15} = \frac{1}{15}(5 + 9) = \frac{1}{15}(14) = \frac{14}{15}$$

Consider the two operations § and Ω.
Use the tables for Exercises 1–6.

1. What is the value of a § c?

   _____

2. What is the value of b Ω c?

   _____

3. What is the value of a § $(b$ Ω $c)$?

   _____

4. What is the value of $(a$ § $b)$ Ω $(a$ § $c)$?

   _____

5. Are the two operations § and Ω commutative?
   Why or why not?

   _____

   _____

6. Based on your results, do you think that the
   operation § is distributive over the operation
   Ω? Why or why not?

   _____

   _____

§	a	b	c
a	c	a	b
b	a	b	c
c	b	c	a

Ω	a	b	c
a	b	a	c
b	c	b	a
c	a	c	b

Problem Solving

LESSON 1-4

Simplifying Algebraic Expressions

To find out how much water a dripping showerhead wastes, Marisa catches the drips in a measuring cup. She collects a cup of water in 6 minutes.

1. Write and simplify an expression for the number of cups of water wasted in t minutes.

_____

2. How much water does this showerhead waste in an hour?

_____

3. How many minutes will it take for this showerhead to waste a gallon of water?

_____

4. Write expressions for the amount of water, in cups and in gallons, that the dripping showerhead wastes in d days.

_____

Choose the letter for the best answer.

5. Van budgets $12 a day for groceries for weekdays and $15 a day for weekend days. Which expression could be used to find his grocery budget for w weeks?

   A $w(12 \cdot 5 + 15 \cdot 2)$

   B $7w(12 + 15)$

   C $12w + 15w$

   D $17w$

6. The Spanish Club is planning to make a quilt for the annual fund-raiser. The quilt design includes 30 blue triangles, each with a base of 4 inches and a height of h inches, and 20 blue squares that are each s inches on a side. Which expression could be used to find the total area of blue fabric needed?

   F $(30 \cdot 4)h + 20s$ H $60h + 20s^2$

   G $120h + 20s$ J $240sh$

7. Susanne wrote the expression $25 + 0.15m$ for the monthly cost of her cell phone where m is the number of minutes she uses. What will her bill be this month if she makes 55 minutes of calls?

   A $8.25   C $63.25

   B $33.25   D $80.00

8. The width of a rectangle is $3g^2$. The length of the rectangle is $h^2 - 2h + 5$. Which represents the area of the rectangle?

   F $3g^2 + h^2 - 2h + 15$

   G $3g^2h^2 + 6gh - 15g^2$

   H $18g^2h^2 - 6gh$

   J $3g^2h^2 - 6g^2h + 15g^2$

Holt Algebra 2

LESSON 1-4 Reading Strategies
Understand Vocabulary

To **evaluate an algebraic expression**, substitute a number for each variable. Then simplify the numerical expression.

Evaluate $x - 2xy + y^2$ for $x = 24$ and $y = 3$.

$-4 - 2(-4)(3) + (3)^2$ ← *Substitute.*

$-4 - 2(-4)(3) + 9$ ← *Evaluate exponents.*

$-4 + 24 + 9$ ← *Multiply.*

29 ← *Add.*

> Follow the correct order of operations.

The evaluation of $x - 2xy + y^2$ for $x = -4$ and $y = 3$ is 29.

To **simplify an algebraic expression**, identify like terms. Then add or subtract the coefficients of the variables.

Simplify $3(a - 2b) + a + 5b$.

$3a - 6b + a + 5b$ ← *Distribute.*

$3a + a - 6b + 5b$ ← *Find like terms.*

$4a - b$ ← *Add coefficients.*

> Like terms are $3a$ and a and $-6b$ and $5b$.

Answer each question.

1. What is the first step to evaluate $b + 2bc - 5c$ for $b = -1$ and $c = 6$?

   _____

2. What is the coefficient of x in $2w - x + y$?

   _____

3. What are the like terms in $g^2 + 5g^2h - 3g^2 - 4h^2 + 6g^2 + 8h^2 - 2g^2h^2 + 7g^2h$?

   _____

4. List the steps you would use to evaluate $m^2 - 8mn + 3n - 5$ for $m = 2$ and $n = -5$. What is the result?

   _____

   _____

5. Jalen simplifies the expression $a(a + 1) - 3a + a^2$ to $a^2 - 2a$. Then he evaluates the expression for $a = 4$. His result is 8. Is he correct? If not, explain why.

   _____

   _____

    Holt Algebra 2

LESSON 1-5

Practice A
Properties of Exponents

Fill in the blanks to expand each expression.

1. $4^3 =$ ___ · ___ · ___

2. $a^5 = ·$ ___ · ___ · ___ · ___ · ___

3. $(3d)^4 = ($___$)($___$)($___$)($___$)$

4. $\left(\dfrac{x}{7}\right)^3 = ($___$)($___$)($___$)$

Fill in the blanks to evaluate each expression.

5. $3^{-3} = \left(\underline{}\right)^3 = $ ___ · ___ · ___ = ___

6. $\left(\dfrac{-5}{6}\right)^{-2} = \left(\underline{}\right)^2 = $ ___ · ___ = ___

Simplify each expression. Use the multiplication properties of exponents.

7. $3r^2(-3r^3)$ 8. $(4f^5g)^2(2fg^3)$

Multiply a power of a power	no power of a power	_____
Add exponents with same base	_____	_____
Multiply whole numbers	_____	_____

Simplify each expression. Use the division properties of exponents.

9. $\dfrac{9k^3m^8}{3k^5m^2}$ 10. $\dfrac{16p^{-2}q^{-3}}{2p^{-5}q^{-4}}$

Substitute reciprocals	no negative exponents	_____
Subtract exponents with same base	_____	_____
Divide whole numbers	_____	_____

Evaluate each expression. Write the answer in scientific notation.

11. $(4.2 \times 10^3)(2.0 \times 10^2)$ 12. $\dfrac{1.4 \times 10^6}{7.0 \times 10^2}$

_____   _____

13. $\dfrac{4.5 \times 10^4}{9.0 \times 10^7}$ 14. $(3.5 \times 10^{-3})(5.8 \times 10^5)$

_____   _____

        Holt Algebra 2

LESSON 1-5

Practice B
Properties of Exponents

Write each expression in expanded form.

1. $-3x^5$

2. $(j - 3k)^3$

3. $7t^2(-4r)^4$

_____ _____ _____

Evaluate each expression.

4. $-(-2)^{-4}$

5. $\left(\dfrac{5}{8}\right)^{-2}$

6. $\left(-\dfrac{3}{2}\right)^{-3}$

_____ _____ _____

Simplify each expression. Assume all variables are nonzero.

7. $\dfrac{68f^5 g^{-3}}{4f^{-3} g^6}$

8. $(-4a^3 b^7)^{-2}$

9. $6m^4 n^9 (-3m^2 n^3)^{-2}$

_____ _____ _____

Evaluate each expression. Write the answer in scientific notation.

10. $(7.2 \times 10^{-5})(4.5 \times 10^3)$

11. $\dfrac{1.7 \times 10^5}{3.4 \times 10^9}$

12. $(7.8 \times 10^8)(2.8 \times 10^{11})$

_____ _____ _____

Solve.

13. The A-1 Moving and Storage Company sells crates that measure $x^2 y$ units wide, x units long, and y^2 units tall. Find the volume of the crate.

_____

14. The average lifespan for an adult living today is about 82 years. Some scientists believe that people born in the early part of this century may live up to 150 years. Calculate the number of minutes an 82-year-old and a 150-year-old could live. Round to the nearest million. Record the difference in scientific notation.

_____

15. A movie made 6.7×10^7. It took 250 hours to film it. How much money was earned for each hour of filming? Write your answer in scientific notation.

_____

LESSON
1-5

Practice C
Properties of Exponents

Write and simplify an expression for the volume of each figure.

1.

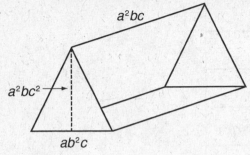

a^2bc

$a^2bc^2 \rightarrow$

ab^2c

$V =$ area of base × height

_____

2.

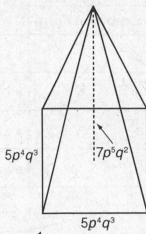

$5p^4q^3$ $7p^5q^2$

$5p^4q^3$

$V = \dfrac{1}{3}$ area of base × height

_____

Simplify each expression. Assume all variables are nonzero.

3. $(-5x^5y^{-3}z^8)^3$

4. $7g^2h^3(-2h^5k^0)^{-3}$

5. $\left(\dfrac{24m^7n^3}{4mn^{-5}}\right)^{-2}$

_____   _____   _____

One cubic foot of pennies is 49,152 pennies. Use this fact for Exercises 6–8. Write your answers in scientific notation rounded to the nearest tenth.

6. The Empire State Building in New York City has an approximate volume of 3.7×10^7 ft^3. About how many pennies would fit in the Empire State Building?

_____

7. If the Sears Tower in Chicago were filled with pennies, it would hold about 2.6×10^{12} pennies. What is the approximate volume of the Sears Tower?

_____

8. Think about covering the entire earth with two layers of pennies. The total number of pennies needed could be stacked in a cube that measures 2.73×10^4 ft on each side. How many pennies are in this cube?

_____

Holt Algebra 2

LESSON 1-5

Reteach
Properties of Exponents

Write		Read
Expanded Form	**Exponent Form**	
$a \cdot a$	a^2	a squared
$a \cdot a \cdot a$	a^3	a cubed
$a \cdot a \cdot a \cdot a$	a^4	a to the fourth power
$a \cdot a \cdot \ldots \cdot a$	a^n	a to the nth power

$-4x^5 = -4(x \cdot x \cdot x \cdot x \cdot x)$
$-(4x^5) = -(4x)(4x)(4x)(4x)(4x)$
$(-4x)^5 = (-4x)(-4x)(-4x)(-4x)(-4x)$
$4x^3(y+6)^2 = 4(x)(x)(x)(y+6)(y+6)$

> List the factors to expand exponential expressions.

Zero Exponent Property: $a^0 = 1$; a is not zero $38^0 = 1$

Negative Exponent Property: $a^{-n} = \dfrac{1}{a^n}$ and $\left(\dfrac{a}{b}\right)^{-n} = \left(\dfrac{b}{a}\right)^{n}$; a is not zero.

$3^{-4} = \dfrac{1}{3^4} = \dfrac{1}{3 \cdot 3 \cdot 3 \cdot 3} = \dfrac{1}{81}$

$\left(\dfrac{2}{5}\right)^{-3} = \left(\dfrac{5}{2}\right)^{3} = \dfrac{5}{2} \cdot \dfrac{5}{2} \cdot \dfrac{5}{2} = \dfrac{125}{8}$

Write each expression in expanded form.

1. $-8c^3$

   $-8(c \cdot$ _____$)$

2. $(3xy)^4$

   _____

3. $a^3(b-c)^2$

   _____

Evaluate each expression.

4. 6^{-1}

   _____

5. 10^0

   _____

6. 12^{-2}

   _____

7. $(-4)^{-3}$

   _____

8. $\left(\dfrac{1}{7}\right)^{-2}$

   _____

9. $\left(\dfrac{3}{4}\right)^{-3}$

   _____

10. -5^0

    _____

11. $\left(\dfrac{-2}{5}\right)^{2}$

    _____

12. $-\left(\dfrac{1}{3}\right)^{-2}$

    _____

Holt Algebra 2

LESSON
1-5

Reteach

Properties of Exponents *(continued)*

Properties of Exponents *(m and n are integers; a and b are nonzero real numbers.)*

Same Base: $a^m \cdot a^n = a^{m+n}$ $\dfrac{a^m}{a^n} = a^{m-n}$ $(a^m)^n = a^{m \cdot n}$

| To multiply, add exponents. | To divide, subtract exponents. | To raise to a power, multiply exponents. |

Different Bases: $(ab)^m = a^m b^m$

Distribute the exponent.

$$\left(\frac{a}{b}\right)^m = \frac{a^m}{b^m}$$

Combine properties of exponents to simplify expressions with exponents.

$(2x^5)^4$		$c^4 d(c^{-3}d^2)$	
$2^4(x^5)^4$	*Distribute the exponent.*	$c^4 c^{-3} dd^2$	*Group like variables.*
$2^4 x^{5 \cdot 4}$	*Multiply exponents.*	$c^{4-3}d^{1+2}$	*Add exponents.*
$2^4 x^{20}$	*Simplify.*	cd^3	*Simplify.*
$16x^{20}$			

$$\frac{3rs^5}{r^4 s^3}$$

$3r^{1-4}s^{5-3}$ *Subtract exponents.*

$3r^{-3}s^2$ *Simplify.*

$$\frac{3s^2}{r^3}$$ *Record answer with positive exponents.*

Simplify each expression. Assume all variables are nonzero.

13. $(-5ab^3)^2$

     $(-5)^2 a^2 b^{3 \cdot 2}$

_____

14. $w^2 x^5(w^4 x^3)$

     $w^{2+4}x^{5+3}$

_____

15. $y^4 z^3(y^{-1}z)^2$

     $y^4 y^{-2}z^3 z^2$

_____

16. $\dfrac{6s^3 t}{3st^2}$

     $\dfrac{6}{3}s^{3-1}t^{1-2}$

_____

17. $\left(\dfrac{a^4}{b^2}\right)^3$

     $\dfrac{a^{4 \cdot 3}}{b^{2 \cdot 3}}$

_____

18. $-3x^{-2}y^3(9x^{-1}y^5)$

     $-3(9)x^{-2-1}y^{3+5}$

_____

Challenge

Parentheses Make the Difference

Compare the expressions -3^2 and $(-3)^2$. How are they different? In the expression -3^2, the base is 3 and the exponent is 2. Only 3 is squared, not -3. Think of -3^2 as $(-1)3^2$. In the expression $(-3)^2$, the base is -3 since the value is shown in parentheses. Evaluating each expression gives $-3^2 = -9$ and $(-3)^2 = 9$.

1. Evaluate -5^3 and $(-5)^3$. _____

2. Evaluate -2^4 and $(-2)^4$. _____

3. Write a general rule for $-a^n$ and $(-a^n)$ where $a > 0$.

_____

_____

Insert parentheses to make each equation true or determine that the equation is true as written.

4. $-5^2 + 11 + 14 = 0$

_____

5. $-3^2 + 81 - 3^4 - 3^2 = 0$

_____

6. $4x^2 + 36x^4y^4 - 6(x^2y^2)^2 - 2x^2 = 0$

_____

7. $-12a^3 + 2b^2 + 1728a^3 - 2b^2 - 2b^2 = 0$

_____

8. $2g^2 + 2h^3 - 4^0 + 24 = 25$

_____

9. $4p^0 + 81^1 - 9^2 - 2^2 = 0$

_____

10. $-12abc^0 - 25d^2 + 34ab^0 + 5d^2 = 2$

_____

Holt Algebra 2

Problem Solving

Properties of Exponents

Joan made a presentation to her technology class about the history of the Internet. Use the data in her table for Exercises 1–6.

1. About how many million Internet users were there in the world in 1997?

   _____

2. When did the estimated number of Internet users in the United States show the greatest increase?

   _____

3. What was the first year the number of Internet users in the United States exceeded 10 million?

   _____

4. During which year was there about the same number of Internet users in the United States as in the world?

   _____

5. During which two years was the number of Internet users in the world almost double the number of Internet users in the United States?

   _____

6. By what factor did the number of Internet users increase in the United States from 1992 to 2002?

   _____

Number of Internet Users (estimated)		
Year	**U.S.**	**World**
1992	4.5×10^6	1.2×10^7
1993	5.5×10^6	1.5×10^7
1994	8.5×10^6	1.75×10^7
1995	2.0×10^7	2.37×10^7
1996	3.0×10^7	5.5×10^7
1997	4.5×10^7	1.01×10^8
1998	7.3×10^7	1.6×10^8
1999	1.02×10^8	2.7×10^8
2000	1.24×10^8	3.85×10^8
2001	1.43×10^8	4.99×10^8
2002	1.64×10^8	5.44×10^8

Choose the letter for the best answer.

7. In 1790 the population of the United States was about 3.9×10^6. By 2000 the population had grown to around 2.8×10^8. By what factor did the population increase?

   A 720

   B 72

   C 7.2

   D 0.72

8. Lee is packing three congruent storage boxes. Each box is $2b^3$ high, b^4 long, and $3b^{-2}$ wide. Which expression gives the total volume of the 3 boxes?

   F $6b^5$

   G $4b^7$

   H $18b^5$

   J $12b^7$

Name _____ Date _____ Class _____

Reading Strategies
Compare and Contrast

Compare these properties of exponents.

For each statement, m and n are
exponents, a and b are bases.
Bases are nonzero real numbers.

Same Base	Different Bases
$a^m \cdot a^n = a^{m+n}$	$(ab)^m = a^m b^m$
$\dfrac{a^m}{a^n} = a^{m-n}$	$\left(\dfrac{a}{b}\right)^m = \dfrac{a^m}{b^m}$
$a^{-n} = \left(\dfrac{1}{a}\right)^n = \dfrac{1}{a^n}$	$\left(\dfrac{a}{b}\right)^{-n} = \left(\dfrac{b}{a}\right)^n = \dfrac{b^n}{a^n}$
$(a^m)^n = a^{m \cdot n}$	

To simplify an expression with exponents:
- use properties
- eliminate grouping symbols
- rewrite all negative exponents as positive exponents
- combine like terms

Complete each statement.

1. In g^5, _____ is the base and _____
   is the exponent.

2. Write a power with base 6 and exponent 8. _____

3. How would you find the product of k^u and k^v? Give an
   example with numbers.

   _____

4. Express h to the negative 7 power in 2 different ways.

   _____

5. In which expression are the bases the same: x^3y^3 or xx^5? _____

6. Which expression has different bases: $-2p^3(3s^3)$ or $-4p^2(5p^5)$? _____

7. Which expression is not simplified: $\dfrac{3a^3}{b^2}$ or $\dfrac{2a^5}{a^2}$? Explain. Then simplify.

   _____

8. Explain how to simplify $\left(\dfrac{x}{y}\right)^{-2}$.

   _____

Original content Copyright © by Holt McDougal. Additions and changes to the original content are the responsibility of the instructor.

Holt Algebra 2

LESSON 1-6 Practice A

Relations and Functions

Complete each sentence to make a true statement.

1. The domain of a relation corresponds to the _____-values in the ordered pairs.

2. The range of a relation corresponds to the _____-values in the ordered pairs.

Give the domain and range for each relation.

3.

Daily CD Sales	
Day	**CDs Sold**
Mon	287
Tue	395
Wed	128
Thu	326
Fri	649

4.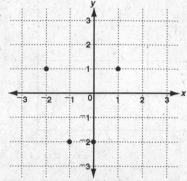

_____

_____

Determine whether each relation is a function. Write *yes* or *no*.

5. {(2, 3), (5, 4), (0, 3), (4, 1)}

6.

_____   _____

Determine whether each relation is a function. Write *yes* or *no*. Use the vertical-line test.

7.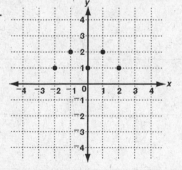

8.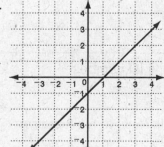

9.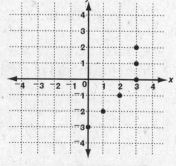

_____   _____   _____

LESSON 1-6

Practice B

Relations and Functions

Give the domain and range for each relation. Then determine whether each relation is a function.

1.

Average High Temperatures	
Month	Temperature
Jun	82°
Jul	88°
Aug	93°
Sep	82°

2.

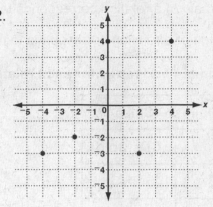

_____   _____

_____   _____

Use the vertical-line test to determine whether each relation is a function. If not, identify two points a vertical line would pass through.

3.
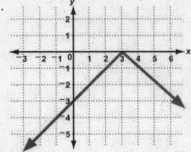

4.
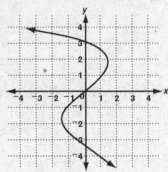

5.
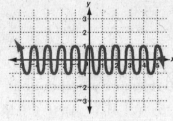

_____   _____   _____

Explain whether each relation is a function.

6. {(1, 1), (2, 2), (3, 3), (4, 4)}

_____

7. from the model of car to the car's ID number

_____

8. from the dates James took math tests to his test scores

_____

LESSON 1-6 Practice C
Relations and Functions

Give the domain and range of each relation and make a mapping diagram.

1. {(1, 4), (−2, −3), (6, −3), (3, 4)}

2. {(3, −1), (2, −2), (0, 2), (2, 1)}

_____

_____

3.

Basketball Scoring Record	
Game	Points Scored
1	37
2	44
3	38
4	59

4.

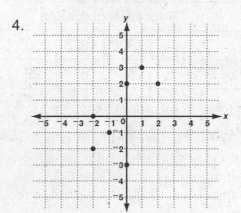

_____

_____

Determine whether the relation from A to B is a function, the relation from B to A is a function, or both are functions.

	A	B	A→B	B→A
5.	Date of getting a driver's license	Person		
6.	Fishing contest participants	Number of fish caught		
7.	Zip code	State		
8.	Age of a tree	Type of tree		
9.	Type of bird	Month bird migrates		
10.	Number of days in birth month	Person		

LESSON	**Reteach**
1-6	*Relations and Functions*

A **relation** pairs input values (*x*) and output values (*y*).

Domain
Set of input values
or *x*-coordinates

Range
Set of output values
or *y*-coordinates

List domain and range elements from least to greatest.

Soccer Registration					
Year	1996	1998	2000	2002	2004
Number of Players	56	82	95	136	212

Domain: {1996, 1998, 2000, 2002, 2004}   Set of *x*-coordinates

Range: {56, 82, 95, 136, 212}   Set of *y*-coordinates

The domain of a set of ordered pairs is
the *x*-coordinates. The range is the
y-coordinates. Each value is listed only once.

For the graph at right:

Domain: {−4, −2, 0, 2, 4}; Range: {0, 2, 3}

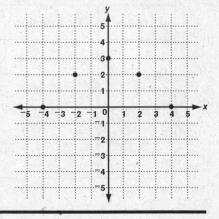

Give the domain and range for each relation.

1.

Concert Ticket Price					
Year	2001	2002	2003	2004	2005
Price ($)	25	28	35	42	46

Domain: {2001, _____   Range: {25, _____

2.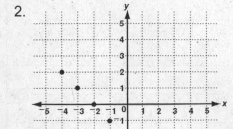

Domain: {−4, _____

Range: {−2, _____

Holt Algebra 2

LESSON 1-6 Reteach

Relations and Functions (continued)

A **function** is a special type of relation.
A function has only one output for each input.

Use the **vertical-line test** to decide whether a relation is a function.

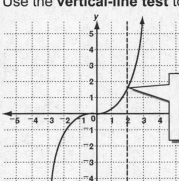

Draw a vertical line. The line passes through no more than one point on the graph. This *is* a function.

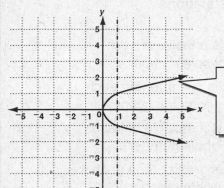

Draw a vertical line. The line passes through two points on the graph, at (1, −1) and (1, 1). This is *not* a function.

Use the vertical-line test to determine whether each relation is a function. If not, identify two points a vertical line would pass through.

3.

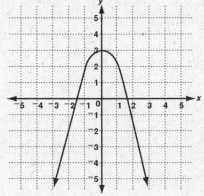

4.

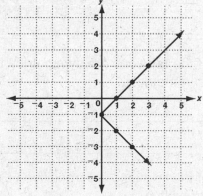

_____   _____

Holt Algebra 2

Challenge
Relating Relations

A relation is said to be **reflexive** if for every element *r* in the relation, the ordered pair (*r*, *r*) is in the relation. For example, if 3 is an element in a relation, then the relation is reflexive if the ordered pair (3, 3) is in the relation.

A relation is said to be **symmetric** if whenever the ordered pair (*r*, *s*) is in the relation, then (*s*, *r*) is also in the relation. For example, if (5, 6) is an ordered pair in a relation, then the relation is symmetric if the ordered pair (6, 5) is in the relation.

A relation is said to be **transitive** if whenever the ordered pairs (*r*, *s*) and (*s*, *t*) are in the relation, then the ordered pair (*r*, *t*) is in the relation. For example, if (3, 7) and (7, 12) are ordered pairs in a relation, then the relation is transitive if the ordered pair (3, 12) is in the relation.

Any relation that has all 3 properties is called an **equivalence relation**.

The following relations are described in words. Use these relations for Exercises 1–4.

> *V* is a set of ordered pairs such that each first element is a factor of each second element, and every element in the relation is a whole number.

> *W* is a set of ordered pairs such that each first element is congruent to each second element, and every element in the relation is a geometric figure.

> *X* is a set of ordered pairs such that each first element is a multiple of each second element, and every element in the relation is a whole number.

> *Y* is a set of ordered pairs such that each first element is greater than each second element, and every element in the relation is a whole number.

> *Z* is a set of ordered pairs such that each first element is similar to each second element, and every element in the relation is a geometric figure.

1. Which of the relations are reflexive? Explain why the other relations are not reflexive.

   _____

2. Which of the relations are symmetric? Explain why the other relations are not symmetric.

   _____

   _____

3. Which of the relations are transitive? Explain why the other relations are not transitive.

   _____

4. Which, if any, of the relations are equivalence relations? _____

LESSON 1-6 Problem Solving
Relations and Functions

In order to make a nutrition plan, Richard wants to compare different types of milk. Use the table for Exercises 1–7.

1. Is the relation from calories to saturated fat a function? Explain why or why not.

   _____

   _____

2. Is the relation from calories to carbohydrates a function? Explain why or why not.

   _____

   _____

MILK FACTS (1 cup)			
A	**B**	**C**	**D**
Type	Calories	Carbo-hydrates (g)	Saturated Fat (g)
Whole	146	11	4.4
2%	122	11.4	3.1
1%	102	12.2	1.5
Nonfat	83	12.2	0.3

3. Is the relation from carbohydrates to calories a function? Explain why or why not.

   _____

Choose the letter for the best answer.

4. Richard is drawing graphs of some of the relations from the table above. Which of these graphs fails the vertical-line test if he graphs the data as follows?

   A column B along the x-axis, column C along the y-axis

   B column D along the x-axis, column B along the y-axis

   C column D along the x-axis, column C along the y-axis

   D column C along the x-axis, column B along the y-axis

5. For the function (B, D) that relates calories to saturated fat, which column shows the domain?

   F column A

   G column B

   H column C

   J column D

6. Which column shows the range of a function that relates the type of milk to the number of calories?

   A column A

   B column B

   C column C

   D column D

7. Richard makes a mapping diagram from each type of milk to the number of students in his class of 25 who prefer that type of milk. Which is the best statement about this diagram?

   F It is a relation, but not a function.

   G It is a function, but not a relation.

   H It is a function and a relation.

   J It is not a relation or a function.

LESSON 1-6

Reading Strategies

Read a Table

A **function** is a **relation** in which the input is never repeated. A relation is a pairing of 2 sets of numbers, such as pairing a year with the number of students enrolled in school. Use a table to help you determine if a relation is a function.

The **domain** is the set of input values. The domain is the *x* values.

Lakeside School Enrollment	
Year	**Number of Students**
2000	356
2001	372
2002	422
2003	455

The **range** is the set of output values. The range is the *y* values.

Because no input values are repeated, the relation is a function.

x	−10	−5	−1	−1	0
y	2	3	4	5	6

−1 is an input value. It is repeated. The relation is not a function.

Use the table for Exercises 1–3.

x	−2	−2	0	1	2
y	4	2	0	−4	−6

1. What is the domain of the relation? How do you know?

_____

2. What is the range of the relation? How do you know?

_____

3. Is the relation a function? Explain.

_____

4. Make a table to show the ordered pairs in the set. Is the relation a function? Explain.
   {(9, 6), (1, 4), (0, 2), (1, 4), (4, 6)}

_____

LESSON
1-7

Practice A

Function Notation

Find each value of the function.

1. $f(x) = -5x + 9$ $f(3) = -5(\_\_\_\_) + 9 = -\_\_\_\_ + 9 = \_\_\_\_\_$

2.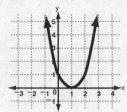

3.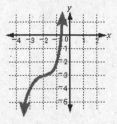

4.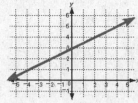

$f(0) = _____$

$f(1) = _____$

$f(2) = _____$

$f(-1) = _____$

$f(-2) = _____$

$f(-3) = _____$

$f(-4) = _____$

$f(0) = _____$

$f(2) = _____$

Graph each function.

5.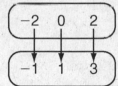

6. $f(x) = 2x - 3$

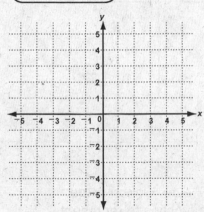

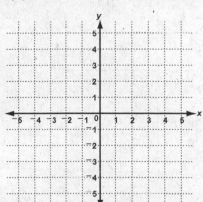

7. Ty uses the function $g(x) = 0.5 + 0.2(x - 1)$ to calculate the cost in dollars of using a calling card to make a long-distance call lasting x minutes. The variable x must be a whole number. Graph the function. Then determine the cost of a 10-minute call.

_____

Calling Card Costs

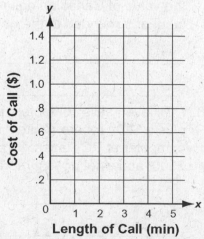

LESSON 1-7

Practice B
Function Notation

For each function, evaluate $f(-1)$, $f(0)$, $f\left(\dfrac{3}{2}\right)$.

1. $g(x) = -4x + 2$ _____

2. $h(x) = x^2 - 3$ _____

3. $f(x) = 3x^2 + x$ _____

4. $f(x) = \dfrac{x}{2} - 1$ _____

Graph each function. Then evaluate $f(-2)$ and $f(0)$.

5. $f(x) = x^2 - 4$

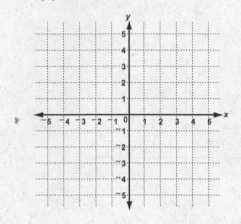

6. $f(x) = -\dfrac{3}{2}x + 1$

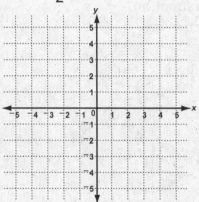

_____   _____

Solve.

7. On one day the value of $1.00 U.S. was equivalent to 0.77 euro. On the same day $1.00 U.S. was equivalent to $1.24 Canadian. Write a function to represent the value of Canadian dollars in euros. What is the value of the function for an input of 5 rounded to the nearest cent, and what does it represent?

_____

_____

8. PC Haven sells computers at a 15% discount on the original price plus a $200 rebate. Write a function to represent the final price of a computer at PC Haven. What is the value of the function for an input of 2500, and what does it represent?

_____

_____

LESSON 1-7

Practice C

Function Notation

A set of input values is sometimes referred to as the *replacement set* for the independent variable. Evaluate each function for the given replacement set.

1. $f(x) = \dfrac{-x}{4} + 6; \left\{-8, \dfrac{1}{2}, 1.6, 3\right\}$

2. $g(x) = x(-2x + 3); \left\{-4\dfrac{1}{2}, -\dfrac{1}{3}, 3, 6\right\}$

_____ _____

3.

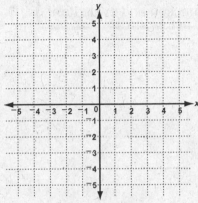

$\left\{-3, -2.5, 1\dfrac{1}{4}, 3\right\}$

4.

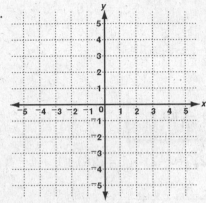

$\left\{-3, -\dfrac{1}{2}, 1.5, 3\right\}$

_____ _____

Explain what a reasonable domain and range would be for each situation.

5. the number of 8-slice pizzas needed to feed *x* people at a party where each person will eat 3 slices of pizza

_____

_____

6. the time it takes to bicycle *m* miles at a rate of 15 miles per hour

_____

_____

Write a function to represent each situation.

7. Sharon earns $30 for each lawn she mows. _____

8. Each large tub of ice cream makes 80 single-dip cones. A single-dip cone sells for $1.49. _____

LESSON 1-7

Reteach
Function Notation

You can use function notation to write a function.

Read: *f* of *x* equals 2*x* – 3.

$$f(x) = 2x - 3$$

Output *f*(*x*)

Input *x*

Evaluate $f(0)$, $f\left(\dfrac{1}{2}\right)$, and $f(-2)$ for $f(x) = 2x^2 - x + 1$.

$$f(0) = 2(0)^2 - 0 + 1 = 1$$

Subsitute 0 for *x* in the function and evaluate.

$$f\left(\frac{1}{2}\right) = 2\left(\frac{1}{2}\right)^2 - \frac{1}{2} + 1 = 2\left(\frac{1}{4}\right) - \frac{1}{2} + 1 = \frac{1}{2} - \frac{1}{2} + 1 = 1$$

Substitute $\dfrac{1}{2}$ for *x*.

$$f(-2) = 2(-2)^2 - (-2) + 1 = 2(4) + 2 + 1 = 8 + 2 + 1 = 11$$

Substitute –2 for *x*.

For each function, evaluate $f(0)$, $f\left(\dfrac{3}{2}\right)$, and $f(-1)$.

1. $f(x) = 4x^2 - 2$

   $f(0) = 4(0)^2 - 2$ $f\left(\dfrac{3}{2}\right) = 4\left(\dfrac{3}{2}\right)^2 - 2$ $f(-1) = 4(-1)^2 - 2$

   _____   _____   _____

2. $f(x) = -2x + 10$

   $f(0) =$ _____ $f\left(\dfrac{3}{2}\right) =$ _____ $f(-1) =$ _____

3. $f(x) = x^2 + 6x$

   $f(0) =$ _____ $f\left(\dfrac{3}{2}\right) =.$ _____ $f(-1) =$ _____

Holt Algebra 2

Reteach
Function Notation (continued)

Plot ordered pairs on a coordinate plane to graph a function.

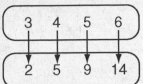

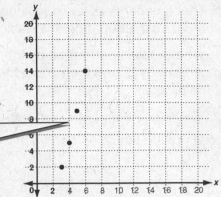

Values between given points are not defined. Do *not* connect the points.

To graph $f(x) = -2x + 3$, make a table of values.

x	−2x + 3	f(x)
−2	−2(−2) + 3	7
−1	−2(−1) + 3	5
0	−2(0) + 3	3
1	−2(1) + 3	1
2	−2(2) + 3	−1

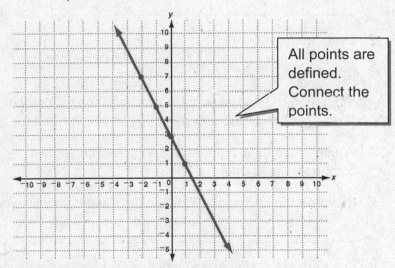

All points are defined. Connect the points.

Graph each function on the coordinate plane given.

4.

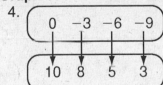

5. $g(x) = 2x - 4$

x	2x − 4	g(x)
0		
1		
2		
3		
4		

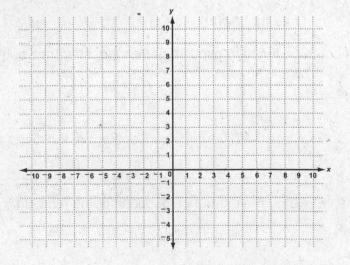

Holt Algebra 2

LESSON 1-7 Challenge
Function Togetherness

You can think of a function as a process. The process has an input, the independent variable. That independent variable is put into the function, processed, and then output as the dependent variable.

So $f(x) = 3x + 7$ defines the process performed by the function f. The variable, x, is input, multiplied by 3, and then 7 is added to the result. The output is the result of the process.

Consider the functions $f(x) = 2x - 3$ and $g(x) = x^2 + x - 5$.

1. Describe the process of the functions f and g in words.

   _____

   _____

2. Evaluate $f(5x^2)$.   _____

3. Evaluate $g(2x)$.   _____

A combination of the functions $f(x)$ and $g(x)$ form a composite function, $f(g(x))$. In $f(g(x))$ the output of $g(x)$ is used as the input for $f(x)$.

4. Which function or process is performed first in the
   composite function $f(g(x))$?   _____

5. Evaluate the composite function $f(g(x))$ and simplify your result.

   _____

6. Evaluate the composite function $g(f(x))$ and simplify your result.

   _____

7. Is it true that $f(g(x)) = g(f(x))$?   _____

A common function used in math is the difference quotient.

$$\frac{f(x+h) - f(x)}{h}$$

8. Evaluate the difference quotient for the function f and simplify your result.

   _____

9. Evaluate the difference quotient for the function g and simplify your result.

   _____

Holt Algebra 2

LESSON
1-7

Problem Solving

Function Notation

Juan is analyzing cell phone plans. The graph shows two plans he is considering. Use the graph for Exercises 1–4.

1. For which value of x does each function have a value of $40?

   _____

2. The graphs of the functions cross at x = 150. Explain what this represents.

   _____

3. Use function notation and estimation to represent the value of each function for 200 minutes.

   _____

4. Juan expects to use about 300 minutes per month. Which plan should he buy? Why?

   _____

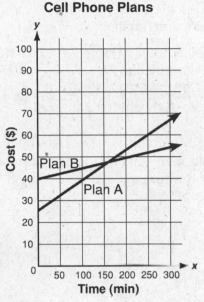

Cell Phone Plans

In September, Harley puts $1035 that he earned during the summer in a bank account to use during the school year for his personal expenses. He budgets d dollars a month for expenses. Choose the letter for the best answer.

5. Which shows a function representing the amount left in his account after 4 months?

   A $f(d) = \$1035 - 4d$

   B $f(d) = \$1035 - d$

   C $f(d) = (\$1035 - 4)d$

   D $f(d) = \dfrac{\$1035}{4d}$

6. Harley writes the function

   $g(a) = \dfrac{\$1035}{9} - a$ to show his monthly

   budgeted amount remaining in a month when a, the actual amount he spends, is less than the amount of his budget. What is the value of this function for a month when he spends $87.50?

   F $12.50   H $115.00

   G $27.50   J $202.50

7. Fay uses the function $f(x) = \dfrac{3}{2}x + 1$ to find the number of boxes of tile to buy for each 10 square feet of floor. How many boxes of tiles does she need to cover 600 square feet?

   A 901 boxes

   B 401 boxes

   C 91 boxes

   D 41 boxes

8. Rasheed uses the function $f(e) = 4e$ to find the distance around a square barbecue pit. What is the length of the side of the pit that has a perimeter of 55.2 ft?

   F 13.8 ft

   G 27.6 ft

   H 110.4 ft

   J 220.8 ft

Holt Algebra 2

LESSON 1-7

Reading Strategies
Understand Notation

Function notation, $f(x)$, allows you to keep track of the dependent variable. The dependent variable is x.

> Read $f(x)$ as "f of x."

In function notation, $y = f(x)$.

> Write ordered pairs as (x, y) or $(x, f(x))$.

To evaluate $f(x) = x^2 + 2x - 1$ for $f(3)$, substitute 3 for x in the function.

$f(3) = (3)^2 + 2(3) - 1 = 9 + 6 - 1 = 14$
For $y = f(x)$, when $x = 3$, $y = 14$.

> Read $f(x) = x^2 + 2x - 1$ as "f of x is equal to x squared plus $2x$ minus 1."

You can graph $y = f(x)$. Use the graph to evaluate $f(-2)$: find the point on the graph where $x = -2$.

> $f(-2)$ is the corresponding y-value where $x = -2$.

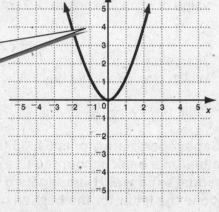

$f(-2) = 4$

Answer each question.

1. Use function notation to write: "f of x is equal to x cubed minus x squared."

   _____

2. Describe the function in words: $f(x) = 5x^2 + 4x - 3$.

   _____

3. Explain how to evaluate $f(x) = x^3 + 6x$ for $f(-1)$.

   _____

4. Explain how to use the graph to evaluate $f(2)$.

   _____

   _____

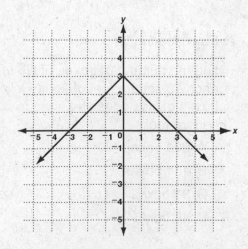

Holt Algebra 2

LESSON
1-8

Practice A
Exploring Transformations

Use the graph to perform each transformation described.

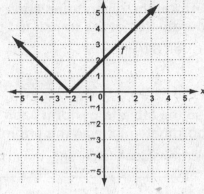

1. Plot point *A* at (4, 3). Translate point *A* left 5 units. Label this point *B*. Give the coordinates of point *B*.

   _____

2. Plot point *C* at (1, 1). Translate point *C* right 2 units and down 3 units. Label this point *D*. Give the coordinates of point *D*.

   _____

3. Transform *y* = *f*(*x*) by translating it right 2 units. Label the new function *g*. Compare the points that make up the 2 functions. Which coordinate changes, *x* or *y*?

   _____

4. Transform *y* = *f*(*x*) by reflecting it across the *x*-axis. Label the new function *h*. Which coordinate changes, *x* or *y*?

   _____

Use the graph to perform each transformation described.

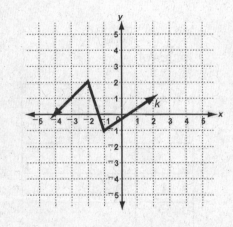

5. Transform *y* = *k*(*x*) by compressing it horizontally by a factor of $\frac{1}{2}$. Label the new function *m*. Which coordinate is multiplied by $\frac{1}{2}$, *x* or *y*?

   _____

6. Transform *y* = *k*(*x*) by translating it down 3 units. Label the new function *p*. What happens to the *y*-coordinate in each new ordered pair?

   _____

7. Transform *y* = *k*(*x*) by stretching it vertically by a factor of 2. Label the new function *q*. Which coordinate is multiplied by 2, *x* or *y*?

   _____

8. Describe how the coordinates of a function change when it is translated 2 units to the left and 4 units up.

   _____

9. Describe how the coordinates of a function change when you vertically compress a function by a factor of $\frac{2}{3}$.

   _____

Holt Algebra 2

Practice B
Exploring Transformations

Perform the given translation on the point (2, 5) and give the coordinates of the translated point.

1. left 3 units

2. down 6 units

3. right 4 units, up 2 units

_____   _____   _____

Use the table to perform each transformation of y = f(x). Use the same coordinate plane as the original function.

4. translation left 1 unit, down 5 units

x	y	
−3	3	
−1	1	
1	2	
2	1	
3	2	

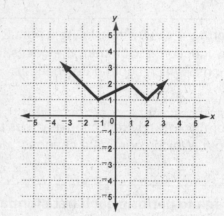

5. vertical stretch
   factor of $\frac{3}{2}$

x	y	
−3	3	
−1	1	
1	2	
2	1	
3	2	

6. horizontal compression
   factor of $\frac{1}{2}$

x	y	
−3	3	
−1	1	
1	2	
2	1	
3	2	

7. reflection across x-axis

x	y	
−3	3	
−1	1	
1	2	
2	1	
3	2	

Solve.

8. George has a goal for the number of computers he wants to sell each month for the next 6 months at his computer store. He draws a graph to show his projected profits for that period. Then he decides to discount the prices by 10%. How will this affect his profits? Identify the transformation to his graph and describe how to find the ordered pairs for the transformation.

_____

LESSON
1-8

Practice C
Exploring Transformations

Transform trapezoid *ABCD* as indicated.
Estimate the area of each transformed
trapezoid as compared to the area of
trapezoid *ABCD*.

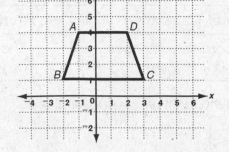

1. reflection across the *x*-axis

   _____

2. horizontal compression by a factor of $\frac{1}{2}$ 3. horizontal stretch by a factor of 2

   _____   _____

4. vertical compression by a factor of $\frac{1}{2}$ 5. vertical stretch by a factor of $\frac{3}{2}$

   _____   _____

Tucci's House of Music rents practice space and
musical instruments. Use of a practice room costs
$10 for the first 2 hours and $4 for each additional
hour. An electric guitar rents for $15 for the first
2 hours and $3 for each additional hour.

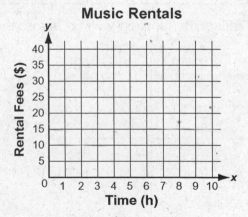

Music Rentals

6. Sketch a graph of two functions, one for the cost of
   renting a practice room and another for the cost of
   renting an electric guitar.

**Identify the transformation of the original graphs
represented by the following changes.**

7. The charge for the first 2 hours' rental of a practice room increases to $12.

   _____

8. As a special promotion, Tucci's House of Music cuts the practice room
   charges by 50% for first-time users.

   _____

9. The cost of renting a guitar increases to $30 for the first 4 hours and
   $6 for each additional hour.

   _____

LESSON 1-8

Reteach

Exploring Transformations

A **translation** moves a point, figure, or function right, left, up, or down.

Horizontal Translation (right or left)	**Vertical Translation** (up or down)
The *x*-coordinate changes. $(x, y) \rightarrow (x + h, y)$	The *y*-coordinate changes. $(x, y) \rightarrow (x, y + k)$

Translate the function $y = f(x)$ left 2 units.

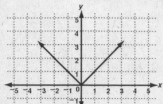 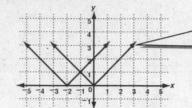

Move each point 2 units left. Connect the points. $(x, y) \rightarrow (x - 2, y)$

A **reflection** flips a point, figure, or function across a line.

Reflection Across *y*-axis	**Reflection Across *x*-axis**
The *x*-coordinate changes. $(x, y) \rightarrow (-x, y)$	The *y*-coordinate changes. $(x, y) \rightarrow (x, -y)$

Reflect the function $y = f(x)$ across the *x*-axis.

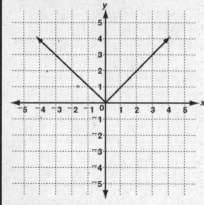 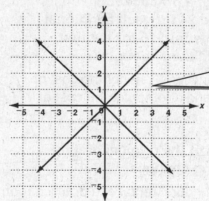

Flip each point across the axis. Connect the points. $(x, y) \rightarrow (x, -y)$

Perform each transformation of $y = f(x)$.

1. translation up 2 units

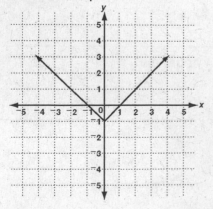

2. reflection across *x*-axis

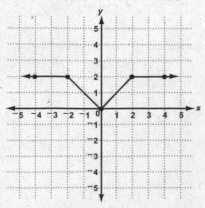

Holt Algebra 2

Reteach
Exploring Transformations (continued)

In a stretch or a compression, the new figure has a different shape than the original.

Horizontal Stretch (away from *y*-axis)	The *x*-coordinate changes. $(x, y) \rightarrow (bx, y)$; $|b| > 1$
Vertical Stretch (away from *x*-axis)	The *y*-coordinate changes. $(x, y) \rightarrow (x, ay)$; $|a| > 1$
Horizontal Compression (toward the *y*-axis)	The *x*-coordinate changes. $(x, y) \rightarrow (bx, y)$; $0 < |b| < 1$
Vertical Compression (toward the *x*-axis)	The *y*-coordinate changes. $(x, y) \rightarrow (x, ay)$; $0 < |a| < 1$

Perform a vertical stretch of the function $y = f(x)$ by a factor of 2.
In a vertical stretch $(x, y) \rightarrow (x, ay)$. In this case, $a = 2$.

Original Figure (solid line)	x	2y	Stretched Figure (dashed line)
(−3, 3)	−3	6	(−3, 6)
(−1, 1)	−1	2	(−1, 2)
(0, 2)	0	4	(0, 4)
(1, 1)	1	2	(1, 2)
(3, 3)	3	6	(3, 6)

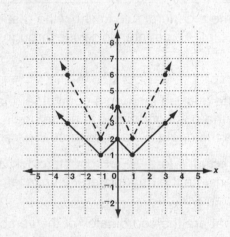

Perform each transformation of $y = f(x)$.

3. horizontal stretch by a factor of 2

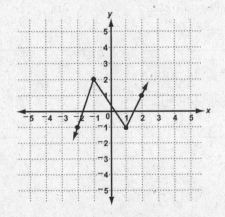

4. vertical compression by a factor of $\frac{1}{2}$

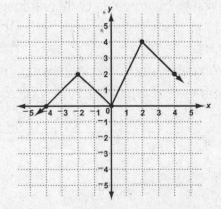

Holt Algebra 2

LESSON
1-8

Challenge

Turn it Around

Translations and reflections are transformations in the position of a
figure. A third transformation that preserves congruence is called a
rotation. Point *A* is at (4, 0). Move point *A* along the semicircle 90°
in a counterclockwise direction. The rotated point has coordinates
(0, 4). This is called a rotation of 90° counterclockwise centered at
the origin.

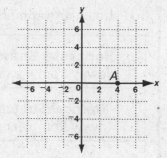

Use the graph at right for Exercises 1–6.

Rotate figure *EFGH* 90° clockwise through the origin.

1. What are the coordinates of the vertices of the
   rotated figure?

   _____

2. Write a general rule to show the result of rotating
   a point 90° clockwise through the origin.

   _____

3. Write a general rule to show the result of rotating
   a point 90° counterclockwise through the origin.

   _____

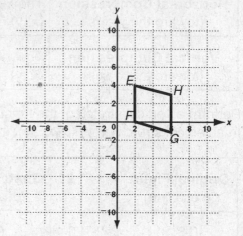

To rotate a figure through a point other than the origin, translate the figure
so that the point of rotation is at the origin. Then perform the rotation
through the origin. Finally, reverse the translation.

Rotate quadrilateral *EFGH* counterclockwise 90° through the point (2, 0).
First translate the quadrilateral 2 units left to move the point of rotation,
(2,0), to the origin.

4. What are the coordinates of the vertices of the translated quadrilateral?

   _____

Now, rotate the translated quadrilateral 90° counterclockwise through
the origin.

5. What are the coordinates of the vertices of the rotated quadrilateral?

   _____

Finally, reverse the translation by moving the quadrilateral 2 units right.

6. What are the coordinates of the vertices of the final quadrilateral?

   _____

LESSON 1-8

Problem Solving

Exploring Transformations

Harry is working on a budget for a concert. The graph shows the total cost of renting the hall. A cleaning fee of $40 for each rental is included in the graph. Use the graph for Exercises 1–6.

1. What is the cost of renting the hall for 2 hours? for 3 hours? for 6 hours? for 7 hours?

   _____

Concert Hall Rental

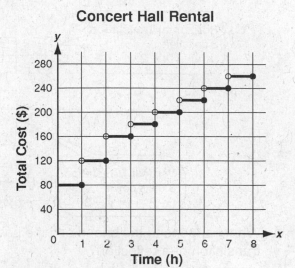

2. What is the rate per hour not including the cleaning fee if Harry rents the hall for up to 3 hours?

   _____

3. What is the rate per hour after the first 3 hours?

   _____

4. Describe the effect on the graph if the cleaning fee were changed to $25.

   _____

5. The managers decide that the minimum time for which the hall can be rented is 3 hours. Describe the effect this change would have on the graph above. How would the range change?

   _____

   _____

6. The Art Center gives Harry a graph showing its charges. This graph is the same shape as the graph above, but every point has been translated up 10 units. What would be the effect on Harry's budget if he chose to have the concert at the Art Center?

   _____

   _____

Choose the letter for the best answer.

7. Martha's profits from her bagel store last year were $0.35 per dozen bagels sold. This year her profits decreased 10%. What kind of transformation does this represent?

   A vertical compression

   B vertical stretch

   C horizontal compression

   D horizontal stretch

8. Shana drew the graph for a quadratic function. Then she did a horizontal stretch of the curve. Which transformation did she perform?

   F $(x, y) \rightarrow (x, ay); |a| > 1$

   G $(x, y) \rightarrow (bx, y); 0 < |b| < 1$

   H $(x, y) \rightarrow (x, ay); 0 < |a| < 1$

   J $(x, y) \rightarrow (bx, y); |b| > 1$

Holt Algebra 2

LESSON 1-8

Reading Strategies
Understand Vocabulary

A diagram can help you connect transformation vocabulary to corresponding graphs. When you perform a transformation on a graph, the figure is moved according to the type of transformation.

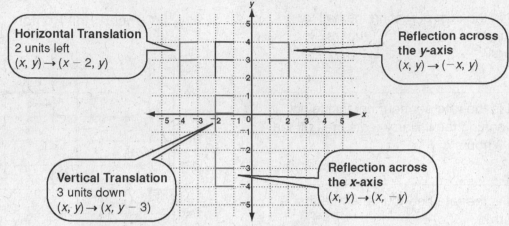

Horizontal Translation
2 units left
$(x, y) \rightarrow (x - 2, y)$

Reflection across the y-axis
$(x, y) \rightarrow (-x, y)$

Vertical Translation
3 units down
$(x, y) \rightarrow (x, y - 3)$

Reflection across the x-axis
$(x, y) \rightarrow (x, -y)$

1. What happens to the shape and the position of a figure during a translation or a reflection?

_____

Use the graph for Exercises 2–5.

2. How will the coordinates change if the function is translated 3 units right?

_____

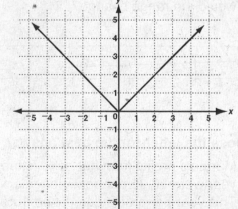

3. How will the coordinates change if the function is translated 5 units down?

_____

4. How will the coordinates change if the function is reflected across the x-axis?

_____

5. How will the coordinates change if the function is translated 4 units left and 2 units up?

_____

LESSON
1-9

Practice A

Introduction to Parent Functions

Identify the parent function for g from its function rule.

1. $g(x) = (x - 6)^2$

2. $g(x) = x^3 + 1$

3. $g(x) = 3x$

_____

_____

_____

Identify the parent function for each graph. Then describe which transformation of the parent function it represents.

4.

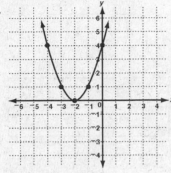

5.

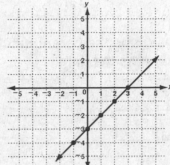

6.

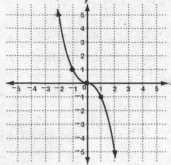

_____

_____

_____

_____

_____

_____

Graph the data from the table. Describe the parent function and the transformation that best approximates the data set.

7.

x	−2	−1	0	1	2
y	6	3	2	3	6

8.

x	−4	−2	0	2	4
y	−8	−1	0	1	8

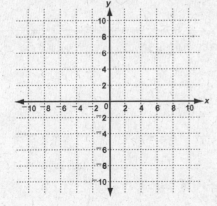

_____

_____

_____

_____

Holt Algebra 2

LESSON 1-9
Practice B
Introduction to Parent Functions

Identify the parent function for *h* from its function rule. Then graph *h* on your calculator and describe what transformation of the parent function it represents.

1. $h(x) = \sqrt{x + 4}$

_____

_____

2. $h(x) = (x - 4)^3$

_____

_____

3. $h(x) = 4x^2$

_____

_____

Graph the data from the table. Describe the parent function and the transformation that best approximates the data set.

4.

x	−2	−1	0	1	2
y	−9	−2	−1	0	7

5.

x	0	2	8	18	32
y	0	1	2	3	4

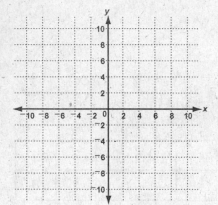

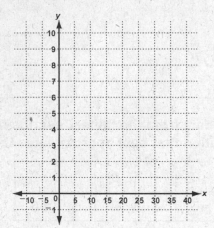

_____   _____

6. Compare the domain and the range for the parent quadratic function to the domain and the range for the parent linear function.

_____

_____

_____

7. Compare the domain and the range for the parent square-root function to the domain and the range for the parent cubic function.

_____

_____

_____

Holt Algebra 2

LESSON
1-9

Practice C

Introduction to Parent Functions

Graph each function on a graphing calculator. Identify the domain and range of the function, and describe the transformation from its parent function.

1. $g(x) = -\sqrt{4x}$ _____

_____

2. $g(x) = \dfrac{1}{2}(x-2)^3$ _____

_____

Graph the function. Identify the parent function that best describes the set of points, and describe the transformation from the parent function.

3. $\{(-2, 9), (-1, 3), (0, 1), (1, 3), (2, 9)\}$

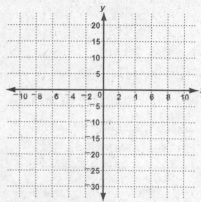

_____

_____

Sketch a graph for each situation and identify the related parent function. Then identify a reasonable domain and range for the function.

4. distance traveled in *t* hours at 55 mi/h

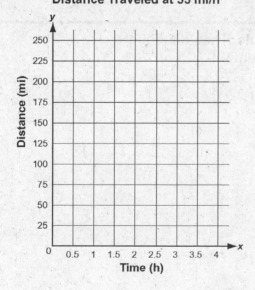

Distance Traveled at 55 mi/h

_____

_____

5. surface area of a cube with side length *c*

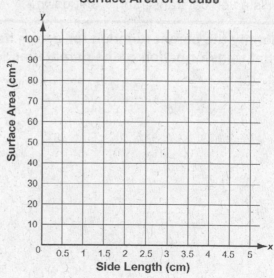

Surface Area of a Cube

_____

_____

Holt Algebra 2

LESSON 1-9

Reteach

Introduction to Parent Functions

Functions can be classified into families. In the families, similar-looking functions represent transformations of a parent function.

Parent Functions			
Linear $f(x) = x$	**Quadratic** $f(x) = x^2$	**Cubic** $f(x) = x^3$	**Square Root** $f(x) = \sqrt{x}$
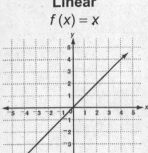	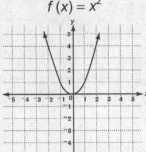		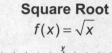

The parent function of $g(x) = x^3 - 1$ is *cubic*.

x has a power of 3.

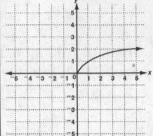

Compare the graph to the graph of the parent function.

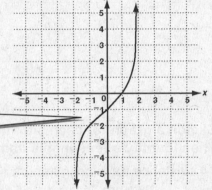

$g(x) = x^3 - 1$ is a transformation from the parent function.
It is a vertical translation 1 unit down.

Identify the parent function for g from its function rule. Then describe what transformation of the parent function it represents.

1. $g(x) = -x^2$

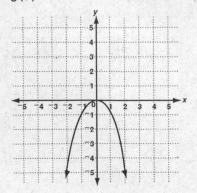

Parent function _____

_____

2. $g(x) = \sqrt{x} + 2$

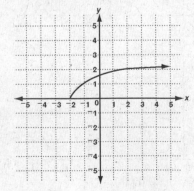

Parent function _____

_____

Holt Algebra 2

LESSON **Reteach**
1-9

Introduction to Parent Functions (continued)

You can graph data to identify a parent function.

x	2	1	3	0	4
y	0	1	1	4	4

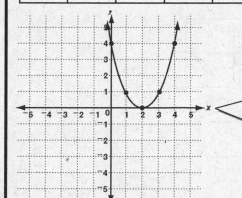

Plot the points.

Connect the points with a smooth curve.

Compare shape to graphs of parent functions.

The shape looks like the quadratic parent function $f(x) = x^2$.

It looks like a horizontal translation 2 units right.

Graph the data from each table. Describe the parent function and the transformation that best approximates the data set.

3.

x	−2	−1	0	1	2
y	1	−2	−3	−2	1

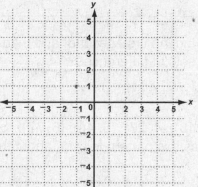

Parent function _____

_____

_____

4.

x	−2	−1	0	1	2
y	2	1	0	−1	−2

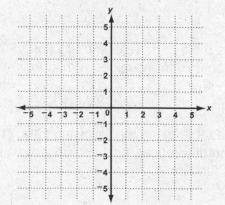

Parent function _____

_____

_____

LESSON	**Challenge**
1-9	*All in the Family*

Sometimes it is necessary to identify parent functions from data points obtained through experiments or trials. Look at the data below for the quadratic function $y = x^2 + 2x + 4$. Notice that the second differences have a constant value of 2. Since the second differences are constant, the parent function is a quadratic function.

x	1	2	3	4	5	6
y	7	12	19	28	39	52
First Difference		5	7	9	11	13
Second Difference			2	2	2	2

A linear function is indicated by constant first differences.

Find the differences in each set of data.

1.

x	1	2	3	4	5	6
y	5	9	25	59	117	205

a. Which differences have a constant value?

_____

b. Identify the parent function.

_____

2.

x	−1	0	1	2	3	4	5
y	11	4	11	44	139	356	779

a. Which differences have a constant value?

_____

b. Identify the parent function.

_____

3. Make a table of data for the function $y = 2^x$ for $1 \le x \le 6$. Find the first, second, and third differences in the y values. What do you notice about the sets of differences?

_____

4. Make a table using the following data: (1, 10), (2, 13), (3, 18), (4, 27), (5, 44), (6, 77). Find the differences until you observe a pattern. What does this pattern tell you about the parent function?

_____

_____

Holt Algebra 2

Name _____ Date _____ Class _____

Problem Solving

Introduction to Parent Functions

Katy and Peter are writing a paper about the history and use of cell phones. They make a graph of the data in the table. They want to determine the parent function for the graph.

Cell Phone Subscribers in the United States (estimated in millions)			
1991	7.6	1997	55.3
1992	11.0	1998	69.2
1993	16.0	1999	86.0
1994	24.1	2000	109.5
1995	33.8	2001	128.4
1996	44.0	2002	140.8

U.S. Cell Phone Subscribers

1. Peter wants to compare the graph to the function $f(x) = 7x + 2$. How would the graph of $f(x) = 7x + 2$ compare to its parent function $f(x) = x$?

_____

2. What is the value $f(x) = 7x + 2$ for 1996, when $x = 6$? Does that point fit the graph? Try some other values of x for the function $f(x) = 7x + 2$. How well do the results fit the range of the graph?

_____

3. Katy wants to compare the graph to the function $f(x) = x^2 + 5$. How would the graph of $f(x) = x^2 + 5$ compare to its parent function $f(x) = x^2$?

_____

4. Find the value of $f(x) = x^2 + 5$ for 1996, when $x = 6$? Does that point fit the graph? Try some other values of x for the function $f(x) = x^2 + 5$. How well do the results fit the range of the graph?

_____

5. Which parent function and transformation best models these data?

_____

Holt Algebra 2

LESSON 1-9

Reading Strategies
Use a Model

Every function belongs to a family of other functions whose graphs have similar shapes. Each family has a parent function. There may be lots of functions in the family, but there is only 1 parent function. Look at the models of the different parent functions in the table below. All linear functions are straight lines just like the function $f(x) = x$. The line may not be in exactly the same position on the coordinate plane, but it is still a straight line.

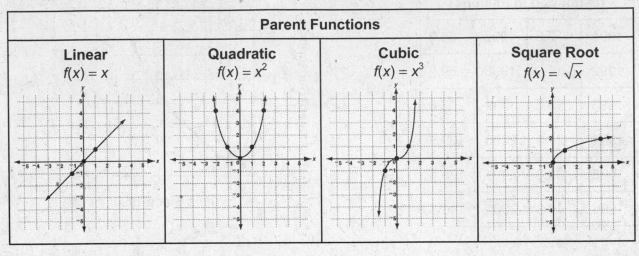

Parent Functions			
Linear $f(x) = x$	**Quadratic** $f(x) = x^2$	**Cubic** $f(x) = x^3$	**Square Root** $f(x) = \sqrt{x}$

Use the graphs below and the table above for Exercises 1–6.

1. How is this function like the parent quadratic function? How is it different?

   _____

   _____

   _____

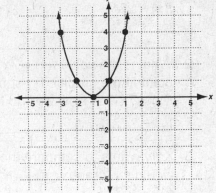

2. What is the transformation of this function?

   _____

3. How is this function like the parent square root function? How is it different?

   _____

   _____

   _____

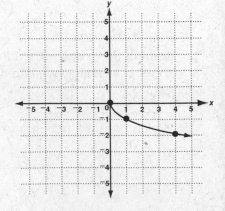

4. What is the transformation of this function?

   _____

Holt Algebra 2

Date _____

Dear Family,

In Chapter 2, your child will study linear and absolute-value equations, inequalities, and functions.

An **equation** is a statement that two expressions are equal. The equation $5(1 - 2x) = -4x + 15$ is a **linear equation in one variable** because the variable x is not in a radical, not in a denominator, not used as an exponent, and not raised to an exponent other than 1.

A **solution** to an equation is a value of the variable that makes the equation true. To solve a linear equation, isolate the variable on one side of the equation.

Many equations have only one solution. For example, the only solution to $x + 2 = 7$ is $x = 5$. An equation that is always true is called an **identity.** An equation that is never true is called a **contradiction.**

Identity:	$x + 2 = x + 2$	Any value of x is a solution.
Contradiction:	$x + 2 = x + 3$	No value of x is a solution.

An **inequality** compares two expressions with $<$, $\le$, $>$, $\ge$, or $\ne$. An inequality can be solved in the same way as an equation, except for one difference:

Solving Linear Inequalities

When you multiply or divide both sides of an inequality by a negative number, the inequality sign reverses direction.

original inequality: $10 > 3$ **multiplied by −5:** $-50 < -15$

the inequality sign reverses direction

A **ratio** relates two quantities, such as 2 to 5, or $\frac{2}{5}$. A **proportion** states that two ratios are equal, such as $\frac{2}{5} = \frac{12}{30}$. When a proportion contains a variable, you can solve it by using **cross products**: if $\frac{a}{b} = \frac{c}{d}$, then $a \cdot d = b \cdot c$. Ratios and proportions have many useful applications, including percents.

Chapter 1 introduced **linear functions**. Chapter 2 shows how linear functions can be written in two useful forms:

Slope-intercept form:	$y = mx + b$
Point-slope form:	$y - y_1 = m(x - x_1)$

Slope-intercept form highlights the slope (m) and the y-intercept (b), so it is helpful when graphing a linear function or writing the equation of a line.

Holt Algebra 2

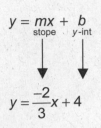

$$y = \underset{\text{stope}}{mx} + \underset{\text{y-int}}{b}$$

$$y = \frac{-2}{3}x + 4$$

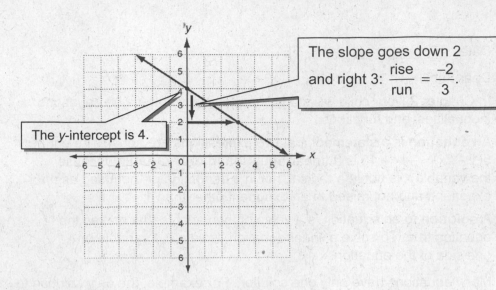

The slope goes down 2 and right 3: $\dfrac{\text{rise}}{\text{run}} = \dfrac{-2}{3}$.

The y-intercept is 4.

Linear inequalities in two variables, such as $y > 2x - 4$, are graphed by first drawing either a dashed line (for < or >) or a solid line (for ≤ or ≥). Then the region above or below that line is shaded to show which points satisfy the inequality.

Chapter 1 also introduced transformations. In Chapter 2, your child will further investigate transformations of linear functions and summarize the transformations algebraically.

Real-world data sometimes show a linear relationship. If you calculate a **line of best fit**, then you can use it to make predictions about the data. In general, the study of relationships between variables is called **regression.**

The **absolute value** of a number x, written $|x|$, represents its distance from zero on a number line. The value of x could be positive, negative, or zero, but its absolute value is always nonnegative. To solve an absolute value equation or inequality, you must consider each possibility.

$|x| = 4$
The distance from zero is 4.

$x = -4$ OR $x = 4$

$|x| \geq 4$
The distance is greater than or equal to 4.

$x \leq -4$ OR $x \geq 4$

$|x| \leq 4$
The distance is less than or equal to 4.

$x \geq -4$ AND $x \leq 4$

Because an absolute value is never negative, the graph of the **absolute-value function** $f(x) = |x|$ has two linear pieces that form a V shape with a vertex at (0, 0). As shown at right, a variety of absolute-value functions can be created by transforming $f(x) = |x|$.

For additional resources, visit go.hrw.com and enter the keyword MB7 Parent.

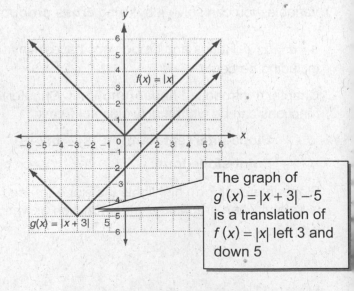

The graph of $g(x) = |x + 3| - 5$ is a translation of $f(x) = |x|$ left 3 and down 5

Holt Algebra 2

LESSON 2-1 Practice A

Solving Linear Equations and Inequalities

Tell which operation(s) you could use to solve each equation or inequality.

1. $x - 61 = 12.5$

2. $2y \leq -3$

3. $\dfrac{t}{5} + 7 = -1$

_____   _____   _____

_____

Solve.

4. $c + 19 = 82$

5. $j - 7 > 10$

6. $\dfrac{w}{3} \leq 6$

$c + 19 - \underline{\quad} = 82 - \underline{\quad}$ $j - 7 + \underline{\quad} > 10 + \underline{\quad}$ $\dfrac{w}{3} \cdot \underline{\quad} \leq 6 \cdot \underline{\quad}$

$c = \underline{\qquad}$ $j > \underline{\qquad}$ _____

7. $-3x + 7 = 4$

8. $-8r < -24$

9. $\dfrac{g}{4} - 6 = -5$

_____   _____   _____

10. $5(n + 3) = -5$

11. $4 - d < 3 + 2d$

12. $-2 + 7z > 3(2z + 1)$

_____   _____   _____

Solve. Then graph the solution set on a number line.

13. $\dfrac{s}{3} < -1$ _____

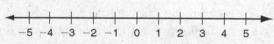

14. $8 - h \geq 12$ _____

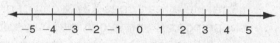

15. $2m + 6 \leq 12$ _____

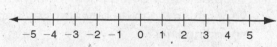

16. $-2(8 - k) > -12$ _____

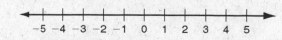

17. $1 - \dfrac{y}{3} \leq 2$ _____

LESSON
2-1

Practice B

Solving Linear Equations and Inequalities

Solve.

1. $2(x-3)=-4$

2. $12-3(w+7)=15$

3. $4(8-p)-(7-p)=22$

_____ _____ _____

4. $18-4y=-2(6+2y)$

5. $7t+6-2\left(5+\dfrac{3t}{2}\right)=5t-11$

6. $32+4(c-1)=-(4c+5)$

_____ _____ _____

Solve and graph.

7. $-5x+7\geq-3$

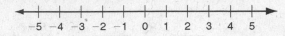

_____

8. $4-(-7-k)>2(k+3)$

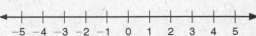

_____

9. $-18d+5(8+3d)\leq7(3d-8)$

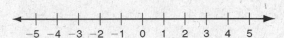

_____

Solve.

10. Yvonne's cell phone plan gives her a maximum of 200 minutes each month.

   a. Suppose Yvonne's calls average 7 minutes. What is the maximum number of calls she can make each month?

                                           _____

   b. Yvonne knows she has used 61 minutes during the first week of this month. If she limits her calls to 15 per week for the remaining 3 weeks this month, what is the maximum length of time rounded to the nearest minute that she can use for each call?

                                           _____

11. Blair wants to spend less than $50 at the grocery store. He already has $37 worth of groceries in his shopping cart and is going to buy some fresh vegetables for $0.75 each. What numbers of vegetables *v* can he buy and stay under his spending limit?

                                           _____

Holt Algebra 2

LESSON 2-1

Practice C

Solving Linear Equations and Inequalities

Find the measure of each angle in the quadrilaterals below to the nearest tenth of a degree. (Hint: The sum of angle measures in a quadrilateral is 360°.)

1.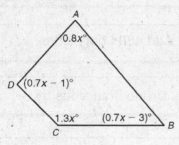

∠A _____ ∠B _____

∠C _____ ∠D _____

2.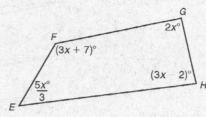

∠E _____ ∠F _____

∠G _____ ∠H _____

3.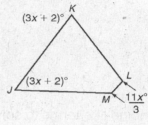

∠J _____ ∠K _____

∠L _____ ∠M _____

Write an equation or inequality to solve each problem. Then solve. Tell what the solution represents.

4. Harriet set up a website to sell jewelry. The web hosting fee is $39.95 per month. There is a one-time setup fee of $50.00. There is also a 1.5% fee on every sale.

   a. During her first month in business, Harriet paid $95.95 to her web host. This includes the setup fee. What was her sales total for her first month?

   _____

   b. During her second month, Harriet makes a goal of selling at least $500 worth of jewelry. If Harriet meets her goal, what is the minimum she will pay in web hosting fees?

   _____

   c. To increase her earnings, Harriet's current goal is for her web hosting fees to be no greater than 5% of sales. What is the minimum her sales must be each month to meet this goal?

   _____

5. What value(s) of k will make the equation
   $-2(x+7) - 11k = -(3 - x)$ an identity? _____

6. What value(s) of q will make the equation
   $2(x - q) = 2x - 1$ a contradiction? _____

Holt Algebra 2

LESSON 2-1 Reteach

Solving Linear Equations and Inequalities

Use the Distributive Property to solve equations.

$$8(y - 6) = 64$$

| Distribute the 8 to both terms. Think: |

$$8y - 48 = 64$$

$$+48 + 48$$

| Add 48 to both sides. |

$$8y = 112$$

$$\frac{8y}{8} = \frac{112}{8}$$

| Divide both sides by 8. |

$$y = 14$$

Combine like terms to solve equations.

$$4x + 18 - 3 = 3x - 45 + 5x$$

| 3x and 5x are like terms. |

$$4x + 15 = 8x - 45$$

$$-4x \qquad -4x$$

| Subtract 4x from both sides. |

$$15 = 4x - 45$$

$$+45 \qquad +45$$

| Add 45 to both sides. |

$$60 = 4x$$

$$\frac{60}{4} = \frac{4x}{4}$$

| Divide both sides by 4. |

$$15 = x$$

Solve.

1. $3(x + 9) = 63$

   $3x + \underline{\quad} = 63$

   $3x = \underline{\quad}$

   $x = \underline{\quad}$

2. $7(y - 4) = 98$

   $7y - \underline{\quad} = 98$

   $7y = \underline{\quad}$

   $y = \underline{\quad}$

3. $8(w - 6) = 168$

   $\underline{\qquad} = 168$

   $\underline{\quad} = \underline{\quad}$

   $w = \underline{\quad}$

4. $5a + 3 = 2a + 9$

   $-2a \qquad -2a$

   $3a + 3 = \underline{\quad}$

   $3a = \underline{\quad}$

   $a = \underline{\quad}$

5. $8y + y = 3y + 30$

   $\underline{\quad} = 3y + 30$

   $\underline{\quad} = 30$

   $y = \underline{\quad}$

6. $x + 5 = 29 - 3x$

   $+3x \qquad\qquad +3x$

   $\underline{\quad} + \underline{\quad} = 29$

   $\underline{\quad} = \underline{\quad}$

   $x = \underline{\quad}$

LESSON 2-1 Reteach

Solving Linear Equations and Inequalities (continued)

Reverse the inequality symbol if you multiply or divide both sides by a negative number.

Combine like terms.

$x - 3 \le 5x + 9$
$\underline{-5x \qquad -5x}$

x and 5x are like terms.
3 and 9 are like terms.

$-4x - 3 \le 9$
$\underline{+3 \ +3}$

$-4x \le 12$

$\dfrac{-4x}{-4} \ge \dfrac{12}{-4}$

Divide by –4. Reverse the inequality symbol.

$x \ge -3$

Graph the solution: $x \ge -3$

The $\ge$ symbol means that –3 is included in the graph.

$-5 \ -4 \ -3 \ -2 \ -1 \ \ 0 \ \ 1 \ \ 2 \ \ 3 \ \ 4 \ \ 5$

Substitute test values into the original inequality to check:

Pick a value that should be a solution.	Pick a value that should NOT be a solution.
Try $x = 0$. $0 - 3 \le 5(0) + 9$? $-3 \le 9$ True	Try $x = -4$. $-4 - 3 \le 5(-4) + 9$? $-7 \le -11$ False

---

Solve each inequality. Check your solutions.

7. $2x > 8x - 24$
$\underline{-8x \quad -8x}$

_____ > -24

$\dfrac{\boxed{}x}{\boxed{}} < \dfrac{-24}{\boxed{}}$

$x < $ _____

8. $5w + 2 < 8w + 23$
$\underline{-8w \qquad -8w}$

_____ + _____ < 23

_____ $<$ _____

$\dfrac{\boxed{}w}{\boxed{}} > \dfrac{\boxed{}}{\boxed{}}$

$w > $ _____

9. $7y - 1 \ge 12y + 29$
$\underline{\qquad \qquad}$

_____ – _____ ≥ 29

_____ $\ge$ _____

$\dfrac{\boxed{}y}{\boxed{}} \le \dfrac{\boxed{}}{\boxed{}}$

$y \le $ _____

Holt Algebra 2

LESSON	**Challenge**
2-1	*How Many Points in an Interval?*

How many points are in the interval $0 \le x \le 10$? Of course there are the 10 points whose coordinates are integers: 1, 2, 3, ..., 10. There are also points like $\frac{1}{2}, 4\frac{1}{8}, 7\frac{3}{4}$, and 9.9999. How many other points are in this interval?

1. Consider the interval $0 \le x \le 10$.

    a. Write a fraction using the endpoints to find the midpoint. _____

    b. Use the left endpoint and the midpoint to find the midpoint of this half-interval. _____

    c. Use the pattern from parts *a* and *b* to generate three more points that lie in the original interval.

    _____

    d. For the original interval, begin with the midpoint and the right endpoint and generate three more points that lie in the original interval.

    _____

    e. How many points are in the original interval?

    _____

Find three points that lie in the left half of each interval and three points that lie in the right half of each interval.

2. $0.01 \le x \le 0.02$

3. $\frac{1}{3} \le x \le \frac{1}{2}$

_____   _____

Let *n* be a positive real number.

4. a. How many points are in the interval $0 \le x \le n$? _____

    b. How do you think the number of points in the interval $-n \le x \le n$ compares to the number of points in the interval $0 \le x \le n$?

    _____

LESSON 2-1

Problem Solving
Solving Linear Equations and Inequalities

Trish keeps track of a leak in her outside water faucet by measuring the depth of the water that collects in a barrel under the faucet. Her results (rounded to the nearest 0.5 centimeter) are shown in the table. Use the data in the table for Exercises 1–3.

Water Leak						
Day	1	2	3	4	5	6
Water in Barrel (cm)	3.5	8	12.5	17	21.5	26

1. After the first day, what is the depth of the water that leaks each day? _____

2. Write an equation for the total depth of the water in the barrel, y, in terms of the number of days that the faucet leaks, x. _____

3. If this pattern continues, and assuming no evaporation of the water in the barrel, when will the depth of the water be greater than 45 centimeters? _____

Choose the letter for the best answer.

4. A ream of computer paper is 2.1 in. high. Which inequality can be used to find the maximum number of reams that will fit in one stack between two shelves that are 1.5 ft apart?

   A $2.1x \leq 1.5$ C $2.1x \leq 18$

   B $\dfrac{2.1}{x} \leq 1.5$ D $\dfrac{2.1}{x} \leq 18$

5. Kevin is 5 years older than Keith, but 3 years younger than Kara. The total of their ages is 49. Which equation can be used to find Keith's age?

   A $x + (x + 5) + (x + 3) = 49$

   B $x + (x - 3) + (x + 8) = 49$

   C $x + (x + 5) + (x - 3) = 49$

   D $x + (x + 5) + (x + 8) = 49$

Tell whether each problem is solved correctly. If not, explain why and find the correct solution.

6. Ana wants to find a solution to a problem by solving this inequality: $-3x < 42$. She multiplies both sides by $-\dfrac{1}{3}$ and found the solution $x < -14$.

7. Tyler writes this equation to solve a problem: $3(b - 4) = 9 + 6b$. He divides both sides of the equation by 3 to get $b - 4 = 3 + 2b$ so he concludes that $b = -7$.

_____

_____

Holt Algebra 2

LESSON 2-1	**Reading Strategies**
	Compare and Contrast

A **linear equation** has one solution.	A **linear inequality** has many solutions.
$x - 3 = 8$	$x - 3 < 8$
$x - 3 + 3 = 8 + 3$	$x - 3 + 3 < 8 + 3$
$x = 11$	$x < 11$
The solution is 11.	The solution set is $x < 11$.

Answer each question.

1. Circle the linear equations. Cross out the linear inequalities.

$c + 7 = 13$ $\qquad$ $3 + 5 = 8$ $\qquad$ $4 \cdot m > 36$ $\qquad$ $7 - 2r = 23$ $\qquad$ $22 \le 3g - 2$ $\qquad$ $48 = \dfrac{w}{6}$

2. How is solving an equation like solving an inequality?

   _____

3. What is the solution of an equation?

   _____

4. How can you check that 11 is the solution of the
   equation $x - 3 = 8$?

   _____

   _____

5. What is the solution set of an inequality?

   _____

6. How can you check that $x < 11$ is the solution set for the
   inequality $x - 3 < 8$?

   _____

7. How are the solution of an equation and the solution set of
   an inequality different?

   _____

   _____

LESSON
2-2

Practice A

Proportional Reasoning

Determine if each pair of fractions is a proportion. Show cross products. Then write *proportion* or *not a proportion*.

1. $\dfrac{2}{3} \overset{?}{=} \dfrac{84}{126}$

2. $\dfrac{5.2}{2.6} \overset{?}{=} \dfrac{4}{2}$

3. $\dfrac{3.5}{8} \overset{?}{=} \dfrac{19}{44}$

_____

_____

_____

_____

_____

_____

Solve each proportion.

4. $\dfrac{5}{8} = \dfrac{c}{24}$

5. $\dfrac{4.2}{7} = \dfrac{2.1}{d}$

6. $\dfrac{x}{6} = \dfrac{3.5}{9}$

_____

_____

_____

7. $\dfrac{0.5}{-6} = \dfrac{4}{f}$

8. $\dfrac{k}{5} = \dfrac{0.4}{7}$

9. $\dfrac{72}{w} = \dfrac{-8}{3}$

_____

_____

_____

Write a proportion to solve each problem. Then find the solution.

10. The morning absentee report shows that 15% of the students are absent. There are 1360 students enrolled in the school. How many students are absent?

_____

11. A 10k run is a distance of 10 kilometers. One kilometer is about 0.62 miles. How far is a 10k run in miles?

_____

12. Isaiah is raising the flag in the school yard. He knows that the flagpole is 20 feet tall. He wants to know the height of the office building across the street. He measures the shadow cast by the building to be 31 feet and the shadow cast by the flagpole to be 8 feet. How tall is the office building to the nearest foot?

_____

Name _____ Date _____ Class_____

Practice B
Proportional Reasoning

Solve each proportion.

1. $\dfrac{28}{36} = \dfrac{g}{81}$

2. $\dfrac{z}{1.75} = \dfrac{64}{21}$

3. $\dfrac{3}{0.6} = \dfrac{1.05}{n}$

_____

_____

_____

4. $\dfrac{5}{8} = \dfrac{f-1}{56}$

5. $\dfrac{2.4}{1.8} = \dfrac{0.004}{y}$

6. $\dfrac{5}{v+6} = \dfrac{4}{12}$

_____

_____

_____

Solve.

7. $\triangle XYZ$ has vertices X (0, 0), Y (0, 10), and Z (−10, 10). $\triangle XWT$ is similar to $\triangle XYZ$ and has a vertex at W (0, 4). Graph $\triangle XYZ$ and $\triangle XWT$ on the same grid.

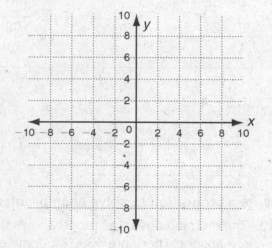

8. Dan works as a house painter. He knows that it is safe to place the base of his 10-foot ladder 3 feet from the base of a house. Today he has to use a 25-foot ladder. Dan wants to keep the same ratios in order to be safe. How far should Dan place the base of his 25-foot ladder from the base of the house?

_____

9. The school newspaper took a survey. Of the students polled, 15% said they did not have too much homework. Sixty students were polled for the survey. How many students said they did not have too much homework?

_____

10. Cheryl wants to measure the distance across a stream. She took some measurements and drew a diagram. How wide is the stream?

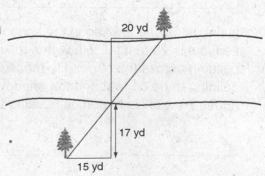

_____

Holt Algebra 2

LESSON 2-2

Practice C
Proportional Reasoning

Solve.

1. $\dfrac{6n}{16} = \dfrac{112.5}{40}$

2. $\dfrac{-3}{0.5} = \dfrac{-9}{w-5}$

3. $\dfrac{1+a}{2.5} = \dfrac{144}{45}$

4. $\dfrac{30}{105} = \dfrac{d+18}{35}$

5. $\dfrac{36}{24m} = \dfrac{3.3}{8.8}$

6. $\dfrac{2.55}{0.9} = \dfrac{1.7}{0.3c}$

The circle graph shows the annual revenue sources for a local baseball team. Use the graph for Exercises 7 and 8.

Baseball Team Revenue

7. If the revenue from ticket sales is $386,152, what is the total revenue for the year?

8. If the total revenue for the year is $1,742,800, what is the revenue from parking fees and food sales together?

9. If the combined revenue from parking and the TV/Radio license is $629,629.17, what is the total revenue for the year?

Solve.

10. Last year, 22% of the students at the high school had perfect attendance. If 165 students had perfect attendance, how many students are enrolled at the high school?

11. Sammy is 5 feet 3 inches tall. He casts a shadow that is 31 feet 6 inches long. He is standing next to a stop sign that casts a shadow that is 40 feet 6 inches long. How tall is the stop sign in feet and inches?

12. Each day the exchange rate between U.S. dollars and foreign currency changes. One day, 4 dollars were equivalent to approximately 3 euro. On the same day 3 euro were equivalent to approximately 168.37 Indian rupees. To the nearest rupee, how many Indian rupees are equivalent to 1 dollar?

LESSON 2-2 Reteach
Proportional Reasoning

Set cross products equal to solve a proportion.

$$\frac{5}{48} = \frac{12.5}{y}$$

5 · y is a cross product.

48 · 12.5 is a cross product.

$$5 \cdot y = 48 \cdot 12.5$$

$5y = 600$ *Simplify cross products.*

$\dfrac{5y}{5} = \dfrac{600}{5}$ *Solve for y. Divide both sides by 5.*

$y = 120$

A proportion can be used to solve percent problems: $\dfrac{percent}{100} = \dfrac{part}{whole}$.

Find 35.5% of 4800.

$\dfrac{35.5}{100} = \dfrac{x}{4800}$ *Write a proportion.*

$100x = 35.5 \cdot 4800$ *Find cross products.*

$\dfrac{100x}{100} = \dfrac{35.5 \cdot 4800}{100}$ *Solve for x. Divide both sides by 100.*

$x = 1704$

Solve.

1. $\dfrac{3}{26} = \dfrac{n}{78}$

   $26n = 3 \cdot$ _____

   $\dfrac{26n}{26} = \dfrac{\boxed{}}{26}$

   $n =$ _____

2. $\dfrac{9}{x} = \dfrac{40.5}{9}$

   $40.5x =$ _____ · _____

   $\dfrac{40.5x}{\boxed{}} = \dfrac{\boxed{}}{\boxed{}}$

   $x =$ _____

3. $\dfrac{4}{17} = \dfrac{32}{t}$

   _____ = _____ · _____

   $\dfrac{\boxed{}}{\boxed{}} = \dfrac{\boxed{}}{\boxed{}}$

   $t =$ _____

4. Find 42% of 300.

   $\dfrac{42}{100} = \dfrac{x}{300}$

   $100x = 42 \cdot 300$

   _____

5. Find 15% of 680.

   $\dfrac{\boxed{}}{100} = \dfrac{x}{680}$

   $100x =$ _____

   _____

6. Find 72% of 5000.

   $\dfrac{\boxed{}}{100} = \dfrac{x}{\boxed{}}$

   _____

   _____

LESSON 2-2

Reteach

Proportional Reasoning (continued)

A proportion can be used to solve problems about indirect measurement.

Jake is 6 feet tall and casts a shadow 15 feet long. At the same time, a tree casts a shadow 50 feet long. How tall is the tree?

Draw and label a diagram.

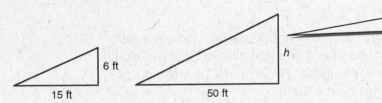

6 ft

15 ft

h

50 ft

> The objects and their shadows form similar triangles.

Use the diagram to write a proportion.

$$\frac{\text{Jake's height}}{\text{Jake's shadow}} = \frac{\text{tree's height}}{\text{tree's shadow}}$$

> Notice that **like** things are related in a proportion. Both numerators are height. Both denominators are shadows.

$$\frac{6}{15} = \frac{h}{50}$$

$15h = 50 \cdot 6$ *Set cross products equal.*

$15h = 300$

$\dfrac{15h}{15} = \dfrac{300}{15}$ *Solve for h. Divide both sides by 15.*

$h = 20$ The tree is 20 feet tall.

Solve.

7. A school building is 40 feet tall. It casts a shadow that is 104 feet long at the same time as the flagpole casts a shadow that is 169 feet long. How tall is the flagpole?

Label the diagram.

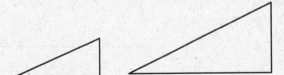

Use a proportion to solve.

$$\frac{40}{104} = \frac{h}{\boxed{}}$$

$104h = $ _____

$104h = $ _____

$\dfrac{104h}{104} = \dfrac{\boxed{}}{\boxed{}}$

$h = $ _____

The flagpole is _____ feet tall.

Holt Algebra 2

LESSON 2-2 | Challenge

Proportional Population

Alfred Lord Tennyson (1809–1892) was an English poet of the Victorian Age. One of his more famous poems, "The Vision of Sin," includes the following verses.

> Every minute dies a man,
>
> Every minute one is born.

Charles Babbage (1791–1871), an English mathematician and engineer, noted that if these lines were indeed true, the population of England would remain stable, neither growing nor decaying. He wrote to Tennyson and suggested the following lines in his next edition.

> Every minute dies a man,
>
> Every minute $1\frac{1}{16}$ is born.

1. a. If Babbage were correct in his revised lines of verse, what would be the ratio of the number of people born to the number who die?

    _____

    b. How many births would there be in England during a week in which 592 people died?

    _____

    c. How many births would there be in England during a week in which the population grew by 23 people?

    _____

In a more recent era with the growth of new medical techniques, there is now a birth approximately every 9 seconds and a death approximately every 15 seconds.

2. At these revised rates, what would be the ratio of births to deaths in England today?

    _____

3. If 1215 new babies were born in England in a week, how many deaths would there be for the same week?

    _____

4. If in one week the population of England increased by 438 people including only births and deaths, determine how many people were born and how many died.

    _____

5. Using Tennyson's lines of verse:

    Every minute dies a man,
    Every minute x is born.

    What value would Babbage replace today for x in these lines of verse?

    _____

LESSON 2-2

Problem Solving

Proportional Reasoning

Leon likes to build model sets of his favorite movies. Solve.

1. In *The Incredible Shrinking Man* (1957), the hero shrinks from about 5 feet 10 inches to about 1 inch tall. If Leon starts with a model character that is $8\frac{3}{4}$ inches tall and shrinks by the same proportion, what is the character's final height?

2. In a scene in *King Kong* (1933), the giant gorilla is about 22 feet tall. An ordinary gorilla is about 5 feet tall. In his model, Leon made the giant gorilla 9 inches tall. How tall would an ordinary gorilla be in his model set?

3. In *The Amazing Colossal Man* (1957), a man of about 6 feet becomes 100 feet tall. How tall will Leon's character become if he starts with a model $\frac{1}{2}$ inch tall?

4. Leon wants to build a model in a shoe box of the movie *Mothra* (1962), in which a caterpillar with a radius of about $\frac{1}{2}$ inch grew to have a radius of about 30 feet. He starts with a model of an ordinary caterpillar with a radius of $\frac{1}{8}$ inch. Will his final model fit in the shoe box? Why or why not?

Choose the letter for the best answer.

5. There are 372 students, or 30% of the student enrollment, in the 10th grade at Highland School. What is the total student enrollment at the school?

   A 1240

   B 1116

   C 744

   D 37.2

6. In this year's city election, 23.6% of the 13,457 registered voters went to the polls. About how many people voted this year?

   A 236

   B 3176

   C 9877

   D 317,585

7. Elijah is 5 feet 6 inches tall. He casts a shadow that is 20 feet long. He is standing next to a palm tree that casts a shadow that is 76 feet 6 inches long. How tall is the palm tree to the nearest foot?

   A 19 ft   C 25 ft

   B 21 ft   D 278 ft

8. How many inches are there in 100 miles?

   A 6.336×10^3 in.

   B 6.336×10^4 in.

   C 6.336×10^5 in.

   D 6.336×10^6 in.

LESSON 2-2

Reading Strategies
Identify Relationships

A **ratio** compares two numbers. You can compare the numbers in any order. The table shows the numbers of boys and girls in three different choirs. The ratio of boys to girls is the same in all three choirs.

Choir	Girls	Boys
Children's	10	15
Junior	50	75
Senior	30	y

Look at the Children's Choir.

The ratio of girls to boys is $\dfrac{10}{15}$.

The ratio of boys to girls is $\dfrac{10}{15}$.

Answer each question.

1. What is the ratio of girls to boys in the Junior Choir? _____

2. What is the ratio of boys to girls in the Junior Choir? _____

3. What is the ratio of girls to boys in the Senior Choir? _____

An equation showing two ratios are equal is called a **proportion**.

$$\dfrac{10}{15} \bowtie \dfrac{50}{75} \text{ is a proportion.}$$

The **cross products** of a proportion are equal.

$$10 \times 75 = 15 \times 50$$

$$750 = 750$$

Answer each question.

4. Write a proportion showing that the boy to girl ratio is the same for the Children's and Senior choirs. _____

5. What do you multiply to find the cross products?

_____

6. How can you find y?

_____

7. How many boys are in the Senior Choir? _____

Holt Algebra 2

LESSON 2-3

Practice A

Graphing Linear Functions

Determine if the rate of change, $\dfrac{\text{change in } f(x)}{\text{change in } x}$ is constant. Then

tell whether each data set represents a linear or nonlinear function.

1.
+2 _____ _____

x	1	3	5	7
f(x)	5	10	15	20

+5 _____ _____

2.
_____ _____ _____

x	0	3	6	9
f(x)	1	3	7	10

_____ _____ _____

_____

_____

Plot the given point. Use the slope to find a second point. Then graph the line.

3. point: (0, –3); slope: 2

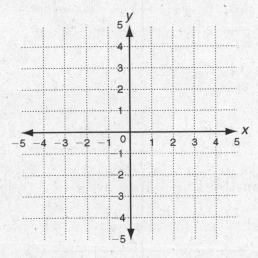

4. point: (–3, 4); slope: $\dfrac{-1}{3}$

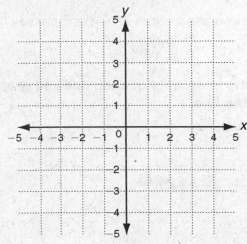

Identify the x-intercept and the y-intercept for each line.

5. $4x + y = 8$

$y = 0; x =$ _____

$x = 0; y =$ _____

6. $3x + 2y = -6$

$y = 0; x =$ _____

$x = 0; y =$ _____

7. $2x - 5y = 8$

$y = 0; x =$ _____

$x = 0; y =$ _____

Write each function in slope-intercept form, $y = mx + b$.

8. $-5x + y = 7$

$-5x + y + 5x = 7 + 5x$

$y =$ _____

9. $2y = 4x - 12$

_____

_____

10. $4x - 3y = -1$

_____

_____

Holt Algebra 2

Practice B
Graphing Linear Functions

Determine whether each data set could represent a linear function.

1.

x	9	7	5	3
f(x)	2	5	10	15

_____

2.

x	0.5	1	1.5	2
f(x)	9	6	3	0

_____

Use the coordinate plane at right to graph and label each line.

3. Line *a* has a slope of –2 and passes through (1, 4).

4. Line *b* has a slope of 1 and passes through (–4, –2).

5. Line *c* has a slope of $\frac{2}{3}$ and passes through (3, –2).

6. Line *d* has a slope of $\frac{-5}{4}$ and passes through (–1, 0).

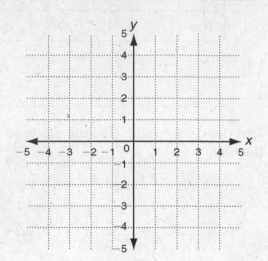

Find the intercepts of each line and graph and label the line.

7. line *e*: $5x + y = -5$

_____

8. line *f*: $6x + 2y = 6$

_____

Write each function in slope-intercept form. Then graph and label the function.

9. line *g*: $-3x - y = 9$

_____

10. line *h*: $4x + 3y = 6$

_____

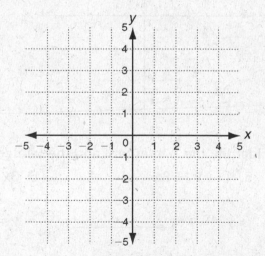

Determine whether each line is vertical or horizontal.

11. $x = -5$

12. $y = \frac{8}{3}$

13. $x = 4.6$

_____   _____   _____

Holt Algebra 2

LESSON 2-3 Practice C

Graphing Linear Functions

1. Every time Imani buys gas for her car, she records the number of gallons required to fill the tank and the number of miles she has driven since the last fill-up.

Car Mileage Records				
Distance (mi)	250	137	238	356
Gas (gal)	10.2	5.5	9.8	14.2

   a. Does the data set represent a linear function? Explain how you know.

   _____

   b. What does it mean, in terms of the way a car uses gas, for the data to be linear or nonlinear?

   _____

2. Julian read in a book that he could predict the temperature based on the number of times a cricket chirps per minute. To test this theory, he records cricket chirps and the temperature for several nights.

Cricket Chirps vs. Temperature				
Chirps (per min)	218	198	204	212
Temperature (°F)	93.5	88.5	90	92

   a. Does the data that Julian collects represent a linear function? Explain how you know.

   _____

   b. Julian wrote the equation $T = \dfrac{c}{4} + 39$ to calculate the temperature (T) based on c chirps per minute. Graph the equation on a graphing calculator. Find the c- and T-intercepts.

   c. About how many times per minute should a cricket chirp at 76°F?

   _____

3. Graph each equation. Identify the polygon formed by the intersecting lines. Give the coordinates of the vertices of the polygon.

$$y = 4 \qquad\qquad -4x - 2y = -8$$

$$x + 2y = -4 \qquad\qquad 24 + 3y + 6x = 0$$

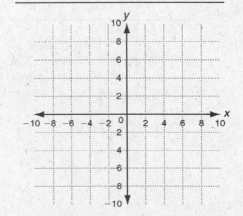

   _____

   _____

Holt Algebra 2

LESSON
2-3

Reteach

Graphing Linear Functions

Use intercepts to sketch the graph of the function $3x + 6y = 12$.

The x-intercept is where the graph crosses the x-axis. To find the x-intercept, set $y = 0$ and solve for x.

$3x + 6y = 12$
$3x + 6(0) = 12$
$3x = 12$
$x = 4$

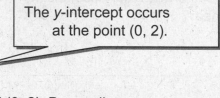

The x-intercept occurs at the point (4, 0).

The y-intercept is where the graph crosses the y-axis. To find the y-intercept, set $x = 0$ and solve for y.

$3x + 6y = 12$
$3(0) + 6y = 12$
$6y = 12$
$y = 2$

The y-intercept occurs at the point (0, 2).

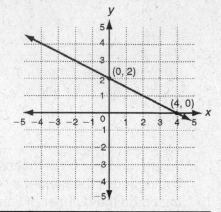

Plot the points (4, 0) and (0, 2). Draw a line connecting the points.

Find the intercepts and graph each line.

1. $3x + 2y = 6$

   a. $3x + 2 ($ _____ $) = 6$

   x-intercept = _____

   b. $3 ($ _____ $) + 2y = 6$

   y-intercept = _____

2. $6x - 3y = -12$

   a. $6x - 3 ($ _____ $) = -12$

   x-intercept = _____

   b. $6 ($ _____ $) - 3y = -12$

   y-intercept = _____

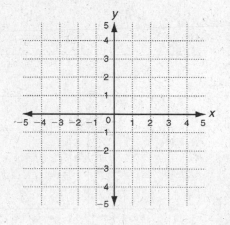

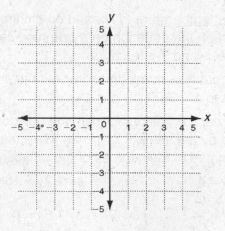

LESSON 2-3 Reteach
Graphing Linear Functions (continued)

Use the slope and the y-intercept to graph a linear function.

To write $2y + x = 6$ in slope-intercept form, solve for y.

$$2y + x = 6$$
$$\ -x \ \ -x$$

$$2y = -x + 6$$

$$\frac{2y}{2} = -\frac{x}{2} + \frac{6}{2}$$

$$y = -\frac{1}{2}x + 3$$

$y = mx + b$ is the slope-intercept form. m represents the slope and b represents the y-intercept.

Compare $y = -\frac{1}{2}x + 3$ to $y = mx + b$.

$m = -\frac{1}{2}$, so the slope is $-\frac{1}{2}$.

$b = 3$, so the y-intercept is 3.

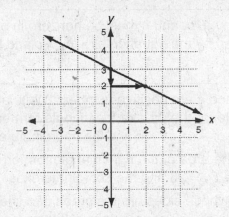

Write each function in slope-intercept form. Use m and b to graph.

3. $2x - y = 1$

    a. $y =$ _____ $x -$ _____

    b. $m =$ _____

    c. $b =$ _____

4. $y - \dfrac{x}{2} = 1$

    a. $y =$ _____

    b. $m =$ _____

    c. $b =$ _____

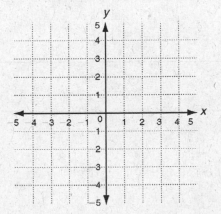

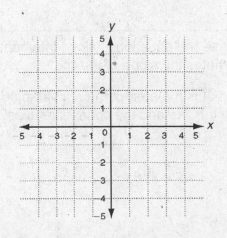

     Holt Algebra 2

LESSON 2-3

Challenge

Intercepts and Triangles

Every linear equation in x and y can be written in the form $ax + by = c$, where a and b cannot both be 0. If a, b, and c are not zero, then the graph is a line that crosses both the x-axis and the y-axis at points other than the origin, such as in the diagram at right.

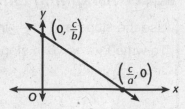

You can use the equation of a line to find the area of a triangle.

1. a, b, and c are nonzero constants and $ax + by = c$. Show that the x-intercept of the graph is $\dfrac{c}{a}$ and that the equation y-intercept is $\dfrac{c}{b}$.

   _____   _____

2. Explain why a, b, and c must be nonzero in order to form a triangle whose sides are the line represented by the equation $ax + by = c$ and the coordinate axes.

   _____

3. a. a, b, and c are positive numbers. Write a formula for the area of the triangle formed by the graph of $ax + by = c$ and the coordinate axes.   _____

   b. Find the area of the right triangle formed by the graph of $4x + 5y = 20$ and the coordinate axes.   _____

4. A triangle whose sides are the graph of a line and the coordinate axes has an area of 100 square units. Write an equation of the form $ax + by = c$ for the hypotenuse of the triangle.   _____

Solve.

5. a. Draw the graph of a line with x-intercept 5 and y-intercept 8.

   b. Find the constants a, b, and c for the line.

   _____

   c. Write the equation for the line.

   _____

   d. Write the equation in slope-intercept form. What is the slope of the line?   _____

   e. What is the area of the right triangle formed by the line and the coordinate axes?   _____

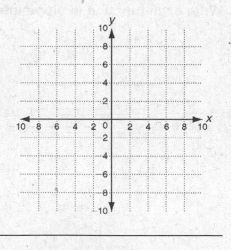

Holt Algebra 2

LESSON 2-3

Problem Solving
Graphing Linear Functions

Solve

1. Nathan made a table to record the balance in his savings account when he made a deposit every other month.

Savings Balance						
Month	2	4	6	8	10	12
Balance ($)	575	810	1025	1280	1545	1850

Is this data set linear? How do you know?

_____

2. Sally runs a landscape service business. The table shows her fee schedule.

Landscape Services						
Time (h)	1	2	3	4	5	6
Price ($)	8	14	20	26	32	38

a. Why is the data set linear?

_____

_____

b. Find the slope of the line that passes through the points.

_____

c. Graph these data.

d. Estimate the cost for 9 hours of landscape services.

_____

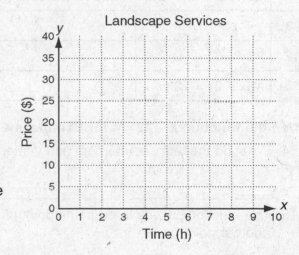

Choose the letter for the best answer.

3. Jan built a skateboard ramp from her back porch to the ground. The porch is 30 inches above the ground. The ramp extends 9 feet from the base of the porch. Find the slope of the ramp.

   A 3.6   C 0.3

   B 3.33   D 0.278

4. When Rafiq left home on a business trip he noted that the odometer on his car read 47,823. He drove 3 h 15 min and then noted that the odometer read 48,017. Find his average speed in miles per hour.

   A 55.6   C 61.6

   B 59.7   D 63.5

Holt Algebra 2

LESSON 2-3

Reading Strategies
Graphic Organizer

Definition	Facts
A function with a constant rate of change is called a **linear function**. $$f(x) = mx + b$$ m is the slope. b is the y-intercept.	The graph of a linear function is always a straight line. You can use the equation of a linear function to find its slope and intercepts: $y = mx + b$.
Example	**Useful Hints**
Linear function: $2x + y = 4$ Slope-intercept form of the linear function: $y = -2x + 4$ Slope $= -2$ y-intercept $= 4$	You can use any two points on a line to draw its graph. The intercepts give you two points on the line. You can also graph a line using its slope and one point on the line.

Complete the table

	Linear Function	Slope-Intercept Form	Slope	y-intercept
1.	$4x + y = 7$			
2.	$3y - 3x = -9$			
3.	$-6x + 2y = 12$			

Use the function $x - 2y = 4$ for Exercises 4 – 6.

4. What do the terms x-intercept and y-intercept mean?

   _____

5. The function passes through the point $(2, -1)$. Describe how to use the slope to find another point on the line.

   _____

   _____

6. Describe how to graph the function using its intercepts.

   _____

   _____

Holt Algebra 2

LESSON
2-4

Practice A
Writing Linear Functions

Identify the slope and *y*-intercept for each equation.

1. $y = 3x + 2$

2. $y = \dfrac{x}{2} - 7$

3. $2y = 5x - 4$

_____

_____

Find the slope of each line.

4. line through (2, 4) and (5, 3)

5. line through (0, 0) and (−1, −3)

_____

Write the equation of each line in slope-intercept form, $y = mx + b$.

6. line with slope 3 and intercept 2

7. line with slope $\dfrac{-1}{2}$ and intercept −1

_____

8. line with slope 2 passing through (1, 1)

9. line with slope $\dfrac{2}{3}$ passing through (4, −1)

_____

10. line parallel to $y = -x + 6$

   passing through (5, 0)

11. line perpendicular to $y = \dfrac{x}{3} - 4$

   passing through (−3, 1)

_____

Solve.

12. Daniela and Jack are hiking a steady incline. They use their GPS device to determine their elevation every 15 minutes. At 15 minutes and 30 minutes they were at elevations of 10,300 feet and 10,900 feet, respectively.

   a. Write an equation expressing their elevation in relation to time.

_____

   b. Based on the formula you found above, what is their elevation after one hour?

_____

Holt Algebra 2

Name _____ Date _____ Class _____

Practice B
Writing Linear Functions

Find the slope of each line.

1.

x	–5	1	4	9
y	–9	3	9	19

2.

x	–7	–2	6	13
y	–0.5	2	6	9.5

_____

Write the equation of each line in slope-intercept form.

3.

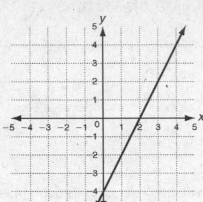

_____

4.

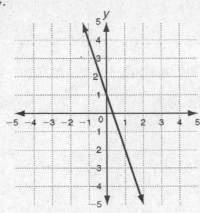

_____

5.

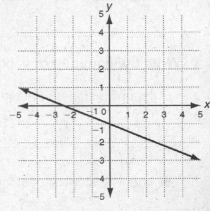

_____

6. line passing through (–3, –4)
   with a slope of $\frac{1}{5}$

_____

7.

x	–2	3	8	11
y	–1	1.5	4	5.5

_____

8. line parallel to $y = -\frac{3}{2}x + 4$
   and through (1, 5)

_____

9. line perpendicular to $y = -2x + 11$
   and through (4, –2)

_____

Solve.

10. The pool at the Barnes Community Center is heated.
    The table shows the temperature of the water at
    various time intervals after the heater is turned on.

    a. Express the temperature of the water as a
       function of time.

    _____

    b. Find the temperature of the water after 12 hours.

    _____

Swimming Pool Heater	
Time (h)	**Temperature (T)**
0	56°F
3	62°F
5	66°F
9	74°F

Holt Algebra 2

LESSON
2-4

Practice C

Writing Linear Functions

Tell whether each pair of lines is parallel, perpendicular, or neither.

1. $y = \frac{2}{5}x - 7$

   $y = \frac{5}{2}x - 7$

   _____

2. $y = 10 - 3x$

   $y = \frac{1}{3}x + 7$

   _____

3. $12 + 2y = 8x$

    $-12x + 3y = 24$

    _____

Write the equation of the line with the given properties.

4. slope −4, passing through (5, 4)

   _____

5. passing through (−4, 2) and (2, 6)

   _____

6.

x	−12	−2	8	21
y	8	3	−2	−8.5

_____

7.

x	−2.4	−0.3	5.7	8.7
y	0.2	0.9	2.9	3.9

_____

Write each linear function.

8. $f(x)$, where $f(4) = 1$ and $f(1) = 4$

   _____

9. $f(x)$, where $f(-1) = -10$ and $f(-5) = 0$

   _____

Solve.

10. Each week, Michelle records the average length of her standing long jump.

   a. Write an equation for the length of Michelle's jumps as a function of the number of weeks she has been practicing.

   _____

   b. If Michelle continues to improve at the same rate, what will be the average length of her jumps by the 8th week?

Long Jump Record	
Week	**Jump Distance (cm)**
1	175
2	178
3	181
4	184

   _____

   c. Will this function continue to be linear? Explain your reasoning.

   _____

   _____

LESSON 2-4

Reteach

Writing Linear Functions

Write the equation of the line shown in the graph in slope-intercept form.

Slope-intercept form: $y = mx + b$

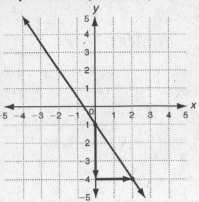

The point $(2, -4)$ lies on the line.

From $(0, -1)$, move 3 units down, or a rise of -3 units, and 2 units right, or a run of 2 units, to $(2, -4)$.	$m = \dfrac{\text{rise}}{\text{run}} = \dfrac{-3}{2} = -\dfrac{3}{2}$	Note that when the rise is a drop the slope is negative.

Substitute $m = -\dfrac{3}{2}$ and $b = -1$ into $y = mx + b$ to get the equation $y = -\dfrac{3}{2}x - 1$.

Write the equation of each line in slope-intercept form.

1.

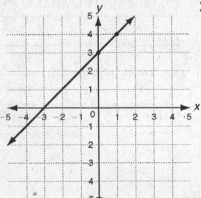

$b = $ _____

$m = \dfrac{\text{rise}}{\text{run}} = \dfrac{1}{1} = $ _____

$y = $ _____ $x + $ _____

2.

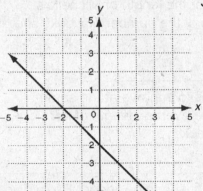

$b = $ _____

$m = \dfrac{\text{rise}}{\text{run}} = \dfrac{\boxed{}}{1} = $ _____

$y = $ _____

3.

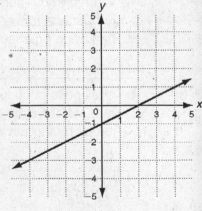

$b = $ _____

$m = \dfrac{\text{rise}}{\text{run}} = \dfrac{\boxed{}}{\boxed{}} = $ ____

$y = $ _____

LESSON
2-4

Reteach

Writing Linear Functions (continued)

The slopes of parallel and perpendicular lines have a special relationship.

The slopes of **parallel** lines are **equal**. $y = -2x + 1$ and $y = -2x - 2$ are parallel lines since both equations have a slope of -2. Note: The slopes of parallel vertical lines are undefined.	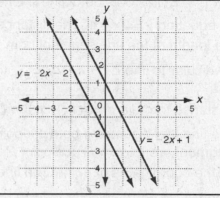
The slopes of **perpendicular** lines are **negative** **reciprocals**. Their product is -1. $y = -2x + 1$ and $y = \frac{1}{2}x - 1$ are perpendicular since $-2 \cdot \frac{1}{2} = -1$.	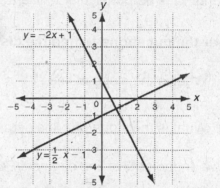

The point-slope form of the equation of a line is $y - y_1 = m(x - x_1)$.

The line has slope m and passes through the point (x_1, y_1).

Write the equation of the line perpendicular to $y = \frac{1}{3}x + 2$ through $(2, 5)$.

Substitute values for m and (x_1, y_1) in $y - y_1 = m(x - x_1)$.

$(x_1, y_1) = (2, 5)$, so $x_1 = 2$, $y_1 = 5$, and $m = -3$

$y - y_1 = m(x - x_1) \rightarrow y - 5 = -3(x - 2)$

$\qquad\qquad y - 5 = -3x + 6$

$\qquad\qquad\quad y = -3x + 11$

> The negative reciprocal of $\frac{1}{3}$ is
>
> -3 because $\frac{1}{3} \cdot (-3) = -1$.

Write the equation of each line.

4. parallel to $y = 4x - 3$ through the point $(-1, 2)$

   $m = $ _____ $(x_1, y_1) = ($ _____, _____ $)$

   $y - y_1 = m(x - x_1) \rightarrow y - $ _____ $= $ _____ $(x - $ _____ $)$ $y = $ _____

5. perpendicular to $y = -\frac{1}{2}x + 4$ through the point $(1, -1)$

   $m = $ _____ $(x_1, y_1) = ($ _____, _____ $)$

   $y - y_1 = m(x - x_1) \rightarrow y - $ _____ $= $ _____ $(x - $ _____ $)$ $y = $ _____

Holt Algebra 2

Name _____ Date _____ Class_____

Challenge

Distance from a Point to a Line

How can you find the shortest distance from a point to a line?
Point P $(-4, 8)$ lies outside of line ℓ. Line ℓ can be represented
by the equation $y = 2x - 4$. The distance from point P to line
ℓ is the length of the line segment from point P to line ℓ that is
perpendicular to line ℓ.

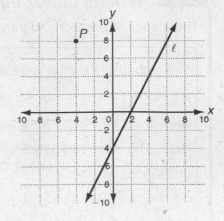

The distance formula $d = \sqrt{(x_2 - x_1)^2 + (y_2 - y_1)^2}$ can be
used to find this distance if both endpoints of the perpendicular
line segment are known. Since point P is given, the problem is
to find the coordinates of point Q on line ℓ such that line
segment PQ is perpendicular to line ℓ.

Answer the questions to find the distance from point P to line ℓ.

1. a. What is the slope of line ℓ? _____

   b. What is the slope of a line perpendicular to line ℓ? _____

2. The endpoint Q of line segment PQ must lie on line ℓ
   and line segment PQ must be perpendicular to line ℓ.
   Let the coordinates of point Q be (x_Q, y_Q). Use the
   equation of line ℓ to write y_Q as a function of x_Q. _____

3. Use the point-slope form to write an expression for
   the slope of line segment PQ as a function of x_Q. _____

4. Use the numerical slope from Exercise 1b and the
   slope expression from Exercise 3 to solve for the
   values of x_Q and y_Q. _____

5. Finally, use the distance formula to find the distance
   from point P to line ℓ. _____

**Find the distance from each point to the line represented by the given
equation.**

6. $(7, 4)$, $3x + 4y = 12$ 7. $(2, -14)$, $6x - 8y = 24$

   _____   _____

8. $(-7, 8)$, $15x - 8y = 120$ 9. $(7, -17)$, $-7x + 24y = 168$

   _____   _____

Holt Algebra 2

LESSON	**Problem Solving**
2-4	***Writing Linear Functions***

Solve.

1. As an image consultant, Antonio is well paid by his celebrity clients. For 20 hours of work, his fee is $1625. He charges $3500 for 45 hours of his time.

   a. Express his fee as a function of his hourly rate.

   _____

   b. What does the *y*-intercept represent?

   _____

   c. What is the fee for 40 hours of his time?

   _____

2. A child's cough medicine has a dosage table on the package.

Medicine Dosage	
Child's Weight (kg)	**Dosage (mL)**
10	6.0
16	7.5
28	10.5
30	11.0

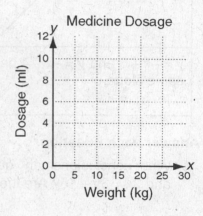

Medicine Dosage

   a. Express the dosage in milliliters as a function of the child's weight in kilograms.

   _____

   b. Graph the function.

   c. Find the dosage for a child who weighs 22 kg.

   _____

Choose the letter for the best answer.

3. Kayla's cell phone plan charges a fee of $25 per month and $0.25 per minute. She just received a notice that the fee is being increased to $35 per month. Which equation models her new cell phone plan?

   A $y = 0.25x + 25$

   B $y = 0.35x + 35$

   C $y = 0.25x + 35$

   D $y = 0.35x + 25$

4. Henry drew 2 lines on a coordinate grid. The red line passes through points $(-2, -4)$ and $(2, -2)$. The blue line is perpendicular to the red line and includes point $(-2, 8)$. What is the equation of the blue line?

   A $y = \frac{1}{2}x - 3$ C $y = -\frac{1}{2}x - 3$

   B $y = -2x + 4$ D $y = 2x + 4$

Holt Algebra 2

Reading Strategies
Draw Conclusions

The slopes of parallel or perpendicular lines are related.

Lines are **parallel** if their slopes are equal.	Lines are **perpendicular** if the product of their slopes is −1.
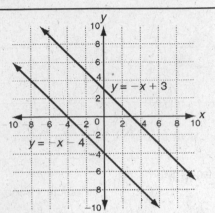	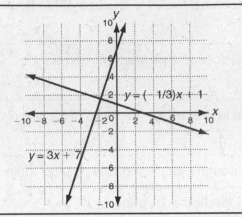
$y = -x + 3$ and $y = -x - 4$ have the same slope.	The product of the slopes of $y = 3x + 7$ and $y = -\dfrac{1}{3}x + 1$ is −1.

Answer each question.

1. What conclusions can you draw about the lines represented by $12x + 8y = 8$ and $2x = 3y + 15$? Are they parallel, perpendicular or neither? Why?

_____

2. a. Write the equation of a line that is parallel to $x + y = 3$. _____

   b. The line $x + y = 3$ is parallel to $y = -x - 4$. Is the line for the equation you just wrote also parallel to $y = -x - 4$? Explain why or why not.

_____

3. Why are the lines $y = 3x + 7$ and $2y - 6x = 2$ parallel?

_____

4. What conclusion can you draw about the slope of a line that is perpendicular to $2y = -4x - 1$? _____

5. Line A is perpendicular to line B. Line C is also perpendicular to line B. What conclusion can you draw about the slopes of lines A and C?

_____

Holt Algebra 2

LESSON 2-5

Practice A

Linear Inequalities in Two Variables

Choose a point in the shaded solution region of each graph and test it in the inequality. Does it satisfy the inequality? Tell whether the solution region is *correct* or *incorrect*.

1. $y > 3x - 1$

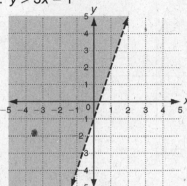

2. $y \geq -x - 1$

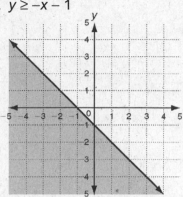

3. $x < 4$

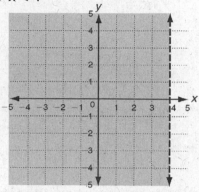

_____   _____   _____

Graph each inequality.

4. $y > x + 3$

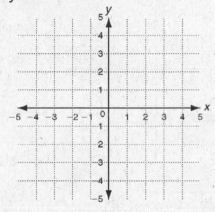

5. $y \leq -2x + 3$

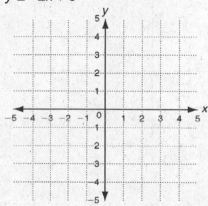

Solve each inequality for *y*. Graph the solution.

6. $2x + 3y < -6$

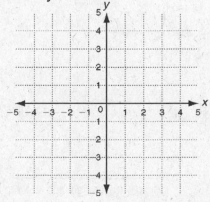

7. $5x - 10y \geq 30$

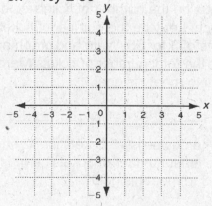

Holt Algebra 2

Practice B
Linear Inequalities in Two Variables

Graph each inequality.

1. $y < x + 2$

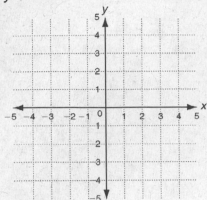

2. $y \geq 3x - 5$

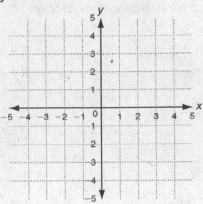

Solve each inequality for *y*. Graph the solution.

3. $-2(3x + 2y - 3) \geq 12$

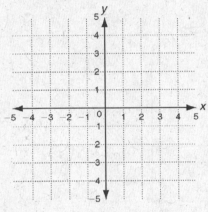

4. $\dfrac{-x}{5} + \dfrac{2y}{3} > 0$

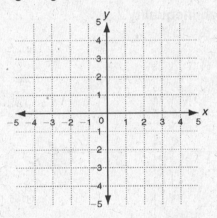

Solve.

5. Marcus volunteers to work at a carnival booth selling raffle tickets. The tickets cost $2 each or 3 for $5. His goal is to have at least $250 in sales during his shift.

   a. Let *x* be the number of tickets sold for $2 each. Let *y* be the number of tickets sold in sets of 3 for $5. Write and graph an inequality for the total number of tickets Marcus must sell to meet his goal.

   _____

   b. If Marcus sells 75 tickets for $2 each, what is the least number of tickets he must sell in sets of 3 to meet his goal?

   _____

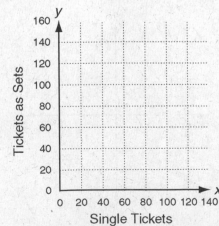

Holt Algebra 2

LESSON 2-5

Practice C
Linear Inequalities in Two Variables

Solve.

1. Ticket prices for Wonderful Wave Water Park are $25.00 for each child under 12 and $35.00 for each adult. When Cassie ends her shift, the total value of her credit card receipts is $2400. She also has cash receipts. Let x be the number of child tickets sold and y be the number of adult tickets sold.

   a. Write an inequality that shows the minimum number of tickets Cassie could have sold during her shift. _____

   b. Graph the inequality on a graphing calculator. If Cassie sold 25 adult tickets, what is the minimum number of child tickets she could have sold? _____

2. The cost to rent a car from Jumpin' Jalopies is $15.00 a day from Monday through Thursday. Friday through Sunday the rental fee is $10.75 a day. Let x be the number of days Monday through Thursday that a car is rented. Let y be the number of weekend days that a car is rented.

   a. Write an inequality that shows the maximum you would pay to rent the car for 10 consecutive days. _____

   b. Graph the inequality on a graphing calculator. Describe the appropriate domain of x and y. _____

   c. Explain why the domain is limited.

   _____

   d. How should you configure the 10 consecutive days in order to spend the minimum to rent a car? Explain your answer.

   _____

Write an inequality for each graph.

3.

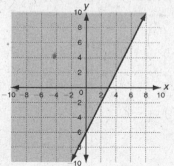

_____

4.

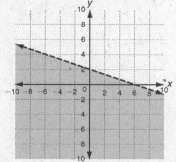

_____

5.

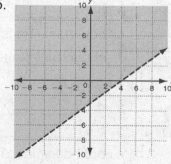

_____

Holt Algebra 2

LESSON 2-5

Reteach

Linear Inequalities in Two Variables

Graphing a linear inequality is similar to graphing a linear function.

Graph $y \le \frac{2}{3}x + 1$ using the slope-intercept form.

Step 1   Write the corresponding equation. Then identify the slope and the y-intercept.

$$y = \frac{2}{3}x + 1$$

$$m = \frac{2}{3} \text{ and } b = 1$$

Step 2   Draw the graph of $y = \frac{2}{3}x + 1$.

Draw a solid boundary line for $\le$ or $\ge$.

Draw a dashed boundary line for $<$ or $>$.

Step 3   Shade the half-plane below the line for $<$ or $\le$. Shade the half-plane above the line for $>$ or $\ge$.

Step 4   Check using a point in the shaded region. Use (0, 0).

$$y \le \frac{2}{3}x + 1$$

$$0 \overset{?}{\le} \frac{2}{3}(0) + 1$$

$$0 \overset{?}{\le} 1 \checkmark$$

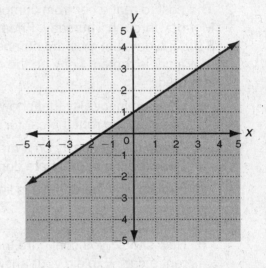

Graph each inequality.

1. $y \le x + 2$

     a. $m =$ _____

     b. $b =$ _____

     c. boundary line is _____

     d. shade half-plane _____ the line

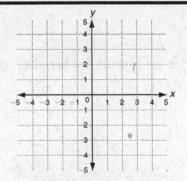

2. $y > -2x + 1$

     a. $m =$ _____

     b. $b =$ _____

     c. boundary line is _____

     d. shade half-plane _____ the line

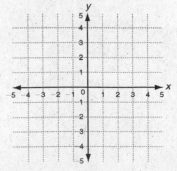

Holt Algebra 2

LESSON
2-5

Reteach

Linear Inequalities in Two Variables (continued)

The intercepts can be used to graph a linear inequality.

Graph $2x + y > 4$ using the intercepts.

Step 1 Write the corresponding equation. Then identify the *x*-intercept and the *y*-intercept.

$2x + y = 4$.

When $y = 0$, $x = 2$; plot $(2, 0)$.

When $x = 0$, $y = 4$; plot $(0, 4)$.

Step 2 Draw the graph of $2x + y = 4$ using a dashed line.

Step 3 Choose a point to check which half-plane to shade. Use $(0, 0)$.

$2x + y > 4$

$2(0) + (0) \overset{?}{>} 4$

$0 \overset{?}{>} 4 \times$

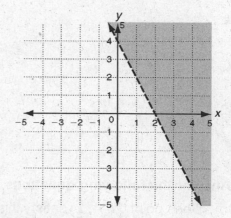

Step 4 The inequality is false, so shade the half-plane above the line.

Graph each inequality.

3. $2x + 4y > 8$

   a. *x*-intercept _____

   b. *y*-intercept _____

   c. boundary line _____

   d. test $(0, 0)$ _____

   e. shade _____ the line

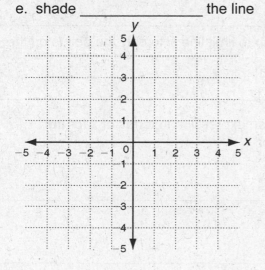

4. $-3x + y \le -1$

   a. *x*-intercept _____

   b. *y*-intercept _____

   c. boundary line _____

   d. test $(0, 0)$ _____

   e. shade _____ the line

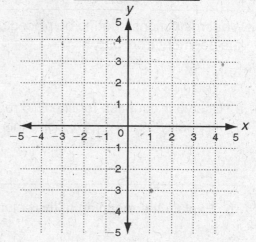

Holt Algebra 2

Challenge
What's in the Solution Region?

The graph shows the linear inequality $3x + 4y < 12$. The solution is represented by the shaded half-plane below the dashed line.

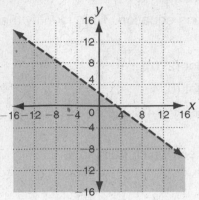

Answer the following questions.

1. Does point J (–4, 2) satisfy this inequality? Why or why not?

   _____

2. Does point K (4, –2) satisfy this inequality? Why or why not?

   _____

3. Write an equation for line R that passes through points J and K. Give the equation in slope-intercept form.

   _____

4. Draw a line segment from point J to point K on the graph. Do all points on this line segment satisfy the inequality $3x + 4y < 12$? How do you know?

   _____

5. What restrictions need to be placed on the domain to limit line R to only the points on the line segment from J to K?

   _____

6. a. Use your equation for line R to replace y with an expression in terms of x for the inequality $3x + 4y < 12$. Solve this inequality for x.

   _____

   b. Explain the meaning of this solution.

   _____

   _____

LESSON
2-5

Problem Solving

Linear Inequalities in Two Variables

Mr. and Mrs. Zaragosa are planning a landscape garden for their new house. They have set a budget of $200 for native grasses, at $12 each, and flowering plants, at $8.50 each.

1. Let n be the number of native grasses and p be the number of flowering plants. Write an inequality for the number of each that they can buy.

2. Find the intercepts of the boundary line.

   n-intercept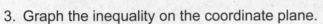

   p-intercept _____

3. Graph the inequality on the coordinate plane.

4. Define the domain for variables n and p. _____

5. Should the boundary line be dashed or solid? Why?

   _____

6. What is the solution region on the graph? How do you know?

   _____

   _____

7. Use your graph to determine if they can buy 10 flowering plants and 15 native grasses. How do you know?

   _____

   _____

8. What is the greatest number of grasses they can buy if they want to buy at least 5 flowering plants? _____

9. Use your graph to estimate the number of each they could buy if they want the same number of each type of plant. _____

Choose the letter for the best answer.

10. What is the greatest number of grasses they can buy if they have already bought 8 flowering plants?

    A 8

    B 9

    C 10

    D 11

11. What is the greatest number of flowering plants they can buy if they decide to buy a dozen native grasses?

    A 6

    B 7

    C 8

    D 9

LESSON 2-5 Reading Strategies
Understand Symbols

The solution set of a linear inequality is a region in the plane. The linear equation $y = x + 1$ is shown on the graph. The line is the boundary between the two shaded portions. You can describe each shaded portion with or without the boundary by using one of the four inequality symbols: $\leq, <, \geq,$ or $>$. The resulting inequalities are:

$$y \leq x + 1 \qquad y < x + 1 \qquad y \geq x + 1 \qquad y > x + 1$$

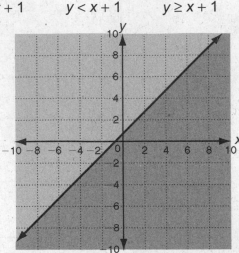

Answer each question. Use the inequalities shown above.

1. a. Which inequality describes both the shaded area
       above the line and the boundary line?   _____

    b. Give two points that are solutions of that inequality.

    _____

    c. Is the point (–4, –3) a solution of that inequality?   _____

2. Write the inequality that describes just the shaded
   area above the line.   _____

3. How would you change the graph to show that the boundary line is not
   included in the solution region?

   _____

4. Describe the region represented by $y \leq x + 1$.

   _____

5. Write the inequality that describes just the shaded area
   below the line?   _____

6. The points (0, –3) and (1, 2) are in the solution region
   of which inequality?   _____

Holt Algebra 2

LESSON
2-6

Practice A

Transforming Linear Functions

Describe the change in terms of *f*(*x*) for the transformation described.

1. vertical translation 3 units down

   $f(x) \rightarrow f(x) -$ _____

2. horizontal stretch by a factor of 4

   _____

3. vertical compression by a factor of $\frac{1}{4}$

4. horizontal translation 5 units left

   _____

   _____

5. horizontal compression by a factor of $\frac{2}{3}$

6. reflection across the *y*-axis

   _____

   _____

Let *g*(*x*) be the indicated transformation of. *f*(*x*). Write the rule for *g*(*x*).

7. $f(x) = 2x$; shift the graph vertically 2 units   _____

8. $f(x) = x - 3$; horizontal stretch by a factor of 3   _____

9. $f(x) = \frac{x}{4}$; vertical compression by a factor of $\frac{3}{4}$ _____

Let *g*(*x*) be the indicated combined transformation of *f*(*x*) = *x*. Write the rule for *g*(*x*).

10. horizontal stretch by a factor of 5 followed by a horizontal
    shift right 2 units   _____

11. vertical shift down 3 units followed by a vertical compression
    by a factor of $\frac{1}{8}$ _____

12. reflection across the *y*-axis followed by
    a vertical shift up 4 units   _____

Solve.

13. Tia's earnings can be represented by the function $f(x) = 5x + 120$,
    where *x* is the number of hours she works. If she works 3 additional
    hours, her earnings function is $g(x) = 5(x + 3) + 120$. What type of
    transformation can be applied to the graph of *f* to get the graph of *g*?

    _____

Name _____ Date _____ Class_____

Practice B

Transforming Linear Functions

Let $g(x)$ be the indicated transformation of $f(x)$. Write the rule for $g(x)$.

1.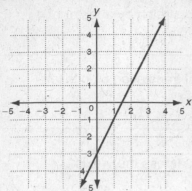

    horizontal translation

    left 3 units

    _____

2.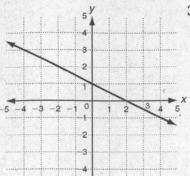

    vertical compression by

    a factor of $\frac{1}{5}$

    _____

3.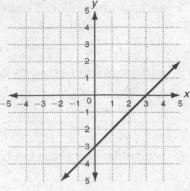

    reflection across the

    y-axis

    _____

4. linear function defined by the table; horizontal stretch by
   a factor of 2.3

    _____

x	−5	0	7
y	−3	7	21

5. $f(x) = 1.7x - 3$; vertical compression by a factor of 0.7   _____

Let $g(x)$ be the indicated combined transformation of $f(x) = x$. Write the rule for $g(x)$.

6. vertical translation down 2 units followed by a

   horizontal compression by a factor of $\frac{2}{5}$ _____

7. horizontal stretch by a factor of 3.2 followed by
   a horizontal translation right 3 units   _____

Solve.

8. The Red Cab Taxi Service used to charge $1.00 for the first $\frac{1}{5}$ mile and $0.75 for each

   additional $\frac{1}{5}$ mile. The company just raised its rates by a factor of 1.5.

   a. Write a new price function $g(x)$ for a taxi ride.

   _____

   b. Describe the transformation(s) that have been applied.

   _____

Holt Algebra 2

Practice C
Transforming Linear Functions

Graph f(x). Write the rule for gf(x), using the transformation given, and then graph g(x).

1.

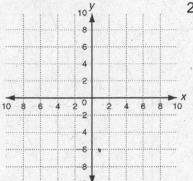

$f(x) = 3x$

horizontal translation

left 3 units

_____

2.

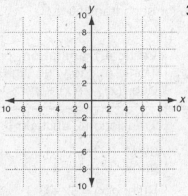

$f(x) = -x - 5$

vertical compression by

a factor of $\frac{1}{5}$

_____

3.

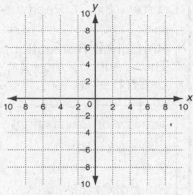

$f(x) = \frac{x}{3} + 2$

reflection across the

x-axis

_____

Solve.

4. The rate of increase in a certain city's population in 2000 was 1.4%. The rate in 2001 was 1.9%.

   a. Write a function to represent the increase in population in 2000.

   _____

   b. Write a function to represent the increase in population in 2001.

   _____

   c. Describe the transformation that can be applied to the first function to get the second function.

   _____

   d. Find the difference between the two possible growth rates if the population in 2030 is 8.5 billion.

   _____

5. Let g(x) be the reflection of f(x) across the x-axis. Let h(x) = x − 1 be the reflection of g(x) across the y-axis.

   a. Find the rule for g(x).   _____

   b. Find the rule for f(x).   _____

   c. Graph all three functions on a graphing calculator. Describe the transformation from f(x) to h(x).

   _____

Holt Algebra 2

LESSON 2-6

Reteach
Transforming Linear Functions

Translating linear functions vertically or horizontally changes the intercepts of the function. It does NOT change the slope.

Let $f(x) = 3x + 1$. Read the rule for each translation.

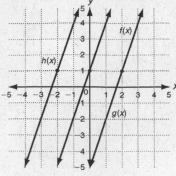

Horizontal Translation ⇔ Think: Add to *x*, go west. Use $f(x) \rightarrow f(x - h)$.	**Vertical Translation** ↕ Think: Add to *y*, go high. Use $f(x) \rightarrow f(x) + k$.
Translation 2 units right ⇒ $g(x) = f(x - 2)$ $g(x) = 3(x - 2) + 1$ Rule: $g(x) = 3x - 5$	Translation 2 units up ⇑ $g(x) = f(x) + 2$ $g(x) = 3x + 1 + 2$ Rule: $g(x) = 3x + 3$
Translation 2 units left ⇐ $h(x) = f(x - (-2)) = f(x + 2)$ $h(x) = 3(x + 2) + 1$ Rule: $h(x) = 3x + 7$	Translation 2 units down ⇓ $h(x) = f(x) + (-2) = f(x) - 2$ $h(x) = 3x + 1 - 2$ Rule: $h(x) = 3x - 1$

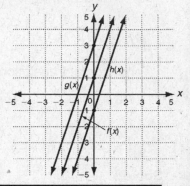

Let $f(x) = 2x - 1$. Write the rule for $g(x)$.

1. horizontal translation 5 units right

   $g(x) = f(x - \underline{\hspace{0.6cm}})$

   $g(x) = 2(x - \underline{\hspace{0.6cm}}) - 1$

   $g(x) = \underline{\hspace{2.5cm}}$

2. vertical translation 4 units down

   $g(x) = f(x) - \underline{\hspace{0.6cm}}$

   $g(x) = \underline{\hspace{0.9cm}} - \underline{\hspace{0.6cm}}$

   $g(x) = \underline{\hspace{2.5cm}}$

3. vertical translation 3 units up

   $g(x) = f(x) + \underline{\hspace{0.6cm}}$

   $g(x) = \underline{\hspace{0.9cm}} + \underline{\hspace{0.6cm}}$

   $g(x) = \underline{\hspace{2.5cm}}$

4. horizontal translation 1 unit left

   $g(x) = f(x + \underline{\hspace{0.6cm}})$

   $g(x) = 2(\underline{\hspace{0.9cm}}) - 1$

   $g(x) = \underline{\hspace{2.5cm}}$

5. vertical translation 7 units down

   _____

6. horizontal translation 9 units right

   _____

7. vertical translation 1 unit up

   _____

8. horizontal translation $\dfrac{1}{2}$ unit to the left

   _____

LESSON 2-6

Reteach

Transforming Linear Functions *(continued)*

Compressing or stretching linear functions **changes** the slope.

Let $f(x) = 3x + 1$. Read the rule for each translation.

Horizontal stretch or compression by a factor of b	**Vertical stretch or compression by a factor of a**
Use $f(x) \to f\left(\dfrac{1}{b}x\right)$.	Use $f(x) \to a \cdot f(x)$.
Horizontal stretch by a factor of 2 $$g(x) = f\left(\dfrac{1}{b}x\right) = f\left(\dfrac{1}{2}x\right)$$ $$g(x) = 3\left(\dfrac{1}{2}x\right) + 1$$ Rule: $g(x) = \dfrac{3}{2}x + 1$	Vertical stretch by a factor of 2 $$g(x) = a \cdot f(x) = 2 \cdot f(x)$$ $$g(x) = 2(3x + 1)$$ Rule: $g(x) = 6x + 2$
Horizontal compression by a factor of $\dfrac{1}{2}$ $$h(x) = f\left(\dfrac{1}{b}x\right) = f\left(\dfrac{1}{\left(\frac{1}{2}\right)}\right) = f(2x)$$ $h(x) = 3(2x) + 1$ Rule: $h(x) = 6x + 1$	Vertical compression by a factor of $\dfrac{1}{2}$ $$h(x) = a \cdot f(x) = \dfrac{1}{2} \cdot f(x)$$ $$h(x) = \dfrac{1}{2}(3x + 1)$$ Rule: $h(x) = \dfrac{3}{2}x + \dfrac{1}{2}$

Let $f(x) = 2x + 1$. Write the rule for $g(x)$.

7. vertical compression by a factor of $\dfrac{1}{4}$

   $f(x) \to$ _____ $\cdot f(x)$

   $g(x) =$ _____ $(2x + 1)$

   $g(x) =$ _____

8. horizontal stretch by a factor of 3

   $f(x) \to f($_____$)$

   $g(x) = 2($_____$) + 1$

   $g(x) =$ _____

9. horizontal compression by a factor of $\dfrac{1}{3}$

   $f(x) \to$ _____

   $g(x) =$ _____

10. vertical stretch by a factor of 5

    _____

    _____

LESSON 2-6

Challenge

Reflecting a Line Across a Line

A reflection is a type of transformation. Lines can be reflected across the
x-axis or the y-axis. However, lines can also be reflected across other lines.
You can explore reflections across the lines $y = x$ and $y = -x$. The graph
shows the linear function $y = 2x - 4$. The line $y = x$ is also shown.

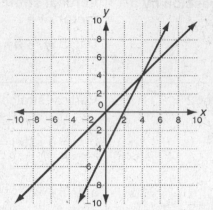

Answer the following questions.

1. What are the slope, x-intercept, and y-intercept of the
   line $y = 2x - 4$?
   _____

2. At what point do the lines of the two equations intersect?
   _____

3. On the graph, draw the reflection of the line $y = 2x - 4$
   across the line $y = x$.

4. What are the slope, x-intercept, and y-intercept of the
   reflected line?
   _____

5. What general pattern do you see in the slope, x-intercept,
   and y-intercept for the reflected line comparing it to the original line?

   _____

   _____

6. Write an equation for the reflected line in slope-intercept form. _____

7. On the graph, draw the line $y = -x$. Now draw the reflection of the
   line $y = 2x - 4$ across the line $y = -x$.

8. Write an equation for this new line in slope-intercept form. _____

9. Examine the two reflected lines and their equations. What general
   statement can you make about these two lines?

   _____

   _____

LESSON 2-6

Problem Solving

Transforming Linear Functions

The students in Ms. Hari's English class are planning to print a booklet of their creative writings. Use the table of publishing prices.

1. The students decide to print a booklet containing black and white text only. Write a function, $C(p)$, to show the cost of printing a booklet of p pages with a cover that also has text only.

   _____

Publishing Prices		
	Text Only	Color Graphic
Per page	$0.55	$1.25
Cover	$2.25	$3.50

2. Julie wants the booklet cover to have a color graphic. Write a new function, $J(p)$, to show this cost for a booklet of p pages.

   _____

3. What is the slope of each function? What does the slope tell you about the relationship of the lines?

   _____

4. What is the y-intercept of each function? What is represented by the y-intercept?

   _____

5. Describe the transformation that has been applied to the graph by the decision to change the cover.

   _____

6. Oscar suggests that the booklet have 30 pages, one for each person in the class. What is the cost of printing 50 booklets, using the function $J(p)$?

   _____

Choose the letter for the best answer.

7. Lee writes a function for the cost of p pages, all in color, with a plain text cover. What transformation does this apply to the graph of $C(p)$?

   A Horizontal stretch

   B Horizontal compression

   C Vertical stretch

   D Vertical compression

8. Tina finds a printer who will print text pages at $0.25 a page, with a color cover for $2.00. Using this printer, what is the cost of 50 booklets of 30 pages each?

   A $950

   B $725

   C $600

   D $475

LESSON 2-6

Reading Strategies

Read a Table

You can shift the graph of a linear function up or down and right or left.
These transformations are called translations.

Transformation	Example	Result
To translate the function **up**, add a constant >0 to the function.	$f(x) = 3x$ $f(x) = 3x + 2$	When $x = 0$ point (0, 0) becomes (0, 2).
To translate the function **down**, subtract a constant >0 from the function.	$f(x) = 3x$ $f(x) = 3x - 1$	When $x = 0$ point (0, 0) becomes (0, −1).

1. How does the graph of $f(x) = 3x$ change when you add 2 to the function?

   _____

2. How does the graph of $f(x) = 3x$ change when you subtract 1 from the function?

   _____

3. Do the graphs of $f(x) = 3x + 2$ and $f(x) = 3x - 1$ intersect? Explain why or why not.

   _____

Transformation	Example	Result
To translate the function **to the left**, add a constant >0 to the variable x.	$f(x) = 3x$ $f(x) = 3(x + 2)$ $f(x) = 3x + 6$	When $y = 0$ point (0, 0) becomes (−2, 0).
To translate the function **to the right**, subtract a constant >0 from the variable x.	$f(x) = 3x$ $f(x) = 3(x - 1)$ $f(x) = 3x - 3$	When $y = 0$ point (0, 0) becomes (1, 0).

4. How does the graph of $f(x) = 3x$ change when you add 2 to the variable?

   _____

5. How does the graph of $f(x) = 3x$ change when you subtract 1 from the variable?

   _____

Holt Algebra 2

Name _____ Date _____ Class_____

Practice A
Curve Fitting with Linear Models

Sketch the line of best fit for each scatter plot. Name the type of correlation.

1.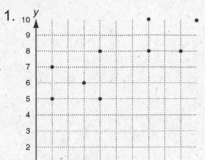

2.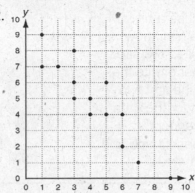

3.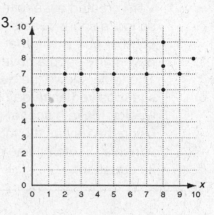

_____   _____   _____

As a science experiment, Keith recorded the percent humidity and the number of stars he could see at 10:00 P.M. each evening. Use the data in the table for Exercises 4 – 9.

Star Counting Experiment										
Humidity (%)	84	76	79	88	95	82	87	88	75	82
Number of Visible Stars	12	22	25	15	11	19	13	18	20	22

4. Make a scatter plot of the data using the humidity as the independent variable.

5. Sketch the line of best fit.

6. Find the slope of the line.

_____

7. Write the equation of the line.

_____

8. Would you expect the correlation coefficient for the line of best fit to be between –1 and 0 or between 0 and 1? Why?

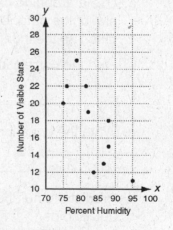

_____

9. Describe the relationship Keith found between the percent humidity and the number of stars visible.

_____

_____

Practice B
Curve Fitting with Linear Models

Solve.

1. Vern created a website about his
   school's sports teams. He has a hit
   counter on his site that lets him know
   how many people have visited the site.
   The table shows the number of hits the
   site received each day for the first two
   weeks. Make a scatter plot for the data
   using the day as the independent
   variable. Sketch a line of best fit and find
   its equation.

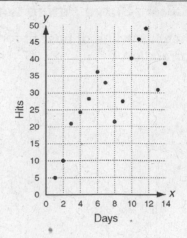

Lincoln High Website													
Day	1	2	3	4	5	6	7	8	9	10	11	12	13	14
Hits	5	10	21	24	28	36	33	21	27	40	46	50	31	38

2. A photographer hiked through the Grand
   Canyon. Each day she filled a photo memory
   card with images. When she returned from the
   trip, she deleted some photos, saving only the
   best. The table shows the number of photos she
   kept from all those taken for each memory card.

   a. Use a graphing calculator to make a scatter
      plot of the data. Use the number of photos
      taken as the independent variable.

   b. Find the correlation coefficient.

   _____

   c. Write the equation of the line of best fit.

   _____

Grand Canyon Photos	
Photos Taken	**Photos Kept**
117	25
128	31
140	39
157	52
110	21
188	45
170	42

   d. Predict the number of photos this photographer will keep if she takes
      200 photos.

   _____

3. What is the relationship between the slope of a line and its correlation coefficient?

   _____

   _____

Holt Algebra 2

Name _____ Date _____ Class_____

Practice C
Curve Fitting with Linear Models

Estimate the correlation coefficient for each scatter plot.

1.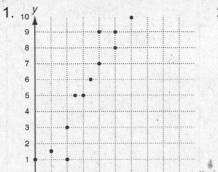

2.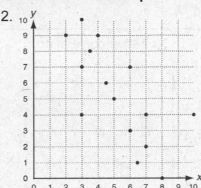

3.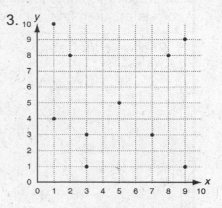

_____ _____ _____

Solve.

4. Over several years, the Bird-Watchers Club members recorded the number of chipping sparrows that have visited the bird feeders they placed in the park. The graph shows the average number of chipping sparrows that appeared per visit.

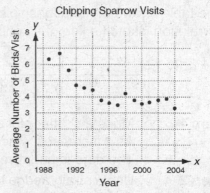

Chipping Sparrow Visits

a. Estimate the line of best fit. Draw the line on the graph.

b. What does the slope of the line mean for the visiting chipping sparrows?

_____

_____

c. Use your line of best fit to predict the average number of chipping sparrows that will visit the bird feeders in the park in 2020. How accurate do you think your prediction is?

_____

_____

_____

_____

5. How do lines of best fit help make predictions considering that all of the data do not fall exactly on the line?

_____

_____

_____

LESSON 2-7

Reteach
Curve Fitting with Linear Models

Use a scatter plot to identify a correlation. If the variables appear correlated, then find a line of fit.

Positive correlation	Negative correlation	No correlation
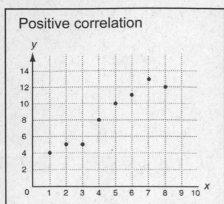	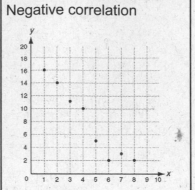	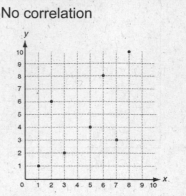

The table shows the relationship between two variables. Identify the correlation, sketch a line of fit, and find its equation.

x	1	2	3	4	5	6	7	8
y	16	14	11	10	5	2	3	2

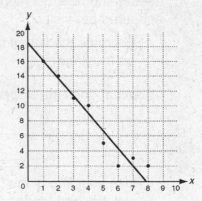

Step 1   Make a scatter plot of the data.
As x increases, y decreases.
The data is negatively correlated.

Step 2   Use a straightedge to draw a line.
There will be some points above and below the line.

Step 3   Choose two points on the line to find the equation:
(1, 16) and (7, 2).

Step 4   Use the points to find the slope:

$$m = \frac{\text{change in } y}{\text{change in } x} = \frac{16-2}{1-7} = \frac{14}{-6} = -\frac{7}{3}$$

Step 5   Use the point-slope form to find the equation of a line that models the data.

$$y - y_1 = m(x - x_1)$$

$$y - 2 = -\frac{7}{3}(x - 7)$$

$$y = -\frac{7}{3}x + 18$$

Use the scatter plot of the data to solve.

1. The correlation is _____.

2. Choose two points on the line and find the slope.

_____

3. Find the equation of a line that models the data.

_____

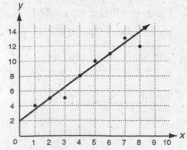

         Holt Algebra 2

LESSON 2-7

Reteach

Curve Fitting with Linear Models (continued)

A line of best fit can be used to predict data.

Use the correlation coefficient, *r*, to measure how well the data fits.

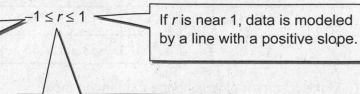

$-1 \le r \le 1$

If *r* is near –1, data is modeled by a line with a negative slope.

If *r* is near 1, data is modeled by a line with a positive slope.

If *r* is near 0, data has no correlation.

Use a graphing calculator to find the correlation coefficient of the data and the line of best fit. Use STAT EDIT to enter the data.

x	1	2	3	4	5	6	7	8
y	16	14	11	10	5	2	3	2

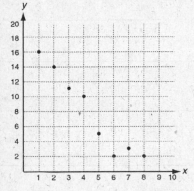

Use LinReg from the STAT CALC menu to find the line of best fit and the correlation coefficient.

LinReg
$y = ax + b$
$a = -2.202$
$b = 17.786$
$r^2 = .9308$
$r = -.9648$

The correlation coefficient is –0.9648. The data is very close to linear with a negative slope.

Use the linear regression model to predict *y* when $x = 3.5$.

$$y \approx -2.2x + 17.79$$
$$y \approx -2.2(3.5) + 17.79$$
$$y \approx 10.09$$

Use a calculator and the scatter plot of the data to solve.

4. Find the correlation coefficient, *r*. _____

5. Find the equation of the line of best fit.

_____

6. Predict *y* when $x = 2.6$. _____

7. Predict *y* when $x = 5.3$. _____

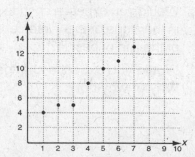

LESSON 2-7

Challenge

Transforming the Correlation Coefficient

The correlation coefficient, r, measures the strength and direction of the linear relationship for a set of data. What happens to r as transformations are applied to the graphs of the data?

x	2	6	9	14	16	21	25	28
y	3	7	15	33	38	35	40	41

1. Make a scatter plot using the data in the table.

2. Use a graphing calculator to find the slope and y-intercept for the line of best fit and the correlation coefficient, r.

_____

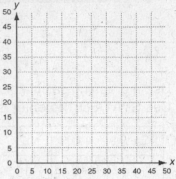

Apply each transformation to the original data.

3. horizontal translation 10 units to the right

    a. Describe how the graph would change._____

    b. How would the relationship between data points change? _____

    c. Would you expect a change in the slope
       or the y-intercept of the line of best fit? _____

    d. Would you expect a change in r?
       Why or why not? _____

4. vertical compression by a factor of 0.5

    a. Describe how the graph would change. _____

    b. How would the relationship between
       data points change? _____

    c. Would you expect a change in the slope or the
       y-intercept of the line of best fit? _____

    d. Would you expect a change in r?
       Why or why not?_____

5. reflection across the x-axis

    a. Describe how the graph would change._____

    b. How would the relationship between data points change? _____

    c. Would you expect a change
       in the slope or the y-intercept
       of the line of best fit? _____

    d. Would you expect a change in r?
       Why or why not? _____

          Holt Algebra 2

Problem Solving

Curve Fitting with Linear Models

As a science project, Shelley is studying the relationship of car mileage (miles per gallon) and speed (miles per hour). The table shows the data Shelley gathered using her family's hybrid vehicle.

Speed (miles per hour)	30	40	50	60	70
Mileage (miles per gallon)	34.0	33.5	31.5	29.0	27.5

1. Make a scatter plot of the data. Identify the correlation.

   _____

2. Sketch a line of best fit on the graph.

3. Use two points on the line to find the slope.

   _____

4. Use the point-slope form to write an equation that models the data.

   _____

5. Use a graphing calculator to plot the data. Find the value of the correlation coefficient r.

6. What does the value of r tell you about the data?

   _____

7. What equation do you find with the calculator for the line of best fit?

   _____

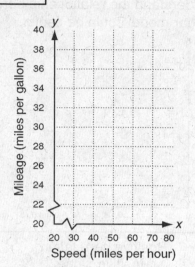

Use the equation you wrote in Exercise 3. Choose the letter for the best answer.

8. Predict the mileage for a speed of 55 miles per hour.

   A 30

   B 34

   C 39

   D 46

9. Predict the speed if the mileage is 28 miles per gallon.

   A 32

   B 35

   C 67

   D 75

Holt Algebra 2

**LESSON
2-7**

Reading Strategies
Use a Model

Some real-world relationships are very close to being linear. For example, your heating bill and the average winter temperature may be almost directly related; as the temperature drops your heating bill increases. In the summer you could see the opposite; as the temperature increases your air-conditioning bill also increases. Some things have no relationship like the temperature and your phone bill. You can use a scatter plot to understand the relationship between two variables and find whether a linear model could be useful.

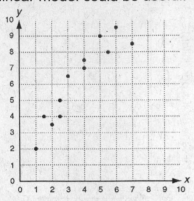 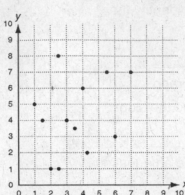 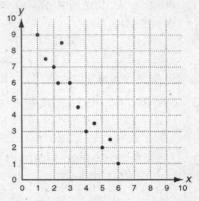

Positive correlation Positive slope	Relatively no correlation	Negative correlation Negative slope

The plotted data points may lie around a straight line. This straight line is a linear model.		A correlation coefficient, r, measures how close the relationship is to being linear. $-1 \leq r \leq 1$

Answer each question.

1. In a linear model, what is the relationship between the sign of r and the sign of the slope?

_____

2. If the value of r is close to 0, would a linear model be useful? Explain.

_____

3. Describe the correlation coefficient you might expect between the number of hours you spend studying and your grade on a test.

_____

4. Describe the correlation coefficient you might expect between the number of days of rain in July and the crowds at the beach.

_____

Holt Algebra 2

LESSON 2-8

Practice A
Solving Absolute-Value Equations and Inequalities

Solve each compound inequality. Then graph the solution.

1. $2x < 8$ and $x + 3 > 3$

_____

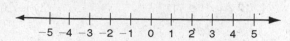

2. $x - 13 \geq -15$ or $4x < -12$

_____

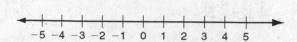

3. $4x \geq -16$ and $x + 1 \leq 0$

_____

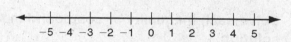

Solve each equation.

4. $|3x| = 36$

$3x = $ _____ or $3x = $ _____

$x = $ _____ or $x = $ _____

5. $|x| - 7 = -1$

_____

6. $|8x| - 13 = 11$

_____

Determine whether each inequality is a conjunction or a disjunction and whether you would use *and* or *or*.

7. $|4x| + 10 > 30$

_____

8. $|5x + 11| < 21$

_____

9. $3|x - 1| \geq 6$

_____

Solve each inequality. Then graph the solution.

10. $\dfrac{|3x - 1|}{2} \leq 3$

11. $5|2x| > 10$

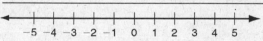

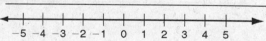

12. Phil told his friend that if you subtract 12 from his age and then take the absolute value, you'll get an answer of 3. How old is Phil?

_____

Holt Algebra 2

Name _____ Date _____ Class_____

Practice B

Solving Absolute-Value Equations and Inequalities

Solve each equation.

1. $|2x + 1| = 7$

2. $|-7x| = 28$

3. $3|3x| - 7 = 2$

_____ _____ _____

4. $|2x - 5| = 5$

5. $2|x + 1| = 14$

6. $|4 - x| + 2 = 9$

_____ _____ _____

Solve each inequality or compound inequality. Then graph the solution.

7. $-4x + 2 > -10$ and $5x - 12 < 8$

8. $3x - 4 \geq 8$ or $-x + 12 > 16$

_____

_____

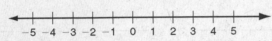

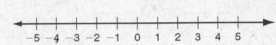

9. $|9x| \geq 18$

10. $|3x - 7| > 8$

_____

_____

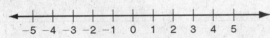

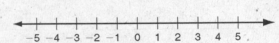

11. $|0.3x| > 1$

12. $|7x| - 12 \leq 9$

_____

_____

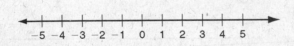

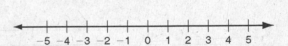

Solve.

13. Any measurement is accurate within ±0.5 of the measurement unit. For example, if you measure your pencil to the nearest inch, your measurement could be 0.5 inch too long or 0.5 inch too short. Write an absolute-value inequality that shows the maximum and minimum actual measure of a nail measured to be 4.4 centimeters to the nearest 0.1 centimeter.

_____

Holt Algebra 2

Name _____ Date _____ Class_____

Practice C

Solving Absolute-Value Equations and Inequalities

Solve each equation.

1. $|2x - 3| = 15$

2. $\frac{1}{2}|x + 9| = 1$

3. $11 - |4 - x| = 4$

_____ _____ _____

Solve and graph.

4. $5(7 - 2x) < 40$ and $5x + 2 < 12$

5. $\frac{7x - 10}{6} \leq 3$ or $3x + 2 > 5x - 8$

_____

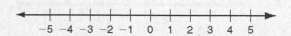

_____

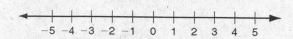

6. $\left|\frac{4x - 1}{6}\right| \geq 1$

7. $-3|5x - 2| < -12$

_____

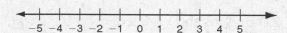

_____

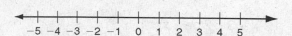

8. $2|3x - 6| + 6 \geq 24$

9. $\frac{|9x + 1|}{4} < 2$

_____

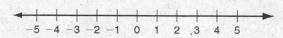

_____

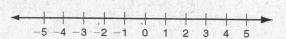

Solve.

10. Ben says that there is no solution for this absolute-value inequality. Is he correct? If not, solve the inequality. Explain how you know you are correct.

$$32 + \frac{|x - 7|}{13} < 7$$

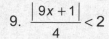

_____

_____

_____

Holt Algebra 2

LESSON 2-8

Reteach

Solving Absolute-Value Equations and Inequalities

To solve compound inequalities, solve both inequalities. Then graph.

Solve $x + 6 < 4$ or $2x \geq 8$.

$$x + 6 < 4 \qquad \text{OR} \qquad 2x \geq 8$$
$$x < -2 \qquad \text{OR} \qquad x \geq 4$$

> This inequality uses OR. Its graph has two parts.

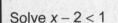

Solve $x - 2 < 1$ and $-3x \leq 12$.

$$x - 2 < 1 \qquad \text{AND} \qquad -3x \leq 12$$
$$x < 3 \qquad \text{AND} \qquad x \geq -4$$

> Reverse the inequality when dividing by a negative number.

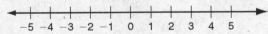

> This inequality uses AND. Its graph has one part.

Solve and graph each compound inequality.

1. $x + 3 < 2$ or $\dfrac{1}{2}x > 1$

   $x <$ ____ OR $x >$ ____

   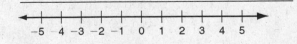

2. $-6x \leq 18$ and $x + 6 \leq 6$

   $x \geq$ ____ AND $x \leq$ ____

   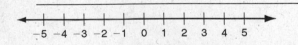

3. $x - 4 < -7$ or $-4x \leq 4$

   _____ OR _____

4. $-3x \leq 6$ and $x + 2 < 5$

   _____ AND _____

5. $3x < 12$ and $-3x < 12$

6. $\dfrac{1}{2}x - 2 \leq 0$ or $2 - \dfrac{1}{2}x \leq -1$

LESSON 2-8

Reteach

Solving Absolute-Value Equations and Inequalities (continued)

Solving absolute-value inequalities is like solving compound inequalities.

Solve: $\|x\| < 2$ Solution: $-2 < x < 2$	Solve: $\|x\| \leq 2$ Solution: $-2 \leq x \leq 2$
Solve: $\|x\| > 2$ Solution: $x < -2$ OR $x > 2$	Solve: $\|x\| \geq 2$ Solution: $x \leq -2$ OR $x \geq 2$

Remember:
$|x| = x$ if $x \geq 0$

Solve $|x - 2| \leq 3$.

> Use the solutions from the table to write the inequalities

$$-3 \leq x - 2 \leq 3$$

$$-3 + 2 \leq x - 2 + 2 \leq 3 + 2 \qquad \textbf{\textit{Add 2.}}$$

$$-1 \leq x \leq 5 \qquad \textit{Simplify.}$$

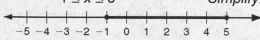

Solve $|2x - 1| > 5$.

$2x - 1 > 5$	OR	$2x - 1 < -5$
$2x > 6$	OR	$2x < -4$ *Add 1.*
$x > 3$	OR	$x < -2$ *Divide by 2.*

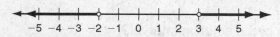

Solve and graph.

7. $|x + 3| < 2$

_____ $< x + 3 <$ _____

_____ $< x <$ _____

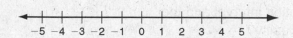

8. $|2x + 1| \geq 3$

$2x + 1 \geq$ _____ OR $2x + 1 \leq$ _____

$2x \geq$ _____ OR $2x \leq$ _____

$x \geq$ _____ OR $x \leq$ _____

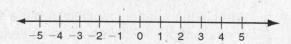

Challenge

Relating the Length of a Solution Interval to a Coefficient

Changing the value of a coefficient in an absolute-value linear inequality
results in a change in the solution interval.

Solve.

1. $|ax + b| \leq c$, where $a > 0$ and $c > 0$.

   a. Solve the inequality for x in terms of a, b, and c. _____

   b. Verify that your solution is equivalent to $\dfrac{-(b+c)}{a} \leq x \leq \dfrac{c-b}{a}$.

   _____

Apply the general solution to solve each inequality.

2. $|2x + 3| \leq 5$ _____   3. $|4x + 3| \leq 5$ _____

Refer to the inequalities in Exercises 2 and 3.

4. a. Compare the values of a, b, and c in the two inequalities.

   _____

   b. How does the value of a affect the length of the solution interval?

   _____

   c. Predict the solution interval for the inequality $|8x + 3| \leq 5$. _____

   d. Use the general solution to determine if your prediction was correct.

   _____

   e. What is the relationship between the solution interval and the
      coefficient of x in this absolute-value inequality?

   _____

Solve.

5. a. Use the general solution to solve $|3x - 6| \leq 21$. _____

   b. Predict the solution interval of $|6x - 6| \leq 21$. _____

   c. Predict the solution interval of $|12x - 6| \leq 21$. _____

Problem Solving
Solving Absolute-Value Equations and Inequalities

Gita's science class is making a set of posters about North American wildlife. The table shows some of the data collected.

1. What is the center of each weight group?

   a. W_1 _____

   b. W_2 _____

   c. W_3 _____

2. Express each weight group as an absolute-value expression.

   a. W_1 _____

   b. W_2 _____

   c. W_3 _____

3. Write inequalities to show the amount of food required each day for animals in each weight group.

   a. W_1 _____

   b. W_2 _____

   c. W_3 _____

North American Wildlife		
Weight Groups (kg)	**Animal**	**Daily Food Requirement (kg)**
W_1 135–450	Grizzly bear	10.5
	Polar bear	9.9
	Black bear	3.9
W_2 10–90	Mule deer	2.8
	Arctic wolf	2.3
	River otter	0.8
W_3 3–8	Nutria	0.38
	Opossum	0.19
	Rabbit	0.18

4. Gita wants to use the term *disjunction* or *conjunction* on her poster showing the inequalities. Which term should she use? Why?

   _____

5. Les includes the following on his poster:
   Solve this equation to find the number of kilograms of food consumed each day by an animal in one of the weight groups:

   $$|f - 7.2| \le 3.3.$$

   Find the solution.

   _____

6. Write an absolute-value inequality to represent the maximum weight difference between a grizzly bear, g, and a black bear, b.

   _____

Reading Strategies
LESSON 2-8
Understand Vocabulary

Equations and inequalities can be combined to make compound statements. **Disjunctions** and **conjunctions** are two types of compound statements.

Compound Statement	Definition and Symbol	Example
Disjunction	Two statements joined by the word *or*	$x > 1$ or $x \leq -2$
	Symbol: $\cup$	
Conjunction	Two statements joined by the word *and*	$x > 0$ and $x \leq 6$
	Symbol: $\cap$	

Answer each question.

1. $x > 1$ or $x \leq -2$

   a. Is the compound statement true for $x = 6$? Explain.

   _____

   b. Is the compound statement true for $x = 0$? Explain.

   _____

   c. For which values of x is the disjunction false?

   _____

2. $x > 0$ and $x \leq 6$

   a. Describe the values of x for which the conjunction is true.

   _____

   b. Describe the values of x for which the conjunction is false?

   _____

3. $|x| > 5$

   a. Describe in words the values of x for which the inequality is true.
   Then write a compound statement for those values of x.

   _____

   b. Write a compound statement to show all the values of x for which the inequality is false.

   _____

Holt Algebra 2

LESSON **Practice A**
2-9 *Absolute-Value Functions*

Perform each transformation on $f(x) = |x|$. Write the transformed function, $g(x)$.

1. up 3 units

2. right 3 units

3. reflect across y-axis

_____ _____ _____

4. stretch horizontally by a factor of 3

5. reflect across x-axis

6. compress vertically by a factor of 0.1

_____ _____ _____

Translate $f(x) = |x|$ so that the vertex is at the given point.

7. (6, 4)

8. (−1, 5)

9. (3, −3)

_____ _____ _____

Perform each transformation. Then graph.

10. Translate $f(x) = |x - 4| + 1$ up 2 units and left 3 units.

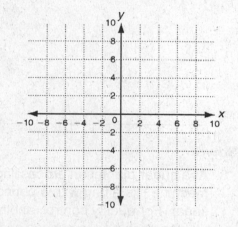

_____

11. Stretch $f(x) = 2|x - 1|$ horizontally by a factor of 5.

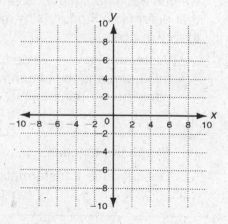

_____

LESSON 2-9 Practice B
Absolute-Value Functions

Perform each transformation on $f(x) = |2x| + 3$. Write the transformed function $g(x)$.

1. down 7 units

2. reflect across *y*-axis

3. left 5 units

_____

_____

_____

Translate $f(x) = |x|$ so that the vertex is at the given point.

4. (6, –3)

5. (–8, –1)

6. (–7, 2)

_____

_____

_____

Perform the transformation. Then graph.

7. Compress $f(x) = |3x - 4|$ vertically by a factor of $\frac{1}{3}$.

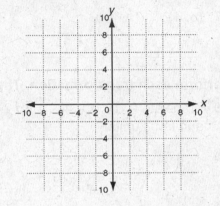

_____

Solve.

8. At a sugar plantation processing plant, a machine fills a bag with 5 pounds of white sugar. For quality control, another machine weighs each bag in ounces and rejects bags that differ from 5 pounds by more than *y* ounces.

   a. Write an absolute-value function to show the minimum and maximum weight of sugar that could be in each bag.

   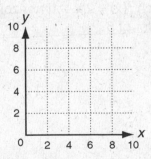

   _____

   b. Graph the function.

   c. Describe the transformation from $f(x) = |x|$.

_____

Holt Algebra 2

LESSON 2-9

Practice C

Absolute-Value Functions

State the transformation that maps the graph of $f(x) = |x|$ **onto the graph of each function.**

1. $g(x) = |x + 2|$ 2. $g(x) = |2x|$ 3. $g(x) = 4(|x - 5| + 3)$

_____   _____   _____

Find the vertex of the graph of each function.

4. $g(x) = |x - 3| + 7$ 5. $g(x) = -4 + |x|$ 6. $g(x) = |x + 8| - 1$

_____   _____   _____

Find an absolute-value function for each graph.

7.   8.   9.

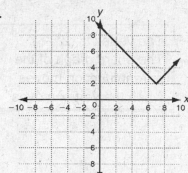   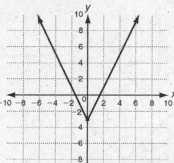   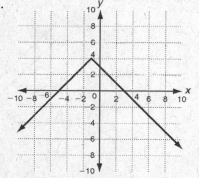

_____   _____   _____

Solve.

10. Gwen transformed the function $f(x) = |x|$ by translating it up 2 units and then reflecting it across the *x*-axis. She named the new function $g(x)$.

a. Write the equation of $g(x)$.

_____

b. Joe transformed $g(x)$ and named the new function $h(x)$. The function $h(x)$ is shown on the graph. Write the equation for $h(x)$.

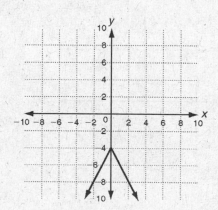

_____

c. Describe the transformation from $g(x)$ to $h(x)$.

_____

Holt Algebra 2

LESSON 2-9

Reteach

Absolute-Value Functions

The graph of the absolute-value parent function looks like a V.

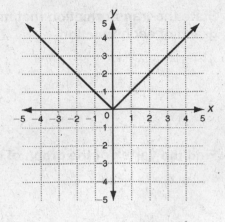

To translate $f(x) = |x|$ to a new vertex (h, k), use $g(x) = |x - h| + k$.

Translate $f(x) = |x|$ so that the vertex is at $(2, -3)$.

$g(x) = |x - h| + k$	*Write the transformation.*
$g(x) = |x - 2| + (-3)$	*Substitute $h = 2$, $k = -3$.*
$g(x) = |x - 2| - 3$	*Simplify.*

Graph to check:

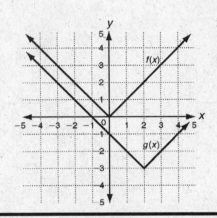

The vertex is $(2, -3)$. The entire graph of the parent function moves when the vertex moves.

Translate $f(x) = |x|$ to each new vertex. Then graph the transformation.

1. vertex $(1, 2)$

$g(x) = |x - \underline{\hspace{1cm}}| + \underline{\hspace{1cm}}$

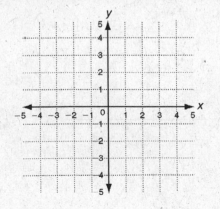

2. vertex $(-3, -1)$

$g(x) = |\underline{\hspace{1cm}}| + \underline{\hspace{1cm}}$

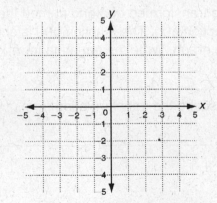

LESSON
2-9
Reteach
Absolute-Value Functions (continued)

To **vertically** stretch or compress $f(x)$ by a factor of a, use $f(x) \rightarrow a \cdot f(x)$.

To **horizontally** stretch or compress $f(x)$ by a factor of b, use $f(x) \rightarrow f\left(\dfrac{1}{b}x\right)$.

Stretch the graph of $f(x) = \|x\| + 1$ vertically by a factor of 2. $g(x) = a \cdot f(x)$ $g(x) = 2(\|x\| + 1)$ *Substitute.* $g(x) = 2\|x\| + 2$ *Distribute.*	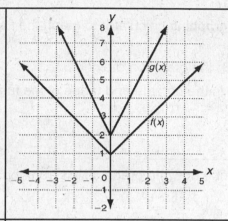
Compress the graph of $f(x) = \|x - 2\|$ horizontally by a factor of $\dfrac{1}{2}$. $g(x) = f\left(\dfrac{1}{b}x\right)$ $g(x) = f\left(\dfrac{1}{\left(\dfrac{1}{2}\right)}x\right) = f(2x)$ *Substitute,* $g(x) = \|(2x) - 2\| = \|2x - 2\|$ *Simplify.*	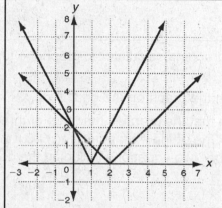

Perform each transformation.

3. Stretch $f(x) = \|x\| - 1$ vertically by a factor of 3.

    $g(x) = a \cdot f(x)$ $g(x) = 3(_____)$ $g(x) = _____$

4. Stretch $f(x) = \|4x + 1\|$ horizontally by a factor of 2.

    $g(x) = f\left(\dfrac{1}{b}x\right) = f\left(\_\_\_ x\right)$ $g(x) = \left|4\left(\_\_\_ x\right) + \_\_\_\right|$ $g(x) = _____$

5. Compress $f(x) = \|4x\| - 2$ vertically by a factor of $\dfrac{1}{2}$.

    $g(x) = a \cdot f(x)$ $g(x) = \_\_\_\_ (_____)$ $g(x) = _____$

LESSON
2-9

Challenge

The Absolute Value of Absolute Value

Absolute-value graphs of the form $y = |x - h| + k$ have
a V shape or an inverted V shape that may have its vertex
translated from the origin. The graph shows the following
absolute-value function.

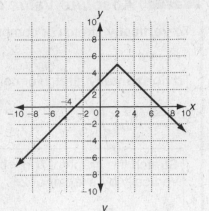

$$y = 5 - |x - 2|$$

What happens when you introduce the absolute value of an
absolute value?

1. Use your graphing calculator to graph the function
   $y = |5 - |x - 2||$.

   a. Sketch the graph on the grid.

   b. What is the domain and range of the function?

   _____

   c. Describe how the graph differs from the graph of
      $y = 5 - |x - 2|$.

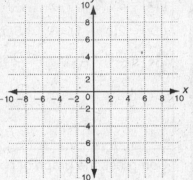

   _____

2. Use your graphing calculator to graph the function
   $y = |x + 2| - |x - 3|$.

   a. Sketch the graph on the grid.

   b. Notice that the graph is made up of three straight
      lines. One of the equations is $y = -5$ if $x \le -2$. Write
      the other two equations including the domain for each.

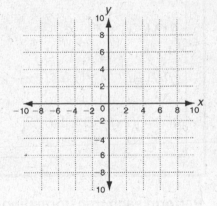

   _____

3. Use your graphing calculator to graph the function
   $y = |x + 2| - |x - 3||$.

   a. Sketch the graph on the grid.

   b. Describe how the graph differs from the graph of
      $y = |x + 2| - |x - 3|$.

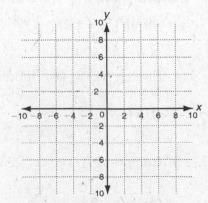

   _____

   c. Write an equation for each straight line section of
      the graph giving the domain for each.

   _____

LESSON 2-9	# Problem Solving

Absolute-Value Functions

Linette and Dylan are observing people passing by an outdoor art exhibit in the park. The graph shows the average path of a person walking past the exhibit at a rate of 1 block per minute.

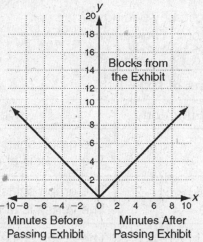

Blocks from
the Exhibit

Minutes Before   Minutes After
Passing Exhibit   Passing Exhibit

1. Write an absolute-value equation that represents the graph. Express the distance in blocks from the exhibit, $D(t)$, as a function of minutes (t) before and after arriving at the exhibit.

   _____

2. Find the value of $D(t)$ for $t = 3$ and for $t = -3$. What do these values mean about the position of a person walking past the exhibit?

   _____

3. What is the domain of the function?   _____

4. What is the range of the function?   _____

5. A person rides past the exhibit on a bicycle at a rate of 5 blocks per minute.

   a. Write an absolute-value function, $C(t)$, to represent the distance the bicycle is from the exhibit at any time, t.

   _____

   b. Sketch $C(t)$ on the graph. Describe the transformation.

   _____

   c. Compare the vertex of $C(t)$ to the vertex of $D(t)$.

   _____

LESSON 2-9 Reading Strategies
Read a Table

The graph of an absolute-value function can be identified by its shape. The graph of $f(x) = |x|$ is V-shaped. Its vertex is at the origin (0, 0).

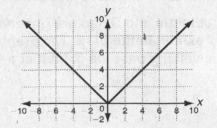

You can shift, or translate the graph of this function by adding to or subtracting from the function or the value of x. Translation doesn't change the shape of the graph.

Translations of $f(x) = |x|$		
Transformation	Function	Result
To translate the function **up**, add a constant > 0 to the function.	$f(x) = |x| + 3$	The graph shifts 3 units up. The vertex is at (0, 3).
To translate the function **down**, subtract a constant > 0 to the function.	$f(x) = |x| - 2$	The graph shifts 2 units down. The vertex is at (0, –2).
To translate a function **to the right**, subtract a constant > 0 inside the absolute value function.	$f(x) = |x - 1|$	The graph shifts 1 unit to the right. The vertex is at (1, 0).
To translate a function **to the left**, add a constant > 0 inside the absolute value function.	$f(x) = |x + 3|$	The graph shifts 3 units to the left. The vertex is at (–3, 0).

Answer each question.

1. What is the domain and range of the function $f(x) = |x|$? Explain why the range is limited.

_____

2. What is the difference in the function between shifting $f(x) = |x|$ 3 units down or 3 units to the right?

_____

4. The graph of $f(x) = |x|$ is shifted 2 units left and 1 unit up.

   a. Write the equation of the resulting figure. _____

   b. Give the coordinates of the vertex. _____

5. Except at 0, all the values of the function $f(x) = |x|$ are positive. Is this also true for $f(x) = |x| - 2$? Explain.

_____

Holt Algebra 2

Date _____

Dear Family,

In Chapter 3, your child will learn to solve systems of linear equations and linear inequalities.

A **system of equations** is a set of two or more equations containing two or more variables. The solution of a system is the point or set of points that make all of its equations true.

A **linear system** contains only linear equations. The graph of a linear system of two equations in two variables is two lines. If two lines intersect, their point of intersection is the solution to the system.

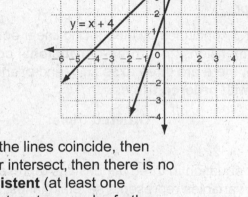

Linear system:

$$\begin{cases} y = 3x + 2 \\ y = x + 4 \end{cases}$$

Solution to system:

$$(1, 5)$$

Not all linear systems have exactly one solution. If the lines coincide, then there are infinitely many solutions. If the lines never intersect, then there is no solution. A system can be classified as either **consistent** (at least one solution), or **inconsistent** (no solution). A consistent system can be further classified as **dependent** (same slope and y-intercept) or **independent** (different slopes).

graph			
solutions	one	infinitely many	none
classification	consistent and independent	consistent and dependent	inconsistent

Your child will also learn two algebraic methods of solving systems. In **substitution**, you solve one equation for one variable and then substitute the expression into the other equation. In **elimination**, you add or subtract multiples of the equations in order to get rid of one of the variables.

Holt Algebra 2

A **system of linear inequalities** is two or more linear inequalities with the same variables. The solution is the region where the shadings overlap.

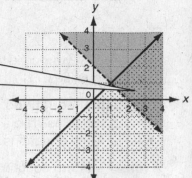

System of linear inequalities:

$$\begin{cases} y \leq x \\ y > -x + 2 \end{cases}$$

solution to system: all of the points in the overlapping region and on its solid boundary line

Systems can be applied to solve many real-world problems. A special application of systems of linear inequalities is **linear programming**, a method of finding optimal values of a function given a set of **constraints.** Linear programming often has business applications. For example, you may want to maximize a production function under constraints of material and labor.

Chapter 3 concludes by introducing linear equations in three-dimensions. In a **three-dimensional coordinate system,** there are three axes (*x, y,* and *z*) and points are plotted with **ordered triples.**

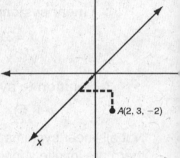

Ordered triple: $\left(\underset{x}{2}, \underset{y}{3}, \underset{z}{-2}\right)$

A linear equation in three dimensions represents a *plane.* A linear system in three variables represents several planes, and the intersection of those planes is the solution.

Because it can be difficult to graph planes and visualize their points of intersection, linear systems in three variables are usually solved using elimination.

Step 1:
Add the first two equations to eliminate *z:*

$$\begin{array}{l} x + 2y + z = 8 \\ 2x + y - z = 4 \\ \hline 3x + 3y \quad\;\; = 12 \end{array}$$

Step 3:
Use $\begin{cases} 3x + 3y = 12 \\ 7x + 4y = 19 \end{cases}$ to solve for *x* and *y.*

Solve: $\begin{cases} x + 2y + z = 8 \\ 2x + y - z = 4 \\ x + y + 3z = 7 \end{cases}$

Step 2:
Add multiples of the second two equations to eliminate *z:*

$$\begin{array}{l} 6x + 3y - 3z = 12 \\ x + y \quad + 3z = 7 \\ \hline 7x + 4y \quad\quad = 19 \end{array}$$

Step 4:
Find *z* by substituting *x* and *y* into one of the original equations.

For additional resources, visit go.hrw.com and enter the keyword MB7 Parent.

Holt Algebra 2

LESSON	**Practice A**
3-1	*Using Graphs and Tables to Solve Linear Systems*

Does the given ordered pair solve the system of equations?
Substitute each value for *x* and *y* into the equations. Write *yes* or *no*.

1. $(2, -1)$ $\begin{cases} 3x + y = 3 \\ x - y = 5 \end{cases}$ 2. $(4, 5)$ $\begin{cases} x - 6y = -26 \\ 2x + y = 13 \end{cases}$ 3. $(-3, -7)$ $\begin{cases} -x + 2y = 1 \\ 4x - 3y = 19 \end{cases}$

$3(2) + (-1) \overset{?}{=} 3$

$(2) - (-1) \overset{?}{=} 5$

_____   _____   _____

Use a table and a graph to solve the system.

4. $\begin{cases} y = x + 1 \\ x = 2y + 2 \end{cases}$

a. Make a table of values for each equation.

$y = x + 1$

x	y
-2	
-1	
0	
1	
2	

$x = 2y + 2$

x	y
-2	
-1	
0	
1	
2	

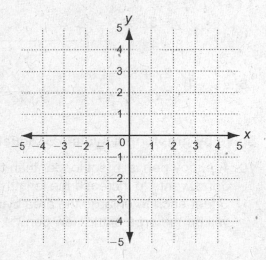

b. Use the values in the tables to graph each equation.

c. Which ordered pair solves both equations? _____

Use a graph to solve each system.

5. $\begin{cases} x + y = 2 \\ x - y = 4 \end{cases}$ _____   6. $\begin{cases} y = 3x - 2 \\ x + y = 6 \end{cases}$ _____

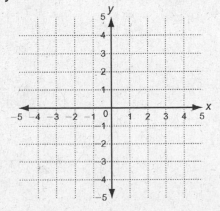   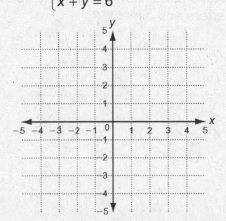

Holt Algebra 2

LESSON 3-1

Practice B

Using Graphs and Tables to Solve Linear Systems

Classify each system, and determine the number of solutions.

1. $\begin{cases} y = -4x + 7 \\ 12x + 3y = 21 \end{cases}$

2. $\begin{cases} 5y = x - 10 \\ y = \dfrac{x}{5} + 3 \end{cases}$

3. $\begin{cases} x + 6y = -2 \\ 12x - 6y = 0 \end{cases}$

_____   _____   _____

_____   _____   _____

Use substitution to determine if the given ordered pair is an element of the solution set for the system of equations. If it is not, give the correct solution.

4. $(-4, 8) \begin{cases} y = -2x \\ 3x + y = -4 \end{cases}$ _____

5. $(11, 3) \begin{cases} y = x - 8 \\ x + 4y = -2 \end{cases}$ _____

6. $(4, 1) \begin{cases} y = 5x - 1 \\ 8 = 4x + y \end{cases}$ _____

7. $(5, -5) \begin{cases} x + y = 10 \\ x - y = 0 \end{cases}$ _____

8. $(2, -1) \begin{cases} 2x + 3y = -8 \\ 3x - 4y = 5 \end{cases}$ _____

9. $(0, 3) \begin{cases} 3x + 5y = 15 \\ x - y = -3 \end{cases}$ _____

Solve by graphing a system of equations.

10. A puppy pen is 1 foot longer than twice its width. John wants to increase the length and width by 5 feet each to enlarge the area by 90 square feet. What will be the area of the new pen?

_____

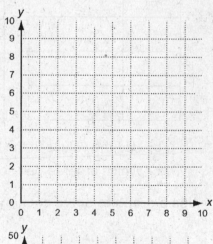

11. Keesha has 10 more quarters than dimes, which, together, total $11.25. How many coins does she have in quarters and dimes?

_____

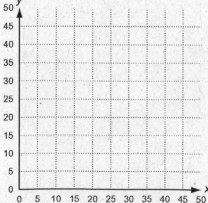

LESSON 3-1

Practice C
Using Graphs and Tables to Solve Linear Systems

Match each system of equations with the corresponding conditions that it satisfies.

1. The system is consistent and dependent.

$$\begin{cases} y = \dfrac{2}{3}x + 10 \\ y = 3x + 1 \end{cases}$$

2. The system is inconsistent.

$$\begin{cases} y = \dfrac{2}{3}x + 10 \\ 6y - 4x = 60 \end{cases}$$

3. The system is consistent and independent.

$$\begin{cases} y = \dfrac{2}{3}x + 10 \\ 3y + 9 = 2x \end{cases}$$

Solve.

4. A tub containing 16 gallons of water is draining at a rate of 1 gallon per hour. A basin of 3.5 gallons of water is draining at a rate of 1 gallon every 6 hours.

   a. Write a system of equations that represents y, the number of gallons left in the container after x hours.

   _____

   b. If both containers began draining at the same time, how soon will the tub and basin hold the same amount of water?

   _____

   c. When the amounts are equal, how much water will be in each container?

   _____

5. Jenna has $1500 in a savings account. She adds $30 to her account each month. Luis has $2400 in his savings account. He withdraws $30 from his account each month.

   a. In how many months will they have the same
      balance in their savings accounts?   _____

   b. What will be the balance in each account?   _____

LESSON 3-1

Reteach

Using Graphs and Tables to Solve Linear Systems

A **linear system** of equations is a set of two or more linear equations. To **solve a linear system**, find all the ordered pairs (x, y) that make both equations true. Use a table and a graph to solve a system of equations.

$$\begin{cases} y + x = 2 \\ y - 2x = 5 \end{cases} \quad \text{Solve each equation for } y. \rightarrow \begin{cases} y = -x + 2 \\ y = 2x + 5 \end{cases}$$

Make a table of values for each equation.

$y = -x + 2$	
x	y
-2	4
-1	3
0	2
1	1

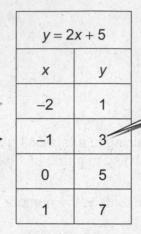

$y = 2x + 5$	
x	y
-2	1
-1	3
0	5
1	7

> When $x = -1$, $y = 3$ for both equations.

On a graph, the point where the lines intersect is the solution.

Use the table to draw the graph of each equation.

The lines appear to intersect at $(-1, 3)$.

Substitute $(-1, 3)$ into the original equations to check.

$$y + x = 2 \qquad y - 2x = 5$$

$$3 + (-1) \overset{?}{=} 2 \qquad 3 - 2(1) \overset{?}{=} 5$$

$$2 = 2 \checkmark \qquad 5 = 5 \checkmark$$

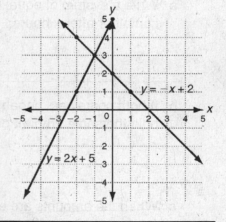

Solve the system using a table and a graph. Give the ordered pair that solves both equations.

1. $\begin{cases} x + y = 1 \\ 2x - y = 5 \end{cases}$ Solution: _____

$y = -x + 1$	
x	y
0	
1	
2	
3	

$y = 2x - 5$	
x	y
0	
1	
2	
3	

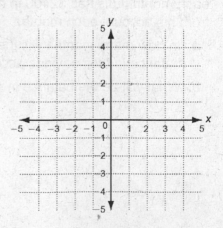

Holt Algebra 2

<table>
<tr><td>LESSON
3-1</td><td></td></tr>
</table>

Reteach

Using Graphs and Tables to Solve Linear Systems (continued)

To classify a linear system:

		Remember: m = slope and b = y-intercept.
Step 1	Write each equation in the form $y = mx + b$.	
Step 2	Compare the slopes and y-intercepts.	
Step 3	Classify by the number of solutions of the system.	

Exactly One Solution Independent	Infinitely Many Solutions Dependent	No Solution Inconsistent
The lines have **different slopes** and intersect at one point.	The lines have the **same slope and y-intercept.** Their graph is the same line.	The lines have the **same slope and different y-intercepts.** The lines are parallel.
$\begin{cases} x + y = 3 \\ x - y = 1 \end{cases}$	$\begin{cases} 2x = y - 1 \\ 4y - 8x = 4 \end{cases}$	$\begin{cases} y + 2x = -3 \\ y - 1 = -2x \end{cases}$
Solve each equation for y.	Solve each equation for y.	Solve each equation for y.
$\begin{cases} y = -x + 3; m = -1 \\ y = x - 1; m = 1 \end{cases}$	$\begin{cases} y = 2x + 1; m = 2, b = 1 \\ y = 2x + 1; m = 2, b = 1 \end{cases}$	$\begin{cases} y = -2x - 3; m = -2, b = -3 \\ y = -2x + 1; m = -2, b = 1 \end{cases}$
The slopes are different. The system has one solution and is independent.	The slopes and the y-intercepts are the same. The system has infinitely many solutions and is dependent.	The slopes are the same but the y-intercepts are different. The system has no solution and is inconsistent.
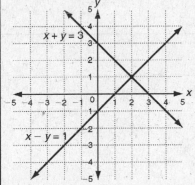	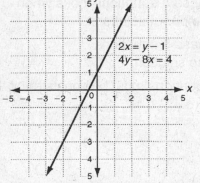	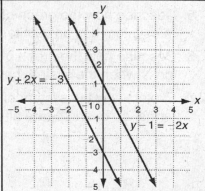

Classify each system and determine the number of solutions.

2. $\begin{cases} y + x = 2 \\ y + 1 = -x \end{cases}$

$y =$ _____ , $m =$ ____, $b =$ ____
$y =$ _____ , $m =$ ____, $b =$ ____
Number of solutions: _____

3. $\begin{cases} y + 1 = 3x \\ 2y - 6x = -2 \end{cases}$

$y =$ _____ , $m =$ ____, $b =$ ____
$y =$ _____ , $m =$ ____, $b =$ ____
Number of solutions: _____

_____ _____

LESSON
3-1

Challenge

System Classifications

A system of linear equations can be consistent and independent, consistent and dependent, or inconsistent. **Use the following system of equations for Exercises 1–3.**

$$\begin{cases} x - 3y = 12 \\ 3x + by = c \end{cases}$$

1. Find values of b and c so that the system is consistent and dependent.

   _____

2. Find values of b and c so that the system is inconsistent.

   _____

3. Find values of b and c so that the system is consistent and independent.

   _____

Use this system of equations for Exercises 4–7.

$$\begin{cases} a_1x + b_1y = c_1 \\ a_2x + b_2y = c_2 \\ a_3x + b_3y = c_3 \end{cases}$$

4. Describe how the graph of these 3 equations looks when the system has exactly one solution.

   _____

5. Describe how the graph of these 3 equations looks when the system has an infinite number of solutions.

   _____

6. Describe how the graph of these 3 equations looks when the system has no solution.

   _____

7. Explain why the system of equations must be consistent if the 3 constant terms, c_1, c_2 and c_3 are all zero.

   _____

Use this system of equations for Exercise 8.

$$\begin{cases} ax + by = e \\ cx + dy = f \end{cases}$$

8. Under what conditions will this system be consistent and independent?

   _____

   _____

LESSON 3-1

Problem Solving
Using Graphs and Tables to Solve Linear Systems

Solve.

1. After the lesson, Carl takes the wakeboarding class to the *Glass Cafe*. He pays $26 for 8 large and 4 small juice drinks. A large glass costs $1 more than a small glass.

   a. Write a linear system of equations to find the cost of each size drink.

   _____

   b. Write one equation at the top of each table and complete the table.

   c. What is the cost of each size drink?

   _____

x	y
1	
1.5	
2	
2.5	
3	

x	y
1	
1.5	
2	
2.5	
3	

2. Sandy rented a jet ski for $95 plus $15 per hour. Pauline rented a jet ski for $80 plus $20 per hour.

   a. Write a linear system of equations to find the number of hours for which the rental cost is the same.

   _____

   b. Graph the system.

   c. For what number of hours would Sandy and Pauline pay the same to rent a jet ski?

   _____

   d. How much would it cost to rent the jet ski for this amount of time?

   _____

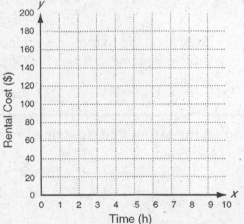

Choose the letter for the best answer.

3. Juan started with 50 gallons of water in his pool, and he is filling it at a rate of 10 gallons per minute. His next-door neighbor Sam started with 20 gallons of water in his pool, and he is filling it at a rate of 15 gallons per minute. Which system of equations could you use to find when the pools will contain the same amount of water?

   A $\begin{cases} y = 50 + 15x \\ y = 20 + 10x \end{cases}$ C $\begin{cases} y = 50 - 15x \\ y = 20 - 10x \end{cases}$

   B $\begin{cases} y = 50 + 10x \\ y = 20 + 15x \end{cases}$ D $\begin{cases} y = 50 - 10x \\ y = 20 - 15x \end{cases}$

LESSON 3-1

Reading Strategies

Use Graphic Aids

A system of linear equations can be classified.

Linear Equations

Consistent   **Inconsistent**

Dependent   **Independent**

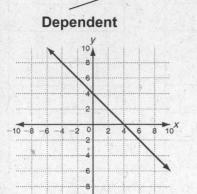

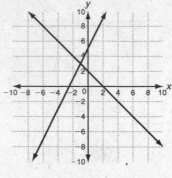

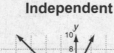

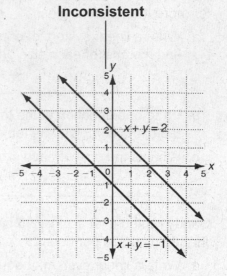

Both lines the same
Infinitely many
solutions

Lines intersect
One solution

Lines parallel
No solutions

Ring all the terms that describe the system.

1. $\begin{cases} y = -x + 1 \\ y = x + 3 \end{cases}$

   a. Consistent

   b. Inconsistent

   c. Dependent

   d. Independent

2. $\begin{cases} x + y = 5 \\ x + y = 2 \end{cases}$

   a. Consistent

   b. Inconsistent

   c. Dependent

   d. Independent

3. $\begin{cases} 3x - y = 3 \\ 3y = 9x - 9 \end{cases}$

   a. Consistent

   b. Inconsistent

   c. Dependent

   d. Independent

Draw a line from each system of equations to the matching graph.

4. $\begin{cases} 2x + y = 1 \\ 2y = -4x + 2 \end{cases}$

5. $\begin{cases} y = x - 3 \\ y = -x + 1 \end{cases}$

6. $\begin{cases} x - y = 5 \\ 2x + y = 4 \end{cases}$

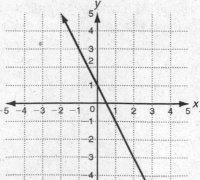

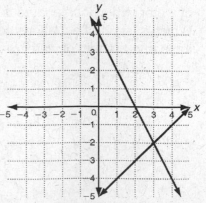

Holt Algebra 2

LESSON
3-2

Practice A

Using Algebraic Methods to Solve Linear Systems

Use substitution to solve each system of equations.

1. $\begin{cases} y = x - 3 \\ x + 2y = 6 \end{cases}$

   a. Substitute $x - 3$ for y in $x + 2y = 6$. Then solve the equation for x.

   _____

   b. Substitute your value for x in $y = x - 3$ and solve for y.

   _____

   c. Write the solution as an ordered pair.   _____

2. $\begin{cases} x = 5 - y \\ 2x + 5y = 16 \end{cases}$ 3. $\begin{cases} y = 3x + 2 \\ 2x + 3y = 17 \end{cases}$ 4. $\begin{cases} x - y = 2 \\ y = 4x + 1 \end{cases}$

_____   _____   _____

Use elimination to solve each system of equations.

5. $\begin{cases} 4x - 5y = 7 \\ 3x - 4y = 6 \end{cases}$

   a. Multiply the first equation by -3 and the second equation by 4.

   _____

   b. Add the two equations, which eliminates x. Solve for y.

   _____

   c. Substitute your value for y into the first equation. Solve for x.
      Write the solution as an ordered pair.   _____

6. $\begin{cases} 5x + y = 19 \\ -2x - y = -7 \end{cases}$ 7. $\begin{cases} -x + 3y = 12 \\ 6x - y = -21 \end{cases}$ 8. $\begin{cases} 2x + 3y = 4 \\ 4x - 2y = -8 \end{cases}$

_____   _____   _____

    Holt Algebra 2

LESSON 3-2

Practice B

Using Algebraic Methods to Solve Linear Systems

Use substitution to solve each system of equations.

1. $\begin{cases} x = 7y - 4 \\ 2x - 3y = 14 \end{cases}$

2. $\begin{cases} y - 3x = 5 \\ 2x = 3y + 6 \end{cases}$

3. $\begin{cases} 3x - 4y = 20 \\ y - 2x = 0 \end{cases}$

_____ _____ _____

Use elimination to solve each system of equations.

4. $\begin{cases} x + 6y = 1 \\ 3x + 5y = -10 \end{cases}$

5. $\begin{cases} 3x + 4y = 6 \\ 2x + 3y = 3 \end{cases}$

6. $\begin{cases} 3x - 5y = 1 \\ 2x + 3y = -12 \end{cases}$

_____ _____ _____

Use substitution or elimination to solve each system of equations.

7. $\begin{cases} x + y = 13 \\ 2x - 3y = 1 \end{cases}$

8. $\begin{cases} 9x + 2y = 5 \\ 3x - y = -10 \end{cases}$

9. $\begin{cases} 2x + y = 1 \\ x = 5 + y \end{cases}$

_____ _____ _____

10. $\begin{cases} x = -8y \\ x + y = 14 \end{cases}$

11. $\begin{cases} 2x + 4y = 12 \\ -3x + 3y = 63 \end{cases}$

12. $\begin{cases} 5x - 2y = -1 \\ 3x - y = -2 \end{cases}$

_____ _____ _____

Solve.

13. Bill leaves his house for Makayla's house riding his bicycle at 8 miles per hour. At the same time, Makayla leaves her house heading toward Bill's house walking at 3 miles per hour.

   a. Write a system of equations to represent the distance, d, each is from Makayla's house in h hours. They live 8.25 miles apart.

   _____

   b. Solve the system to determine how long they travel before meeting.

   _____

LESSON
3-2

Practice C

Using Algebraic Methods to Solve Linear Systems

Use substitution or elimination to solve each system of equations.

1. $\begin{cases} x = y - 5.2 \\ 2x + 3y = 9.6 \end{cases}$

2. $\begin{cases} 3x - 4y = 5 \\ x = y + \dfrac{1}{2} \end{cases}$

3. $\begin{cases} x + 4y = \dfrac{1}{4} \\ 4x - 3y = 39 \end{cases}$

_____ _____ _____

4. $\begin{cases} 2x + 20y = 3 \\ 2x = -7y - 10 \end{cases}$

5. $\begin{cases} x + y = 5 \\ 3x + 2y = 4 \end{cases}$

6. $\begin{cases} 3x + 4y = 35 \\ 4x - 2y = 21 \end{cases}$

_____ _____ _____

7. $\begin{cases} 3\dfrac{1}{4}x + 3y = 42 \\ 5x = 4y \end{cases}$

8. $\begin{cases} 5x - 5y = 6 \\ 4x + 7y = -4 \end{cases}$

9. $\begin{cases} 2x - 8y = 24 \\ x - 21 = 16y \end{cases}$

_____ _____ _____

Solve.

10. Cora bought 4 pounds of nuts and 2 pounds of raisins for $23.50. Mark bought 2 pounds of nuts and 4 pounds of raisins for $18.50.

    a. Write a system of equations that represents the price of the nuts, *n,* and the price of the raisins, *r.* _____

    b. Solve the system. How much should a pound of nuts and a pound of raisins cost together? _____

11. Kate and Riley are reading the same book. Kate reads $\dfrac{1}{3}$ page

    per minute, and Riley reads $\dfrac{3}{4}$ page per minute. Kate has already

    read 70 pages, while Riley has read 30 pages. If they both resume reading together, eventually Riley will catch up to Kate.

    a. On what page will that occur?

    _____

    b. How many minutes have they read when Riley catches up?

    _____

Holt Algebra 2

Reteach

Using Algebraic Methods to Solve Linear Systems

To use the **substitution method** to solve a system of linear equations:
1. Solve one equation for one variable.
2. Substitute this expression into the other equation.
3. Solve for the other variable.
4. Substitute the value of the known variable in the equation in Step 1.
5. Solve for the other variable.
6. Check the values in both equations.

> Use this equation.
> It is solved for y.

$$\begin{cases} y = x + 2 \\ 2x + y = 17 \end{cases}$$

> Use the substitution method when the coefficient of one of the variables is 1 or −1.

$$2x + y = 17$$

$$2x + (x + 2) = 17 \qquad \textit{Substitute } x + 2 \textit{ for } y.$$

$$3x + 2 = 17 \qquad \textit{Simplify and solve for } x.$$

$$3x = 15$$

$$x = 5$$

Substitute $x = 5$ into $y = x + 2$ and solve for y: $y = x + 2$

$$y = 5 + 2$$

$$y = 7$$

The solution of the system is the ordered pair (5, 7).

Check using both equations: $\qquad y = x + 2; \qquad 7 \overset{?}{=} (5) + 2; \qquad 7 = 7\checkmark$

$$2x + y = 17; \qquad 2(5) + 7 \overset{?}{=} 17; \qquad 17 = 17\checkmark$$

Use substitution to solve each system of equations.

1. $\begin{cases} y = 2x - 5 \\ 3x + y = 10 \end{cases}$

   Use $y = 2x - 5$.

   $3x +$ _____ $= 10$

   _____

   _____

   _____

   Ordered pair solution: _____

2. $\begin{cases} 3x + 2y = 1 \\ x - y = 2 \end{cases}$

   Solve for x: $x - y = 2$.

   $x =$ _____

   $3($ _____ $) + 2y = 1$

   _____

   _____

   Ordered pair solution: _____

Holt Algebra 2

LESSON	**Reteach**
3-2	***Using Algebraic Methods to Solve Linear Systems*** *(continued)*

To use the **elimination method** to solve a system of linear equations:
1. Add or subtract the equations to eliminate one variable.
2. Solve the resulting equation for the other variable.
3. Substitute the value for the known variable into one of the original equations.
4. Solve for the other variable.
5. Check the values in both equations.

$$\begin{cases} 3x + 2y = 7 \\ 5x - 2y = 1 \end{cases}$$

The *y* terms have opposite coefficients, so add.

Use the elimination method when the coefficients of one of the variables are the same or opposite.

$$\begin{array}{r} 3x + 2y = 7 \\ + 5x - 2y = 1 \\ \hline \end{array}$$ *Add the equations.*

$$8x = 8 \qquad \text{Solve for x.}$$
$$x = 1$$

Substitute $x = 1$ into $3x + 2y = 7$ and solve for y:
$$3x + 2y = 7$$
$$3(1) + 2y = 7$$
$$2y = 4$$
$$y = 2$$

The solution to the system is the ordered pair (1, 2).

Check using both equations:

$$3x + 2y = 7 \qquad\qquad 5x - 2y = 1$$
$$3(1) + 2(2) \overset{?}{=} 7 \qquad 5(1) - 2(2) \overset{?}{=} 1$$
$$7 = 7 ✓ \qquad\qquad 1 = 1 ✓$$

Use elimination to solve each system of equations.

3. $\begin{cases} 2x + y = 1 \\ -2x - 3y = 5 \end{cases}$

$$\begin{array}{r} 2x + y = 1 \\ + (-2x - 3y = 5) \\ \hline \end{array}$$

$$-2y = \underline{\quad\quad}$$

$$y = \underline{\quad\quad}$$

$$\underline{\hspace{4cm}}$$

Ordered pair solution: _____

4. $\begin{cases} 3x + 4y = 13 \\ 5x - 4y = -21 \end{cases}$

$$\begin{array}{r} 3x + 4y = 13 \\ + 5x - 4y = -21 \\ \hline \end{array}$$

$$\underline{\hspace{3cm}}$$

$$x = \underline{\quad\quad}$$

$$\underline{\hspace{4cm}}$$

Ordered pair solution: _____

LESSON 3-2

Challenge

Using Linear Systems to Find the Equation of a Line

Linear systems of equations can be used to find the equation of a line. Determine the equation of the line passing through points $(-4, 2)$ and $(2, 14)$ using $y = mx + b$. Substituting the x- and y-coordinates for the values of x and y in the slope-intercept form of the line gives the system.

$$\begin{cases} 2 = -4m + b \\ 14 = 2m + b \end{cases}$$

Solve this system to find the slope and y-intercept of the line passing through points $(-4, 2)$ and $(2, 14)$. Finding $m = 2$ and $b = 10$ from the table or the graph allows you to write the equation of the line $y = 2x + 10$.

m	$2 = -4m + b$ b	$14 = 2m + b$ b
0	2	14
1	6	12
2	10	10
3	14	8
4	18	6

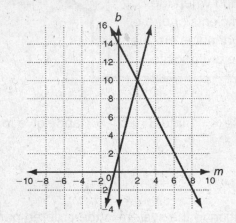

Use a system of equations to find the equation of the line passing through the given points.

1. $(5, 7)$ and $(1, 19)$ _____

2. $(-2, 4)$ and $(2, 8)$ _____

3. $(3, -5)$ and $(5, 1)$ _____

4. $(1, 1)$ and $(5, -9)$ _____

5. $(-1, 8)$ and $(1, -8)$ _____

The equation of a parabola in standard form is $y = ax^2 + bx + c$. There are three constants, a, b, and c. Three points not on a line will determine a unique parabola.

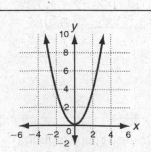

Find the equation of the parabola passing through the given points.

6. $(0, 1)$, $(1, 0)$, and $(2, 1)$ _____

7. $(1, 5)$, $(2, 4)$, and $(4, 8)$ _____

Holt Algebra 2

LESSON 3-2

Problem Solving

Using Algebraic Methods to Solve Linear Systems

Shanae mixes feed for various animals at the zoo so that the feed has the right amount of protein. Feed X is 18% protein. Feed Y is 10% protein. Use this data for Exercises 1–4.

1. How much of each feed should Shanae mix to get 50 lb of feed that is 15% protein?

   a. Write a linear system of equations. _____

   b. Solve the system. How much of each feed should she mix?

   _____

2. Shanae has 15 lb of Feed Y left. She wants to make a mixture that is 12% protein. She needs to know how much of Feed X to use, and how much of the mixture she can make.

   a. Write a linear system of equations. _____

   b. How much of Feed X should she use? _____

   c. How much of the mixture will she make? _____

Choose the letter for the best answer.

3. Raul mixes 12 lb of Feed X with 20 lb of Feed Y. Which equation gives the percent of protein (*c*) in the mixture?

   A $12(0.18) + 20(0.10) = 32c$

   B $32[12(0.18) + 20(0.10)] = c$

   C $12(0.18) + 20(0.10) = c$

   D $[12(0.18) + 20(0.10)]c = 32$

4. Alonzo needs to know how much of Feed X and Feed Y to mix to get 25 lb of a mixture that is 12% protein. Which equation can be used as part of a system of equations to find the solution?

   A $(0.10 + 0.18)(x + y) = (0.12)25$

   B $(0.18)x + (0.10)y - (0.12)25$

   C $25(0.18 + 0.10) = (0.12)x$

   D $10 + 18 = (0.12)25$

5. Billie reorders Feed X and Feed Y. Feed X costs $58 per 100 lb. Feed Y costs $45 per 100 lb. The order comes to $470 for 900 lb. How much of each did she order?

   A Feed X: 350 lb; Feed Y: 550 lb

   B Feed X: 400 lb; Feed Y: 500 lb

   C Feed X: 450 lb; Feed Y: 540 lb

   D Feed X: 500 lb; Feed Y: 400 lb

6. Shanae earns $8.00 per hour during the daytime and $9.50 per hour in the evenings after 6 P.M. Last week she earned $314.00 for 37 hours. How many daytime and evening hours did she work?

   A 35 daytime; 2 evening

   B 30 daytime; 7 evening

   C 25 daytime; 12 evening

   D 20 daytime; 17 evening

Holt Algebra 2

Reading Strategies

Understand Vocabulary

There are two ways you can solve a system of equations algebraically.

Substitution	**Elimination**
Use substitution when you can easily solve one equation for one variable.	Use elimination to add or subtract equations to remove one of the variables.

Substitution

Use substitution when you can easily solve one equation for one variable.

Memory tip: You can *substitute* salad for fries with your order.

For the system $\begin{cases} x - y = 4 \\ 2x - 3y = 7 \end{cases}$

it is easy to solve $x - y = 4$ for x:

$x = \boxed{4 + y}$

Then *substitute* for x in the second equation and solve for y:

$2x - 3y = 7$

$2(\boxed{4 + y}) - 3y = 7$

$8 + 2y - 3y = 7$

$-y = -1$ or $y = 1$

Finally, solve for x:

$x = 4 + y$

$x = 4 + 1 = 5$

The solution to the system is (5, 1).

Elimination

Use elimination to add or subtract equations to remove one of the variables.

Memory tip: The Tigers were *eliminated* from the basketball tournament.

For the system $\begin{cases} 5x - 2y = -9 \\ 3x + 2y = 1 \end{cases}$

if you add the 2 equations together, the y-term is *eliminated* because $-2y + 2y = 0$.

Addition gives $8x = -8$, so $x = -1$.

Finally, solve for y.

$3x + 2y = 1$

$3(-1) + 2y = 1$

$-3 + 2y = 1$

$2y = 1 + 3 = 4$

$y = 2$

The solution to the system is (−1, 2).

Tell which method you would use to solve each system of equations and explain why.

1. $\begin{cases} 2x + y = 3 \\ 3x + 4y = 9 \end{cases}$ _____

2. $\begin{cases} 3x - 4y = 9 \\ -3x + 5y = -9 \end{cases}$ _____

3. $\begin{cases} -2x + 5y = 3 \\ x - 2y = 0 \end{cases}$ _____

4. $\begin{cases} 3x - y = -1 \\ 4x + \dfrac{1}{2}y = 1 \end{cases}$ _____

LESSON 3-3

Practice A

Solving Systems of Linear Inequalities

Graph each system of inequalities.

1. $\begin{cases} y \le 4 \\ y > x - 2 \end{cases}$

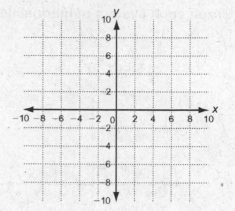

   a. In order to graph $y \le 4$, draw the line for $y = 4$.

   b. Now shade the area below the line to show $y \le 4$.

   c. In order to graph $y > x - 2$, draw the line that
      represents $y = x - 2$. Make the line dashed since
      the line is not included in the inequality.

   d. Shade the area above the line.

   e. Describe the solution region of this system of inequalities.

2. $\begin{cases} y > x \\ y > -x \end{cases}$ 3. $\begin{cases} x \le -4 \\ y \ge 2 \end{cases}$

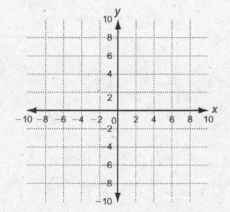   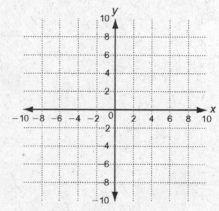

4. $\begin{cases} y < 2x + 1 \\ y \ge x \end{cases}$ 5. $\begin{cases} y < x - 4 \\ y > -3x + 2 \end{cases}$

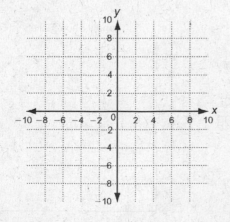   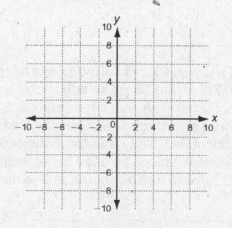

Holt Algebra 2

LESSON
3-3

Practice B

Solving Systems of Linear Inequalities

Graph each system of inequalities.

1. $\begin{cases} y \le 3x - 5 \\ y < -\dfrac{1}{2}x + 4 \end{cases}$

2. $\begin{cases} y < x + 5 \\ y \ge 4x - 2 \end{cases}$

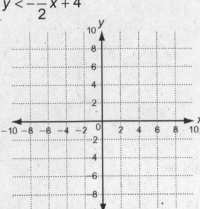

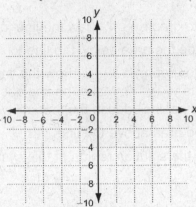

Graph the system of inequalities, and classify the figure created by the solution region.

3. $\begin{cases} x \le 2 \\ x \ge -3 \\ y \le 2x + 2 \\ y \ge 2x - 1 \end{cases}$ _____

4. $\begin{cases} y \le -x + 4 \\ y \le 3 \\ y \ge 0 \\ y \ge -2x - 1 \end{cases}$ _____

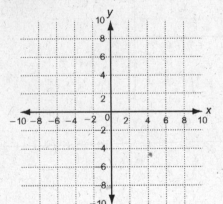

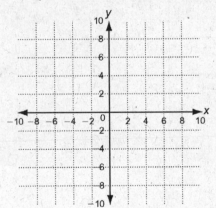

Solve.

5. The Thespian Club is selling tickets to its annual variety show. Prices are $8 for an adult ticket and $4 for a student ticket. The club needs to raise $1000 to pay for costumes and stage sets. The auditorium has a seating capacity of 240. Write and graph a system of inequalities that can be used to determine how many tickets have to be sold for the club to meet its goal.

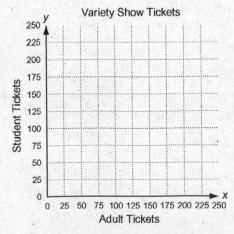

_____

LESSON 3-3

Practice C

Solving Systems of Linear Inequalities

Graph the system of inequalities, and classify the figure created by the solution region.

1.
$$\begin{cases} y \le -x + 2 \\ y \le x + 2 \\ y \ge -x - 2 \\ y \ge x - 2 \end{cases}$$
_____

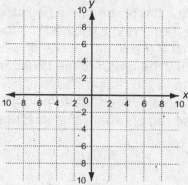

2.
$$\begin{cases} y < -3x + 4 \\ y > -8 \\ y < x + 5 \\ x > -6 \end{cases}$$
_____

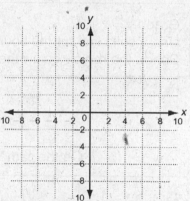

3.
$$\begin{cases} y \le -\dfrac{2}{3}x + 3 \\ y \le x \\ y \ge -\dfrac{2}{3}x - 5 \\ x \le 4 \end{cases}$$
_____

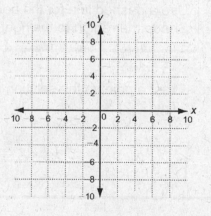

Solve.

4. Anton wants to divide a maximum of $20,000 between two simple interest investment accounts. One pays 6% interest and the other pays 7.5% interest. Write and graph a system of inequalities that shows the amounts Anton can invest in each account and still earn at least $1300 per year.

_____

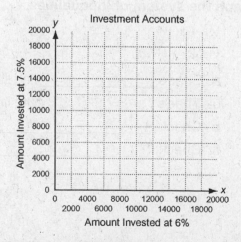

LESSON	**Reteach**
3-3	*Solving Systems of Linear Inequalities*

To use graphs to find the solution to a system of inequalities:

1. Draw the graph of the boundary for the first inequality. Remember to use a solid line for $\leq$ or $\geq$ and a dashed line for $<$ or $>$.
2. Shade the region above or below the boundary line that is a solution of the inequality.
3. Draw the graph of the boundary for the second inequality.
4. Shade the region above or below the boundary line that is a solution of the inequality using a different pattern.
5. The region where the shadings overlap is the solution region.

Graph $\begin{cases} y \leq x + 2 \\ x > 1 \end{cases}$ Graph $y \leq x + 2$.

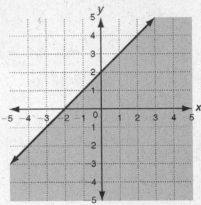

Graph $y = x + 2$.
Use a solid line for the boundary.
Shade the region below the line.

On the same plane, graph $x > 1$.

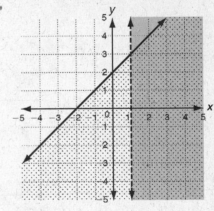

Graph $x = 1$.
Use a dashed line for the boundary.
Shade the region to the right of the line.

Check: Test a point in the solution region in both inequalities.
Try (2, 2).

$y \leq x + 2$ $x > 1$

$2 \overset{?}{\leq} 2 + 2$ $2 > 1 \checkmark$

$2 \leq 4 \checkmark$

Graph the system of inequalities.

1. $\begin{cases} y > -x + 1 \\ y \leq 2 \end{cases}$

   a. Shade _____ the line for $y > -x + 1$.

   b. Shade _____ the line for $y \leq 2$.

   c. Check: _____

   d. Check: _____

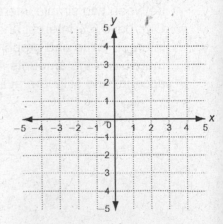

Holt Algebra 2

LESSON 3-3

Reteach

Solving Systems of Linear Inequalities (continued)

The solution of a system of inequalities may create a geometric figure.

Graph $\begin{cases} y \le \dfrac{1}{2}x + 2 \\ y \ge -2 \\ x \le 3 \\ x \ge -2 \end{cases}$

> The graph of $y = -2$ is a horizontal line. The graphs of $x = 3$ and $x = -2$ are vertical lines.

Graph $y \le \dfrac{1}{2}x + 2$ and $y \le -2$.

> Use solid boundary lines.
> Shade the region below $y \le \dfrac{1}{2}x + 2$ and above $y \le -2$.

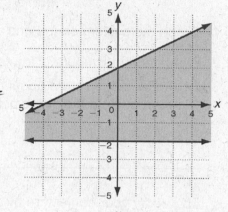

On the same plane, graph $x \le 3$ and $x \ge -2$.

> Use solid boundary lines.
> Shade the region to the left of $x \le 3$ and to the right of $x \ge -2$.

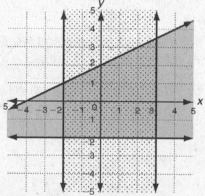

The figure created by the overlapping pattern is a quadrilateral with one pair of parallel sides. The figure is a trapezoid.

Graph the system of inequalities. Classify the figure created by the solution region.

2. $\begin{cases} y \le 2x + 1 \\ y \ge -x + 1 \\ x \le 3 \end{cases}$

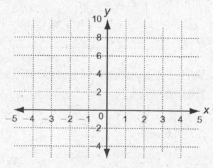

a. Shade _____ the line for $y \le 2x + 1$.

b. Shade _____ the line for $y \ge -x + 1$.

c. Shade to the _____ of the line for $x \le 3$.

d. The figure is a _____.

Holt Algebra 2

LESSON 3-3

Challenge

Systems of Absolute-Value Inequalities

The absolute value function is known for the V-shape of its graph. Some systems of absolute value inequalities have graphs that form geometric figures.

Use the system $\begin{cases} |x| \le 2 \\ |y| \le 2 \end{cases}$ **for Exercises 1-5.**

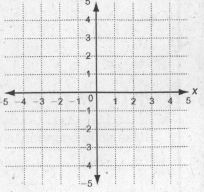

1. Graph the system on the grid at right.

2. What geometric figure is formed by the system? _____

3. a. Make a conjecture about how the graph of $|x| + |y| \le 2$ compares to the graph of the given system.

   _____

   b. Verify your conjecture by graphing $|x| + |y| \le 2$ on the same grid.

4. What geometric figure would be formed if the constant terms of the system were not equal? _____

5. What transformation(s) will change the original figure into the figure formed by each of the following systems?

   a. $\begin{cases} |x - 3| \le 2 \\ |y| \le 2 \end{cases}$

   b. $\begin{cases} |x| \le 2 \\ |y + 3| \le 2 \end{cases}$

   c. $\begin{cases} |2x| \le 2 \\ |y| \le 2 \end{cases}$

   _____   _____   _____

Write the coordinates of the vertices of the figure determined by the given system.

6. $\begin{cases} |x - 3| \le 4 \\ |y + 2| \le 2 \end{cases}$

7. $\begin{cases} |x + 3| \le 2 \\ |y - 2| \le 4 \end{cases}$

8. $\begin{cases} |2x| \le 4 \\ |y| \le 4 \end{cases}$

   _____   _____   _____

Write a system of inequalities to represent the specified geometric figure.

9. $x = \pm 5$
   when $y = \pm 5$

10. $x = 2$ or -8
    when $y = 4$ or 6

11. $x = \pm 0.5$
    when $y = 0$ or 2

   _____   _____   _____

Holt Algebra 2

Name _____ Date _____ Class_____

Problem Solving

Solving Systems of Linear Inequalities

Marshall and Zack plan a hike-and-canoe vacation in a national park. They plan to hike for *m* hours at a steady 3 miles per hour and canoe for *n* hours at 6 miles per hour. They want to travel no more than 8 hours and cover at least 40 miles in a day.

1. Marshall makes a table to find the number of hours they can hike and canoe and still meet their goal.

   a. Complete the table.

   b. What different options do they have in whole numbers of hours of hiking and canoeing while still meeting their goal?

Hiking Time (*m*)	Canoeing Time (*n*)	Total Miles per day
1	7	
2	6	
3	5	
4	4	
5	3	

---

2. a. Write a system of inequalities to model the conditions.

   _____

   b. Graph the boundary lines. Shade the areas to show the inequalities and the overlapping region.

   c. Describe how the overlapping shaded region relates to the solution to the inequalities.

   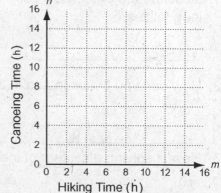

   _____

   d. Name a point within the solution region.

   _____

Choose the letter for the best answer.

3. Which point is NOT in the region that satisfies the goals?

   A (4, 4)

   B (2, 6)

   C (1, 6.75)

   D (0, 7)

4. How could you interpret the point of intersection of the boundary lines?

   A They will travel exactly the same number of hours hiking as canoeing.

   B This represents the only possible solution.

   C It is the only impossible combination of hiking hours and canoeing hours.

   D They will travel exactly 40 miles in exactly 8 hours.

Holt Algebra 2

LESSON 3-3

Reading Strategies

Compare and Contrast

A system of linear equations may have one solution, which is an ordered pair. $$\begin{cases} y = 2x + 5 \\ y = -x + 2 \end{cases}$$ The system can be solved by graphing. The solution is the point where the lines intersect.	A system of linear inequalities may have an infinite number of ordered pair solutions. $$\begin{cases} y < 2x + 5 \\ y \geq -x + 2 \end{cases}$$ The system can be solved by graphing. The solution is the region where the shadings overlap.
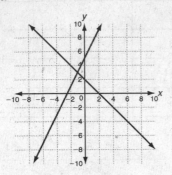	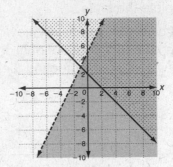

Answer each question.

1. Describe the process to determine if a given ordered pair is a solution to a system of inequalities.

_____

2. How can you check to see if (3, 2) is a solution to the system $\begin{cases} x + y \geq 4 \\ 2x - y < -1? \end{cases}$

_____

3. How is solving a system of inequalities like solving a system of equations?

_____

4. How is solving a system of inequalities different from solving a system of equations?

_____

5. Describe the solution set of a system of inequalities.

_____

6. When would you use a dashed line in graphing an inequality? When would you use a solid line? What is the difference?

_____

Name _____ Date _____ Class_____

Linear Programming

Maximize or minimize each objective function.

1. Maximize $P = 2x + y$ for the constraints $\begin{cases} x \geq 0 \\ y \geq 0 \\ x + y \leq 6 \end{cases}$

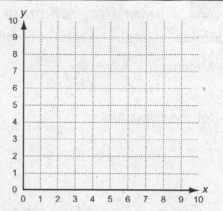

   a. Graph the constraints.

   b. Write the vertices of the feasible region.

   _____

   c. Use the table to evaluate P for the x- and y-values at each vertex.

   d. Compare the values for P. Write the coordinate pair that gives the maximum value.

   _____

x	y	$P = 2x + y$

2. Minimize $P = 4x + 3y$ for the constraints $\begin{cases} x \leq 4 \\ y \leq 6 \\ x + y \geq 7 \end{cases}$

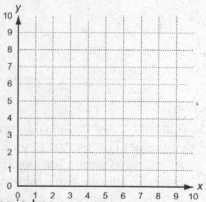

   _____

Solve.

3. Jasmine is planting a maximum of 40 bulbs of lilies and tulips in her backyard. She wants more tulips, x, than lilies, y.

   a. Write a system of inequalities.

   _____

   b. Graph the system.

   c. What is the maximum number of lily bulbs Jasmine could plant?

   _____

   d. What is the minimum number of tulip bulbs Jasmine could plant?

   _____

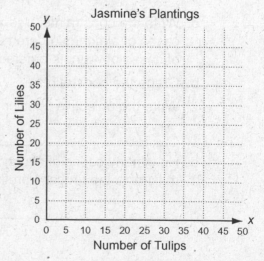

Jasmine's Plantings

Number of Lilies

Number of Tulips

LESSON
3-4

Practice B
Linear Programming

Maximize or minimize each objective function.

1. Maximize $P = 5x + 2y$

   for the constraints $\begin{cases} y \geq 0 \\ x \geq 0 \\ y \leq -x + 10 \\ y \leq 2x + 1 \end{cases}$

   _____

2. Minimize $P = 4x + 6y$

   for the constraints $\begin{cases} 0 \leq x \leq 4 \\ y \geq 1 \\ y \geq -x + 4 \end{cases}$

   _____

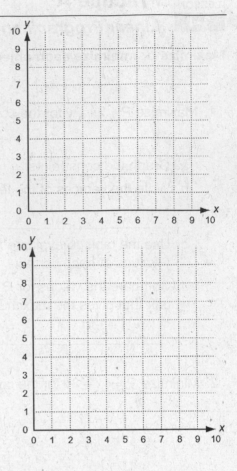

Solve.

3. A grocer buys cases of almonds and walnuts. Almonds are packaged 20 bags per case. The grocer pays $30 per case of almonds and makes a profit of $17 per case. Walnuts are packaged 24 bags per case. The grocer pays $26 per case of walnuts and makes a profit of $15 per case. He orders no more than 300 bags of almonds and walnuts together at a maximum cost of $400.

   a. Write the constraints. Use *x* for the number of cases of almonds ordered and *y* for the number of cases of walnuts ordered.

   b. Graph the constraints.

   c. Write the objective function for the profit.

   _____

   d. How many cases of almonds and walnuts maximize the grocer's profit?

   _____

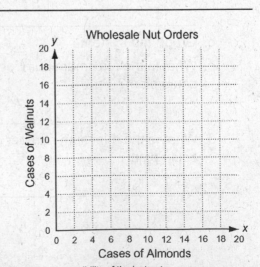

Wholesale Nut Orders

Cases of Walnuts / Cases of Almonds

Holt Algebra 2

Practice C

Linear Programming

Solve.

1. Maximize $P = 4.5x + 2.5y$

   for the constraints $\begin{cases} y \geq 0 \\ x \geq 0 \\ y \geq x \\ y \leq -2x + 9 \end{cases}$ _____

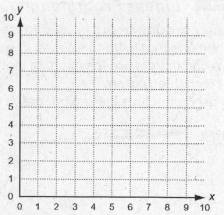

2. Rita is production manager at a company that is manufacturing a new athletic training machine. There are 4 models. Models B and D are needed for the next shipment. Between 10 and 30 of model B are needed. Rita can use no more than 100 hours of production time and she wants to maximize the profit. Use the table to determine how many of each machine Rita should produce for the next shipment.

Athletic Trainer		
Model	**Production Time (h)**	**Profit per Item**
A	6.5	$125
B	2.5	$80
C	4.25	$90
D	5.0	$100

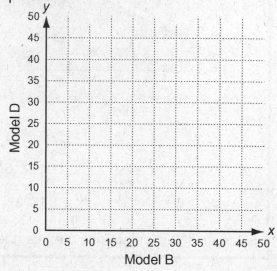

_____

3. A department store is planning to hire up to 24 temporary employees for a tent sale. Experienced workers will be paid $20 per hour and inexperienced workers $15 per hour. The company can pay up to $400 per hour for the temporary employees. An experienced worker produces 1.5 times the profit that an inexperienced worker produces. How many of each type of worker should be hired?

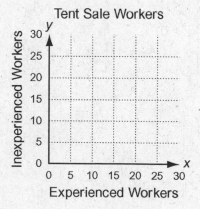

_____

Holt Algebra 2

LESSON 3-4

Reteach

Linear Programming

Linear programming is used to maximize or minimize a function based on conditions that have to be met. These conditions are called **constraints**. The constraints are a system of inequalities. The graph of their solution is the **feasible region**.

To graph the feasible region, graph the system of inequalities.

$$\begin{cases} x \geq 0 \\ y \geq 0 \\ y \leq 0.5x + 1 \\ y \leq -1.5x + 9 \end{cases}$$

When $x \geq 0$ and $y \geq 0$, the graph lies in the first quadrant, so the x- and y-values must be positive.

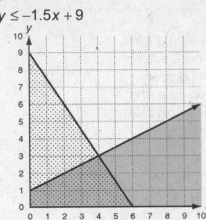 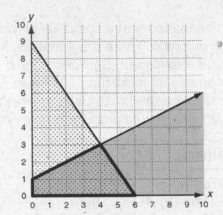

Check a point in the feasible region. Try (2, 1).

$x \geq 0$	$y \geq 0$	$y \leq 0.5x + 1$	$y \leq -1.5x + 9$
$2 \geq 0$ ✓	$1 \geq 0$ ✓	$1 \overset{?}{\leq} 0.5(2) + 1$	$1 \overset{?}{\leq} -1.5(2) + 9$
		$1 \leq 2$ ✓	$1 \leq 6$ ✓

Since all of the inequalities are true, the constraints are satisfied.

Graph each feasible region.

1. $$\begin{cases} x \geq 0 \\ y \geq 0 \\ y \leq 1.5x + 1 \\ y \leq -x + 6 \end{cases}$$

2. $$\begin{cases} x \geq 0 \\ y \geq 0 \\ y \geq 2x + 1 \\ y \leq -2x + 9 \end{cases}$$

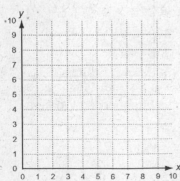 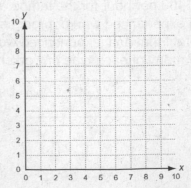

Holt Algebra 2

LESSON	**Reteach**
3-4	*Linear Programming* *(continued)*

The **objective function** is the best combination of values to maximize or minimize a function subject to the constraints graphed in the feasible region. The maximum or minimum occurs at one or more of the vertices of the feasible region. Evaluate the objective function for each vertex to find the maximum or minimum.

Maximize $P = 5x + 7y$ for the constraints $\begin{cases} x \geq 0 \\ y \geq 0 \\ y \leq 0.5x + 1 \\ y \leq -1.5x + 9 \end{cases}$

Step 1 Graph the feasible region.

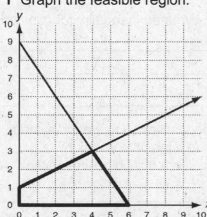

Step 2 Identify the vertices.

$(0, 0), (0, 1), (4, 3), (6, 0)$

Step 3 Evaluate the objective function at each vertex. Find the maximum value.

$P = 5x + 7y$

$P(0, 0) = 5(0) + 7(0) = 0$

$P(0, 1) = 5(0) + 7(1) = 7$

$P(4, 3) = 5(4) + 7(3) = 41$ ⟵

$P(6, 0) = 5(6) + 7(0) = 30$

The objective function is maximized at $(4, 3)$.

Solve using your graphs from Exercises 1–2 on the previous page.

3. Maximize $P = 2x + 5y$ for:

$\begin{cases} x \geq 0 \\ y \geq 0 \\ y \leq 1.5x + 1 \\ y \leq -x + 6 \end{cases}$

Vertices: _____

$P(\_\_\_, \_\_\_) =$ _____

$P(\_\_\_, \_\_\_) =$ _____

$P(\_\_\_, \_\_\_) =$ _____

$P(\_\_\_, \_\_\_) =$ _____

Maximum value at _____

4. Minimize $P = 3x + 6y$ for:

$\begin{cases} x \geq 0 \\ y \geq 0 \\ y \geq 2x + 1 \\ y \leq -2x + 9 \end{cases}$

Vertices: _____

_____

_____

_____

Minimum value at _____

LESSON 3-4

Challenge

Linear Programming with Three Variables

For a linear programming problem with three variables, the feasible region is defined by a polyhedron, and the maximum or minimum value of the objective function occurs at one of the vertices. There is a method for solving a three-variable problem that does not require drawing the polyhedron.

> A *polyhedron* is a three-dimensional figure bounded by polygons.

A crafter has a budget of $6300 and wants to produce a maximum 100 ornate boxes, some of wood, others with jeweled inlays, and others of stained glass. The table at right shows the cost and profit data per box, in dollars. The crafter wants to maximize profit.

	Wood	Inlay	Glass
Cost	35	80	70
Profit	60	75	90

Let w, i, and g represent the number of boxes of each type. There will be 5 constraints: A, B, C, D, E.

1. Three of the constraints are A: $w \geq 0$, B: $i \geq 0$, C: $g \geq 0$. Write an inequality for constraint

   a. D, the number of boxes. _____

   b. E, the budget. _____

2. Write the objective function, P. _____

3. In the table below, write all 10 possible systems of 3 inequalities. Solve each system to find the intersection. Check whether the intersection is a feasible vertex by testing the coordinates in the constraints A–E. Then evaluate the objective function for all feasible vertices.

System of inequalities	Intersection	Feasible	Dollar value of P
A, B, C	(0, 0, 0)	Yes	0
A, B, D	(0, 0, 100)	No	—
A, B, E			

4. How can the crafter maximize profit? _____

5. What is the maximum profit? _____

Name _____ Date _____ Class_____

Problem Solving
Linear Programming

At the local fair, Tamara wants to demonstrate her "build-it-yourself" products. She decides to hire some skilled technicians and some students to build her garden chairs. Technicians can build 2 chairs in 8 hours; students can build only 1 chair in 8 hours. She wants at least 1 technician to work with every 3 students, but can find only 6 technicians. She will pay $12 per hour for technicians and $7 per hour for students, and can spend up to $800. What combination of technicians and students can build the greatest number of chairs in an 8-hour day?

1. Write the constraints needed to graph the feasible region.

_____

2. Graph the feasible region.

3. List the vertices of the feasible region.

_____

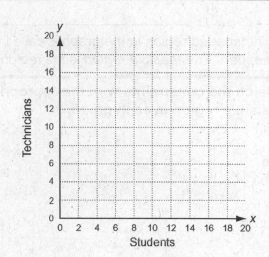

4. Write the objective function, *C*, to show the total number of chairs that can be built.

_____

5. At which vertex is the objective function maximized?

_____

6. How many technicians and students should Tamara hire to achieve her goal?

_____

Choose the letter for the best answer.

7. Tamara decides that at least 1 technician should work with every 2 students. How does this change her hiring plan?

   A She should hire only the 6 technicians.

   B She should hire 4 technicians and 7 students.

   C She should hire 6 technicians and 12 students.

   D Her hiring plan will not change.

8. Tamara finds 1 more technician. How does this change her hiring plan?

   A She should hire only the 7 technicians.

   B She should hire 3 technicians and 9 students.

   C She should hire 7 technicians and 2 students.

   D Her hiring plan will not change.

Holt Algebra 2

LESSON 3-4

Reading Strategies
Identify Relationships

Linear programming is used to find the value of a function that satisfies some conditions. The conditions are called **constraints**. A constrained region is defined by its boundaries.

Graph each constraint. Instead of shading the solution region, mark an X in the area that you would shade:

1. $y \geq 0$

2. $x \geq 2$

3. $x \leq 4$

4. $x + y \leq 5$

5. Are all the Xs in the same region? What is the shape of that region? Shade that region.

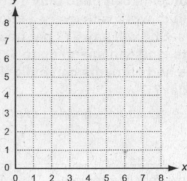

The shaded region in the graph is called the **feasible region**. Something is *feasible* if it can happen. The *feasible region* is the region containing the possible solutions of the function.

Match the constraints with the appropriate graph. Then shade the feasible region in each graph.

6. $\begin{cases} x \geq 2 \\ x \leq 5 \\ y \geq 2 \\ x + y \leq 8 \end{cases}$

7. $\begin{cases} x \leq 2 \\ x \geq 0 \\ y \geq 2 \\ x + y \leq 8 \end{cases}$

8. $\begin{cases} x \geq 5 \\ y \geq 0 \\ y \leq 2 \\ x + y \leq 8 \end{cases}$

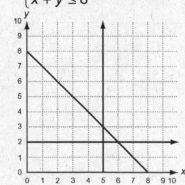
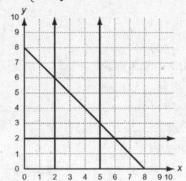
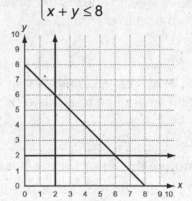

9. Graph each constraint. Mark an X in the area you would shade and then shade the feasible region.

$\begin{cases} y \geq 0 \\ x \geq 0 \\ y \leq x \\ x \leq 5 \end{cases}$

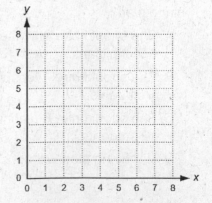

Holt Algebra 2

LESSON 3-5

Practice A
Linear Equations in Three Dimensions

Graph each point in three-dimensional space.

1. (3, –2, 4)

   a. Locate the *x*-axis and estimate 3 units forward.

   b. Estimate 2 units to the left (*y*-axis).

   c. Estimate 4 units up (*z*-axis).

2. (–4, 0, –3)

3. (2, 2, 2)

Find the *x*-, *y*-, and *z*-intercepts for each equation.

4. $2x - 6y - 3z = 12$ _____

5. $9x + 3y - 6z = 18$ _____

6. $3x - 5y + 10z = 15$ _____

Graph the linear equation in three-dimensional space.

7. $10x + 4y + 5z = 20$

   a. Find the point that represents each intercept.

      x-intercept _____

      y-intercept _____

      z-intercept _____

   b. Plot the three points.

   c. Draw a plane through the points.

Solve.

8. Andrea's fish tank holds 30 gallons of water. Andrea estimates that every inch of a fish's length requires a gallon of water. She wants to purchase some corydoras that are 2 inches long, angelfish that are 5 inches long, and fancy guppies that are 3 inches long.

   a. Write an equation for the situation.

      _____

   b. Complete the table for the maximum number of each type of fish Andrea can purchase.

Corydoras	Angelfish	Guppies
4		4
	1	3
5	1	
	4	2

Holt Algebra 2

3-5

Practice B

Linear Equations in Three Dimensions

Graph each linear equation in three-dimensional space.

1. $8x + 16y + 4z = 16$

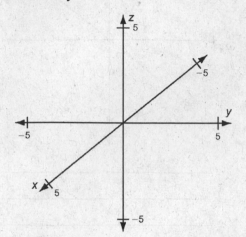

2. $-6x + 8y - 12z = 24$

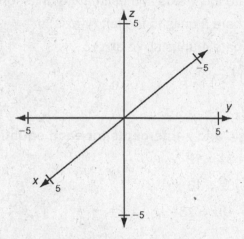

3. $4x + 3y + 6z = -12$

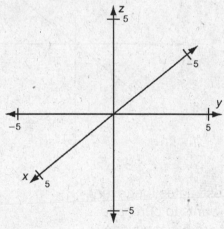

4. $10x + 15y - 6z = -30$

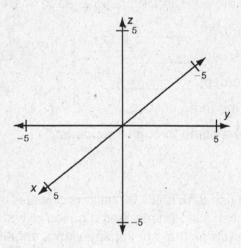

Solve.

5. Bill is buying bulbs for his flower garden. Bags of iris bulbs are $4 each, bags of tulip bulbs are $3 each, and bags of daffodil bulbs are $2 each. He spends $24 in all.

   a. Write an equation to represent the situation.   _____

   b. Bill wants to buy 3 bags of iris bulbs and at least 2 bags of daffodil bulbs. What is the maximum number of bags of tulip bulbs he can buy?   _____

   c. Bill buys 5 bags of daffodil bulbs and the same number of bags of tulip bulbs as iris bulbs. How many bags of each does he buy?   _____

Holt Algebra 2

LESSON 3-5

Practice C

Linear Equations in Three Dimensions

Graph each linear equation in three-dimensional space.

1. $4x - 2y - 8z = -8$

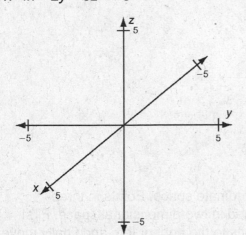

2. $-10x + 2y - 5z = 10$

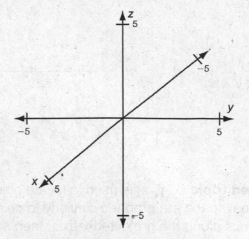

3. $\frac{2}{5}x + 2y - \frac{1}{2}z = -2$

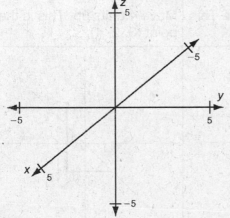

4. $9x - 18y - 6z = 18$

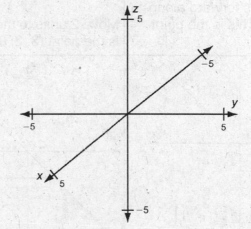

Solve.

5. Cars, vans, and minibuses have been rented to provide transportation to a company retreat. Cars hold 5 employees, vans hold 7 employees, and minibuses hold 14 employees. There are 72 employees to be transported.

a. Write an equation to show x, the number of cars, y, the number of vans, and z, the number of minibuses needed to transport the employees.

_____

b. If only 1 minibus and 5 cars are available on the day of the retreat, how many vans will be needed to transport all of the employees?

_____

c. The same number of vans as minibuses were used for transportation. There were no empty seats in any van or minibus or in any of the cars that were rented. How many cars were rented?

_____

Holt Algebra 2

LESSON 3-5

Reteach
Linear Equations in Three Dimensions

In a three-dimensional coordinate system, the *x*-axis projects out from the paper and the *y*- and *z*-axes lie in the plane of the paper.

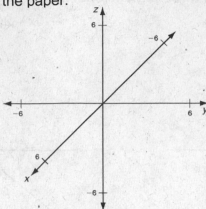

An **ordered triple** (*x, y, z*) is used to locate points in coordinate space. Points in three-dimensional space are graphed similarly to points graphed in two-dimensional space. First count *x* units along the projected *x*-axis, then move *y* units to the right or left, and finally move *z* units up or down.

To graph (3, 2, 4), start at the origin.

Move 3 units forward along the x-axis. This is the point (3, 0, 0).	Move 2 units to the right. This is the point (3, 2, 0).	Move 4 units up. This is the point (3, 2, 4).
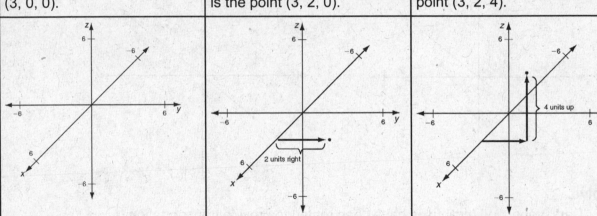		

Graph each point in three-dimensional space.

1. (–2, 3, 1)

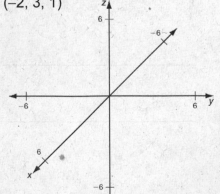

2. (2, 4, –3)

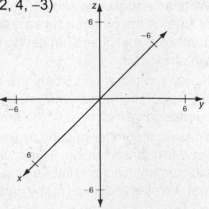

LESSON 3-5

Reteach

Linear Equations in Three Dimensions *(continued)*

In three-dimensional space, the graph of a linear equation is a plane. You can graph the plane by finding its x-, y-, and z-intercepts.

Graph $2x - 4y + 3z = 12$.

Step 1 Find the intercepts.

Find the x-intercept.	Find the y-intercept.	Find the z-intercept.
Set $y = z = 0$.	Set $x = z = 0$.	Set $x = y = 0$.
$2x - 4(0) + 3(0) = 12$	$2(0) - 4y + 3(0) = 12$	$2(0) - 4(0) + 3z = 12$
$2x = 12$	$-4y = 12$	$3z = 12$
$x = 6$	$y = -3$	$z = 4$
The x-intercept is	The y-intercept is	The z-intercept is
at $(6, 0, 0)$.	at $(0, -3, 0)$.	at $(0, 0, 4)$.

Step 2 Plot each point. Use a dashed line to connect the points. The triangle represents the plane.

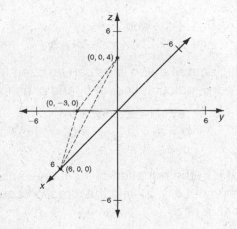

Graph each linear equation in three-dimensional space.

3. $3x + 4y + 6z = 12$

   x-intercept is at $(4, \underline{\hspace{1cm}}, \underline{\hspace{1cm}})$

   y-intercept is at $(\underline{\hspace{1cm}}, 3, \underline{\hspace{1cm}})$

   z-intercept is at $(\underline{\hspace{1cm}}, \underline{\hspace{1cm}}, 2)$

4. $2x - 2y + 5z = 10$

   x-intercept is at $\underline{\hspace{3cm}}$

   y-intercept is at $\underline{\hspace{3cm}}$

   z-intercept is at $\underline{\hspace{3cm}}$

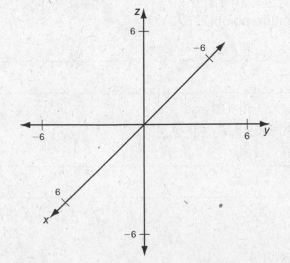

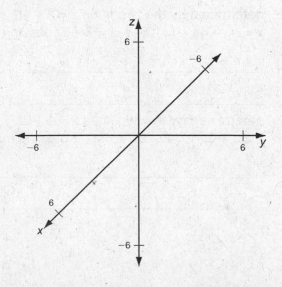

Holt Algebra 2

| LESSON | **Challenge** |
| 3-5 | **Linear Equations in Three Dimensions** |

A line, $y = mx + b$, is uniquely determined by a point and a direction, commonly called the slope. A plane, $ax + by + cz = d$, can also be uniquely determined by a point and a direction. However, for a plane, it is not the direction of the plane. It is the direction of a line that is perpendicular to the plane as shown at the right.

This line perpendicular to the plane has the parametric equations

$$x = x_0 + at, \qquad y = y_0 + bt, \qquad z = z_0 + ct$$

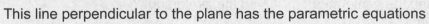

where the point (x_0, y_0, z_0) can be any arbitrary point in the plane and the coefficients a, b, and c describe the direction of that perpendicular line. The coefficients a, b, and c are the same as in the equation of the plane. Consider two lines that lie in the plane given by the following equations.

$$\begin{array}{ll} x = x_1 + a_1 t & x = x_2 + b_1 t \\ y = y_1 + a_2 t \quad \text{and} \quad & y = y_2 + b_2 t \\ z = z_1 + a_3 t & z = z_2 + b_3 t \end{array}$$

The direction coefficients of these lines can be used to find the direction coefficients of the perpendicular line, a, b, and c, as follows.

$$a = a_2 \times b_3 - a_3 \times b_2$$
$$b = a_3 \times b_1 - a_1 \times b_3$$
$$c = a_1 \times b_2 - a_2 \times b_1$$

To find the value of d in the equation of the plane, substitute the coordinates of one point (x, y, z) with the direction coefficients a, b, and c and solve for the value of d.

Find the equation of each plane as described.

1. determined by the two lines $x = t$, $y = 1 - t$, $z = 1 + t$ and $x = 1 + 2t$, $y = 2 - 3t$, $z = 5 + t$ passing through the point $(0, 1, 1)$

_____

_____

2. determined by the two lines $x = 2 + 4t$, $y = 5 - 3t$, $z = 3 + t$ and $x = -3 - 4t$, $y = 10 + t$, $z = 8 + 7t$ passing through the point $(2, 5, 3)$

_____

_____

3. determined by the two lines $x = 4 + 2t$, $y = -3 - t$, $z = 1 + 6t$ and $x = 1 + 3t$, $y = 2 - 5t$, $z = 2 - t$ passing through the point $(6, -4, 7)$

_____

_____

Holt Algebra 2

LESSON
3-5

Problem Solving

Linear Equations in Three Dimensions

To play *Space Force,* Lily, Alicia, and Van must define a space plane relative to the mother ship at the origin. They choose 5 in the *x*-dimension, 4 in the *y*-dimension, and 10 in the *z*-dimension, and a total space force of 60. The *Space Force* software creates the plane that they have defined, and places Alicia at the *x*-intercept, Lily at the *y*-intercept, and Van at the *z*-intercept. It then constrains them to move only in the space plane. The objective is to move to the same location using the least number of moves based on each other's moves.

1. a. Write a linear equation in three dimensions that defines the plane.

   _____

   b. Complete the table to show the *x*-, *y*-, and *z*-intercept starting positions for each player.

2. Plot the starting locations for each player on the grid and draw the space plane.

3. To play the game, each player moves by defining a change in two dimensions. The *Space Force* software then uses the linear equation to find the third dimension and relocates the player in the space plane. Find the new location for each player.

   a. Alicia changes her location by $(-2, 1, z)$.

   _____

   b. Lily changes her location by $(x, -10, 2)$.

   _____

   c. Van changes his location by $(1, y, -2)$.

   _____

Starting Positions			
	x	*y*	*z*
Alicia			
Lily			
Van			

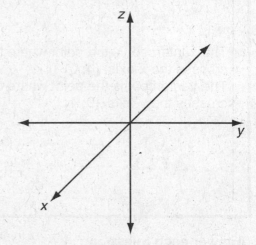

Choose the letter for the best answer.

4. Which point is NOT in the space plane?

   A $(0, 6, 3.6)$

   B $(1, 1.25, 5)$

   C $(4, 3.4, 2)$

   D $(8, 2.5, 1)$

5. Which player is the greatest distance from the mother ship at the start of the game?

   A Alicia

   B Lily

   C Van

   D They are all the same distance from the mother ship.

Holt Algebra 2

Reading Strategies
Compare and Contrast

In a two-dimensional coordinate system there are 2 axes: the *x-axis* and the *y*-axis. Each point is represented by an ordered pair.

(3, 2)
↑   ↑
x   y

The graph of a linear equation such as $x + y = 4$ is a line.

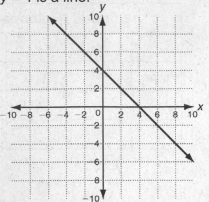

The *x*-intercept is the point where the line crosses the *x*-axis, (4, 0).
The *y*-intercept is the point where the line crosses the *y*-axis, (0, 4).

In a three-dimensional coordinate system there are 3 axes, the *x*-axis, the *y*-axis, and the **z-axis**. Each point is represented by an **ordered triple.**

(3, 4, 2)
↑   ↑   ↑
x   y   z

Tip: *Tri* means 3-as in *tricycle* or *triangle*. The graph of a linear equation such as $x + y + z = 4$ is a plane.

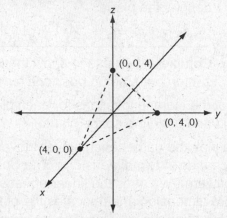

The *x*-intercept is the point where the plane crosses the *x*-axis, (4, 0, 0).
The *y*-intercept is the point where the plane crosses the *y*-axis, (0, 4, 0).
The *z*-intercept is the point where the plane crosses the *z*-axis, (0, 0, 4).

Answer each question.

1. Give an example of a two-dimensional space in your home.
   Then give an example of a three-dimensional space.

_____

2. State one way in which a two-dimensional graph of a linear equation is similar to a three-dimensional graph of a linear equation.

_____

3. State one way in which a two-dimensional graph of a linear equation is different from a three-dimensional graph of a linear equation.

_____

4. Explain how a line is different from a plane.

_____

Practice A
Solving Linear Systems in Three Variables

Use elimination to solve each system of equations.

1. $\begin{cases} x + y + z = 4 \\ 2x - y + z = 3 \\ -4x + 2y - z = -1 \end{cases}$

   a. Eliminate the variable z by
      adding the last 2 equations.

      $2x - y + z = 3$

      $-4x + 2y - z = -1$

      _____

   b. Then add the first and
      third equations.

      $x + y + z = 4$

      $-4x + 2y - z = -1$

      _____

   c. Solve this system of 2 equations
      for x and y using elimination.

   d. Substitute x and y into one of the
      original equations and solve for z.

      _____

   e. Write the solution as an ordered triple.

      _____

2. $\begin{cases} x + y + 2z = 3 \\ x - y - z = 0 \\ 3x - 2y - z = 1 \end{cases}$

   _____

3. $\begin{cases} 4x + y + 3z = 0 \\ 2x - 2y - z = 10 \\ 3x - 2y + 2z = 11 \end{cases}$

   _____

4. $\begin{cases} 3x + 4y - z = 1 \\ 3x - y - 4z = -3 \\ x + 3y - 3z = 9 \end{cases}$

   _____

5. $\begin{cases} 2x + y + z = 1 \\ 3x - 2y - z = 3 \\ 4x - 3y - 2z = 5 \end{cases}$

   _____

Solve.

6. In a souvenir shop, Jodi purchased 2 small picture
   frames and 1 large one for $28. Mike bought
   3 medium-size frames and 2 large ones for $56.
   Shelly bought a small, a medium, and a large frame for
   $30. Write and solve a system of equations to find
   the price of each size of picture frame.

   _____

LESSON 3-6

Practice B

Solving Linear Systems in Three Variables

Use elimination to solve each system of equations.

1. $\begin{cases} x + y - 2z = 10 \\ 8x - 9y - z = 5 \\ 3x + 4y + 2z = -10 \end{cases}$

2. $\begin{cases} 6x + 3y + 4z = 3 \\ x + 2y + z = 3 \\ 2x - y + 2z = 1 \end{cases}$

_____

3. $\begin{cases} x + y + z = 0 \\ x - y + z = 14 \\ x - y - z = 16 \end{cases}$

4. $\begin{cases} 8x + 3y - 6z = 4 \\ x - 2y - z = 2 \\ 4x + y - 2z = -4 \end{cases}$

_____

5. $\begin{cases} 2x - y - z = 1 \\ 3x + 2y + 2z = 12 \\ x - y + z = 9 \end{cases}$

6. $\begin{cases} 2x - y + 3z = 7 \\ 5x - 4y - 2z = 3 \\ 3x + 3y + 2z = -8 \end{cases}$

_____

Classify each system as consistent or inconsistent, and determine the number of solutions.

7. $\begin{cases} 2x - 6y + 4z = 3 \\ -3x + 9y - 6z = -3 \\ 5x - 15y + 10z = 5 \end{cases}$

8. $\begin{cases} -4x + 2y + 2z = -2 \\ 2x - y - z = 1 \\ x + y + z = 2 \end{cases}$

_____

Solve.

9. At the arcade Sami won 2 blue tickets, 1 yellow ticket and 3 red tickets for 1500 total points. Jamal won 1 blue ticket, 2 yellow tickets, and 2 red tickets for 1225 total points. Yvonne won 2 blue tickets, 3 yellow tickets, and 1 red ticket for 1200 total points Write and solve a system of equations to determine the point value of each type of ticket.

_____

 Holt Algebra 2

LESSON
3-6

Practice C
Solving Linear Systems in Three Variables

Use elimination to solve each system of equations.

1. $\begin{cases} 3x + 3y + z = -3 \\ 2x - 3y - 4z = -5 \\ 5x + 4y - z = 10 \end{cases}$

2. $\begin{cases} 3x + 4y + 2z = 8 \\ 5x - 6y - 3z = 26 \\ 4x + 8y + 5z = 1 \end{cases}$

_____   _____

Classify each system as consistent or inconsistent, and determine the number of solutions.

3. $\begin{cases} -4.5x + 3y + 1.5z = 9 \\ x + y - z = 0 \\ 3x - 2y - z = 4 \end{cases}$

4. $\begin{cases} 4x + 2y + 5z = 5 \\ 3x - 4y + 10z = 21 \\ 3x + 6y + 15z = 42 \end{cases}$

_____   _____

Solve.

5. The band members sold pumpkins in October to raise money for their annual tour. Rick sold 4 small pumpkins, 2 medium-sized pumpkins, and 8 large pumpkins for $45.20. Valerie sold 7 small, 2 medium, and 5 large pumpkins for $35.45. Therese sold 2 small, 9 medium, and 16 large pumpkins for $93.40. Write and solve a system of equations to find the price of each of the three sizes of pumpkins.

_____

6. Mr. Reese counts homework and class participation as well as tests toward a student's grade each quarter. Use the table to determine what percent each accounts for in the final grade.

Student	Homework	Class Participation	Tests	Final Grade
Fabian	90	85	80	83.75
Ingrid	85	90	95	91.25
Nesita	80	75	90	82.75

_____

LESSON 3-6

Reteach

Solving Linear Systems in Three Variables

You know how to solve a system of two linear equations in two variables using the **elimination method**. The same method can be used to solve a system of three linear equations in three variables.

$$\begin{cases} x - y + 2z = 8 \\ 2x + y - z = -2 \\ x + 2y + z = 2 \end{cases}$$

The first and second equations have opposite coefficients of y. So adding these two equations will eliminate y.

$$\begin{aligned} x - y + 2z &= 8 \\ \underline{+2x + y - z} &= \underline{-2} \\ 3x + z &= 6 \end{aligned}$$

Multiply the first equation by 2 and add to the third equation to eliminate y.

$$\begin{aligned} 2x - 2y + 4z &= 16 \\ \underline{+ x + 2y + z} &= \underline{2} \\ 3x + 5z &= 18 \end{aligned}$$

Now you have two equations in two variables. Solve using the elimination method for a system of two equations.

$$\begin{cases} 3x + z = 6 \\ 3x + 5z = 18 \end{cases}$$

Solving this system gives $x = 1$ and $z = 3$. Substituting these values in any of the original equations gives $y = -1$.

So the solution is the ordered triple $(1, -1, 3)$

Show the steps you would use to eliminate the variable z.

1. $\begin{cases} 2x - y + z = -3 \\ x + 2y - z = 2 \\ x + 3y - 2z = 3 \end{cases}$

a. $\begin{aligned} 2x - y + z &= -3 \\ + \underline{\hspace{3cm}} \\ \underline{\hspace{4cm}}. \end{aligned}$

b. $\begin{aligned} 2(\underline{\hspace{3cm}}) &= \underline{\hspace{3cm}} \\ \underline{+ x + 3y - 2z} &= \underline{3} \\ \underline{\hspace{3cm}} \end{aligned}$

c. Give the resulting system of two equations. _____

LESSON 3-6 Reteach
Solving Linear Systems in Three Variables (continued)

Linear systems in three variables are classified by their solutions.

Exactly One Solution Independent	Infinitely Many Solutions Dependent	No Solution Inconsistent
Three planes intersect at one point.	Three planes intersect at a line.	All three planes never intersect.

Classify: $\begin{cases} x + z = 1 \\ x + y + z = 2 \\ x - y + z = 1 \end{cases}$

Add the second and third equations to eliminate y.

$$\begin{aligned} x + y + z &= 2 \\ +\ x - y + z &= 1 \\ \hline 2x + 2z &= 3 \end{aligned}$$

Solve: $\begin{cases} x + z = 1 \\ 2x + 2z = 3 \end{cases}$

Multiply the first equation by –2. Then add.

$$\begin{aligned} -2x - 2z &= -2 \\ +\ 2x + 2z &= 3 \\ \hline 0 &= 1 \quad \textbf{X} \end{aligned}$$

Since 0 does not equal 1, the system has no solution and is inconsistent.

Classify: $\begin{cases} x + 2y + 4z = 3 \\ 4x - 2y - 6z = 2 \\ 2x - y - 3z = 1 \end{cases}$

Add the first and second equations.

$$\begin{aligned} x + 2y + 4z &= 3 \\ +\ 4x - 2y - 6z &= 2 \\ \hline 5x \qquad -2z &= 5 \end{aligned}$$

Multiply the third equation by 2. Add to the first equation.

$$\begin{aligned} 4x - 2y - 6z &= 2 \\ +\ x + 2y + 4z &= 3 \\ \hline 5x \qquad -2z &= 5 \end{aligned}$$

Now you have a system with two identical equations.

Subtracting the equations gives 0 = 0.

The system has infinitely many solutions and is dependent.

$\begin{cases} 5x - 2z = 5 \\ 5x - 2z = 5 \end{cases}$

Classify each system and determine the number of solutions.

2. $\begin{cases} x + z = 0 \\ x + y + 2z = 3 \\ y + z = 2 \end{cases}$

3. $\begin{cases} y - z = 0 \\ x - 3z = -1 \\ -x + 3y = 1 \end{cases}$

Challenge

LESSON
3-6

Solving Linear Systems in Three Variables

Two nonparallel planes in three-dimensional space will
always intersect in a line. This line can be written in
parametric form. Consider the planes defined by this
system of equations.

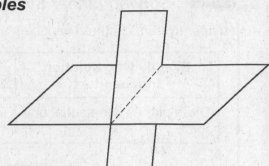

$$\begin{cases} 2x + 5y - 5z = -8 \\ 2x + 4y - 2z = 4. \end{cases}$$

Since the coefficients are different and not multiples of one another, the
planes are not parallel to each other and so they intersect in a line. To find
the parametric equations of the line subtract the two equations to eliminate
x, giving the following equation.

$$y - 3z = -12$$

This is a linear equation in two variables y and z. Substitute the parameter t
for z and solve the equation for y.

$$z = t \qquad y = 3t - 12$$

Now substitute for y and z in the first equation and solve for x.

$$2x + 5y - 5z = 2x + 5(3t - 12) - 5(t) = -8$$
$$x = -5t + 26$$

This gives the parametric equations of the line of intersection.

$$x = -5t + 26$$
$$y = 3t - 12$$
$$z = t$$

Find the parametric equations of the line of intersection of the planes.

1. two planes $\begin{cases} x + y + z = 5 \\ x + 2y + 3z = 6 \end{cases}$

2. two planes $\begin{cases} x + y = 2 \\ y + z = -4 \end{cases}$

_____   _____

3. two planes $\begin{cases} 3x + 2y + z = 10 \\ -2x + 4y + 6z = 8 \end{cases}$

4. three planes $\begin{cases} x + 2y + 3z = 14 \\ 3x + 2y + z = 10 \\ x + y + z = 6 \end{cases}$

_____   _____

Holt Algebra 2

Problem Solving

Solving Linear Systems in Three Variables

LESSON 3-6

For an annual violin competition, judges score the musicians in three categories: technique, creativity, and presentation. Each category is worth a percent of the final score. Use the table for Exercises 1–3.

Musician	Technique	Creativity	Presentation	Final Score
Jonathan	7	8	8	7.6
Miguel	9	4	8	7.4
Travis	6	10	6	7.0

1. Find the value of each category in the judging.

   a. Write a system of equations to
      represent the data in the table.   _____

   b. What percent of the final score is based on technique?   _____

   c. What percent of the final score is based on creativity?   _____

   d. What percent of the final score is based on presentation?   _____

2. How many more points would Miguel have needed to score
   for creativity to win the competition?   _____

3. Leesa scored 8 points for technique and 9 points for creativity.
   Her final score was 7.2. How many points did she score for
   presentation?   _____

A student-written performance is playing at a local high school. Rachelle paid $52 for two adult, two student, and one child tickets; RJ paid $56 for one adult, two student, and three child tickets; and Hong-An paid $44 for one adult and four child tickets. Choose the letter for the best answer.

4. Austin wants to know the cost of each
   type of ticket, a, s, and c. RJ says she
   can write a system of equations using the
   data. Which equation is not part of this
   system?

   A $2a + 2s + c = 52$

   B $a + 2s + 3c = 56$

   C $a + 4c = 44$

   D $2a + s + 2c = 54$

5. Austin solves the correct system of
   equations. What is the price for each type
   of ticket?

   A Adult: $13; student: $9; child: $7

   B Adult: $12; student: $10; child: $8

   C Adult: $11; student: $10; child: $10

   D Adult: $11; student: $9; child: $8

LESSON 3-6

Reading in Math

Analyze Information

A system of three equations in three variables can be solved using the methods you used to solve systems of two equations with two variables.

Elimination	Substitution
$\begin{cases} 2x + y - z = -3 \\ 5x - y - z = -8 \\ -x + 3y + z = 6 \end{cases}$	$\begin{cases} 2x - y = 5 \\ x - 3y - z = 1 \\ 2y - 2z = -10 \end{cases}$
Tip: Remember to *eliminate* means to remove, the plan is to *eliminate* one of the variables.	Tip: Remember you can solve an equation for one of the three variables, then *substitute* that expression in the other equations.
In this system, you can *eliminate* z by adding equations 1 and 3 together and then by adding equations 2 and 3 together $(-z + z = 0)$. This gives the system $\begin{cases} x + 4y = 3 \\ 4x + 2y = -2 \end{cases}$	In this system, you can solve the first equation to find *y* in terms of *x*. Then, *substitute* that value into the other two equations. This gives the system $\begin{cases} -5x - z = -14 \\ 4x - 2z = 0 \end{cases}$
Eliminate *y* from this system by multiplying the second equation by −2 and then adding to find $x = -1$. Substitution yields $y = 1$ and $z = 2$. The solution to the system is $(-1, 1, 2)$	Solve for *z* and substitute to find $x = 2$. Substituting gives $y = -1$ and $z = 4$. The solution to the system is $(2, -1, 4)$

Answer these questions.

1. Explain why a system of three equations with three variables requires a three-dimensional coordinate system to graph.

   _____

2. $x + 2y - z = 3$ is one equation in a dependent system of equations. Write two other equations in that system.

   _____

3. What does it mean if a system of three equations with three variables is independent?

   _____

4. If you solve one of the equations in a system for *x*, why can you substitute that value for *x* in the other equations?

   _____

Date _____

Dear Family,

In Chapter 4, your child will learn about matrices and how to use them to solve linear systems.

A **matrix** is a rectangular array of numbers enclosed in brackets. A matrix is like a table without headings.

The numbers of rows and columns are called the **dimensions** of the matrix. A **square matrix** has the same numbers of rows and columns.

matrix: $A = \begin{bmatrix} 2 & 5 \\ 3 & -4 \\ 1 & 0 \end{bmatrix}$

dimensions: Matrix A is a 3×2 matrix.

address: The address of 3 is a_{21}.

Each value, or **entry**, in the matrix is named by an **address** that gives its row and column.

Several operations can be performed with matrices:

Operation	Requirements	How To	Example
Addition/ Subtraction	The matrices must have the same dimensions.	Add or subtract corresponding entries.	$\begin{bmatrix} 2 & 5 \\ 3 & -4 \\ 1 & 0 \end{bmatrix} + \begin{bmatrix} 3 & 6 \\ -8 & 9 \\ 2 & 5 \end{bmatrix} = \begin{bmatrix} 2+3 & 5+6 \\ 3+(-8) & -4+9 \\ 1+2 & 0+5 \end{bmatrix}$
Scalar Multiplication	No requirements.	Multiply each entry by the same number, or **scalar**.	$4\begin{bmatrix} 2 & 5 \\ 3 & -4 \\ 1 & 0 \end{bmatrix} = \begin{bmatrix} 4(2) & 4(5) \\ 4(3) & 4(-4) \\ 4(1) & 4(0) \end{bmatrix}$
Matrix Multiplication	The *inside* dimensions must be the same. (The dimensions of the product will be the *outside* dimensions.)	Working with row *i* of the first matrix and column *j* of the second matrix, add the products of consecutive entries. The result goes in row *i* column *j* of the matrix product.	The dimensions are 3×2 and 2×2. Same inside dimension. The product will be 3×2. $\begin{bmatrix} 2 & 5 \\ 3 & -4 \\ 1 & 0 \end{bmatrix}\begin{bmatrix} 3 & 6 \\ -8 & 9 \end{bmatrix} = $ $\begin{bmatrix} 2(3)+5(-8) & 2(6)+5(9) \\ 3(3)+(-4)(-8) & 3(6)+(-4)(9) \\ 1(3)+0(-8) & \boxed{1(6)+0(9)} \end{bmatrix}$ The entry at p_{32} is calculated from row 3 of the first matrix and column 2 of the second matrix.

A **multiplicative identity matrix** is a square matrix with 1's along the **main diagonal** (top left to bottom right) and 0's for every other entry. The product of square matrix A and the identity matrix is simply matrix A. The product of a matrix and its **multiplicative inverse** is the identity.

$\begin{bmatrix} 1 & 0 \\ 0 & 1 \end{bmatrix}\begin{bmatrix} 2 & 4 \\ 3 & -1 \end{bmatrix} = \begin{bmatrix} 2 & 4 \\ 3 & -1 \end{bmatrix}$

identity matrix

$\begin{bmatrix} \frac{1}{14} & \frac{2}{7} \\ \frac{3}{14} & \frac{-1}{7} \end{bmatrix}\begin{bmatrix} 2 & 4 \\ 3 & -1 \end{bmatrix} = \begin{bmatrix} 1 & 0 \\ 0 & 1 \end{bmatrix}$

inverse matrix

Holt Algebra 2

A matrix can represent the *x*- and *y*-coordinates of the vertices of a polygon. You can then transform the polygon using matrix operations.

$\triangle ABC$: $\begin{bmatrix} -2 & -3 & -1 \\ 3 & 0 & -2 \end{bmatrix}$ ← *x*-coordinates
← *y*-coordinates

↑ ↑ ↑
A B C

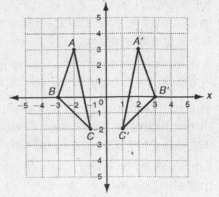

$\triangle A'B'C'$: $\begin{bmatrix} -1 & 0 \\ 0 & 1 \end{bmatrix} \begin{bmatrix} -2 & -3 & -1 \\ 3 & 0 & -2 \end{bmatrix} = \begin{bmatrix} 2 & 3 & 1 \\ 3 & 0 & -2 \end{bmatrix}$

1442443
reflection matrix

Matrices can also represent a linear system in two ways:

Linear System	**Matrix Equation**	**Augmented Matrix**

$\begin{cases} 2x + 4y = 20 \\ 3x - y = 9 \end{cases}$

$\begin{bmatrix} 2 & 4 \\ 3 & -1 \end{bmatrix} \begin{bmatrix} x \\ y \end{bmatrix} = \begin{bmatrix} 20 \\ 9 \end{bmatrix}$

coefficient matrix variable matrix constant matrix

$\begin{bmatrix} 2 & 4 & | & 20 \\ 3 & -1 & | & 9 \end{bmatrix}$

coefficients constants

Cramer's rule allows you to solve a linear system using determinants. A **determinant** is a single number calculated from the entries in the matrix.

determinant of coefficient matrix: $\det \begin{bmatrix} 2 & 4 \\ 3 & -1 \end{bmatrix} = (2)(-1) - (3)(4) = -14$

replace *x*-coefficients with constants: $\det \begin{bmatrix} 20 & 4 \\ 9 & -1 \end{bmatrix} = -56$, so $x = \dfrac{-56}{-14} = 4$

replace *y*-coefficients with constants: $\det \begin{bmatrix} 2 & 20 \\ 3 & 9 \end{bmatrix} = -42$, so $y = \dfrac{-42}{-14} = 3$

You can also solve a linear system with a matrix equation and the multiplicative inverse of the coefficient matrix.

matrix equation: $\begin{bmatrix} 2 & 4 \\ 3 & -1 \end{bmatrix} \begin{bmatrix} x \\ y \end{bmatrix} = \begin{bmatrix} 20 \\ 9 \end{bmatrix}$

solution: $\begin{bmatrix} \frac{1}{14} & \frac{2}{7} \\ \frac{3}{14} & \frac{-1}{7} \end{bmatrix} \begin{bmatrix} 2 & 4 \\ 3 & -1 \end{bmatrix} \begin{bmatrix} x \\ y \end{bmatrix} = \begin{bmatrix} \frac{1}{14} & \frac{2}{7} \\ \frac{3}{14} & \frac{-1}{7} \end{bmatrix} \begin{bmatrix} 20 \\ 9 \end{bmatrix}$ $\begin{bmatrix} x \\ y \end{bmatrix} = \begin{bmatrix} 4 \\ 3 \end{bmatrix}$, so $\begin{matrix} x = 4 \\ y = 3 \end{matrix}$

A third way to solve a linear system uses **row operations** to change the augmented matrix into **reduced row-echelon form**.

augmented matrix: $\begin{bmatrix} 2 & 4 & | & 20 \\ 3 & -1 & | & 9 \end{bmatrix}$

reduced row-echelon form: $\begin{bmatrix} 1 & 0 & | & 4 \\ 0 & 1 & | & 3 \end{bmatrix}$, so $\begin{matrix} x = 4 \\ y = 3 \end{matrix}$

All three methods can be extended to systems with more than two equations and two variables.

For additional resources, visit go.hrw.com and enter the keyword MB7 Parent.

Holt Algebra 2

LESSON 4-1 Practice A
Matrices and Data

Answer the following questions about matrix K.

1. How many rows are in the matrix? _____

2. How many columns are in the matrix? _____

3. What are the dimensions of K? _____

$$K = \begin{bmatrix} 1.2 & 1.5 & 1.8 & 0.7 & 0.4 \\ 2.3 & 0.7 & 1.3 & 3.1 & 4.5 \\ 0.1 & 5.2 & 4.8 & 2.5 & 3.9 \end{bmatrix}$$

4. Look at the point where the third row meets the fourth column. What is the entry k_{34}? _____

5. Find the entry 3.1 in the matrix. What row is it in? what column? What is the address of the entry 3.1? _____

6. What are the dimensions of matrices that can be added to or subtracted from K? _____

Use the following matrices for Exercises 7–9. Add or subtract, if possible.

$$A = \begin{bmatrix} 3 & 6 \\ 5 & 0 \end{bmatrix} \qquad B = \begin{bmatrix} 12 & 7 \\ 5 & 9 \end{bmatrix} \qquad C = \begin{bmatrix} 3 & 6 & 9 \\ 1 & 5 & 7 \end{bmatrix}$$

7. $A + B$

$$A + B = \begin{bmatrix} 3+12 & \underline{}+\underline{} \\ \underline{}+\underline{} & \underline{}+\underline{} \end{bmatrix} = \begin{bmatrix} \underline{} & \underline{} \\ \underline{} & \underline{} \end{bmatrix}$$

8. $B + C$

9. $B - A$

_____   _____

Use the following matrices for Exercises 10–12. Evaluate, if possible.

$$D = \begin{bmatrix} 7 & 0 \\ 3 & 14 \\ 4 & 6 \end{bmatrix} \qquad E = \begin{bmatrix} 2 & 4 \\ 3 & 5 \\ 6 & 9 \end{bmatrix}$$

10. $3D$

$$3D = 3 \cdot \begin{bmatrix} \underline{} & \underline{} \\ \underline{} & \underline{} \\ \underline{} & \underline{} \end{bmatrix} = \begin{bmatrix} 3(\underline{}) & 3(\underline{}) \\ 3(\underline{}) & 3(\underline{}) \\ 3(\underline{}) & 3(\underline{}) \end{bmatrix} = \begin{bmatrix} \underline{} & \underline{} \\ \underline{} & \underline{} \\ \underline{} & \underline{} \end{bmatrix}$$

11. $2E$

12. $3D + 2E$

_____   _____

Holt Algebra 2

LESSON 4-1 Practice B

Matrices and Data

The table shows the prices for various passes to a theme park.

Theme Park Pass Price List				
Type of Pass	1-Day	2-Day	3-Day	5-Day
Basic	$40	$75	$100	$125
Super	$70	$95	$120	$140
Deluxe	$80	$105	$130	$150

1. Display the data in the form of a matrix, P.

2. What are the dimensions of P?   _____

3. What is the entry at p_{31} and what does it represent?

   _____

4. What is the address of the entry $120?   _____

5. Write an expression that represents a matrix that shows
   the cost of buying theme park tickets for a family of four. _____

Use the following matrices for Exercises 6–8. Add or subtract, if
possible.

$$R = \begin{bmatrix} 4 & 12 \\ 0 & -6 \\ 9 & 15 \end{bmatrix} \qquad S = \begin{bmatrix} -3 & 9 & 2 \\ 10 & -5 & 4 \\ 1 & 2 & 3 \end{bmatrix} \qquad T = \begin{bmatrix} -5 & 9 \\ -3 & 6 \\ 10 & 5 \end{bmatrix}$$

6. $S - R$ 7. $T + R$ 8. $R - T$

_____   _____   _____

Use the following matrices for Exercises 9–11. Evaluate, if possible.

$$X = \begin{bmatrix} 5 & -2 & 0 & 9 \\ 4 & 16 & -5 & 6 \end{bmatrix} \qquad Y = \begin{bmatrix} -6 & 4 & 10 & 8 \\ 13 & 6 & 0 & -2 \end{bmatrix}$$

9. $3X$ 10. $3Y + 4X$ 11. $3X - 2Y$

_____   _____   _____

Solve.

12. If $E = \begin{bmatrix} 2 & -3 \\ 5 & 4 \end{bmatrix}$ and $E + F = \begin{bmatrix} 0 & 0 \\ 0 & 0 \end{bmatrix}$, find F.   _____

LESSON 4-1 Practice C
Matrices and Data

Use the following matrices for Exercises 1–6. Evaluate, if possible.

$$A = \begin{bmatrix} 3 & -6 & 9 \\ 0 & 12 & 15 \end{bmatrix} \qquad B = \begin{bmatrix} -3 & 9 & 2 \\ 10 & -5 & 4 \\ 1 & 2 & 3 \end{bmatrix} \qquad C = \begin{bmatrix} -5 & 1 & 4 \\ 11 & 7 & -3 \end{bmatrix} \qquad D = \begin{bmatrix} 17 & -8 & -5 \\ 2 & 1 & 3 \end{bmatrix}$$

1. $2C + A$

2. $10B$

3. $D - (C - A)$

_____

4. $\dfrac{1}{2}B$

5. $-3C + 4D$

6. $-4(2C - 7A)$

_____

Solve.

7. If $M - N = \begin{bmatrix} 3 & -6 \\ -4 & 1 \end{bmatrix}$, find $N - M$. _____

8. If $W = \begin{bmatrix} 2 & 0 \\ -1 & 3 \end{bmatrix}$ and $3W - 2Z = \begin{bmatrix} 8 & 4 \\ 9 & -3 \end{bmatrix}$, find Z. _____

9. Find x and y in this matrix equation: $\begin{bmatrix} 9 & 2x \\ 4x & 5 \end{bmatrix} + \begin{bmatrix} 8 & 3y \\ -2y & 4 \end{bmatrix} = \begin{bmatrix} 17 & 17 \\ 10 & 9 \end{bmatrix}$.

   $x = $ _____, $y = $ _____

The table shows the number of calories in each size and type of Sal's vegetable pizzas.

Sal's Vegetable Pizza Slice Calorie Counter			
Type of Crust	8-inch	12-inch	16-inch
Thin	120	180	240
Thick	160	240	320

10. Use a scalar product to find the calories in each size pizza if Sal increases the calories by $\dfrac{1}{4}$ by adding more cheese to each pizza. _____

11. Use a scalar product to find the calories in each size pizza if Sal reduces the calories in each pizza by 10% by using less cheese on each pizza. _____

LESSON 4-1

Reteach

Matrices and Data

A **matrix** is a rectangular array of numbers. A matrix can be named by a capital letter. Some examples are shown below.

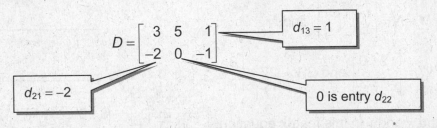

The **dimensions** of a matrix are determined by the number of rows and columns in the matrix. A matrix of dimensions $m \times n$ (read "m by n") has m rows and n columns. Note that the row comes before the column in matrix notation. So, matrix A has dimensions 1×2 and matrix D has dimensions 2×3.

Each value in a matrix is called an **entry**. The **address** of an entry is its location in a matrix. A lowercase letter refers to the entry with the row and column number as subscripts.

$$D = \begin{bmatrix} 3 & 5 & 1 \\ -2 & 0 & -1 \end{bmatrix}$$

$d_{13} = 1$

$d_{21} = -2$

0 is entry d_{22}

Use matrix M to answer the questions. $M = \begin{bmatrix} 2 & 4 & 5 & 8 & 0 \\ -1 & 3 & -2 & 1 & 6 \\ -3 & 0 & 4 & -5 & 7 \end{bmatrix}$

1. a. How many rows does matrix M have? _____

   b. How many columns does matrix M have? _____

   c. What are the dimensions of matrix M? _____

2. What is entry m_{11}?

_____

3. What is entry m_{35}?

_____

4. What is entry m_{23}?

_____

5. What is entry m_{32}?

_____

6. At which two addresses is the entry 4? _____

LESSON 4-1

Reteach

Matrices and Data (continued)

Add or subtract matrices only if they have the same dimensions.

$$A = \begin{bmatrix} 3 & 5 & 1 \\ -2 & 0 & -1 \end{bmatrix} \qquad B = \begin{bmatrix} 1 & -1 & 4 \\ 2 & 3 & -1 \end{bmatrix} \qquad C = \begin{bmatrix} 1 & 2 \\ 3 & -1 \end{bmatrix}$$

A and B have the same dimensions. You can add A and B.

B and C have different dimensions. You CANNOT add B and C.

To add or subtract two matrices, add or subtract the corresponding entries.

$$A + B = \begin{bmatrix} 3 & 5 & 1 \\ -2 & 0 & -1 \end{bmatrix} + \begin{bmatrix} 1 & -1 & 4 \\ 2 & 3 & -1 \end{bmatrix}$$

$$= \begin{bmatrix} 3+1 & 5+(-1) & 1+4 \\ -2+2 & 0+3 & -1+(-1) \end{bmatrix} = \begin{bmatrix} 4 & 4 & 5 \\ 0 & 3 & -2 \end{bmatrix}$$

To multiply a matrix by a number, multiply each entry by that number.

$$3C = 3\begin{bmatrix} 1 & 2 \\ 3 & -1 \end{bmatrix} = \begin{bmatrix} 3(1) & 3(2) \\ 3(3) & 3(-1) \end{bmatrix} = \begin{bmatrix} 3 & 6 \\ 9 & -3 \end{bmatrix}$$

Use the following matrices for Exercises 7–12. Evaluate, if possible.

$$A = \begin{bmatrix} -1 & 0 \\ 2 & -2 \end{bmatrix} \qquad B = \begin{bmatrix} 1 & 2 \\ 3 & 4 \end{bmatrix} \qquad C = [5 \quad 3] \quad D = [-1 \quad 2]$$

7. $A - B = \begin{bmatrix} -1 & 0 \\ 2 & -2 \end{bmatrix} - \begin{bmatrix} 1 & 2 \\ 3 & 4 \end{bmatrix} = \begin{bmatrix} -1-1 & 0-2 \\ 2-3 & -2-4 \end{bmatrix} = \begin{bmatrix} \underline{\quad} & \underline{\quad} \\ \underline{\quad} & \underline{\quad} \end{bmatrix}$

8. $C + D = [5 \quad 3] + [-1 \quad 2]$ _____

9. $C - D = [5 \quad 3] - [-1 \quad 2]$ _____

10. $A + B = \begin{bmatrix} \underline{\quad} & \underline{\quad} \\ \underline{\quad} & \underline{\quad} \end{bmatrix} + \begin{bmatrix} \underline{\quad} & \underline{\quad} \\ \underline{\quad} & \underline{\quad} \end{bmatrix} =$

_____

11. $-A = (-1)\begin{bmatrix} -1 & 0 \\ 2 & -2 \end{bmatrix}$ 12. $4B = 4\begin{bmatrix} \underline{\quad} & \underline{\quad} \\ \underline{\quad} & \underline{\quad} \end{bmatrix}$

_____   _____

Challenge

LESSON
4-1

The Closure Property of Matrix Addition

An operation exhibits the *Closure Property* if performing this operation on two elements of a set always gives another element of that set. We say the set is *closed* under the operation.

Matrix F has dimensions m × n.

1. In order to find the sum of matrix F and a second matrix G, what must be true about the dimensions of matrix G? _____

2. If matrix H represents $F + G$, what must be true about the dimensions of matrix H? _____

3. Is the set of $m \times n$ matrices closed under the operation of addition? _____

Matrices A and B are shown below. None of the elements a–f is 0.

4. How are A and B alike?

$$A = \begin{bmatrix} a & 0 & 0 \\ 0 & b & 0 \\ 0 & 0 & c \end{bmatrix} \quad B = \begin{bmatrix} d & 0 & 0 \\ 0 & e & 0 \\ 0 & 0 & f \end{bmatrix}$$

_____

5. Let $S = A + B$. Write S in the space at right.

_____

6. Compare the dimensions of S with the dimensions of A and B. _____

7. Matrices such as A and B above are called *diagonal matrices*. Is the set of diagonal matrices closed under addition? Explain.

_____

Matrices C and D are called 3 × 3 upper triangular matrices. None of the elements a–f or r–w is 0.

$$C = \begin{bmatrix} a & b & c \\ 0 & d & e \\ 0 & 0 & f \end{bmatrix} \quad D = \begin{bmatrix} r & s & t \\ 0 & u & v \\ 0 & 0 & w \end{bmatrix}$$

8. Is the set of 3×3 upper triangular matrices closed under addition? Justify your response.

_____

9. Modify C and D so that they can be called 3×3 *lower triangular matrices*. Show that the sum of two 3×3 lower triangular matrices is another lower triangular matrix.

_____

Holt Algebra 2

Name _____ Date _____ Class_____

Problem Solving
Matrices and Data

According to the United States Census Bureau, Americans are more educated than ever: about 84% of adults over 25 have at least completed high school and about 26% have at least a bachelor's degree. Olivia is researching whether completing higher levels of education has a payoff in higher lifetime earnings. Use the information in the table to answer the questions.

Average Annual Earnings of Workers in 1999 Dollars (×$1,000)		
Highest Level of Education	Full-Time Workers	All Workers
Bachelor's degree	52.2	45.4
Associate degree	38.2	33.0
High school graduate	30.4	25.9
Not high school graduate	23.4	18.9

1. Display the data in the form of a matrix. Write matrix P.

2. What are the dimensions of matrix P? _____

3. Olivia wants to show the earnings per month, rather than annual earnings. Write an equation with a scalar product that she can use to change matrix P into matrix M. _____

4. Write matrix M.

Choose the letter for the best answer.

5. Olivia's uncle is represented in matrix P by the entry p_{21}. What are the average annual earnings for this entry?

   A $38.20

   B $45.40

   C $38,200

   D $45,400

6. Olivia's cousin graduated from high school and works in the summer only. What is the address for the entry that represents her?

   A p_{13}

   B p_{23}

   C p_{31}

   D p_{32}

Name _____ Date _____ Class_____

Reading Strategies
Use a Model

In a **matrix**, numbers are arranged in rows and columns. The plural of matrix is **matrices**. You can use a matrix to store and show data. The table below shows some results of a high school long jump competition.

Long Jump Competition			
Contestant	Trial 1 (m)	Trial 2 (m)	Trial 3 (m)
Rafael	6.7	5.8	6.1
Kirk	6.6	5.9	6.1
Morgan	6.8	6.0	6.0

This data from the table can be organized in a matrix. A matrix is a model of the information. It is like a table without lines or labels. The **dimensions** of a matrix tell you the number of rows and columns. A 4×3 matrix has 4 rows and 3 columns. You can add or subtract matrices only if they have the same dimensions. The matrices below use the data from the table.

$$A = \begin{bmatrix} 6.7 & 5.8 & 6.1 \\ 6.6 & 5.9 & 6.1 \\ 6.8 & 6.0 & 6.0 \end{bmatrix} \quad B = [6.7 \quad 5.8 \quad 6.1] \quad C = [6.8 \quad 6.0 \quad 6.0] \quad D = \begin{bmatrix} 5.8 \\ 5.9 \\ 6.0 \end{bmatrix}$$

Use the matrices to answer each question.

1. What information is shown in matrix *A*?

   _____

2. What information is shown in matrices *B* and *C*?

   _____

3. What information is shown in matrix *D*?

   _____

4. Give the dimensions of each matrix.

   _____

5. Can you add matrices *A* and *B*? Explain why or why not.

   _____

6. Can you subtract matrix *B* from matrix *C*? Explain why or why not.

   _____

Holt Algebra 2

Practice A
Multiplying Matrices

Tell whether each product is defined. If so, give its dimensions.

1. $A_{3 \times 4}$ and $B_{4 \times 6}$; AB

2. $C_{4 \times 2}$ and $D_{2 \times 1}$; CD

3. $E_{5 \times 2}$ and $F_{5 \times 3}$; EF

_____   _____   _____

Use the following matrices for Exercises 4–7. Evaluate, if possible.

$$A = \begin{bmatrix} 2 & 0 \\ 1 & 3 \end{bmatrix} \qquad B = \begin{bmatrix} 0 & 5 \\ 2 & 1 \\ 0 & 3 \\ 1 & 0 \end{bmatrix} \qquad C = \begin{bmatrix} 8 & 1 & 0 & 1 \\ 0 & 2 & 3 & 1 \end{bmatrix} \qquad D = \begin{bmatrix} 4 & 5 & 0 & 2 \\ 0 & 1 & 3 & 0 \\ 1 & 2 & 1 & 2 \\ 5 & 0 & 1 & 4 \end{bmatrix}$$

4. $A^2 = A \times A = \begin{bmatrix} 2 & 0 \\ 1 & 3 \end{bmatrix} \times \begin{bmatrix} 2 & 0 \\ 1 & 3 \end{bmatrix}$

$$= \begin{bmatrix} 2(2) + 0(1) & 2(\underline{\quad}) + 0(\underline{\quad}) \\ 1(\underline{\quad}) + 3(\underline{\quad}) & 1(\underline{\quad}) + 3(\underline{\quad}) \end{bmatrix}$$ _____

5. CB

6. BA

7. CD

_____   _____   _____

Solve.

8. Julie and Steve are playing the games at the arcade. The first table shows the number of each type of ticket they won. Find the total number of points they each won.

   a. Write a matrix that represents the data in each table.

Tickets Won			
Player	Red	Yellow	Blue
Julie	15	6	2
Steve	17	3	4

_____

   b. Find the product matrix.

Ticket Point Values	
Ticket	Points
Red	5
Yellow	10
Blue	25

_____

   c. How many points did each player win?   _____

Holt Algebra 2

Practice B

Multiplying Matrices

Tell whether each product is defined. If so, give its dimensions.

1. $P_{3 \times 3}$ and $Q_{3 \times 4}$; PQ

2. $R_{3 \times 8}$ and $S_{4 \times 3}$; SR

3. $W_{2 \times 5}$ and $X_{2 \times 5}$; WX

_____   _____   _____

Use the following matrices for Exercises 4–7. Evaluate, if possible.

$$E = \begin{bmatrix} -4 & 1 \\ -2 & 2 \end{bmatrix} \qquad F = \begin{bmatrix} 1 & 0 \\ 4 & -3 \\ -2 & 6 \\ -1 & 5 \end{bmatrix} \qquad G = \begin{bmatrix} -4 & 0 & 3 & 5 \\ 1 & -2 & 0 & 0 \end{bmatrix} \qquad H = \begin{bmatrix} 1 & -2 & -1 & 3 \\ 2 & 0 & 4 & -1 \\ 3 & 5 & -2 & 2 \\ 1 & -1 & 0 & 0 \end{bmatrix}$$

4. EG

5. HF

_____   _____

6. FG

7. E^2

_____   _____

Solve.

8. Jamal, Ken, and Barry are playing a baseball video game. The first table shows the number of singles, doubles, triples, and home runs each scored. Find the total number of points they each scored.

a. Write a matrix that represents the data in each table.

Hits				
Player	**S**	**D**	**T**	**HR**
Jamal	3	2	0	1
Ken	2	4	0	0
Barry	0	1	3	1

Points Scored for Hits	
Hit	**Points**
Single (S)	1
Double (D)	2
Triple (T)	3
Home run (HR)	4

b. Find the product matrix.

_____

c. How many points did each player score?

_____

LESSON 4-2 Practice C
Multiplying Matrices

Use the following matrices for Exercises 1–9. Evaluate, if possible.

$$J = \begin{bmatrix} 1 & -3 & 2 \\ 0 & -4 & 1 \\ 5 & 1 & 0 \end{bmatrix} \qquad K = \begin{bmatrix} 8 & 0 & 1 \\ -2 & 1 & -1 \end{bmatrix} \qquad L = \begin{bmatrix} 0 & 6 & 0 \\ -3 & 1 & 4 \\ 1 & 0 & -2 \end{bmatrix} \qquad M = \begin{bmatrix} 5 & -4 \\ -3 & 3 \end{bmatrix}$$

1. JK

2. KJ

3. JL

_____

4. KL

5. KM

6. M^2

_____

7. MK

8. LJ

9. L^2

_____

Solve.

10. The tables show the prices and amounts of milk sold in a dairy store during one week.

Milk Prices	
Size	**Price**
Quart	$1.65
Half-gallon	$2.10
Gallon	$3.20

Dairy Milk Sales					
Size	**Mon**	**Tue**	**Wed**	**Thu**	**Fri**
Quart	18	21	20	25	12
Half-gallon	12	50	10	5	10
Gallon	60	55	40	60	25

a. To compare milk sales for each day, show the data as matrices.

_____

b. Find the product matrix.

_____

c. Order the days from greatest to least in total sales.

_____

Reteach
Multiplying Matrices

Use the dimensions to decide whether matrices can be multiplied.

To multiply two matrices, the number of columns in A

must equal the number of rows in B.

Matrices: A   ×   B   = AB

Dimensions: $m \times \mathbf{n}$ $\mathbf{n} \times p$ $m \times p$

> Remember, with matrices, AB is NOT the same as BA.

> Inner dimensions are equal: $n = n$.

> Outer dimensions give the dimensions of the product.

To determine which products are defined, check the dimensions.

$$A = \begin{bmatrix} 3 & 5 & 1 \\ -2 & 0 & -1 \end{bmatrix} \qquad B = \begin{bmatrix} 1 & 2 \\ -1 & 4 \\ 0 & 3 \end{bmatrix} \qquad C = \begin{bmatrix} 1 & 2 \\ 3 & -1 \end{bmatrix}$$

A: 2×3 B: 3×2 C: 2×2

AB: 2×3 and 3×2, so AB is defined and has dimensions 2×2.

> Inner dimensions are equal.

AC: 2×3 and 2×2, so AC is not defined.

> Inner dimensions are NOT equal.

Use the following matrices for Exercises 1–3. Tell whether each product is defined. If so, give its dimensions.

$$A = \begin{bmatrix} -1 & 0 \\ 2 & -2 \end{bmatrix} \qquad B = \begin{bmatrix} 3 \\ 1 \end{bmatrix} \qquad C = [4 \quad 3]$$

1. AB

    A: 2×2

    B: 2×1

    Product defined?

    _____

    _____

2. BC

    B: _____

    C: _____

    Product defined?

    _____

    _____

3. AC

    A: _____

    C: _____

    Product defined?

    _____

    _____

LESSON 4-2

Reteach

Multiplying Matrices (continued)

To find a matrix product, first make sure the product is defined.

Find AB. $A = \begin{bmatrix} 3 & 5 & 1 \\ -2 & 0 & -1 \end{bmatrix}$ $B = \begin{bmatrix} 1 & 2 \\ -1 & 4 \\ 0 & 3 \end{bmatrix}$

> A is 2×3 and B is 3×2.
> The product is a 2×2 matrix.

Step 1: Multiply row 1 entries of A by column 1 entries of B. The sum is the first entry in the product.

$$\begin{bmatrix} 3 & 5 & 1 \\ -2 & 0 & -1 \end{bmatrix}\begin{bmatrix} 1 & 2 \\ -1 & 4 \\ 0 & 3 \end{bmatrix} = \begin{bmatrix} 3(1)+5(-1)+1(0) & ? \\ ? & ? \end{bmatrix} = \begin{bmatrix} -2 & ? \\ ? & ? \end{bmatrix}$$

Step 2: Multiply row 1 entries of A by column 2 entries of B. Add.

$$\begin{bmatrix} 3 & 5 & 1 \\ -2 & 0 & -1 \end{bmatrix}\begin{bmatrix} 1 & 2 \\ -1 & 4 \\ 0 & 3 \end{bmatrix} = \begin{bmatrix} -2 & 3(2)+5(4)+1(3) \\ ? & ? \end{bmatrix} = \begin{bmatrix} -2 & 29 \\ ? & ? \end{bmatrix}$$

Step 3: Multiply row 2 entries of A by column 1 entries of B. Add.

$$\begin{bmatrix} 3 & 5 & 1 \\ -2 & 0 & -1 \end{bmatrix}\begin{bmatrix} 1 & 2 \\ -1 & 4 \\ 0 & 3 \end{bmatrix} = \begin{bmatrix} -2 & 29 \\ -2(1)+0(-1)+(-1)0 & ? \end{bmatrix} = \begin{bmatrix} -2 & 29 \\ -2 & ? \end{bmatrix}$$

Step 4: Multiply row 2 entries of A by column 2 entries of B. Add.

$$\begin{bmatrix} 3 & 5 & 1 \\ -2 & 0 & -1 \end{bmatrix}\begin{bmatrix} 1 & 2 \\ -1 & 4 \\ 0 & 3 \end{bmatrix} = \begin{bmatrix} -2 & 29 \\ -2 & -2(2)+0(4)+(-1)(3) \end{bmatrix} = \begin{bmatrix} -2 & 29 \\ -2 & -7 \end{bmatrix}$$

Find each product.

4. $\begin{bmatrix} 3 \\ 1 \end{bmatrix}[4 \quad 3] = \begin{bmatrix} 3(\underline{\quad}) & 3(\underline{\quad}) \\ 1(\underline{\quad}) & 1(\underline{\quad}) \end{bmatrix} = \begin{bmatrix} \underline{\quad} & \underline{\quad} \\ \underline{\quad} & \underline{\quad} \end{bmatrix}$

5. $\begin{bmatrix} -1 & 0 \\ 3 & -2 \end{bmatrix}\begin{bmatrix} 1 & 2 \\ -4 & 0 \end{bmatrix} = \begin{bmatrix} -1(1)+0(-4) & -1(\underline{\quad})+0(\underline{\quad}) \\ 3(\underline{\quad})+-2(\underline{\quad}) & 3(\underline{\quad})+(-2)(\underline{\quad}) \end{bmatrix} = \begin{bmatrix} \underline{\quad} & \underline{\quad} \\ \underline{\quad} & \underline{\quad} \end{bmatrix}$

6. $\begin{bmatrix} -5 & 2 \\ 0 & -3 \end{bmatrix}\begin{bmatrix} 0 & 4 \\ -1 & 2 \end{bmatrix}$

Challenge

LESSON 4-2

Matrix Codes

Matrices can be used to send messages in coded form,
and then another matrix can be used to decode the message.
Use the code shown in the table for letters and characters.
Take a message such as "Math is fun." Code it into numbers and
the message becomes:

Code	
A–Z	1–26
Comma	27
Period	28
Space	29

13 1 20 8 29 9 19 29 6 21 14 28

The message in code can be represented by matrix M. $\begin{bmatrix} 13 & 1 & 20 & 8 \\ 29 & 9 & 19 & 29 \\ 6 & 21 & 14 & 28 \end{bmatrix}$

Notice how the numbers in the message read from left
to right. Multiply matrix M by the coding matrix C.

$$C = \begin{bmatrix} 2 & 0 & 1 \\ 3 & 1 & 2 \\ 1 & 0 & 1 \end{bmatrix}, CM = \begin{bmatrix} 2 & 0 & 1 \\ 3 & 1 & 2 \\ 1 & 0 & 1 \end{bmatrix} \times \begin{bmatrix} 13 & 1 & 20 & 8 \\ 29 & 9 & 19 & 29 \\ 6 & 21 & 14 & 28 \end{bmatrix} = \begin{bmatrix} 32 & 23 & 54 & 44 \\ 80 & 54 & 107 & 109 \\ 19 & 22 & 34 & 36 \end{bmatrix}$$

Since many of the numbers are greater than 29, the greatest number in the
code, divide each number by 29 and record only the remainder. This is
called arithmetic modulo 29.

$$CM \text{ modulo } 29 = \begin{bmatrix} 32 & 23 & 54 & 44 \\ 80 & 54 & 107 & 109 \\ 19 & 22 & 34 & 36 \end{bmatrix} \text{ modulo } 29 = \begin{bmatrix} 3 & 23 & 25 & 15 \\ 22 & 25 & 20 & 22 \\ 19 & 22 & 5 & 7 \end{bmatrix}$$

This gives the coded message CWYOVYTVSVEG. To decode, multiply by

the decoding matrix D, $\begin{bmatrix} 1 & 0 & 28 \\ 28 & 1 & 28 \\ 28 & 0 & 2 \end{bmatrix}$. This gives

$$D \times CM = \begin{bmatrix} 1 & 0 & 28 \\ 28 & 1 & 28 \\ 28 & 0 & 2 \end{bmatrix} \times \begin{bmatrix} 3 & 23 & 25 & 15 \\ 22 & 25 & 20 & 22 \\ 19 & 22 & 5 & 7 \end{bmatrix} = \begin{bmatrix} 535 & 639 & 165 & 211 \\ 638 & 1285 & 860 & 638 \\ 122 & 688 & 710 & 434 \end{bmatrix},$$

which in arithmetic modulo 29 is $\begin{bmatrix} 13 & 1 & 20 & 8 \\ 0 & 9 & 19 & 0 \\ 6 & 21 & 14 & 28 \end{bmatrix}$ and translates back to

"Math is fun."

Note that in the matrix for the decoded message, 0 corresponds to 29.

**When you code a message, be sure to use a matrix with 3 rows. Add
spaces at the end of the message, if necessary.**

1. Code the message "NOT NOW." _____

2. Decode the message "FE RRIQP CCDORI". _____

Holt Algebra 2

LESSON
4-2

Problem Solving
Multiplying Matrices

Members of the Cooking Club entered the Culinary Challenge. In this contest, the score for each entry is multiplied by an assigned degree of difficulty.

Cooking Club Members Scores			
	Appetizer	Main Course	Dessert
Beth	25	38	28
Jon	35	29	37
Lupe	20	31	39
Amy	40	32	36

Culinary Challenge Degrees of Difficulty				
	Beth	Jon	Lupe	Amy
Appetizer	3.1	2.0	3.5	1.5
Main Course	2.1	1.8	3.7	2.8
Dessert	2.3	2.4	3.0	3.5

1. Display each table as a matrix. Matrix S should show the scores and matrix D should show the degrees of difficulty.

2. Write an equation using S, D, and product matrix P you could use to evaluate the final scores. _____

3. Explain how you know that matrix S can be multiplied by matrix D.

_____

4. Write the product matrix P.

5. Roger is writing a story for the school newspaper about the Culinary Challenge. Explain how he can use P to find the final scores for his story.

_____

6. List the contestants and their final scores, in descending order.

_____

Reading Strategies

LESSON 4-2

Compare and Contrast

Like real numbers, matrices can be multiplied. But unlike numbers that can be multiplied in any order, matrices must be multiplied in a specific way.

Multiplication of real numbers is commutative; that is, the order does not matter.	Matrix multiplication is NOT commutative.
$$4 \times 8 = 32$$ and $$8 \times 4 = 32$$ So the product $a \times b$ is the same as $b \times a$. $$a \times b = b \times a$$	$$A = \begin{bmatrix} 2 & 5 \\ 6 & 3 \end{bmatrix} \quad B = \begin{bmatrix} 1 & 4 \\ 7 & 8 \end{bmatrix}$$ $$A \times B = \begin{bmatrix} 37 & 48 \\ 27 & 48 \end{bmatrix} \text{ but } B \times A = \begin{bmatrix} 26 & 17 \\ 62 & 59 \end{bmatrix}$$ $$A \times B \neq B \times A$$

Two matrices can be multiplied if the number of *columns* in the first matrix is the same as the number of *rows* in the second matrix. If matrix R is 2×4 and matrix S is 4×3, then RS is possible but SR is NOT possible.

Matrix R	Matrix S	Product Matrix RS
$$\begin{bmatrix} 5 & 2 & -4 & 1 \\ -1 & 0 & 3 & -2 \end{bmatrix}$$	$$\begin{bmatrix} 3 & 0 & -2 \\ 1 & 4 & 2 \\ 0 & -3 & 1 \\ -5 & 2 & 0 \end{bmatrix}$$	$$\begin{bmatrix} 12 & 22 & -10 \\ 7 & -13 & 5 \end{bmatrix}$$
2×4	4×3	2×3

Use matrices D, E, and F to answer the following questions.

$$D = \begin{bmatrix} -1 & -4 \\ 6 & 3 \end{bmatrix} \qquad E = \begin{bmatrix} -3 & 8 \\ 1 & 5 \\ 7 & -4 \end{bmatrix} \qquad F = \begin{bmatrix} 2 & -1 & 6 \\ 4 & 7 & -3 \end{bmatrix}$$

1. Can you multiply matrices D and E to give DE or ED? Explain.

   _____

2. Can you multiply matrices D and F to give DF or FD? Explain.

   _____

3. Explain why matrix multiplication is not commutative. Give examples.

   _____

   _____

4. Can you multiply matrices E and F? Describe all possibilities. Give the dimensions of any resulting matrices.

   _____

Holt Algebra 2

Name _____ Date _____ Class_____

Practice A

Using Matrices to Transform Geometric Figures

Line segment *GH* has endpoints *G*(–7, 2) and
H(4, 6). Use line segment *GH* for Exercises 1–6.

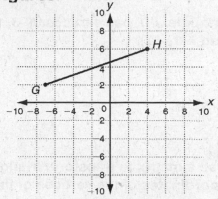

**Use a matrix to transform line segment *GH*. Find the
coordinates of the image endpoints *G'H'*.**

1. Translate 2 units right
   and 8 units down.

$$\begin{bmatrix} -7 & 4 \\ 2 & 6 \end{bmatrix} + \begin{bmatrix} 2 & 2 \\ -8 & -8 \end{bmatrix}$$

$$= \begin{bmatrix} -7+2 & 4+(\underline{}) \\ (\underline{})+(\underline{}) & (\underline{})+(\underline{}) \end{bmatrix}$$

_____

2. Translate 5 units right
   and 1 unit up.

_____

3. Translate 6 units left
   and 3 units down.

_____

4. Enlarge by a factor of 8.

$$8\begin{bmatrix} -7 & 4 \\ 2 & 6 \end{bmatrix}$$

$$= \begin{bmatrix} 8(\underline{}) & 8(\underline{}) \\ \underline{}(\underline{}) & \underline{}(\underline{}) \end{bmatrix}$$

_____

5. Enlarge by a factor of 5.

_____

6. Reduce by a factor of 0.5.

_____

**Use each matrix to reflect the given point. Write the coordinates of
the image. Tell which axis the point is reflected across.**

7. $\begin{bmatrix} -1 & 0 \\ 0 & 1 \end{bmatrix}$; (2, – 3)

$$\begin{bmatrix} -1 & 0 \\ 0 & 1 \end{bmatrix} \cdot \begin{bmatrix} 2 \\ -3 \end{bmatrix}$$

$$= \begin{bmatrix} -1(\underline{})+0(\underline{}) \\ \underline{}(\underline{})+\underline{}(\underline{}) \end{bmatrix}$$

_____

8. $\begin{bmatrix} 1 & 0 \\ 0 & -1 \end{bmatrix}$; (–10, 1)

_____

9. $\begin{bmatrix} -1 & 0 \\ 0 & 1 \end{bmatrix}$; (5, 4)

_____

Holt Algebra 2

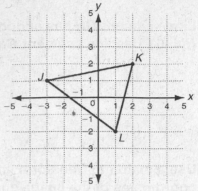

LESSON 4-3 Practice B

Using Matrices to Transform Geometric Figures

**Triangle *JKL* has vertices *J*(−3, 1), *K*(2, 2),
and *L*(1, − 2).**

**Use a matrix to transform triangle *JKL*. Find the
coordinates of the vertices of the image.**

1. Translate 5 units right, 6 units down.   2. Translate 2 units left, 4 units up.

_____   _____

3. Enlarge by a factor of 7.   4. Reduce by a factor of 0.25.

_____   _____

**Reflect or rotate triangle *ABC* with vertices
A(−2, 1), *B*(−1, 4), and *C*(2, 2). Find the coordinates
of the vertices of the image. Describe the transformation.**

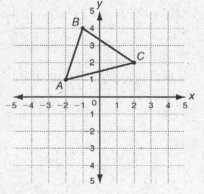

5. $\begin{bmatrix} -1 & 0 \\ 0 & 1 \end{bmatrix}$ 6. $\begin{bmatrix} 0 & 1 \\ -1 & 0 \end{bmatrix}$

_____   _____

7. $\begin{bmatrix} 0 & -1 \\ 1 & 0 \end{bmatrix}$ 8. $\begin{bmatrix} 1 & 0 \\ 0 & -1 \end{bmatrix}$

_____   _____

Solve.

9. a. Natalie drew a figure with vertices
    H(−3, −2), *O*(−3, 3), *U*(0, 5), *S*(3, 3), *E*(3, −2)
    to use as a pattern on a sweatshirt. Write a
    matrix that defines the figure. _____

   b. Natalie wants to enlarge the figure by a factor
      of 5. Describe a method she can use. _____

   c. What are the coordinates of Natalie's enlarged figure?

   *H'*_____ *O'*_____ *U'*_____ *S'*_____ *E'*_____

Holt Algebra 2

LESSON 4-3

Practice C

Using Matrices to Transform Geometric Figures

Use a matrix to transform figure *DEFGH* with
coordinates *D*(1, 3), *E*(3, 2), *F*(1, −1), *G*(−3, −2),
and *H*(−2, 2). Give the transformation matrix or
scalar and the coordinates of the image.

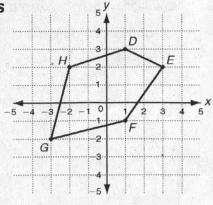

1. Translate 9 units left and 4 units up.

_____

2. Reduce by a factor of 0.1. _____

3. Rotation 90° clockwise _____

4. Rotation 90° counterclockwise _____

5. Reflection across the *x*-axis _____

6. Reflection across the *y*-axis _____

7. Reflection across $y = x$ _____

Solve.

8. Yung Li drew triangle *RST* with coordinates
   R(0, 4), *S*(0, 0), and *T*(3, 0). Then she drew
   triangle *XYZ* with coordinates *X*(0, −4),
   Y(0, 0), and *Z*(−3, 0).

   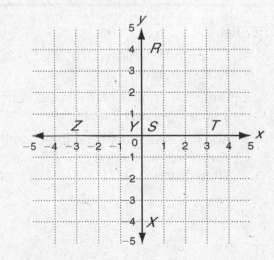

   a. Graph triangles *RST* and *XYZ*.

   b. Write a coordinate matrix to represent
      each triangle.

   c. Use the matrices to show the transformation
      of triangle *RST* into triangle *XYZ*.

_____

Holt Algebra 2

LESSON 4-3

Reteach

Using Matrices to Transform Geometric Figures

A matrix can define a polygon in the coordinate plane.

Vertices of $\triangle ABC$:

$A(4, 3)$, $B(1, -1)$, $C(-1, 2)$

Write each pair of coordinates in a column.

Matrix for $\triangle ABC$: $\begin{bmatrix} 4 & 1 & -1 \\ 3 & -1 & 2 \end{bmatrix}$ 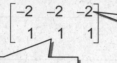 *x*-coordinates

y-coordinates

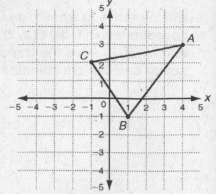

To translate $\triangle ABC$ 2 units left and 1 unit up, add a translation matrix to the matrix for $\triangle ABC$.

Translation matrix: $\begin{bmatrix} -2 & -2 & -2 \\ 1 & 1 & 1 \end{bmatrix}$ The *x*-coordinates are translated 2 units left.

The *y*-coordinates are translated 1 unit up.

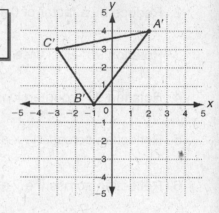

Add the matrices to find the vertices of the translated image.

$$\begin{bmatrix} 4 & 1 & -1 \\ 3 & -1 & 2 \end{bmatrix} + \begin{bmatrix} -2 & -2 & -2 \\ 1 & 1 & 1 \end{bmatrix} = \begin{bmatrix} 2 & -1 & -3 \\ 4 & 0 & 3 \end{bmatrix}$$

Translated image, $A'(2, 4)$, $B'(-1, 0)$, $C'(-3, 3)$.

Solve.

1. $\triangle DEF$ has vertices $D(0, 3)$, $E(-2, 0)$, and $F(1, -2)$.
   Write the matrix for $\triangle DEF$.

   _____

2. Write the translation matrix to translate $\triangle DEF$
   3 units right and 2 units down.

   _____

3. Add the matrices to find the coordinates of the
   vertices of the image $\triangle D'E'F'$.
   Then graph $\triangle D'E'F'$.

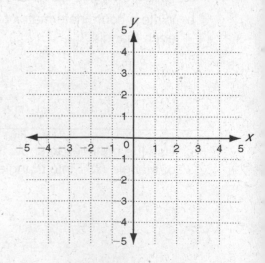

_____

_____

 Holt Algebra 2

LESSON 4-3

Reteach

Using Matrices to Transform Geometric Figures (continued)

To reflect a figure across an axis, multiply by a reflection matrix.

$\triangle QRS$ has vertices $Q(1, 2)$, $R(3, 3)$, and $S(2, -3)$.

To reflect $\triangle QRS$ across the **y-axis**, multiply

by the matrix $\begin{bmatrix} -1 & 0 \\ 0 & 1 \end{bmatrix}$.

$\begin{bmatrix} -1 & 0 \\ 0 & 1 \end{bmatrix}\begin{bmatrix} 1 & 3 & 2 \\ 2 & 3 & -3 \end{bmatrix} = \begin{bmatrix} -1 & -3 & -2 \\ 2 & 3 & -3 \end{bmatrix}$

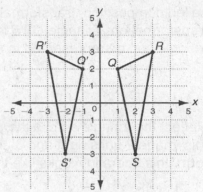

The x-coordinates are multiplied by –1.

The y-coordinates do not change.

$\triangle JKL$ has vertices $J(-3, 1)$, $K(0, 3)$, and $L(4, 2)$.

To reflect $\triangle JKL$ across the **x-axis**, multiply

by the matrix $\begin{bmatrix} 1 & 0 \\ 0 & -1 \end{bmatrix}$.

$\begin{bmatrix} 1 & 0 \\ 0 & -1 \end{bmatrix}\begin{bmatrix} -3 & 0 & 4 \\ 1 & 3 & 2 \end{bmatrix} = \begin{bmatrix} -3 & 0 & 4 \\ -1 & -3 & -2 \end{bmatrix}$

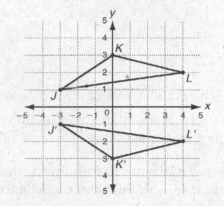

The x-coordinates do not change.

The y-coordinates are multiplied by –1.

$\triangle ABC$ has vertices $A(-2, 1)$, $B(-1, 4)$, and $C(-4, 3)$. Use a reflection matrix to solve. Then graph each reflection on the plane.

4. Reflect $\triangle ABC$ across the y-axis.

$\begin{bmatrix} -1 & 0 \\ 0 & 1 \end{bmatrix}\begin{bmatrix} -2 & -1 & -4 \\ 1 & 4 & 3 \end{bmatrix}$

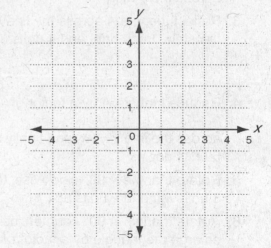

_____

_____

5. Reflect $\triangle ABC$ across the x-axis.

$\begin{bmatrix} 1 & 0 \\ 0 & -1 \end{bmatrix}\begin{bmatrix} -2 & -1 & -4 \\ 1 & 4 & 3 \end{bmatrix}$

_____

_____

Holt Algebra 2

LESSON 4-3

Challenge

Matrix Representations of Transformations

Just as functions can be combined to create a new function in a process called composition, transformations can also be composed to form a new transformation. Triangle *QRS* is shown at right. This triangle can be represented in matrix form by

$$A = \begin{bmatrix} -2 & 1 & 3 \\ -1 & 3 & -2 \end{bmatrix}.$$

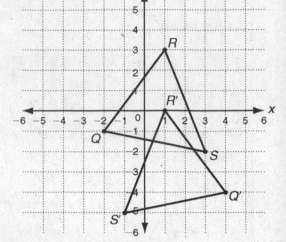

Reflect the triangle across the *y*-axis. Now translate this image 2 units right and 3 units down. In matrix form, this operation looks like the following.

$$\begin{bmatrix} -1 & 0 \\ 0 & 1 \end{bmatrix}\begin{bmatrix} -2 & 1 & 3 \\ -1 & 3 & -2 \end{bmatrix} + \begin{bmatrix} 2 & 2 & 2 \\ -3 & -3 & -3 \end{bmatrix}$$

$$= \begin{bmatrix} 4 & 1 & -1 \\ -4 & 0 & -5 \end{bmatrix}$$

The result is triangle *Q'R'S'* with vertices $(4, -4), (1, 0)$, and $(-1, 5)$

Be careful with the order of transformations. Transformations may or may not be commutative.

Use matrices to transform triangle *A* with vertices at (–2, –2), (1, 2), and (3, –1). Find the coordinates of the vertices of the final image.

1. Reflect triangle *A* across the *x*-axis and translate 4 units left and 3 units up.

   _____

2. Enlarge triangle *A* by a factor of 2, then reflect across the *y*-axis.

   _____

3. Reflect triangle *A* across the line *y* = *x*, then translate 1 unit right and 4 units up.

   _____

4. Reduce triangle *A* by a factor of $\frac{1}{2}$, reflect across the line *y* = –*x*, and finally translate 5 units down.

   _____

5. Rotate triangle *A* 90° clockwise, then translate 3 units left and 2 units up.

   _____

6. Rotate triangle *A* 90° counterclockwise, enlarge the triangle by a factor of 3, and reflect across the *y*-axis. Finally translate 8 units right and 5 units down.

   _____

Holt Algebra 2

LESSON 4-3 Problem Solving

Using Matrices to Transform Geometric Figures

Sherrill is trying to re-create the pattern of a vintage quilt she saw at an antique store. The shaded parts of the figure show the pattern of the quilt.

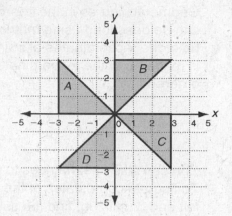

1. What directions would you give Sherrill to help her draw triangle *A* on a grid?

   _____

2. a. What transformation can Sherrill use on triangle *A* to create triangle *B*?

   _____

   b. What transformation matrix should she use to create triangle *B*? _____

3. a. What transformation can Sherrill use on triangle *A* to create triangle *C*? _____

   b. What transformation matrix should she use to create triangle *C*? _____

4. a. What transformation can Sherrill use on triangle *A* to create triangle *D*? _____

   b. What transformation matrix should she use to create triangle *D*? _____

Choose the letter for the best answer.

5. Jesse drew a rectangle represented by

   $R = \begin{bmatrix} 2 & 5 & 5 & 2 \\ -3 & -3 & -5 & -5 \end{bmatrix}$. He added the

   transformation matrix $\begin{bmatrix} 0 & 0 & 0 & 0 \\ 2 & 2 & 2 & 2 \end{bmatrix}$ to *R*

   and drew a second rectangle. Then he added the transformation matrix

   $\begin{bmatrix} -3 & -3 & -3 & -3 \\ 2 & 2 & 2 & 2 \end{bmatrix}$ to *R* and drew a third

   rectangle. Which describes the resulting figure?

   A Rectangle

   B Irregular hexagon

   C Square

   D Irregular octagon

6. Tina drew rectangle *F* with vertices at (0, 0), (0, 5), (3, 5), and (3, 0). She wants to transform *F* into a rectangle that is 6 units wide and 10 units long with the center of the rectangle located at the origin. Which list of transformations will accomplish that?

   A Rotate *F* 90° clockwise, rotate *F* 90° counterclockwise, translate *F* 5 units left and 3 units down

   B Reflect *F* over the *x*-axis, translate *F* 5 units down, rotate *F* 90° counterclockwise

   C Translate *F* 3 units left, translate *F* 3 units down, rotate *F* 90° clockwise

   D Reflect *F* over the *y*-axis, reflect *F* over the *x*-axis, rotate *F* by 180°

Holt Algebra 2

Reading Strategies

LESSON 4-3

Use Graphic Aids

Geometric figures in the coordinate plane such as triangle *ABC* can be described using matrices. The top row of matrix *T* is made up of the *x*-coordinates of points *A*, *B*, and *C*, and the bottom row is made up of the *y*-coordinates. Each column represents an ordered pair.

$$T = \begin{bmatrix} 1 & -6 & 4 \\ 5 & -4 & -3 \end{bmatrix}$$

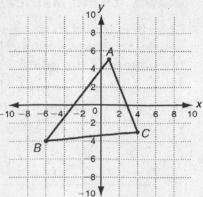

You can also use matrices to transform figures in different ways. To find the coordinates of the translation of triangle *ABC* 2 units left and 3 units up, find the sum of matrix *T* and a **translation matrix**.

$$\begin{bmatrix} 1 & -6 & 4 \\ 5 & -4 & -3 \end{bmatrix} + \begin{bmatrix} -2 & -2 & -2 \\ 3 & 3 & 3 \end{bmatrix} = T'$$

Translation matrix

In the translation matrix, the upper row contains the direction and distance that each *x*-coordinate will be translated. A positive number translates a point to the right and a negative number translates a point to the left. So −2 indicates that the point will shift 2 units left. The bottom row represents the direction and distance that each *y*-coordinate will be translated. A positive number translates a point up and a negative number translates a point down. So 3 indicates that the point will shift 3 units up.

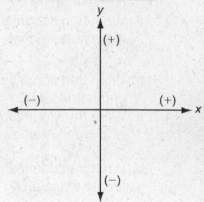

Answer each question.

1. What does the matrix *T'* describe?

_____

2. What are the coordinates of the translated triangle *A'B'C'*?

_____

3. Write a translation matrix to shift triangle *ABC* 1 unit right and 4 units down.

_____

4. What operation would you use on matrix *T* to reduce or enlarge triangle *ABC*? Explain.

_____

Name _____ Date _____ Class_____

Practice A
Determinants and Cramer's Rule

Find the determinant of each matrix.

1. $\begin{bmatrix} 6 & -2 \\ 1 & 10 \end{bmatrix}$

2. $\begin{bmatrix} 3 & -1 \\ -7 & 2 \end{bmatrix}$

3. $\begin{bmatrix} 2 & 9 \\ 1 & -3 \end{bmatrix}$

$= 6(\underline{\quad}) - (\underline{\quad})(\underline{\quad})$

_____   _____   _____

4. $\begin{bmatrix} 5 & 6 & -1 \\ -3 & 2 & 0 \\ 2 & -3 & 4 \end{bmatrix} \longrightarrow \begin{bmatrix} 5 & 6 & -1 \\ -3 & 2 & 0 \\ 2 & -3 & 4 \end{bmatrix} \begin{matrix} 5 & 6 \\ -3 & 2 \\ 2 & -3 \end{matrix} \longrightarrow \begin{matrix} 5 & 6 & -1 & 5 & 6 \\ -3 & 2 & 0 & -3 & 2 \\ 2 & -3 & 4 & 2 & -3 \end{matrix}$

_____

Use Cramer's rule to solve each system of equations.

5. $\begin{cases} x - 2y = -9 \\ 3x + y = 1 \end{cases}$

   a. Write the coefficient matrix. _____

   b. Find D, the determinant of the coefficient matrix. _____

   c. Use Cramer's rule to write the solutions for *x* and *y*.

$$x = \frac{\begin{vmatrix} c_1 & b_1 \\ c_2 & b_2 \end{vmatrix}}{D} = \frac{\begin{vmatrix} \underline{\quad} & \underline{\quad} \\ \underline{\quad} & \underline{\quad} \end{vmatrix}}{\underline{\quad}} \qquad y = \frac{\begin{vmatrix} a_1 & c_1 \\ a_2 & c_2 \end{vmatrix}}{D} = \frac{\begin{vmatrix} \underline{\quad} & \underline{\quad} \\ \underline{\quad} & \underline{\quad} \end{vmatrix}}{\underline{\quad}}$$

   d. Evaluate the determinants in the numerators
      and solve for *x* and *y*.

6. $\begin{cases} 2x + 3y = 4 \\ x - 2y = 9 \end{cases}$ _____

7. $\begin{cases} 3x + y = 5 \\ 2x - 3y = 18 \end{cases}$ _____

8. $\begin{cases} x + 5y = 11 \\ 2x - 3y = 9 \end{cases}$ _____

Holt Algebra 2

LESSON **Practice B**
4-4 *Determinants and Cramer's Rule*

Find the determinant of each matrix.

1. $\begin{bmatrix} 8 & 2 \\ 4 & -1 \end{bmatrix}$

2. $\begin{bmatrix} -6 & 3 \\ 9 & -5 \end{bmatrix}$

3. $\begin{bmatrix} -2 & 8 \\ -3 & 7 \end{bmatrix}$

_____ _____ _____

4. $\begin{bmatrix} 1 & 0 & -1 \\ 5 & -2 & 0 \\ 1 & 6 & 2 \end{bmatrix}$

5. $\begin{bmatrix} 0 & -4 & 5 \\ 2 & 4 & 3 \\ 1 & 1 & -1 \end{bmatrix}$

6. $\begin{bmatrix} -4 & 3 & 1 \\ 7 & -2 & 0 \\ 1 & -1 & 2 \end{bmatrix}$

_____ _____ _____

Use Cramer's rule to solve each system of equations.

7. $\begin{cases} 2x + 3y = -1 \\ 3x + 2y = 16 \end{cases}$

8. $\begin{cases} 4x - 3y = 9 \\ 3x + 5y = 28 \end{cases}$

9. $\begin{cases} 8x - 3y = 20 \\ 3x - 2y = 11 \end{cases}$

_____ _____ _____

10. $\begin{cases} 4y = -5x + 33 \\ 2y = 3x - 11 \end{cases}$

11. $\begin{cases} 27 + 4y = 3x \\ y = \dfrac{1}{3}x - 8 \end{cases}$

12. $\begin{cases} 7 - 5y + 4x = 0 \\ 16 - 2y - 5x = 0 \end{cases}$

_____ _____ _____

Solve.

13. On Monday, Marla babysat for 4 hours, did yard work for 2 hours,
    and earned a total of $41. On Friday, she babysat for 5 hours,
    did yard work for 3 hours, and earned a total of $55.

    a. Write a system of equations.
       Let x = Marla's hourly rate for babysitting,
       and y = her hourly rate for yard work.   _____

    b. Write the coefficient matrix. Evaluate
       its determinant.   _____

    c. Use Cramer's rule to find x and y.   _____

    d. What is Marla's hourly rate for each activity?

       _____

LESSON 4-4 Practice C

Determinants and Cramer's Rule

Find the determinant of each matrix.

1. $\begin{bmatrix} 12 & 5 \\ -14 & -3 \end{bmatrix}$

2. $\begin{bmatrix} -6 & -1 & -2 \\ 2 & 5 & 0 \\ 4 & 3 & 1 \end{bmatrix}$

3. $\begin{bmatrix} 2 & 4 & -1 \\ 0 & 3 & -3 \\ 1 & 0 & 6 \end{bmatrix}$

_____   _____   _____

Use Cramer's rule to solve each system of equations.

4. $\begin{cases} 4x - 3y = 3 \\ -3x + 2y = -1 \end{cases}$

5. $\begin{cases} 5x - 4y = 22 \\ 4x + 3y = -1 \end{cases}$

6. $\begin{cases} 6x - 7y = -11 \\ 5x + 4y = 40 \end{cases}$

_____   _____   _____

7. $\begin{cases} 8x - 5y = 61 \\ 3x + 4y = 17 \end{cases}$

8. $\begin{cases} x - 6y = 21 \\ 3x + 4y = 17 \end{cases}$

9. $\begin{cases} 5x - 6y = -2 \\ 4x - 5y = -3 \end{cases}$

_____   _____   _____

10. $\begin{cases} 3x - 2y + 4z = 0 \\ 6x + 5y - 3z = 7 \\ 5x + 3y + 6z = 11 \end{cases}$

11. $\begin{cases} 4x - 2y + z = -6 \\ 3x + 3y + 5z = -8 \\ 2x - 4y - 3z = 2 \end{cases}$

12. $\begin{cases} -2x + 6y + 3z = -10 \\ 5x - 5y - 4z = 9 \\ 3x + 2y = 0 \end{cases}$

_____   _____   _____

Solve.

13. Travis invested $20,000 in two simple interest accounts. He invested part at 4.5% interest and the rest at 3.5% interest. He earned $785 in total interest per year.

   a. Write the problem as a system of equations.   _____

   b. Find the value of the determinant of the coefficient matrix.   _____

   c. Use Cramer's rule to write the solution for the amount Travis invested at 4.5%.   _____

   d. How much did Travis invest at 4.5% interest?   _____

Holt Algebra 2

LESSON 4-4

Reteach
Determinants and Cramer's Rule

A **square matrix** has the same number of rows as columns. The **determinant** of a square

matrix is shown by $\begin{vmatrix} a & b \\ c & d \end{vmatrix}$.

To find the determinant of a 2 × 2 matrix, find the product of each diagonal, beginning at the upper left corner. Then subtract.

$\det \begin{bmatrix} a & b \\ c & d \end{bmatrix} = \begin{vmatrix} a & b \\ c & d \end{vmatrix} = ad - cb$

$\det \begin{bmatrix} 2 & 3 \\ 5 & 9 \end{bmatrix} = \begin{vmatrix} 2 & 3 \\ 5 & 9 \end{vmatrix} = 2(9) - 5(3) = 18 - 15 = 3$

> Vertical brackets indicate a determinant.

Find the determinant of each matrix.

1. $\det \begin{bmatrix} -1 & 2 \\ -5 & 4 \end{bmatrix} = \begin{vmatrix} -1 & 2 \\ -5 & 4 \end{vmatrix} = -1(4) - (-5)(2) =$ _____

2. $\det \begin{bmatrix} \dfrac{3}{2} & -\dfrac{1}{4} \\ \dfrac{1}{2} & \dfrac{1}{4} \end{bmatrix} = \begin{vmatrix} \dfrac{3}{2} & -\dfrac{1}{4} \\ \dfrac{1}{2} & \dfrac{1}{4} \end{vmatrix} = \dfrac{3}{2}\left(\dfrac{1}{4}\right) - \left(\dfrac{1}{2}\right)\left(-\dfrac{1}{4}\right) =$ _____

3. $\det \begin{bmatrix} -3 & -4 \\ -1 & -6 \end{bmatrix} = \begin{vmatrix} -3 & -4 \\ -1 & -6 \end{vmatrix} = -3(\text{\_\_\_\_}) - (-1)(\text{\_\_\_\_}) =$ _____

4. $\det \begin{bmatrix} -2.4 & 0.5 \\ 1.2 & 2 \end{bmatrix} = \begin{vmatrix} -2.4 & 0.5 \\ 1.2 & 2 \end{vmatrix} =$ _____

5. $\det \begin{bmatrix} \dfrac{1}{6} & 9 \\ \dfrac{2}{3} & -12 \end{bmatrix} = \begin{vmatrix} \dfrac{1}{6} & 9 \\ \dfrac{2}{3} & -12 \end{vmatrix} =$ _____

6. $\det \begin{bmatrix} 8 & \dfrac{2}{5} \\ -15 & \dfrac{3}{4} \end{bmatrix} = \begin{vmatrix} 8 & \dfrac{2}{5} \\ -15 & \dfrac{3}{4} \end{vmatrix} =$ _____

Holt Algebra 2

LESSON	**Reteach**
4-4	***Determinants and Cramer's Rule*** (continued)

Use **Cramer's rule** to solve a system of linear equations. $\begin{cases} x + y = 2 \\ y + 7 = 2x \end{cases}$

Step 1 Write the equations in standard form, $ax + by = c$.

$$x + y = 2$$
$$2x - y = 7$$

Step 2 Write the coefficient matrix of the system of equations. Then find the determinant of the coefficient matrix.

$$\begin{bmatrix} a_1 & b_1 \\ a_2 & b_2 \end{bmatrix} = \begin{bmatrix} 1 & 1 \\ 2 & -1 \end{bmatrix} \quad \boxed{\text{Coefficient matrix}}$$

$$D = \begin{vmatrix} a_1 & b_1 \\ a_2 & b_2 \end{vmatrix} = \begin{vmatrix} 1 & 1 \\ 2 & -1 \end{vmatrix} = 1(-1) - 2(1) = -3 \quad \boxed{\text{Determinant}}$$

Step 3 Solve for x and y using Cramer's rule. Remember to divide by the determinant.

The coefficients of x in the coefficient matrix are replaced by the constant terms.

$$x = \frac{\begin{vmatrix} c_1 & b_1 \\ c_2 & b_2 \end{vmatrix}}{D} = \frac{\begin{vmatrix} 2 & 1 \\ 7 & -1 \end{vmatrix}}{-3} = \frac{-2 - 7}{-3} = \frac{-9}{-3} = 3$$

The coefficients of y in the coefficient matrix are replaced by the constant terms.

$$y = \frac{\begin{vmatrix} a_1 & c_1 \\ a_2 & c_2 \end{vmatrix}}{D} = \frac{\begin{vmatrix} 1 & 2 \\ 2 & 7 \end{vmatrix}}{-3} = \frac{7 - 4}{-3} = \frac{3}{-3} = -1$$

The solution is $(3, -1)$.

Use Cramer's rule to solve each system of equations.

7. $\begin{cases} 2x + y = -1 \\ 4x + y = -5 \end{cases}$

$$D = \begin{vmatrix} 2 & 1 \\ 4 & 1 \end{vmatrix} = \underline{\hspace{3cm}}$$

$$x = \frac{\begin{vmatrix} -1 & 1 \\ -5 & 1 \end{vmatrix}}{D} = \underline{\hspace{3cm}}$$

$$y = \frac{\begin{vmatrix} 2 & -1 \\ 4 & -5 \end{vmatrix}}{D} = \underline{\hspace{3cm}}$$

8. $\begin{cases} x - y = 1 \\ 3x - 2y = 4 \end{cases}$

$$D = \underline{\hspace{3cm}}$$

$$x = \underline{\hspace{3cm}}$$

$$y = \underline{\hspace{3cm}}$$

9. $\begin{cases} y - x = 3 \\ 2x - 2 = y \end{cases}$

$$D = \underline{\hspace{3cm}}$$

$$x = \underline{\hspace{3cm}}$$

$$y = \underline{\hspace{3cm}}$$

10. $\begin{cases} 3y = 4x + 7 \\ 9 - 6x = 2y \end{cases}$

$$x = \underline{\hspace{3cm}}$$

$$y = \underline{\hspace{3cm}}$$

Holt Algebra 2

LESSON 4-4	# Challenge

Determinant Variations with Matrix Operations

What happens to the determinant of a matrix as the entries in the matrix are changed? Certain changes affect the value of the determinant and others do not. Those operations that do not change the determinant are called invariant operations. The determinant of matrix R is -36. Interchange the first and second rows to get matrix S.

$$R = \begin{bmatrix} 1 & 0 & 4 \\ -3 & 2 & 5 \\ 0 & 2 & -1 \end{bmatrix} \qquad S = \begin{bmatrix} -3 & 2 & 5 \\ 1 & 0 & 4 \\ 0 & 2 & -1 \end{bmatrix}$$

1. a. Calculate the determinant of matrix S. _____

    b. Interchange the second and third rows of matrix R. Find the determinant of the new matrix. How do they compare? _____

    c. Make a conjecture about how the value of a matrix changes if you interchange two rows of the matrix. _____

2. a. Multiply the first row of matrix R by 3. Now find the new determinant. How does this value compare to the original determinant? _____

    b. Try this with another 3×3 matrix. Then make a conjecture about how the determinant changes when a row is multiplied by a constant.

    _____

3. a. Multiply matrix R by 3 to get matrix T. Find the determinant of matrix T. _____

    b. Now create a 2×2 matrix and find its determinant. Multiply the matrix by 4 and find the determinant again. Write a conjecture about how the determinant of a matrix changes when the matrix is multiplied by a constant.

    _____

4. a. Use matrix R and add twice the first row to the second row. This becomes the new second row. Write the new matrix U. Find its determinant. _____

    b. Try this with another 3×3 matrix. What conjecture can you make about how this operation affects the determinant?

    _____

Name _____ Date _____ Class_____

Problem Solving
Determinants and Cramer's Rule

As Kristin prepares for a triathlon, she makes a chart of her exercise time, along with the calories burned each day. Part of her chart is shown in the table below. How many calories per hour does she burn for each activity?

Triathlon Training Record			
Day	Swimming (h)	Cycling (h)	Running (h)	Calories Burned
Friday	1.5	2.0	0.5	2450
Saturday	2.5	3.0	1.5	4310
Sunday	2.0	1.5	1.6	3150

1. Write a system of equations that relates Kristin's exercise time to the number of calories burned each day. Use *s*, *c*, and *r* for the calories burned per hour for the three activities.

_____

2. Write the coefficient matrix for the system of equations.

_____

3. What is the value, *D*, for the determinant of the coefficient matrix?

_____

4. Use Cramer's rule to solve this system of equations. Give the values for *s*, *c*, and *r*.

_____

Choose the letter for the best answer.

5. Ty has a bag of pennies, nickels, and dimes. He has 10 times as many pennies as dimes. He has a total of 52 coins and twice as many nickels as dimes. Which coefficient matrix could you use to solve this problem?

A $\begin{bmatrix} 1 & 1 & 1 \\ 1 & 0 & -10 \\ 0 & 1 & -2 \end{bmatrix}$ C $\begin{bmatrix} 1 & 1 & 1 \\ 1 & 0 & -10 \\ 0 & -1 & 2 \end{bmatrix}$

B $\begin{bmatrix} 1 & 1 & 1 \\ 10 & 0 & -1 \\ 0 & 2 & -1 \end{bmatrix}$ D $\begin{bmatrix} 1 & 1 & 1 \\ 10 & 0 & -1 \\ 0 & -2 & 1 \end{bmatrix}$

6. Phyllis collects silver dollars and Kennedy half-dollars. She has 5 times as many half-dollars as dollar coins. She has a total of 192 coins. Which solution could you use to find the number of silver dollars Phyllis has?

A $\dfrac{\begin{vmatrix} 192 & 1 \\ 0 & -5 \end{vmatrix}}{-6}$ C $\dfrac{\begin{vmatrix} 1 & 192 \\ -5 & 0 \end{vmatrix}}{-6}$

B $\dfrac{\begin{vmatrix} 1 & 192 \\ 1 & 0 \end{vmatrix}}{-6}$ D $\dfrac{\begin{vmatrix} 192 & 1 \\ 0 & 1 \end{vmatrix}}{-6}$

Holt Algebra 2

LESSON 4-4

Reading Strategies
Analyze Information

Every square matrix has a determinant. The determinant can be positive, negative, or 0. The determinant of a 2×2 matrix is the difference of the product of the diagonals. Always subtract from the diagonal that starts in the upper left of the matrix.

Matrix	Determinant
$A = \begin{bmatrix} a & b \\ c & d \end{bmatrix}$	$\begin{vmatrix} a & b \\ c & d \end{vmatrix} = ad - cb$
$J = \begin{bmatrix} 4 & -1 \\ -3 & 6 \end{bmatrix}$	$\begin{vmatrix} 4 & -1 \\ -3 & 6 \end{vmatrix} = 4(6) - (-3)(-1) = 24 - 3 = 21$
$K = \begin{bmatrix} -2 & 7 \\ 4 & 9 \end{bmatrix}$	$\begin{vmatrix} -2 & 7 \\ 4 & 9 \end{vmatrix} = -2(9) - 4(7) = -18 - 28 = -46$
$L = \begin{bmatrix} 8 & 4 \\ 16 & 8 \end{bmatrix}$	$\begin{vmatrix} 8 & 4 \\ 16 & 8 \end{vmatrix} = 8(8) - 16(4) = 64 - 64 = 0$

Answer each question.

1. Complete so that each matrix has a positive determinant.

   a. $\begin{bmatrix} 6 & 9 \\ 5 & \_\_ \end{bmatrix}$ b. $\begin{bmatrix} \_\_ & -5 \\ \_\_ & -8 \end{bmatrix}$

2. Complete so that each matrix has a negative determinant.

   a. $\begin{bmatrix} -4 & 3 \\ \_\_ & 7 \end{bmatrix}$ b. $\begin{bmatrix} \frac{1}{4} & -\frac{1}{2} \\ \_\_ & \_\_ \end{bmatrix}$

3. Complete so that each matrix has a determinant of 0.

   a. $\begin{bmatrix} -5 & 7 \\ \_\_ & \_\_ \end{bmatrix}$ b. $\begin{bmatrix} \_\_ & \_\_ \\ \_\_ & -3 \end{bmatrix}$

4. Complete so that each matrix has a determinant of -1.

   a. $\begin{bmatrix} 3 & \_\_ \\ -4 & \_\_ \end{bmatrix}$ b. $\begin{bmatrix} 5 & \_\_ \\ \_\_ & -9 \end{bmatrix}$

5. Matrix W has a determinant of 0. What do you know about the dimensions and the entries of matrix W?

_____

Holt Algebra 2

LESSON 4-5 **Practice A**

Matrix Inverses and Solving Systems

Multiply the matrices two ways to determine if they are inverses.

1. $\begin{bmatrix} 1 & -1 \\ -3 & 2 \end{bmatrix}$ and $\begin{bmatrix} -2 & -1 \\ -3 & -1 \end{bmatrix}$

2. $\begin{bmatrix} 6 & 5 \\ -2 & -2 \end{bmatrix}$ and $\begin{bmatrix} 1 & 2.5 \\ -1 & -3 \end{bmatrix}$

$\begin{bmatrix} 1 & -1 \\ -3 & 2 \end{bmatrix}\begin{bmatrix} -2 & -1 \\ -3 & -1 \end{bmatrix} = \begin{bmatrix} 1 & 0 \\ 0 & 1 \end{bmatrix}$

$\begin{bmatrix} -2 & -1 \\ -3 & -1 \end{bmatrix}\begin{bmatrix} 1 & -1 \\ -3 & 2 \end{bmatrix} = \begin{bmatrix} \underline{\quad} & \underline{\quad} \\ \underline{\quad} & \underline{\quad} \end{bmatrix}$

_____   _____

Find the inverse of the matrix, if it is defined. First find the determinant, and then find the inverse.

3. $\begin{bmatrix} 2 & 5 \\ 2 & 4 \end{bmatrix}$

4. $\begin{bmatrix} 1 & 3 \\ 4 & 2 \end{bmatrix}$

_____   _____

5. $\begin{bmatrix} -3 & 1 \\ 2 & 0 \end{bmatrix}$

6. $\begin{bmatrix} 3 & 1 \\ 1 & -1 \end{bmatrix}$

_____   _____

Write the matrix equation $AX = B$ for each system. Then solve.

7. $\begin{cases} 5x + 3y = -12 \\ 2x + 2y = -4 \end{cases}$

   a. Matrix equation   b. A^{-1} c. Solve for x and y.

_____   _____   _____

8. $\begin{cases} 3x - 2y = 4 \\ 2x - 3y = 11 \end{cases}$ _____

9. $\begin{cases} 3x + y = 3 \\ 2x + 3y = 9 \end{cases}$ _____

10. $\begin{cases} 2x + 3y = -1 \\ x + 4y = -8 \end{cases}$ _____

Practice B
Matrix Inverses and Solving Systems

Determine whether the given matrices are inverses.

1. $\begin{bmatrix} -5 & 0 \\ 4 & 1 \end{bmatrix}\begin{bmatrix} -0.2 & 0 \\ 0.8 & 1 \end{bmatrix}$

_____

2. $\begin{bmatrix} 1 & -4 \\ -2 & 3 \end{bmatrix}\begin{bmatrix} -0.6 & -0.8 \\ -0.4 & -0.2 \end{bmatrix}$

_____

3. $\begin{bmatrix} 2 & -3 \\ -1 & 1 \end{bmatrix}\begin{bmatrix} -1 & -3 \\ -1 & -2 \end{bmatrix}$

_____

Find the inverse of the matrix, if it is defined.

4. $\begin{bmatrix} 1 & 0 \\ 4 & -1 \end{bmatrix}$

5. $\begin{bmatrix} 5 & 2 \\ 7 & 3 \end{bmatrix}$

6. $\begin{bmatrix} 8 & 4 \\ -5 & -3 \end{bmatrix}$

_____   _____   _____

7. $\begin{bmatrix} 3 & -3 \\ -2 & 1 \end{bmatrix}$

8. $\begin{bmatrix} -4 & 4 \\ 5 & -4 \end{bmatrix}$

9. $\begin{bmatrix} 6 & -6 \\ 1 & -1 \end{bmatrix}$

_____   _____   _____

Write the matrix equation for the system, and solve.

10. $\begin{cases} 3x + 2y = -5 \\ 4x + 3y = -9 \end{cases}$

11. $\begin{cases} -6x + 4y = 8 \\ 5x - 3y = -5 \end{cases}$

_____   _____

12. $\begin{cases} 4x + 5y = 0 \\ 5x + 3y = 13 \end{cases}$

13. $\begin{cases} 5x - 3y = 8 \\ 6x - 5y = 4 \end{cases}$

_____   _____

Solve.

14. Keith paid $39 for 3 pounds of pistachios and 2 pounds of cashews.
    Tracey paid $23 for 2 pounds of pistachios and 1 pound of cashews.

   a. Write a system of equations. Let x = the cost
      of a pound of pistachios, and y = the cost of a
      pound of cashews.   _____

   b. Write the matrix equation and solve.   _____

Holt Algebra 2

LESSON 4-5

Practice C
Matrix Inverses and Solving Systems

Find the inverse of the coefficient matrix for the system and solve.

1. $\begin{cases} 4x + 7y = 11 \\ 2x + 5y = 1 \end{cases}$

2. $\begin{cases} 21x - 5y = 5 \\ 13x - 3y = 3 \end{cases}$

_____

3. $\begin{cases} 2x - 7y = -4 \\ -3x + 11y = 6 \end{cases}$

4. $\begin{cases} 3x + 8y = 10 \\ 2x + 7y = 5 \end{cases}$

_____

5. $\begin{cases} 4x + 3y = 3 \\ 9x + 5y = -2 \end{cases}$

6. $\begin{cases} 2x + 7y = -5 \\ 3x + 5y = 9 \end{cases}$

_____

Use the integers 3, –4, –6, and 8.

7. Create a matrix whose inverse is undefined.

8. Create a matrix whose inverse is defined.

_____

Solve.

9. Matrix $A = \begin{bmatrix} e & f \\ g & h \end{bmatrix}$. The determinant of A is –2 and

A^{-1} is $\begin{bmatrix} \dfrac{5}{2} & 4 \\ -\dfrac{1}{2} & -1 \end{bmatrix}$. Find e, f, g, and h.

_____

10. Frank and Juanita sold tickets for the charity fund-raiser. They sold both single tickets and 5-ticket books. Write the appropriate matrix equation and find the price of a single ticket and a book of tickets.

Fund-Raiser Tickets Sold			
	Single	**Book**	**Total Sales**
Frank	12	4	70
Juanita	8	3	50

_____

Holt Algebra 2

Reteach
Matrix Inverses and Solving Systems

The identity matrix of a 2×2 matrix is $\begin{bmatrix} 1 & 0 \\ 0 & 1 \end{bmatrix}$. If a square matrix A has an inverse A^{-1}, then

the product of A and A^{-1} is the identity matrix.

Use the following rule to find the **inverse of a 2×2 matrix.**

The inverse of $A = \begin{bmatrix} a & b \\ c & d \end{bmatrix}$ is $A^{-1} = \dfrac{1}{\det A} \begin{bmatrix} d & -b \\ -c & a \end{bmatrix}$.

> Think: **"Switch ops."** Switch a and d and take the **opposites** of b and c.

> If the determinant is 0, the matrix has no inverse.

To find the inverse of $A = \begin{bmatrix} 2 & 1 \\ 4 & 1 \end{bmatrix}$, first find the determinant.

$\det \begin{bmatrix} 2 & 1 \\ 4 & 1 \end{bmatrix} = \begin{vmatrix} 2 & 1 \\ 4 & 1 \end{vmatrix} = 2 - 4 = -2$

> The determinant exists, so the matrix has an inverse.

Then **switch ops** and multiply by $-\dfrac{1}{2}$.

$A^{-1} = -\dfrac{1}{2} \begin{bmatrix} 1 & -1 \\ -4 & 2 \end{bmatrix} = \begin{bmatrix} -\dfrac{1}{2}(1) & -\dfrac{1}{2}(-1) \\ -\dfrac{1}{2}(-4) & -\dfrac{1}{2}(2) \end{bmatrix} = \begin{bmatrix} -\dfrac{1}{2} & \dfrac{1}{2} \\ 2 & -1 \end{bmatrix}$

Find the inverse of each matrix.

1. $A = \begin{bmatrix} 2 & 7 \\ -1 & -2 \end{bmatrix}$

2. $A = \begin{bmatrix} 6 & 1 \\ 8 & 2 \end{bmatrix}$

$\det \begin{bmatrix} 2 & 7 \\ -1 & -2 \end{bmatrix} = \begin{vmatrix} 2 & 7 \\ -1 & -2 \end{vmatrix} =$ _____

$\dfrac{1}{\det A} =$ _____

$A^{-1} = $ ___ $\begin{bmatrix} -2 & -7 \\ 1 & 2 \end{bmatrix} =$ _____

$\det \begin{bmatrix} 6 & 1 \\ 8 & 2 \end{bmatrix} =$_____

$\dfrac{1}{\det A} =$_____

$A^{-1} =$ _____

3. $A = \begin{bmatrix} -4 & 6 \\ 1 & -2 \end{bmatrix}$ $\det A =$ _____

$A^{-1} =$ _____

Holt Algebra 2

LESSON 4-5

Reteach

Matrix Inverses and Solving Systems *(continued)*

The inverse of a matrix can be used to solve a system of equations.

Solve $\begin{cases} 2x + y = -1 \\ 4x + y = -5 \end{cases}$.

Step 1 Write the matrix equation. $\quad A \quad X = B$

Coefficient matrix $\qquad$ Constant matrix $\qquad$ Variable matrix

$$\begin{bmatrix} 2 & 1 \\ 4 & 1 \end{bmatrix} \begin{bmatrix} x \\ y \end{bmatrix} = \begin{bmatrix} -1 \\ -5 \end{bmatrix}$$

Step 2 Find the determinant of the coefficient matrix A.

$$\det \begin{bmatrix} 2 & 1 \\ 4 & 1 \end{bmatrix} = \begin{vmatrix} 2 & 1 \\ 4 & 1 \end{vmatrix} = 2 - 4 = -2$$

Step 3 Find A^{-1}.

$$A^{-1} = -\frac{1}{2}\begin{bmatrix} 1 & -1 \\ -4 & 2 \end{bmatrix} = \begin{bmatrix} -\frac{1}{2} & \frac{1}{2} \\ 2 & -1 \end{bmatrix}$$

Step 4 Solve $AX = B$ by multiplying both sides by A^{-1}.

$A^{-1}AX = A^{-1}B$

$A^{-1}A = 1$, so $X = A^{-1}B$

$$\begin{bmatrix} x \\ y \end{bmatrix} = \begin{bmatrix} -\frac{1}{2} & \frac{1}{2} \\ 2 & -1 \end{bmatrix}\begin{bmatrix} -1 \\ -5 \end{bmatrix} = \begin{bmatrix} -\frac{1}{2}(-1) + \frac{1}{2}(-5) \\ 2(-1) + (-1)(-5) \end{bmatrix} = \begin{bmatrix} \frac{1}{2} - \frac{5}{2} \\ -2 + 5 \end{bmatrix} = \begin{bmatrix} -2 \\ 3 \end{bmatrix}$$

The solution is (–2, 3).

Write each matrix equation, and solve using the inverse of the matrix.

4. $\begin{cases} x + y = 2 \\ x + 2y = 6 \end{cases}$

a. Write the matrix equation $AX = B$.

_____

b. Find the determinant. _____

c. $A^{-1} =$

_____

d. Solve for x and y.

_____

5. $\begin{cases} 2x + 3y = -1 \\ x + 2y = 1 \end{cases}$

a. Write the matrix equation $AX = B$.

_____

b. Find the determinant._____

c. $A^{-1} =$

_____

d. Solve for x and y.

_____

Name _____ Date _____ Class _____

Challenge
Using Systems of Equations to Determine an Inverse

You know how to use an inverse matrix to solve a system of equations. You can also use systems of equations to find the inverse of a matrix. So, when the inverse matrix exists, it is possible to solve a system of equations with matrices without using a calculator.

Consider the 2 × 2 matrix shown at right and the general form of its inverse.

$$A = \begin{bmatrix} 3 & -3 \\ -6 & 7 \end{bmatrix} \quad A^{-1} = \begin{bmatrix} a & b \\ c & d \end{bmatrix}$$

1. a. Use the definition of inverse to write an equation involving matrix A and the general form of A^{-1}. _____

   b. Use the equation you wrote in part *a* and matrix multiplication to write four equations, two of which involve a and c and two of which involve b and d. _____

   c. Solve the two systems of equations to determine a, b, c, d. Write A^{-1}. _____

   d. Verify your result by using matrix multiplication.

Use the above method to find the inverse of the matrix, if it is defined.

2. $\begin{bmatrix} -6 & -2 \\ 11 & -3 \end{bmatrix}$

3. $\begin{bmatrix} -6 & 9 \\ -4 & 6 \end{bmatrix}$

4. $\begin{bmatrix} 2 & 1 & 3 \\ 1 & 1 & 2 \\ 1 & 4 & 6 \end{bmatrix}$

Solve the sysem of equations by using matrices. Check your results in the given equations.

5. $\begin{cases} 2x - y = -2 \\ 4x + y = 5 \end{cases}$

6. $\begin{cases} x + y + z = -2 \\ 3x + 3y + z = -18 \\ 4x + 2y + z = -20 \end{cases}$

7. $\begin{cases} x + y + z + w = 6 \\ 2x - y + 3z - w = 2 \\ 3x + 2y - z + w = 5 \\ y - 5z - w = -8 \end{cases}$

Holt Algebra 2

LESSON 4-5 Problem Solving

Matrix Inverses and Solving Systems

For his job at a local restaurant, Alex researches and compares prices. He buys three packaged salad lunches from a competitor. He wants to find the price of one ounce of each kind of salad.

Salad Medley	Tasty Threesome	Sampler Salad Plate
Rainbow pasta: 3 oz	Tender tuna: 2 oz	Fruit cup: 2 oz
Tasty tuna: 3 oz	Mixed pasta: 1 oz	Tuna mix: 2 oz
Fresh fruit: 1 oz	Seasonal fruit: 3 oz	Pasta medley: 2 oz
$5.52	$4.59	$4.68

1. Write a system of equations, using p, t, and f as the cost per ounce of each kind of salad. _____

2. Set up the matrix equation, $AX = B$. _____

3. Find the determinant of matrix A.

   _____

4. Find A^{-1}.

   _____

5. Solve $X = A^{-1} B$ for X.

6. What is the price per ounce for each kind of salad? _____

_____

A pharmacist is preparing saline solutions. She has a 2% saline solution and a 12% saline solution. How much of each solution should she mix to prepare 10 liters of a 10% solution? Choose the letter for the best answer.

7. Which represents the matrix equation for this problem?

   A $\begin{bmatrix} 1 & 1 \\ 0.02 & 0.12 \end{bmatrix}\begin{bmatrix} x \\ y \end{bmatrix} = \begin{bmatrix} 1 \\ 10 \end{bmatrix}$

   B $\begin{bmatrix} 1 & 1 \\ 0.2 & 0.12 \end{bmatrix}\begin{bmatrix} x \\ y \end{bmatrix} = \begin{bmatrix} 10 \\ 1 \end{bmatrix}$

   C $\begin{bmatrix} 1 & 1 \\ 0.12 & 0.02 \end{bmatrix}\begin{bmatrix} x \\ y \end{bmatrix} = \begin{bmatrix} 1 \\ 10 \end{bmatrix}$

   D $\begin{bmatrix} 1 & 1 \\ 0.02 & 0.12 \end{bmatrix}\begin{bmatrix} x \\ y \end{bmatrix} = \begin{bmatrix} 10 \\ 1 \end{bmatrix}$

8. Which matrix is the inverse of the coefficient matrix for this problem?

   A $\begin{bmatrix} 1 & 1.2 \\ 10 & 0.2 \end{bmatrix}$

   B $\begin{bmatrix} 1.2 & -10 \\ -0.2 & 10 \end{bmatrix}$

   C $\begin{bmatrix} -1.2 & 1 \\ 0.2 & -1 \end{bmatrix}$

   D $\begin{bmatrix} 1.2 & -10 \\ -0.2 & 1 \end{bmatrix}$

Reading Strategies

LESSON
4-5

Use a Graphic Organizer

Definition	Facts
The identity matrix, *I* is $\begin{bmatrix} 1 & 0 \\ 0 & 1 \end{bmatrix}$. If the product of two matrices is the identity matrix, then they are said to be inverses. The inverse of matrix *A* is written as A^{-1}. $AA^{-1} = A^{-1}A = I$	$A = \begin{bmatrix} a & b \\ c & d \end{bmatrix}$ $A^{-1} = \dfrac{1}{\det A}\begin{bmatrix} d & -b \\ -c & a \end{bmatrix}$
Example $G = \begin{bmatrix} 1 & -1 \\ 4 & -6 \end{bmatrix}$ $G^{-1} = -\dfrac{1}{2}\begin{bmatrix} -6 & 1 \\ -4 & 1 \end{bmatrix} = \begin{bmatrix} 3 & -\dfrac{1}{2} \\ 2 & -\dfrac{1}{2} \end{bmatrix}$ $GG^{-1} = \begin{bmatrix} 1 & -1 \\ 4 & -6 \end{bmatrix}\begin{bmatrix} 3 & -\dfrac{1}{2} \\ 2 & -\dfrac{1}{2} \end{bmatrix} = \begin{bmatrix} 1 & 0 \\ 0 & 1 \end{bmatrix}$	**Useful Hints** The identity matrix has 1 in every position on the main diagonal and 0 in every other position. Not all square matrices have inverses. A square matrix can have an inverse only if its determinant is NOT 0.

Use the information in the graphic organizer to answer the following questions.

1. Matrix $H = \begin{bmatrix} -3 & 5 \\ -3 & 4 \end{bmatrix}$.

    a. Does matrix *H* have an inverse? How do you know?

    _____

    b. Describe the resulting matrix if you multiplied matrix *H* by its inverse.

    _____

2. Explain why a matrix has no inverse if the determinant is 0.

    _____

3. Matrix *F* has an inverse, F^{-1}. What characteristics of matrix *F* can you determine?

    _____

Holt Algebra 2

LESSON 4-6

Practice A

Row Operations and Augmented Matrices

Write the augmented matrix for each system of equations.

1. $\begin{cases} 3x + 2y = 2 \\ x = 4y + 24 \end{cases}$

   a. Write each equation in $Ax + By = C$ form. _____

   b. Use the coefficients and constants to write
      the augmented matrix. _____

2. $\begin{cases} 2x + 5y = 1 \\ x - y = 4 \end{cases}$

3. $\begin{cases} 5x = 2y \\ 3x - 4y = 14 \end{cases}$

4. $\begin{cases} 4x = 9y + 1 \\ y = 2x + 1 \end{cases}$

_____ _____ _____

Use row reduction on each matrix to find the reduced row-echelon form.

5. $\begin{bmatrix} 3 & 2 & 2 \\ 1 & -4 & 24 \end{bmatrix}$

   a. Multiply row 1 by 2.

   b. Add rows 1 and 2.
      Write the sum in row 1.

   c. Divide row 1 by 7. Write
      the quotient in row 1.

_____ _____ _____

   d. Subtract row 2 from
      row 1. Write the result
      in row 2.

   e. Divide row 2 by 4. Write
      the result in row 2.

   f. Solve for x and y.

_____ _____ _____

6. $\begin{bmatrix} 2 & 5 & 1 \\ 1 & -1 & 4 \end{bmatrix}$

7. $\begin{bmatrix} 5 & -2 & 0 \\ 3 & -4 & 14 \end{bmatrix}$

8. $\begin{bmatrix} 4 & -9 & 1 \\ -2 & 1 & -11 \end{bmatrix}$

_____ _____ _____

Holt Algebra 2

LESSON **Practice B**
4-6   ***Row Operations and Augmented Matrices***

Write the augmented matrix for each system of equations.

1. $\begin{cases} 2x + 1 = y \\ x + y + z = 1 \\ 4y + 5z = 3 \end{cases}$ 2. $\begin{cases} 3x = 2y + 4 \\ x - y = 3z \\ 2y + 8z = x \end{cases}$ 3. $\begin{cases} x + z = 1 \\ 3x - 5y = 12 \\ 2y - 3z = 9 \end{cases}$

_____   _____   _____

Write the augmented matrix, and use row reduction to solve.

4. $\begin{cases} 4x + 3y = -11 \\ 2x - 3y = 17 \end{cases}$ 5. $\begin{cases} 3x + 7y = -1 \\ 6x + 11y = 10 \end{cases}$

_____   _____

6. $\begin{cases} 2x = 3y - 1 \\ 5x - 12y = 2 \end{cases}$ 7. $\begin{cases} x + 6y = 0 \\ 2x + 9y = -3 \end{cases}$

_____   _____

Solve.

8. Dimitri has $4.95 in dimes and quarters. He has 3 fewer dimes than quarters.

   a. Write a system of equations.
      Let d = the number of dimes and
      q = the number of quarters.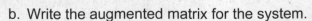

   b. Write the augmented matrix for the system.   _____

   c. How many of each coin does Dimitri have?   _____

9. Clara has a bag of 60 coins with a value of $2.00.
   The coins are all pennies and nickels. How many
   of each coin are in the bag?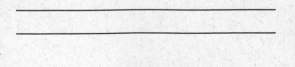

LESSON
4-6

Practice C

Row Operations and Augmented Matrices

Write the augmented matrix, and use row reduction to solve.

1. $\begin{cases} 5x - 3y = 14 \\ 3x + 4y = -9 \end{cases}$

2. $\begin{cases} 9x + 11y + 19 = 0 \\ 15x + 22y + 17 = 0 \end{cases}$

_____

3. $\begin{cases} 7x + 2y + 4 = 0 \\ 5x - 3y = 37 \end{cases}$

4. $\begin{cases} 6x + 5 = 5y \\ 3y + 19 = 8x \end{cases}$

_____

5. $\begin{cases} x + z + 1 = y \\ 4z = y \\ 2x = z + 8 \end{cases}$

6. $\begin{cases} 3y + z = -1 \\ 5y + 2z = 3x \\ x + y = 0 \end{cases}$

_____

Solve.

7. Jonah is buying a cell phone. He has a choice of 2 plans. The monthly base price of each plan includes 500 minutes. There is a charge for each additional minute over 500 minutes.

   a. For what number of minutes is the total monthly cost the same for each plan?

Cell Phone Plan Costs per Month		
	Base Price (500 min)	Additional (per min)
Plan A	$40	$0.50
Plan B	$75	$0.25

_____

   b. Jonah expects to use between 11 and 12 hours of cell phone time each month. Which plan is the better buy for him?

8. Andrea has $2.10 in nickels, dimes, and quarters. She has a total of 18 coins with as many nickels as she has dimes and quarters combined. How many dimes does Andrea have?

_____

Holt Algebra 2

LESSON 4-6

Reteach

Row Operations and Augmented Matrices

To write the **augmented matrix** of a system of linear equations, use the coefficients and the constant terms of the system.

Write linear systems in *two variables* in the form $Ax + By = C$ to write the augmented matrix.

System of Linear Equations   **Augmented Matrix**

$$\begin{cases} x + 6 = 4y \\ y - 3 = 2x \end{cases} \rightarrow \begin{array}{l} x - 4y = -6 \\ 2x - y = -3 \end{array}$$ $$\left[\begin{array}{cc|c} 1 & -4 & -6 \\ 2 & -1 & -3 \end{array}\right]$$

> The line separates the coefficients from the constants.

Write linear systems in *three variables* in the form $Ax + By + Cz = D$ to write the augmented matrix.

System of Linear Equations   **Augmented Matrix**

$$\begin{cases} x + y = z + 5 \\ 2z - x = 3 \\ y = 4z - 1 \end{cases} \rightarrow \begin{array}{l} x + y - z = 5 \\ x + 0y + 2z = 3 \\ 0x + y - 4z = -1 \end{array}$$ $$\left[\begin{array}{ccc|c} 1 & 1 & -1 & 5 \\ -1 & 0 & 2 & 3 \\ 0 & 1 & -4 & -1 \end{array}\right]$$

Write the augmented matrix for the system of equations.

1. $$\begin{cases} 5x - 1 = 7y \\ y - 3 = 2x \end{cases} \rightarrow \begin{array}{l} 5x - 7y = 1 \\ 2x - y = -3 \end{array}$$ 2. $$\begin{cases} 8x = y - 9 \\ -x - 7 = 4y \end{cases}$$

_____

3. $$\begin{cases} x + y = z + 5 \\ 2z - x = 3 \\ y = 4z - 1 \end{cases} \rightarrow \begin{array}{l} x + y - z = 5 \\ -x + 0y + 2z = 3 \\ 0x + y - 4z = -1 \end{array}$$ 4. $$\begin{cases} x - y = 1 - z \\ 3x = 5z + 2 \\ z = 6y - 8 \end{cases}$$

_____

5. $$\begin{cases} z + 3y = x \\ 2x = y - 8z \\ y + 4 = z + z \end{cases}$$ _____

Holt Algebra 2

LESSON
4-6

Reteach

Row Operations and Augmented Matrices (continued)

You can use row operations to change an augmented matrix into **reduced row-echelon form**. In reduced row-echelon form, the solution to the system appears in the constant column of the augmented matrix.

$$\begin{bmatrix} 1 & 0 & 2 \\ 0 & 1 & -3 \end{bmatrix}$$

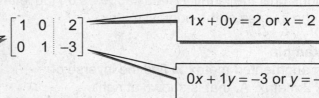

Reduced row-echelon form shows the identity matrix on the left.

$1x + 0y = 2$ or $x = 2$

$0x + 1y = -3$ or $y = -3$

To solve $\begin{cases} x + y = 4 \\ 2x - y = -7 \end{cases}$, use the augmented matrix $\begin{bmatrix} 1 & 1 & 4 \\ 2 & -1 & -7 \end{bmatrix}$.

$$\begin{bmatrix} 1 & 1 & 4 \\ 2 & -1 & -7 \end{bmatrix}$$

Add row 1 to row 2. → $\begin{bmatrix} 1 & 1 & 4 \\ 3 & 0 & -3 \end{bmatrix}$

Row 1 stays the same. The sum becomes row 2.

Switch rows 1 and 2. → $\begin{bmatrix} 3 & 0 & -3 \\ 1 & 1 & 4 \end{bmatrix}$

Divide row 1 by 3. → $\begin{bmatrix} 1 & 0 & -1 \\ 1 & 1 & 4 \end{bmatrix}$

Subtract row 1 from row 2. → $\begin{bmatrix} 1 & 0 & -1 \\ 0 & 1 & 5 \end{bmatrix}$ $x = -1, y = 5$

Solve.

5. $\begin{cases} x + y = -2 \\ x - 2y = 7 \end{cases}$

a. Write the augmented matrix.

b. Subtract row 1 from row 2.

c. Divide row 2 by _____.

d. Subtract row 2 from row 1.

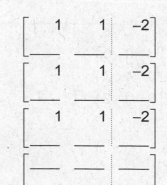

e. $x =$ _____ $y =$ _____

Holt Algebra 2

LESSON
4-6

Challenge

Using an Augmented Matrix to Determine an Inverse

To *augment* means to make greater. Augment a square matrix on its right
side by an identity matrix of the same dimensions and then use row
operations until the identity matrix appears on the left half of the matrix.
This is the inverse of the original matrix.

- **Example**

Use an augmented matrix to find the inverse of
the 2×2 matrix, A, that is shown at right.

$$A = \begin{bmatrix} 1 & 1 \\ 3 & 4 \end{bmatrix}$$

- **Solution**

Augment matrix A by the 2×2 identity matrix on the right.

$$\begin{bmatrix} 1 & 1 & \vdots & 1 & 0 \\ 3 & 4 & \vdots & 0 & 1 \end{bmatrix}$$

Use row operations until the identity matrix appears on the left.

$$(3R_1 - R_2) \to R_2 \begin{bmatrix} 1 & 1 & \vdots & 1 & 0 \\ 0 & -1 & \vdots & 3 & -1 \end{bmatrix} (R_1 + R_2) \to R_1 \begin{bmatrix} 1 & 0 & \vdots & 4 & -1 \\ 0 & -1 & \vdots & 3 & -1 \end{bmatrix} -R_2 \to R_2 \begin{bmatrix} 1 & 0 & \vdots & 4 & -1 \\ 0 & 1 & \vdots & -3 & 1 \end{bmatrix}$$

So, $A^{-1} = \begin{bmatrix} 4 & -1 \\ -3 & 1 \end{bmatrix}$

Some square matrices do not have inverses. If the reduced augmented
matrix you create has one or more rows that contain all zero elements to
the left of the vertical line, then the given matrix has no inverse.

**Use an augmented matrix to find the inverse of the given matrix, if it
is defined. Verify your result.**

1. $\begin{bmatrix} 0 & -1 \\ 1 & 0 \end{bmatrix}$

2. $\begin{bmatrix} 4 & -3 \\ 1 & 2 \end{bmatrix}$

3. $\begin{bmatrix} -2 & 6 \\ -1 & 3 \end{bmatrix}$

_____   _____   _____

4. $\begin{bmatrix} 1 & 0 & 0 \\ 0 & 4 & 7 \\ 0 & 1 & 2 \end{bmatrix}$

5. $\begin{bmatrix} -2 & 2 & 3 \\ 1 & -1 & 0 \\ 0 & 1 & 4 \end{bmatrix}$

6. $\begin{bmatrix} -2 & 5 & 3 \\ 4 & -1 & 3 \\ 4 & -10 & -6 \end{bmatrix}$

_____   _____   _____

LESSON 4-6 Problem Solving
Row Operations and Augmented Matrices

At the annual craft show, the Ceramics Club members sell mugs for $6.00, bowls for $5.50, and plates for $9.50. They have for sale one more bowl than the number of plates and 3 times as many mugs as plates. They sold everything for a total of $236.50. How many of each item did they sell?

1. Write a system of equations to represent the problem, using m, b, and p for the variables. _____

2. Write the augmented matrix for the system of equations. _____

3. Use your calculator to find the reduced row-echelon form of the augmented matrix. _____

4. How many of each item did the Ceramics Club sell? _____

Students earned points for finishing first, second, and third in the field day games. Jake earned a total of 38 points, Wanda earned 33 points, and Jill earned 29 points. How many points were earned for each first-, second-, and third-place finish? Choose the letter for the best answer.

Field Day Tally			
	Jake	Wanda	Jill
First	IIII	I	I
Second		ЖL	III
Third	II		II

5. Which augmented matrix models the problem?

A $\begin{bmatrix} 4 & 1 & 1 & 38 \\ 0 & 5 & 3 & 33 \\ 1 & 0 & 2 & 29 \end{bmatrix}$ B $\begin{bmatrix} 4 & 2 & 0 & 38 \\ 1 & 5 & 0 & 33 \\ 0 & 3 & 2 & 29 \end{bmatrix}$

C $\begin{bmatrix} 4 & 0 & 2 & 38 \\ 1 & 5 & 0 & 33 \\ 1 & 3 & 2 & 29 \end{bmatrix}$ D $\begin{bmatrix} 4 & 1 & 2 & 38 \\ 0 & 3 & 5 & 33 \\ 1 & 2 & 3 & 29 \end{bmatrix}$

6. Which matrix in reduced row-echelon form is the solution to the problem?

A $\begin{bmatrix} 1 & 0 & 0 & 8 \\ 0 & 1 & 0 & 5 \\ 0 & 0 & 1 & 3 \end{bmatrix}$ B $\begin{bmatrix} 1 & 0 & 0 & 10 \\ 0 & 1 & 0 & 6 \\ 0 & 0 & 1 & 3 \end{bmatrix}$

C $\begin{bmatrix} 0 & 0 & 1 & 8 \\ 0 & 1 & 0 & 5 \\ 1 & 0 & 0 & 3 \end{bmatrix}$ D $\begin{bmatrix} 0 & 0 & 1 & 10 \\ 0 & 1 & 0 & 6 \\ 1 & 0 & 0 & 3 \end{bmatrix}$

Holt Algebra 2

Reading Strategies
Understand Vocabulary

Augmented Matrix $\begin{cases} a_1x + b_1y = c_1 \\ a_2x + b_2y = c_2 \end{cases} \rightarrow \begin{bmatrix} a_1 & b_1 & \vert & c_1 \\ a_2 & b_2 & \vert & c_2 \end{bmatrix}$ $\begin{cases} 4x + 3y = 10 \\ x - 2y = -3 \end{cases} \rightarrow \begin{bmatrix} 4 & 3 & \vert & 10 \\ 1 & -2 & \vert & -3 \end{bmatrix}$	A system of linear equations can be represented as an **augmented matrix**. In this form the coefficient terms are to the left of the vertical line, and the constant terms are to the right.
Row Operations For example subtract row 2 from row 1 to create a new row 2. $\begin{bmatrix} a & b & \vert & c \\ d & e & \vert & f \end{bmatrix} = \begin{bmatrix} a & b & \vert & c \\ a-d & b-e & \vert & c-f \end{bmatrix}$ $\begin{bmatrix} 4 & 3 & \vert & 10 \\ 1 & -2 & \vert & -3 \end{bmatrix} = \begin{bmatrix} 4 & 3 & \vert & 10 \\ 3 & 5 & \vert & 13 \end{bmatrix}$	**Row operations** change the form of an augmented matrix in the process of solving a system of equations. The new matrix formed is equivalent to the original matrix.
Row Reduction Use the row reduction feature on your graphing calculator, **rref**, to find the reduced row-echelon form of an augmented matrix. $\begin{bmatrix} 4 & 3 & \vert & 10 \\ 1 & -2 & \vert & -3 \end{bmatrix} = \begin{bmatrix} 1 & 0 & \vert & 1 \\ 0 & 1 & \vert & 2 \end{bmatrix}$ $x = 1$ and $y = 2$	A series of row operations is referred to as **row reduction**. The object is to find an equivalent form of the augmented matrix that solves the system of equations. This form is called the **reduced row-echelon form** $\begin{bmatrix} 1 & 0 & \vert & m \\ 0 & 1 & \vert & n \end{bmatrix}$ where m and n are constants. So $x = m$ and $y = n$.

Use the augmented matrix $\begin{bmatrix} -5 & 10 & \vert & 3 \\ 2 & -4 & \vert & 1 \end{bmatrix}$ **for Exercises 1–3.**

1. Explain how an augmented matrix represents a system of equations.

_____

2. Write the system of equations represented
   by the augmented matrix.

_____

3. Compare multiplying the first equation in the system of equations by 3 and the row operation of multiplying the first row of the augmented matrix by 3. What is the effect of each operation?

_____

Holt Algebra 2

Date _____

Dear Family,

In Chapter 5, your child will graph quadratic functions, solve quadratic equations and inequalities, and learn to operate with complex numbers.

A **quadratic function** is one in which the variable is squared. The parent quadratic function is $f(x) = x^2$, which forms as a U-shaped **parabola** with **vertex** (0, 0).

The parent function can be transformed to form a variety of parabolas. **Vertex form** helps you identify transformations.

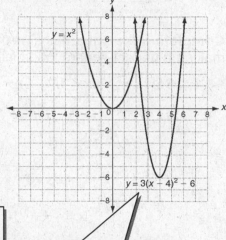

vertex form: $f(x) = a(x - h)^2 + k$

a indicates a reflection across the *x*-axis and/or a vertical stretch or compression.

h indicates a horizontal translation.

k indicates a vertical translation.

$y = 3(x - 4)^2 - 6$ was stretched vertically by a factor of 3, and the vertex is translated to (4, –6).

A quadratic function may also be in **standard form,** which helps identify other properties of the parabola, such as the *y*-intercept (the coefficient *c*).

standard form: $f(x) = ax^2 + bx + c$

The *x*-intercepts of a parabola are input values of *x* that make the output of $f(x) = ax^2 + bx + c$ equal to *zero*. Hence, the *x*-intercepts are also called **zeros**. You can find the zeros of a function by graphing it.

quadratic function: $f(x) = x^2 - 2x - 8$

From the graph, the zeros are $x = -2$ and $x = 4$.

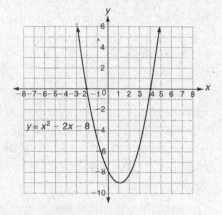

Closely related to a quadratic function is the quadratic equation $ax^2 + bx + c = 0$. The solutions to a quadratic equation are called **roots**. You can find roots by factoring and using the **Zero Product Property.** The roots are equivalent to the zeros.

quadratic equation: $x^2 - 2x - 8 = 0$

$$(x + 2)(x - 4) = 0$$

$$x + 2 = 0 \text{ or } x - 4 = 0$$

$$x = -2 \text{ or } x = 4$$

Zero Product Property
If two quantities multiply to zero, then at least one is zero.

　　　　Holt Algebra 2

Many quadratic expressions are **trinomials** (contain three terms) that factor into two **binomials** (contain two terms). If the two binomial factors are identical, the original expression is called a **perfect-square trinomial**.

$$\underbrace{x^2 - 10x + 25}_{\text{perfect - square trinomial}} = (x - 5)(x - 5) = (x - 5)^2$$

Completing the square is a method of solving a quadratic equation by making a perfect-square trinomial. Then you use a square root to solve.

Solve $x^2 + 6x = 1$.

$x^2 + 6x + \boxed{9} = 1 + \boxed{9}$	*9 makes $x^2 + 6x$ a perfect-square.*
$(x + 3)^2 = 10$	*Factor the left side.*
$x + 3 = \pm\sqrt{10}$	*Take the square root of both sides.*
$x = -3 \pm \sqrt{10}$	*Solve for x.*

If you complete the square for the general equation $ax^2 + bx + c = 0$, you get the **Quadratic Formula:**

If $ax^2 + bx + c = 0$, then the solutions are $x = \dfrac{-b \pm \sqrt{b^2 - 4ac}}{2a}$.

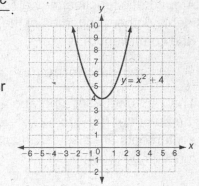

Some quadratic functions, such as $f(x) = x^2 + 4$, have no x-intercepts. Likewise, the equation $0 = x^2 + 4$ has no *real* roots because you get $x = \pm\sqrt{-4}$. The square root of a negative number is called an **imaginary number**, and the **imaginary unit** is $i = \sqrt{-1}$. So, $0 = x^2 + 4$ does have two *imaginary* roots, $x = \pm 2i$.

A **complex number** is one that can be written in the form $a + bi$. For example, in $7 - 2i$, the **real part** is 7 and the **imaginary part** is $-2i$. Complex numbers can be graphed in the **complex plane** (which has a real axis and an imaginary axis), and they can be added, subtracted, multiplied, divided, or raised to powers.

Quadratic inequalities in *two* variables, such as $y \geq 2x^2 - 5x - 2$, are graphed similar to linear inequalities in two variables: solid or dashed boundary line with shading above or below. Quadratic inequalities in *one* variable are graphed on a number line.

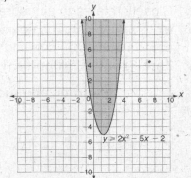

Quadratic equations have many real-world applications, such as the height of a *projectile* (an object that is thrown or launched) as gravity acts on it over time. If the data isn't perfectly quadratic, you might use **regression** to find a best-fit **quadratic model**.

For additional resources, visit go.hrw.com and enter the keyword MB7 Parent.

Holt Algebra 2

LESSON 5-1

Practice A

Using Transformations to Graph Quadratic Functions

Graph the quadratic function by using a table.

1. $f(x) = x^2 - 3$

    a. Complete the table to find ordered pairs for the function.

    b. Plot the ordered pairs on the coordinate plane.

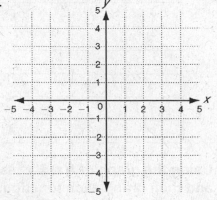

x	$f(x) = x^2 - 3$	$(x, f(x))$
-2	$f(-2) = (-2)^2 - 3$	$(-2, 1)$
-1		
0		
1		
2		

The quadratic parent function is $f(x) = x^2$. Its graph is a parabola with its vertex at the origin (0, 0). Describe each transformation from the parent function.

2. $g(x) = -x^2$

_____

3. $h(x) = (x - 1)^2$

_____

4. $g(x) = x^2 + 7$

_____

5. $h(x) = \left(\dfrac{1}{3}x\right)^2$

_____

6. $g(x) = (x + 3)^2$

_____

7. $h(x) = 5x^2$

_____

The vertex form of a quadratic function is $f(x) = a(x - h)^2 + k$.

8.   a. The parent function $f(x) = x^2$ is translated 2 units left and 3 units up. Write the quadratic function in vertex form.

    _____

    b. Graph the translated function.

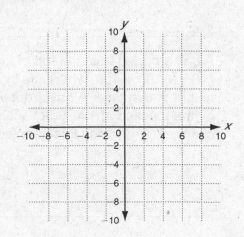

     Holt Algebra 2

LESSON
5-1

Practice B

Using Transformations to Graph Quadratic Functions

Graph the function by using a table.

1. $f(x) = x^2 + 2x - 1$

x	$f(x) = x^2 + 2x - 1$	$(x, f(x))$
-2		
-1		
0		
1		
2		

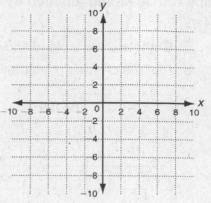

Using the graph of $f(x) = x^2$ as a guide, describe the transformations, and then graph each function. Label each function on the graph.

2. $h(x) = (x - 2)^2 + 2$

_____

3. $h(x) = -(3x)^2$

_____

4. $h(x) = \left(\dfrac{1}{2}x\right)^2$

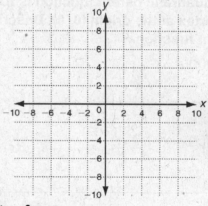

_____

Use the description to write a quadratic function in vertex form.

5. The parent function $f(x) = x^2$ is reflected across the x-axis, horizontally stretched by a factor of 3 and translated 2 units down to create function g.

_____

_____

6. A ball dropped from the top of tower A can be modeled by the function $h(t) = -9.8t^2 + 400$, where t is the time after it is dropped and $h(t)$ is its height at that time. A ball dropped from the top of tower B can be modeled by the function $h(t) = -9.8t^2 + 200$. What transformation describes this change? What does this transformation mean?

_____

_____

Holt Algebra 2

LESSON	**Practice C**
5-1	*Using Transformations to Graph Quadratic Functions*

The height that a baseball reaches when it is thrown can be modeled by the function $h(t) = -16(t - 1.5)^2 + 36$.

1. What is the shape of the ball's path?

   _____

2. What happens to the ball between $t = 0$ and $t = 1.5$ seconds?

   _____

3. Describe the transformation of h from the the parent function $f(t) = t^2$.

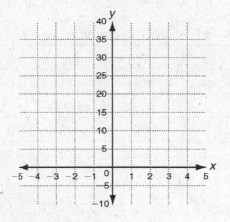

   _____

4. Draw a graph of the baseball's path.

Answer the following questions about functions and transformations.

5. Circle the function that produces the widest parabola.

   $f(x) = 2x^2 - 4$ $\qquad$ $g(x) = -\dfrac{1}{5}x^2 + 2$ $\qquad$ $h(x) = 2(x - 1)^2$

6. Transform the function $m(x) = -3(x + 1)^2 + 4$ so that its vertex is located at $(0, 0)$. Write the transformed function.

   _____

7. Describe the difference and similarity between these two functions: $f(x) = x^2 - 1$ and $f(x) = (x - 1)^2$.

   _____

   _____

Solve.

8. During a flu epidemic last year, a public health official determined that the number of students infected by the flu virus could be approximated by the function $f(t) = -(t - 23)^2 + 625$, where t is the number of days after infection. This year there is a new virus that can be approximated by $f(t) = -(t - 25)^2 + 625$. What kind of transformation describes the change between last year and this year?

   _____

   _____

LESSON
5-1

Reteach

Using Transformations to Graph Quadratic Functions

The graph of a quadratic function is a parabola. A parabola is a curve shaped like the letter U.

Quadratic function $f(x) = a(x - h)^2 + k(a \neq 0)$

You can make a table to graph a quadratic function.

Graph $f(x) = x^2 - 4x + 3$.

x	$f(x) = x^2 - 4x + 3$	$(x, f(x))$
0	$f(0) = 0^2 - 4(0) + 3 = 3$	$(0, 3)$
1	$f(1) = 1^2 - 4(1) + 3 = 0$	$(1, 0)$
2	$f(2) = 2^2 - 4(2) + 3 = -1$	$(2, -1)$
3	$f(3) = 3^2 - 4(3) + 3 = 0$	$(3, 0)$
4	$f(4) = 4^2 - 4(4) + 3 = 3$	$(4, 3)$

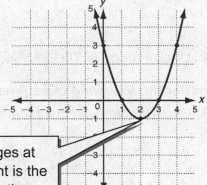

Plot the ordered pairs from the table.

Sketch a smooth curve to connect the points.

The curve changes at $(2, -1)$. This point is the vertex of the function.

Complete the table. Use the ordered pairs to sketch the graph.

1. $f(x) = x^2 - 6x + 7$

x	$f(x) = x^2 - 6x + 7$	$(x, f(x))$
1	$f(1) = 1^2 - 6(1) + 7 = $ _____	
2	$f(2) = $	
3		
4		
5		

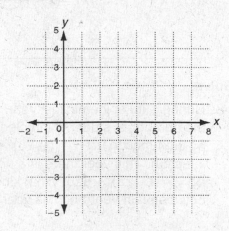

Holt Algebra 2

LESSON
5-1

Reteach

Using Transformations to Graph Quadratic Functions
(continued)

Use the graph of $f(x) = x^2$ as a guide to graph transformations of quadratic functions.

Horizontal and vertical translations change the vertex of $f(x) = x^2$.

Parent Function	Transformation
$f(x) = x^2$	$g(x) = (x - h)^2 + k$
Vertex: $(0, 0)$	Vertex: (h, k)

The translation shifts $f(x) = x^2$:
h units right ($h > 0$) or left ($h < 0$) and
k units up ($k > 0$) or down ($k < 0$).

The vertex of $g(x) = (x - 4)^2 - 2$
is $(4, -2)$.

The graph of $f(x) = x^2$ is shifted
4 units right and 2 units down.

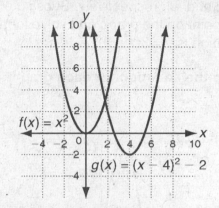

Use the graph of $f(x) = x^2$ as a guide. Find the vertex of each translation. Graph each function and then describe the transformation.

2. $g(x) = (x + 1)^2 - 3$

   Vertex: $(-1, \underline{\quad})$

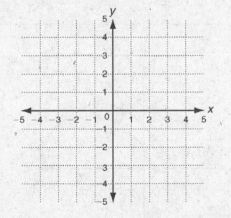

3. $h(x) = (x - 3)^2 + 2$

   Vertex: _____

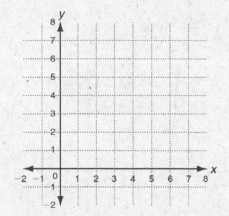

_____

_____

LESSON 5-1

Challenge

Interpreting the Graphs of Quadratic Functions

Functions can be translated, reflected, and/or stretched or compressed to make a new function. Consider the two functions below. You recognize one as the graph of $y = x^2$. You can write the standard equation of the other function, $y = a(x - h)^2 + k$, from the information in the graph.

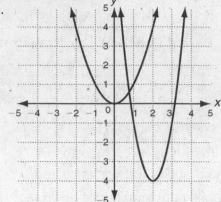

The parabola opens in the upward or positive direction. This indicates that a is a positive number. The vertex has been shifted or translated from the origin to the point $(2, -4)$, so the values of h and k are 2 and -4, respectively. Substitute the coordinates of a point on the graph and solve for a. The resulting equation is $y = 3(x - 2)^2 - 4$.

Write the equation for each graph.

1.

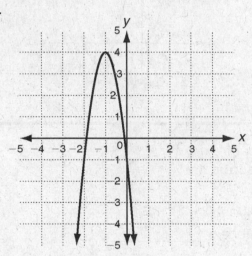

2.

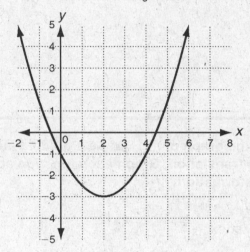

_____

_____

3.

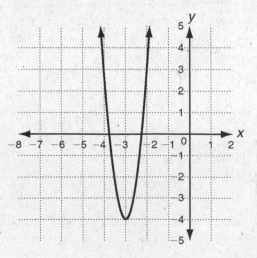

4.

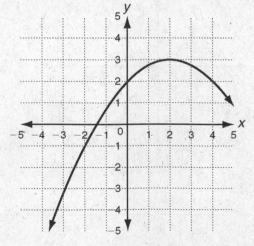

_____

_____

Holt Algebra 2

Problem Solving
Using Transformations to Graph Quadratic Functions

Christa and Jelani are standing at the top of the Leaning Tower of
Pisa in Italy, 185 feet above the ground. Jelani wonders what the
path of a dropped object would be as it falls to the ground from
the top of the tower. The height of an object after t seconds is
given by the function, $f(t) = -16t^2 + 185$.

1. Complete the table to show the height, $f(t)$, of the object for different
   values of t.

2. Plot the ordered pairs from the table and draw the graph to show the
   path of the object.

Time (t)	$f(t) = -16t^2 + 185$	$(t, f(t))$
0	$f(0) = -16(0)^2 + 185$	
1	$f(1) = -16(1)^2 + 185$	
2		
3		
4		

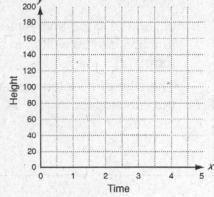

3. What is the parent function for the graph? _____

4. What is the name for this U-shaped curve? _____

5. Describe the transformations of the parent function into $f(t) = -16t^2 + 185$,
   which describes the path of an object falling from 185 feet.

_____

_____

Choose the letter for the best answer.

6. Mario dropped a wrench from the top of
   a sailboat mast 58 feet high. Which
   function describes the path of the falling
   wrench?

   A $f(t) = 16(t - 58)^2 - 185$

   B $f(t) = -16(t - 58)^2 + 185$

   C $f(t) = 16t^2 - 58$

   D $f(t) = -16t^2 + 58$

7. Delle wants to transform the parent
   function $f(t) = t^2$ into
   $f(t) = -4(t - 0.6)^2 + 6$. Which is NOT
   a step in that transformation?

   A Translation 6 units up

   B Translation 0.6 unit left

   C Reflection across the x-axis

   D Vertical stretch by a factor of 4

Holt Algebra 2

LESSON 5-1	# Reading Strategy
	Compare and Contrast

Linear and quadratic functions have some similar properties and some different properties.

Linear Functions	Quadratic Functions
– The graph is a straight line.	– The graph is a parabola.
– The graph has no maximum or minimum.	– The graph has a maximum or a minimum at the vertex (h, k).
– The domain is the set of all real numbers and the range is the set of all real numbers.	– The domain is the set of all real numbers but the range is $[k, \infty)$ when the vertex is a minimum or $(-\infty, k]$ when the vertex is a maximum.
– Given the slope and y-intercept, a linear function can be written in slope-intercept form: $f(x) = mx + b$.	– Given the vertex (h, k) and the value of a (coefficient of x^2), a quadratic function can be written in vertex form: $f(x) = a(x - h)^2 + k$.
– The sign of m determines which direction the line slopes.	– The sign of a determines whether the parabola opens upward or downward.

Answer each question.

1. Determine the type of graph for each function.

   a. $f(x) = 3x + 1$ _____

   b. $f(x) = x^2 - 6x + 5$ _____

   c. $f(x) = 4x - x^2 + 1$ _____

   d. $f(x) = 5 + \dfrac{2}{3}x$ _____

2. Find the domain and range of the function $f(x) = (x - 4)^2 + 3$.

   _____

3. Find the slope of the line $f(x)\, \dfrac{1}{2}x + 8$. Describe how the line slopes.

   _____

4. Find the vertex of the function $f(x) = 2(x + 6)^2 - 3$. Does the parabola open upward or downward?

   _____

Holt Algebra 2

LESSON 5-2

Practice A

Properties of Quadratic Functions in Standard Form

Identify the axis of symmetry for the graph of each function.

1. $f(x) = -(x - 4)^2 - 6$ _____

2. $g(x) = 5(x - 2)^2 + 4$ _____

3. $g(x) = 12(x + 6)^2 - 5$ _____

4. $f(x) = -3(x + 1)^2 - 7$ _____

Tell whether each statement is true or false.

5. The graph of a quadratic function is always a parabola.   _____

6. The graphs of all quadratic functions open upward.   _____

7. The graph of $f(x) = x^2$ has a maximum value at (0, 0).   _____

For the following functions, (a) determine whether the graph opens upward or downward. Then find (b) the axis of symmetry, (c) the vertex, and (d) the y-intercept. Graph each function. Then (e) determine if the function has a minimum or a maximum and (f) find the value of the minimum or maximum.

8. $g(x) = 3x^2 + 2x + 1$ 9. $f(x) = -2x^2 - 4x - 2$

   a._____   a._____

   b._____   b._____

   c._____   c._____

   d._____   d._____

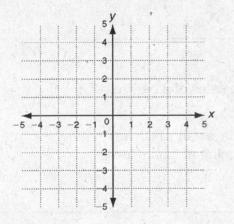   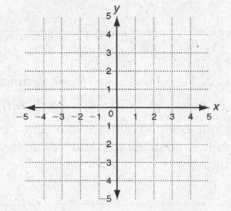

   e._____   e._____

   f._____   f._____

| LESSON | **Practice B** |
| 5-2 | *Properties of Quadratic Functions in Standard Form* |

Identify the axis of symmetry for the graph of each function.

1. $g(x) = x^2 - 4x + 2$

2. $h(x) = -8x^2 + 12x - 11$

3. $k(x) = -4(x + 3)^2 + 9$

_____   _____   _____

For each function, (a) determine whether the graph opens upward or downward, (b) find the axis of symmetry, (c) find the vertex, and (d) find the *y*-intercept. Then graph the function.

4. $f(x) = -x^2 + 3x + 1$

    a. Upward or downward _____

    b. Axis of symmetry _____

    c. Vertex _____

    d. *y*-intercept _____

5. $g(x) = 2x^2 + 4x - 2$

    a. Upward or downward _____

    b. Axis of symmetry _____

    c. Vertex _____

    d. *y*-intercept _____

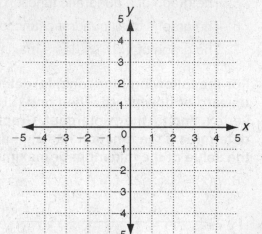

Find the minimum or maximum value of each function. Then state the domain and range of the function.

6. $g(x) = x^2 - 2x + 1$

7. $h(x) = -5x^2 + 15x - 3$

_____   _____

Solve.

8. A record label uses the following function to model the sales of a new release.

$$a(t) = -90t^2 + 8100t$$

The number of albums sold is a function of time, *t*, in days. On which day were the most albums sold? What is the maximum number of albums sold on that day?

_____

Holt Algebra 2

Name _____ Date _____ Class _____

Practice C

Properties of Quadratic Functions in Standard Form

For each function, determine whether the graph opens upward or downward, find the axis of symmetry, the vertex, and the *y*-intercept. Then graph the function.

1. $f(x) = \dfrac{1}{2}x^2 + 2x + 4$

   a. Upward or downward   _____

   b. Axis of symmetry   _____

   c. Vertex   _____

   d. *y*-intercept   _____

2. $g(x) = -2(x + 3)^2 + 1$

   a. Upward or downward   _____

   b. Axis of symmetry   _____

   c. Vertex   _____

   d. *y*-intercept   _____

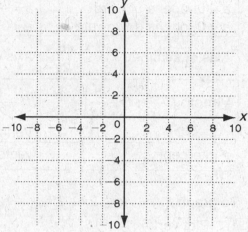

Solve.

3. Write the vertex form of a quadratic function that opens upward and has a *y*-intercept of 3.

   _____

4. The vertex of the function $g(x) = 4x^2 + bx + 16$ is at $(2, 0)$. Find the value of *b* for the function.

   _____

5. The *y*-intercept of $g(x) = 2(x - 3)^2 + k$ is -2. Find the value of *k*.

   _____

6. An airline sells a 3-day vacation package. Sales from this vacation package can be modeled by the quadratic function $s(p) = -40p^2 + 32000p$. Sales are dependent on the price, *p*, of the package. If the price is set too high, the package won't sell, but if the price is too low, prospective buyers will think it is a scam.

   a. At what price, *p*, does the company have the greatest revenue?

     _____

   b. What are the maximum sales possible based on this model?

     _____

   c. What is the revenue from the vacation package if the price is set at $800?

     _____

                                  Holt Algebra 2

Reteach
Properties of Quadratic Functions in Standard Form

You can use the properties of a parabola to graph a quadratic function in standard form:
$f(x) = ax^2 + bx + c$, $a \neq 0$.

Property	Example: $f(x) = -x^2 - 2x + 2$
$a > 0$: opens upward $a < 0$: opens downward	$a = -1$, $b = -2$, $c = 2$ $a < 0$, so parabola opens downward.
Axis of symmetry: $x = -\dfrac{b}{2a}$	Axis of symmetry: $x = -\dfrac{b}{2a} = -\dfrac{(-2)}{2(-1)} = -1$
Vertex: $\left(-\dfrac{b}{2a},\ f\left(-\dfrac{b}{2a}\right)\right)$	$f\left(-\dfrac{b}{2a}\right) = f(-1) = -1(-1)^2 - 2(-1) + 2 = 3$ Vertex: $(-1, 3)$
y-intercept: c	y-intercept is 2, so $(0, 2)$ is a point on the graph.

To graph $f(x) = -x^2 - 2x + 2$:

1. Plot vertex.
2. Sketch axis of symmetry through vertex.
3. Plot y-intercept.
4. Use symmetry to plot $(-2, 2)$.
5. Sketch graph.

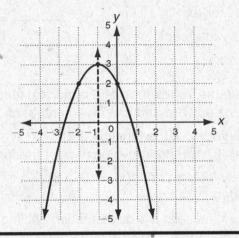

Use the properties of a parabola to graph $f(x) = x^2 - 4x + 3$.

1. $a =$ _____, $b =$ _____, $c =$ _____

2. The graph opens _____.

3. Axis of symmetry: $x = -\dfrac{b}{2a} =$ _____

4. $f\left(-\dfrac{b}{2a}\right) =$ _____

5. Vertex: _____

6. y-intercept: _____

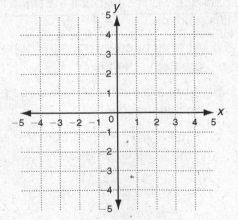

Holt Algebra 2

LESSON 5-2 Reteach

Properties of Quadratic Functions in Standard Form (continued)

The **maximum** or the **minimum** value of a parabola is the y-value of the vertex, or $f\left(-\dfrac{b}{2a}\right)$. If the parabola opens upward, $a > 0$, then it is a minimum value. If the parabola opens downward, $a < 0$, then it is a maximum value.

$f(x) = -2x^2 + 4x - 3$	$f(x) = 3x^2 + 12x + 1$
$a = -2$: Find maximum	$a = 3$: Find minimum.
Evaluate $-\dfrac{b}{2a}$ for $a = -2$ and $b = 4$.	Evaluate $-\dfrac{b}{2a}$ for $a = 3$ and $b = 12$.
$-\dfrac{b}{2a} = -\dfrac{4}{2(-2)} = 1$	$-\dfrac{b}{2a} = -\dfrac{12}{2(3)} = -2$
$f\left(-\dfrac{b}{2a}\right) = f(1)$	$f\left(-\dfrac{b}{2a}\right) = f(-2)$
$\quad = -2(1)^2 + 4(1) - 3 = -1$	$\quad = 3(-2)^2 + 12(-2) + 1 = -11$
Maximum value is -1.	Maximum value is -11.
Range: $\{y \mid y \le -1\}$	Range: $\{y \mid y \ge -11\}$

All other y-values must be less than or equal to the maximum.

All other y-values must be greater than or equal to the minimum.

Find the minimum or maximum value of each function. Then state the range of each function.

7. $f(x) = 2x^2 - 8x + 9$

Minimum or maximum? _____

$-\dfrac{b}{2a} = -\dfrac{(-8)}{2(2)} = $ _____

$f\left(-\dfrac{b}{2a}\right) = $ _____

Range: _____

8. $f(x) = -3x^2 + 6x - 4$

Minimum or maximum? _____

$-\dfrac{b}{2a} = $ _____

$f\left(-\dfrac{b}{2a}\right) = $ _____

Range: _____

Holt Algebra 2

LESSON 5-2

Challenge

Maximizing a Quadratic Function

Quadratic functions are frequently used in optimization problems when a maximum or minimum value is needed for a function. The vertex of a parabola is the minimum value of the function when $a > 0$ and the maximum value of the function when $a < 0$.

Pam just purchased a new house and plans to fence in a portion of the backyard. The house is 40 feet wide and 60 feet long. She will use 260 feet of fencing and wants to fence the area shown below. She wants to place the two short sections of fencing labeled x to enclose the greatest possible area.

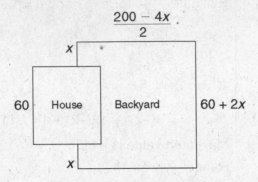

1. The length of the back fence is labeled $60 + 2x$. Explain how this value was derived.

_____

2. The length of the side fence is labeled $\dfrac{200 - 4x}{2}$. Explain how this value was derived.

_____

3. Where should the short sides of the fence labeled x be located?

_____

4. a. Write a quadratic function for the area of the backyard to be fenced.

_____

   b. Find the maximum value of the function. What does this represent?

_____

   c. What dimensions of the backyard will maximize the area of the rectangle?

_____

Holt Algebra 2

LESSON 5-2 Problem Solving

Properties of Quadratic Functions in Standard Form

Kim wants to buy a used car with good gas mileage. He knows that the miles per gallon, or mileage, varies according to various factors, including the speed. He finds that highway mileage for the make and model he wants can be approximated by the function $f(s) = -0.03s^2 + 2.4s - 30$, where s is the speed in miles per hour. He wants to graph this function to estimate possible gas mileages at various speeds.

1. Determine whether the graph opens upward or downward.

   _____

2. Identify the axis of symmetry for the graph of the function.

   _____

3. Find the y-intercept.

   _____

4. Find the vertex.

   _____

5. Graph the function.

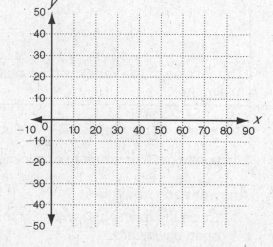

6. a. Does the curve have a maximum or a minimum value?

   _____

   b. What is the value of the y-coordinate at the maximum or minimum?

   _____

   c. Explain what this point means in terms of gas mileage.

   _____

A ball is hit into the air from a height of 4 feet. The function $g(t) = -16t^2 + 120t + 4$ can be used to model the height of the ball where t is the time in seconds after the ball is hit. Choose the letter for the best answer.

7. About how long is the ball in the air?

   A 3.5 seconds

   B 3.75 seconds

   C 7 seconds

   D 7.5 seconds

8. What is the maximum height the ball reaches?

   A 108 feet

   B 124 feet

   C 229 feet

   D 394 feet

Holt Algebra 2

LESSON 5-2

Reading Strategy
Draw Conclusions

The graph of a quadratic function, $f(x) = ax^2 + bx + c$, is a parabola that can open upward or downward. This tells you whether the function has a **minimum** or a **maximum**.

Minimum	Maximum
$a > 0$, the parabola opens up. The function has a minimum. 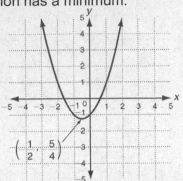	$a < 0$, the parabola opens down. The function has a maximum. 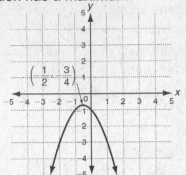
The y-value of the vertex is the function's minimum.	The y-value of the vertex is the function's maximum.

The x-value of the vertex is $-\dfrac{b}{2a}$. Substitute this value of x in the quadratic function to get its maximum or minimum value.

Answer each question.

1. Circle the function(s) whose graph opens upward. Draw a rectangle around those that open downward.

   $f(x) = 2x^2 - 3$ $g(x) = -x^2 + x + 1$ $h(x) = \dfrac{1}{2}x^2 + x + 3$ $k(x) = -6x^2 - x - 5$

2. For the function $f(x) = 3x^2 + 2x + 4$:

   a. What conclusion can you draw about the graph of the function?

   _____

   b. Describe how to find the minimum or maximum of the function.

   _____

3. Can a quadratic function have both a maximum and a minimum? Explain.

   _____

4. The vertex of a function $g(x)$ is at $(3, -5)$. The function opens downward. What is the maximum value of this function?

   _____

Holt Algebra 2

LESSON **Practice A**
5-3
Solving Quadratic Equations by Graphing and Factoring

Tell whether each statement is true or false.

1. Quadratic functions have only one zero.   _____

2. A zero of a function is the value of x that makes $f(x) = 0$.   _____

3. The points $(0, 2)$ and $(0, 5)$ could be the zeros of a
   given quadratic function.   _____

Find the zeros of $f(x) = x^2 - x - 6$ by using a table and a graph.

4. In what direction does the parabola open?

x	-2	-1	0	2	4
$f(x)$					

_____

5. Find the y-intercept.

_____

6. Find the vertex.

_____

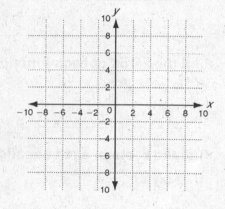

7. Plot the vertex and the y-intercept. Complete
   the table and use the values to draw the graph.

8. What are the zeros of the function?

_____

Find the zeros of each function by factoring.

9. $f(x) = x^2 - 3x - 10$

    a. Set the function equal to 0. $x^2 - 3x - 10 = $ _____

    b. Factor. $(x + $ _____$)(x - $ _____$) = $ _____

    c. Set each factor equal to 0. $(x + $ _____$) = $ _____ or $(x - $ _____$) = $ _____

    d. Solve each equation for x. $x = $ _____ or $x = $ _____

10. $f(x) = x^2 - 1$ _____

Solve.

11. A quadratic function has zeros equal to 1 and 2.

    a. What is the factored form of the function?   _____

    b. Multiply the factors to give the quadratic function.   _____

LESSON 5-3 Practice B

Solving Quadratic Equations by Graphing and Factoring

Find the zeros of each function by using a graph and a table.

1. $f(x) = x^2 + 5x + 6$

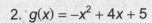

x	−4	−3	−2	−1	0
f(x)					

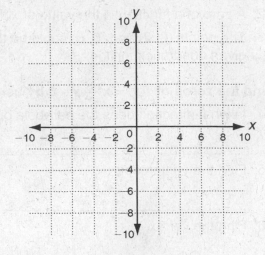

_____

2. $g(x) = -x^2 + 4x + 5$

x	−2	0	2	4	6
f(x)					

_____

Find the zeros of each function by factoring.

3. $h(x) = -x^2 - 6x - 9$ 4. $f(x) = 2x^2 + 9x + 4$ 5. $g(x) = x^2 + x - 20$

_____   _____   _____

Find the roots of each equation by factoring.

6. $12x = 9x^2 + 4$ 7. $16x^2 = 9$

_____   _____

Write a quadratic function in standard form for each given set of zeros.

8. −2 and 7   9. 1 and −8

_____   _____

Solve.

10. The quadratic function that approximates the height of a javelin throw is $h(t) = -0.08t^2 + 4.48$, where t is the time in seconds after it is thrown and h is the javelin's height in feet. How long will it take for the javelin to hit the ground?

_____

LESSON
5-3
Practice C
Solving Quadratic Equations by Graphing and Factoring

Find the zeros or roots of each function or equation.

1. $f(x) = -x^2 - 11x - 30$

2. $g(x) = 2x^2 - 25x + 12$

_____

_____

3. $36x^2 = 4$

4. $56x = 8x^2 + 98$

_____

_____

Solve.

5. Find the zeros of $h(x) = 3x^2 + 4x - 4$ by graphing.

_____

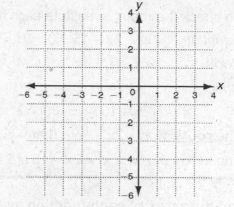

6. Write a quadratic function in standard form with zeros 6 and −1.

_____

7. Write an equation in standard form with roots 3, −2.

_____

8. Write a quadratic function with two zeros that have a sum of 3.

_____

9. Write a quadratic equation with just one nonzero root.

_____

Solve.

10. a. Marilyn hit a golf ball on the ground with her driver. Use the general function for a projectile to write a function that shows the height in feet of her golf ball as a function of time. The ball was hit with an initial vertical velocity of 100 feet per second.

_____

 b. How long will Marilyn's golf ball stay in the air?

_____

LESSON 5-3

Reteach

Solving Quadratic Equations by Graphing and Factoring

Solve the equation $ax^2 + bx + c = 0$ to find the roots of the equation.

Find the roots of $x^2 + 2x - 15 = 0$ to find the zeros of $f(x) = x^2 + 2x - 15$.

$$x^2 + 2x - 15 = 0$$

> Factor, then multiply to check.

$$(x + 5)(x - 3) = 0$$

> Solve each equation for x.

$$(x + 5) = 0 \text{ or } (x - 3) = 0$$

$$x = -5 \text{ or } x = 3$$

> Set each factor equal to 0.

To check the roots, substitute each root into the original equation:

Equation:	$x^2 + 2x - 15 = 0$	$x^2 + 2x - 15 = 0$
Root:	$x = -5$	$x = 3$
Check:	$(-5)^2 + 2(-5) - 15$	$(3)^2 + 2(3) - 15$
	$25 - 10 - 15 = 0 \checkmark$	$9 + 6 - 15 = 0 \checkmark$

The **roots** of $x^2 + 2x - 15 = 0$ are –5 and 3.

The **zeros** of $f(x) = x^2 + 2x - 15$ are –5 and 3.

> The roots of the equation are the zeros of the function.

Find the zeros of each function by factoring. Set the function equal to 0, factor, set each factor equal to 0, and then solve each equation.

1. $f(x) = 4x^2 - 24x$

   $4x^2 - 24x = 0$

   $4x(x - \underline{\qquad}) = 0$

   $\underline{\qquad} = 0 \text{ or } x - \underline{\qquad} = 0$

   _____

2. $f(x) = x^2 + 4x + 3$

   $x^2 + 4x + 3 = 0$

   $(x + \underline{\qquad})(x + \underline{\qquad}) = 0$

   $x + \underline{\qquad} = 0 \text{ or } x + \underline{\qquad} = 0$

   _____

3. $f(x) = x^2 - 5x + 4$

   _____

   _____

   _____

   _____

4. $f(x) = 3x^2 + 12x$

   _____

   _____

   _____

   _____

LESSON 5-3 Reteach

Solving Quadratic Equations by Graphing and Factoring (continued)

Some quadratic equations have special factors.

Difference of Two Squares: $a^2 - b^2 = (a + b)(a - b)$

Perfect Square Trinomials: $a^2 - 2ab + b^2 = (a - b)^2$

$a^2 + 2ab + b^2 = (a + b)^2$

Always write a quadratic equation in standard form before factoring.

$16x^2 = 25$

$16x^2 - 25 = 0$ 16 and 25 are perfect squares. Use the difference of two squares to factor.

$(4x)^2 - (5)^2 = 0$

$(4x - 5)(4x + 5) = 0$

$(4x - 5) = 0 \text{ or } (4x + 5) = 0$ Set each factor equal to 0.

$x = \dfrac{5}{4} \text{ or } x = -\dfrac{5}{4}$

Try to factor a perfect square trinomial if the coefficient of x and the constant term are perfect squares.

$4x^2 - 12x + 9 = 0$ $4x^2$ and 9 are perfect squares.

$(2x)^2 - 2(2x)(3) + (3)^2 = 0$

$(2x - 3)(2x - 3) = (2x - 3)^2 = 0$

$(2x - 3) = 0$ The factors are the same.

$x = \dfrac{3}{2}$

Find the roots of each equation by factoring.

5. $4x^2 = 49$

   $4x^2 - 49 = $ _____

   $(\underline{\quad} x)^2 - (\underline{\quad})^2 = $ _____

   _____

   _____

   _____

6. $x^2 + 16 = 8x$

   $x^2 - 8x + 16 = $ _____

   _____

   _____

   _____

   _____

   Holt Algebra 2

LESSON 5-3

Challenge

Exploring Equations in Quadratic Form

Some equations that are not of the second degree can be rewritten in quadratic form. Once in quadratic form, the equation may be solved by factoring. When you solve an equation in quadratic form, you may obtain a value that does not satisfy the original equation. For this reason, it is important to check all solutions in the original equation.

- **Example**

  Solve: $x^4 - 29x^2 + 100 = 0$

- **Solution**

  $$x^4 - 29x^2 + 100 = 0$$

  Rewrite the equation in x^2. $(x^2)^2 - 29(x^2) + 100 = 0$

  Factor. $(x^2 - 25)(x^2 - 4) = 0$

  Zero Product Property $x^2 - 25 = 0 \text{ or } x^2 - 4 = 0$

  Solve for x. $x = \pm 5 \text{ or } x = \pm 2$

  Check all four values in the original equation, as shown at right.

Check

$$x^4 - 29x^2 + 100 = 0$$
$$(\pm 5)^4 - 29(\pm 5)^2 + 100$$
$$= 625 - 725 + 100$$
$$= 0 \checkmark$$

$$x^4 - 29x^2 + 100 = 0$$
$$(\pm 2)^4 - 29(\pm 2)^2 + 100$$
$$= 0 \checkmark$$

So, there are four solutions:
$-5, -2, 2, 5$

Determine if each equation can be expressed in quadratic form. If so, write the equation in quadratic form. If not, write *no*. Do not solve.

1. $x^4 + 4x^2 - 5 = 0$

2. $x^4 - x^3 + 12 = 0$

3. $x^8 - 17x^4 + 16 = 0$

_____

_____

_____

4. $x^3 - 2x^2 - 5 = 0$

5. $x - 2\sqrt{x} - 8 = 0$

6. $(x - 3)^2 - 4(x - 3) - 21 = 0$

_____

_____

_____

Factor each equation to determine if it contains a quadratic factor. If so, write the factored form of the equation. If not, write *no*. Do not solve.

7. $x^3 - 9x = 0$

8. $x^5 - 4x^4 - 12x^3 = 0$

9. $2x^3 - x^2 - 9 = 0$

_____

_____

_____

Write each equation in quadratic form and solve. Check your answers.

10. $x^4 - 10x^2 + 9 = 0$

11. $9x^4 - 18x^2 + 8 = 0$

12. $x - 3\sqrt{x} - 4 = 0$

_____

_____

_____

Name _____ Date _____ Class_____

Problem Solving

Solving Quadratic Equations by Graphing and Factoring

Erin and her friends launch a rocket from ground level vertically into the air with an initial velocity of 80 feet per second. The height of the rocket, $h(t)$, after t seconds is given by $h(t) = -16t^2 + 80t$.

1. They want to find out how high they can expect the rocket to go and how long it will be in the air.

   a. Use the standard form $f(x) = ax^2 + bx + c$ to find values for a, b, and c. _____

   b. Use the coordinates for the vertex of the path of the rocket to find t, the number of seconds the rocket will be in the air before it starts its downward path. _____

   c. Substitute the value for t in the given function to find the maximum height of the rocket. How high can they expect their rocket to go? _____

   d. Megan points out that the rocket will have a height of zero again when it returns to the ground. How long will the rocket stay in the air? _____

2. Megan gets ready to launch the same rocket from a platform 21 feet above the ground with the same initial velocity. How long will the rocket stay in the air this time?

   a. Write a function that represents the rocket's path for this launch. _____

   b. Factor the corresponding equation to find the values for t when h is zero. _____

   c. Erin says that the roots of the equation are $t = 5.25$ and $t = -20.25$ and that the rocket will stay in the air 5.5 seconds. Megan says she is wrong. Who is correct? How do you know?

   _____

   _____

Choose the letter for the best answer.

3. Which function models the path of a rocket that lands 3 seconds after launch?

   A $h(t) = -16t^2 + 32t + 48$

   B $h(t) = -16t^2 + 32t + 10.5$

   C $h(t) = -16t^2 + 40t + 48$

   D $h(t) = -16t^2 + 40t + 10.5$

4. Megan reads about a rocket whose path can be modeled by the function $h(t) = -16t^2 + 100t + 15$. Which could be the initial velocity and launch height?

   A 15 ft/s; 100 ft off the ground

   B 16 ft/s; 100 ft off the ground

   C 100 ft/s; 15 ft off the ground

   D 171 ft/s; 15 ft off the ground

Holt Algebra 2

LESSON
5-3

Reading Strategy
Compare and Contrast

A **zero** of a function is the value of x that makes $f(x) = 0$. Two different ways of finding the zeros of a function, graphing and factoring, are compared below.

Finding Zeros by Using a Graph	Finding Zeros by Factoring
$f(x) = x^2 + 2x - 3$ The graph opens upward. The vertex is $(-1, -4)$ The y-intercept is -3. 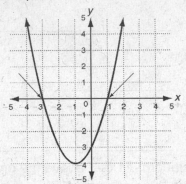 The zeros are 1 and -3.	$f(x) = x^2 + 2x - 3$ Set the function equal to zero. $x^2 + 2x - 3 = 0$ Factor. $(x - 1)(x + 3) = 0$ Set each factor equal to 0 and solve. $x - 1 = 0$ $x = 1$ $x + 3 = 0$ $x = -3$ The zeros are 1 and -3

Answer each question.

1. How can you use a graph to find the zeros of a quadratic function?

   _____

2. Can a quadratic function have more than two zeros? Explain.

   _____

3. Consider the function $f(x) = (x - 1)(x + 1)$.

   a. What are the zeros of the function?   _____

   b. Which method did you use? Why?

   _____

4. A quadratic function opens down and its vertex is $(0, -3)$. How many zeros does this function have? Explain.

   _____

5. Compare and contrast the two methods of finding the zeros of a quadratic function. Describe when you would use one or the other method.

   _____

Practice A
Completing the Square

Solve each equation using square roots.

1. $(x + 1)^2 = 9$

   $x + 1 = $ ____

2. $(x - 2)^2 = 16$

   $x - 2 = $ ____

3. $(x + 3)^2 = 25$

   $x + 3 = $ ____

_____   _____   _____

To complete the square of $x^2 + bx$, add $\left(\dfrac{b}{2}\right)^2$ to the expression. Write

the term needed to complete the square for each expression.

4. $x^2 + 4x$

5. $x^2 + 2x$

6. $x^2 - 8x$

_____   _____   _____

Solve each equation by completing the square.

7. $x^2 + 10x = 20$

   a. Add $\left(\dfrac{b}{2}\right)^2$ to each side of the equation. $x^2 + 10x + $ _____ $= 20 + $ _____

   b. Simplify. $x^2 + 10x + $ ____ $= 20 + $ ____

   c. Factor the square. $(x + $ ___ $)(x + $ ___ $) = $ ____

   d. Take square root of both sides. $x + $ _____ $= \sqrt{\underline{\ \ \ }}$

   e. Solve for x. $x = $ _____

8. $x^2 - 6x - 23 = 0$ 9. $x^2 + 13 = -14x$

_____   _____

Solve.

10. Ralph and Edie each solved the equation $(x - 7)^2 - 100 = 0$.
    Ralph says the correct answer is $x = 17$. Edie says the correct answer
    is $x = -3$. Who is correct? How do you know?

_____

_____

      Holt Algebra 2

LESSON	**Practice B**
5-4	*Completing the Square*

Solve each equation.

1. $2x^2 - 6 = 42$

2. $x^2 - 14x + 49 = 18$

_____   _____

Complete the square for each expression. Write the resulting expression as a binomial squared.

3. $x^2 - 4x +$ _____

4. $x^2 + 12x +$ _____

_____   _____

Solve each equation by completing the square.

5. $2d^2 = 8 + 10d$

6. $x^2 + 2x = 3$

_____   _____

7. $-3x^2 + 18x = -30$

8. $4x^2 = -12x + 4$

_____   _____

Write each function in vertex form, and identify its vertex.

9. $f(x) = x^2 - 6x - 2$

10. $f(x) = x^2 - 4x + 1$

_____   _____

11. $h(x) = 3x^2 - 6x - 15$

12. $f(x) = -2x^2 - 16x + 4$

_____   _____

Solve.

13. Nathan made a triangular pennant for the band booster club. The area of the pennant is 80 square feet. The base of the pennant is 12 feet shorter than the height.

  a. What are the lengths of the base and height of the pennant?

_____

  b. What are the dimensions of the pennant if the base is only 6 feet shorter than the height?

_____

Holt Algebra 2

LESSON **Practice C**
5-4 *Completing the Square*

Complete the square for each expression. Write the resulting expression as a binomial squared.

1. $x^2 - 22x +$ _____

2. $x^2 + 9x +$ _____

_____   _____

Solve each equation by completing the square.

3. $14x + x^2 = 24$

4. $2x^2 - 8x = -2$

_____   _____

5. $x^2 = 3x + 4$

6. $4x^2 + 32x + 16 = 0$

_____   _____

Write each function in vertex form, and identify its vertex.

7. $f(x) = x^2 - 4x - 17$

8. $g(x) = x^2 - \dfrac{1}{2}x + 1$

_____   _____

9. $h(x) = 3x^2 - 24x + 15$

10. $f(x) = -x^2 - 3x + 12$

_____   _____

Solve.

11. Write a quadratic equation with the vertex (3, 1) and $a = 1$ in standard form.   _____

12. What is the y-intercept for the graph of the function $f(x) = 2(x + 2)^2 + 9$?   _____

13. The value of a stock is given by $S(t) = t^2 - 6t + 13$, where t is the number of days after the purchase.

a. Complete the square and write the function in vertex form.   _____

b. What is the value of the stock at $t = 0$? At what other time will the stock have this same value?   _____

c. What is the vertex? What does the vertex represent in terms of the stock price?   _____

LESSON 5-4

Reteach

Completing the Square

You can use the **square root property** to solve some quadratic equations.

Square Root Property	
To solve $x^2 = a$, take the square root of both sides of the equation.	$x^2 = a$ $\sqrt{x^2} = \pm\sqrt{a}$ $x = \pm\sqrt{a}$

Remember:
$2^2 = 4$, and $(-2)^2 = 4$.

Solve $4x^2 - 5 = 43$.

$4x^2 = 48$ *Add 5 to both sides.*

The coefficient of x^2 should be 1 to use the square root property.

$x^2 = 12$ *Divide both sides by 4.*

$\sqrt{x^2} = \pm\sqrt{12}$ *Take the square root of both sides.*

$x = \pm\sqrt{12}$ *Simplify.*

$x = \pm 2\sqrt{3}$

Think: $\sqrt{12} = \sqrt{4 \cdot 3} = \sqrt{4}\sqrt{3} = 2\sqrt{3}$

Solve $x^2 + 12x + 36 = 50$.

$(x + 6)^2 = 50$ *Factor the perfect square trinomial.*

$\sqrt{(x + 6)^2} = \pm\sqrt{50}$ *Take the square root of both sides.*

$x + 6 = \pm\sqrt{50}$ *Subtract 6 from both sides.*

$x = -6 \pm \sqrt{50}$ *Simplify.*

$x = -6 \pm 5\sqrt{2}$

Think: $\sqrt{50} = \sqrt{25 \cdot 2} = \sqrt{25}\sqrt{2} = 5\sqrt{2}$

Solve each equation.

1. $3x^2 + 7 = 31$

    $3x^2 = $ _____

    _____

2. $x^2 - 8x + 16 = 18$

    $(x - $ _____ $)^2 = 18$

    _____

3. $6x^2 - 4 = 38$

    _____

4. $x^2 - 2x + 1 = 10$

    _____

LESSON 5-4

Reteach

Completing the Square *(continued)*

You can use a process called **completing the square** to rewrite a quadratic of the form $x^2 + bx$ as a perfect square trinomial.

To complete the square of $x^2 + bx$, add $\left(\dfrac{b}{2}\right)^2$.	*Think:* Multiply the coefficient of x by $\dfrac{1}{2}$. Then square it.	$x^2 + bx + \left(\dfrac{b}{2}\right)^2 = \left(x + \dfrac{b}{2}\right)^2$

Complete the square: $x^2 - 8x + ?$.

Step 1 Identify b, the coefficient of x: $b = -8$.

Step 2 Find $\left(\dfrac{b}{2}\right)^2$: $\left(\dfrac{b}{2}\right)^2 = \left(\dfrac{-8}{2}\right)^2 = (-4)^2 = 16$

Step 3 Add $\left(\dfrac{b}{2}\right)^2$: $x^2 - 8x + 16$

Step 4 Factor: $x^2 - 8x + 16 = (x - 4)^2$

Use $\dfrac{b}{2}$ as a factor.

Check: $(x - 4)^2 = (x - 4)(x - 4)$
$= x^2 - 8x + 16$ ✓

Complete each square and factor.

5. $x^2 + 9x + ?$

$b = 9$, so $\dfrac{b}{2} = \dfrac{9}{2}$

$\left(\dfrac{b}{2}\right)^2 =$ _____

$x^2 + 9x +$ _____

$\left(x + \underline{}\right)^2$

6. $x^2 - 4x + ?$

$b =$ _____, so $\dfrac{b}{2} =$ _____

$\left(\dfrac{b}{2}\right)^2 =$ _____

$x^2 - 4x +$ _____

_____

7. $x^2 - 10x + ?$

_____

_____

8. $x^2 + 3x + ?$

_____

_____

Holt Algebra 2

LESSON
5-4

Challenge
The Golden Ratio

The ancient Greeks constructed rectangles called golden rectangles
because they were thought to be pleasing to the eye. A rectangle is
considered golden if the dimensions of the rectangle are in a certain ratio.

$$\frac{l}{w} = \frac{l+w}{l}$$

The ratio $\dfrac{l}{w}$ is called the golden ratio. A golden rectangle

with length l and width w has the property that if it is joined
to a square of side length l to form a larger rectangle, the
length-to-width ratio of the larger rectangle is the same as
that of the original rectangle.

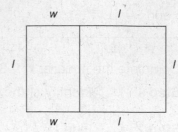

Solve.

1. a. Clear the equation of fractions and collect all the terms that contain
      variables on the left side of the equation.

   _____

   b. Complete the square and solve for l in terms of w. Ignore the negative
      solution since l must be a positive number. Use the result to find both the

      exact value of $\dfrac{l}{w}$ and a decimal approximation.

   _____

2. Measure the length and width of a credit card
   and calculate the ratio of the length and width.
   Does this closely approximate the golden ratio? _____

3. a. In the Fibonacci Sequence, {1, 1, 2, 3, 5, 8, 13, 21, 34, . . .}, each term
      from the third term on is the sum of the previous two terms. Make a list of
      values of the ratio of a term and its predecessor.

   _____

   b. What decimal value do these ratios approximate
      as the list is continued? _____

4. Consider the continued fraction $1 + \cfrac{1}{1 + \cfrac{1}{1 + \cfrac{1}{1 + \cdots}}}$.

   Make a table of decimal values for this fraction when 1 fraction is used, then 2, then 3, and so
   on. Round the values to the nearest thousandth. What value do the fractions seem to
   approach?

   _____

Problem Solving
Completing the Square

Sean and Mason run out of gas while fishing from their boat in the bay. They set off an emergency flare with an initial vertical velocity of 30 meters per second. The height of the flare in meters can be modeled by $h(t) = -5t^2 + 30t$, where t represents the number of seconds after launch.

1. Sean thinks the flare should reach at least 15 meters to be seen from the shore. They want to know how long the flare will take to reach this height.

   a. Write an equation to determine how long it will take the flare to reach 15 meters. _____

   b. Simplify the function so you can complete the square. _____

   c. Solve the equation by completing the square. _____

   d. Mason thinks that the flare will reach 15 meters in 5.4 seconds. Is he correct? Explain.

   _____

   e. Sean thinks the flare will reach 15 meters sooner, but then the flare will stay above 15 meters for about 5 seconds. Is he correct? Explain.

   _____

2. Sean wants to know how high the flare will reach above the surface of the water.

   a. Write the function in vertex form, factoring so the coefficient of t^2 is 1. _____

   b. Complete the square using the vertex form of the function. _____

   c. How high will the flare reach? _____

Choose the letter for the best answer.

3. Use the vertex form of the function to determine how long after firing the flare it will reach its maximum height.

   A 3 s

   B 5 s

   C 9 s

   D 15 s

4. The boys fire a similar flare from the deck 5 meters above the water level. Which statement is correct?

   A The flare will reach 45 m in 3 s.

   B The flare will reach 50 m in 3 s.

   C The flare will reach 45 m in 3.5 s.

   D The flare will reach 50 m in 3.5 s.

LESSON 5-4

Reading Strategy
Use a Model

Just as some numbers are perfect squares, some quadratic expressions are perfect squares.

$$(x + 2)^2 = x^2 + 4x + 4$$ ◁ Perfect square

You can model this expression with the area of algebra tiles. You can use three types of tiles.

Algebraic Term	Type of Tile	Model
x^2	Square with sides x	x · · · x
x	Rectangle with sides x and 1	1 · · · x
1	Square with sides 1	1 · · · 1

$$(x + 2)^2 = x^2 + 4x + 4$$

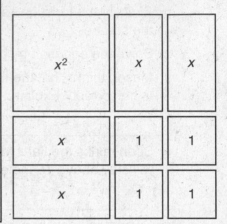

You can make a quadratic expression $x^2 + bx$ into a perfect square.

Not a Perfect Square		Add		Perfect Square
$x^2 + bx$	→	$\left(\dfrac{b}{2}\right)^2$	→	$x^2 + bx + \dfrac{b^2}{4} = \left(x + \dfrac{1}{2}b\right)^2$
$x^2 + 8x$	→	$\left(\dfrac{8}{2}\right)^2 = 4^2 = 16$	→	$x^2 + 8x + 16 = (x + 4)^2$

Answer each question.

1. Circle the expressions that are perfect squares.

   $(x - 1)^2$ $x^2 + 2x + 2$ $(4x - 5)^2$ $x^2 + 6x + 9$ $x^2 + x + 1$ x^2

2. a. What would you add to the expression
      $x^2 - 4x$ to make it a perfect square?   _____

   b. Write this expression as a perfect square.   _____

3. a. Use algebra tiles to draw a model for
      the expression $x^2 + 2x + 1$.

   b. Write this expression as a perfect square. What are the sides of the square created in
      the model?

_____

Holt Algebra 2

Practice A
Complex Numbers and Roots

Answer each question.

1. Circle the complex numbers.

   $3i$ $\qquad$ $(4)^2$ $\qquad$ $3x + 1$ $\qquad$ $7i - 1$ $\qquad$ $-2i$ $\qquad$ $\sqrt{8}$

2. What is another way of expressing $\sqrt{-1}$? $\qquad\qquad$_____

3. What is the value of the square of i ? $\qquad\qquad$_____

4. What is the real part of the complex number $a + bi$? $\qquad$_____

5. What is the imaginary part of the complex number $a + bi$? $\qquad$_____

Express each number in terms of i.

6. $\sqrt{-4}$ $\qquad\qquad\qquad$ 7. $3\sqrt{-9}$ $\qquad\qquad\qquad$ 8. $-\sqrt{-81}$

_____ $\qquad\qquad$ _____ $\qquad\qquad$ _____

9. $2\sqrt{-16}$ $\qquad\qquad\quad$ 10. $\sqrt{-25}$ $\qquad\qquad\qquad$ 11. $3\sqrt{-49}$

_____ $\qquad\qquad$ _____ $\qquad\qquad$ _____

The complex conjugate of $a + bi$ is $a - bi$. What is the complex conjugate of each of the following?

12. $1 + 2i$ $\qquad\qquad\qquad$ 13. $5i$ $\qquad\qquad\qquad\qquad$ 14. $2 - 3i$

_____ $\qquad\qquad$ _____ $\qquad\qquad$ _____

Solve.

15. a. What are the roots of the equation $x^2 = -25$?

    _____

    b. How could you check that these roots are correct?

    _____

16. a. What are the roots of the equation $48 + 3x^2 = 0$?

    _____

    b. How could you check that these roots are correct?

    _____

    _____

$\qquad\qquad\qquad\qquad\qquad\qquad\qquad\qquad$ Holt Algebra 2

LESSON
5-5

Practice B
Complex Numbers and Roots

Express each number in terms of *i*.

1. $\sqrt{-32}$

2. $2\sqrt{-18}$

3. $\sqrt{-\dfrac{1}{9}}$

_____   _____   _____

Solve each equation.

4. $3x^2 + 81 = 0$

5. $4x^2 = -28$

_____   _____

6. $\dfrac{1}{4}x^2 + 12 = 0$

7. $6x^2 = -126$

_____   _____

Find the values of *x* and *y* that make each equation true.

8. $2x - 20i = 8 - (4y)i$

9. $5i - 6x = (10y)i + 2$

_____   _____

Find the zeros of each function.

10. $f(x) = x^2 - 2x + 4$

11. $g(x) = x^2 + 6x + 14$

_____   _____

Find each complex conjugate.

12. $i - 3$

13. $3i - 4$

14. $11i$

_____   _____   _____

Solve.

15. The impedance of an electrical circuit is a way of measuring how much the circuit impedes the flow of electricity. The impedance can be a complex number. A circuit is being designed that must have an impedance that satisfies the function $f(x) = 2x^2 - 12x + 40$, where *x* is a measure of the impedance. Find the zeros of the function.

_____

Holt Algebra 2

LESSON 5-5 Practice C

Complex Numbers and Roots

Solve each equation.

1. $\frac{1}{2}x^2 = -28$

2. $3x^2 + 14 = -19$

_____   _____

Find the zeros of each function.

3. $f(x) = x^2 - 6x + 20$ 4. $g(x) = -2x^2 + 8x - 16$ 5. $h(x) = x^2 - 2x + 3$

_____   _____   _____

Find the values of x and y that make each equation true.

6. $6x - 2i = (-2y)i + 10$ 7. $-40i + 2x = (5y)i - 12$ 8. $-8y + 14i = (7x)i - 2$

_____   _____   _____

Find each complex conjugate.

9. $\sqrt{3i} - 25$ 10. $-5i + \frac{12}{5}$ 11. $-2 - 1.5i$

_____   _____   _____

Solve.

12. Does the function $f(x) = (x - 1)^2 + 5$ have real or imaginary zeros? How can you determine that without any calculations or graphing?

_____

13. Joel wrote the function $s(t) = t^2 + 6t + 34$ to approximate the speed of a model rocket that he built. The function models the speed of the rocket, s, at a given time, t.

   a. What does $s(t) = 0$ represent?

_____

   b. Solve the equation to find the zeros of the function.

_____

   c. Is Joel's function correct? Explain.

_____

           Holt Algebra 2

LESSON
5-5

Reteach

Complex Numbers and Roots

An **imaginary number** is the square root of a negative number.
Use the definition $\sqrt{-1} = i$ to simplify square roots.

Simplify.

$\sqrt{-25}$

$\sqrt{(25)(-1)}$ *Factor out –1.*

$\sqrt{(25)}\sqrt{-1}$ *Separate roots.*

$5\sqrt{-1}$ *Simplify.*

$5i$ *Express in terms of i.*

$-\sqrt{-48}$

$-\sqrt{(48)(-1)}$ *Factor out –1.*

$-\sqrt{(48)}\sqrt{-1}$ *Separate roots.*

$-\sqrt{16}\sqrt{3}\sqrt{-1}$ *Factor the perfect square.*

$-4\sqrt{3}\sqrt{-1}$ *Simplify.*   Real   Imaginary

$-4i\sqrt{3}$ *Express in terms of i.*

Complex numbers are numbers that can be written in the form $a + bi$.

The **complex conjugate** of $a + bi$ is $a - bi$.   Write as $a + bi$
The complex conjugate of $5i$ is $-5i$.   Find $0 - 5i = -5i$

Express each number in terms of *i*.

1. $\sqrt{-72}$

     $\sqrt{(36)(2)(-1)}$

2. $4\sqrt{-45}$

     $4\sqrt{(9)(5)(-1)}$

3. $\sqrt{-100}$

_____   _____   _____

4. $5\sqrt{-54}$

5. $2\sqrt{-64}$

6. $-\sqrt{-98}$

_____   _____   _____

Find each complex conjugate.

7. $-9i$

8. $1 + 4i$

9. $12 - i$

_____   _____   _____

     Holt Algebra 2

LESSON	**Reteach**
5-5	***Complex Numbers and Roots*** *(continued)*

You can use the square root property and $\sqrt{-1} = i$ to solve quadratic equations with imaginary solutions.

Solve $x^2 = -64$.

$\sqrt{x^2} = \pm\sqrt{-64}$ *Take the square root of both sides.*

$x = \pm 8i$ *Express in terms of i.*

Check each root: $(8i)^2 = 64i^2 = 64(-1) = -64$

> Remember: $\left(\sqrt{-1}\right)^2 = i^2 = -1$

$\quad\quad\quad\quad\quad (-8i)^2 = 64i^2 = 64(-1) = -64$

Solve $5x^2 + 80 = 0$.

$5x^2 = -80$ *Subtract 80 from both sides.*

$x^2 = -16$ *Divide both sides by 5.*

$\sqrt{x^2} = \pm\sqrt{-16}$ *Take the square root of both sides.*

$x = \pm 4i$ *Express in terms of i.*

Check each root:

$5(4i)^2 + 80$ $5(-4i)^2 + 80$

$5(16)i^2 + 80$ $5(16)i^2 + 80$

$80(-1) + 80$ $80(-1) + 80$

0 0

Solve each equation.

10. $x^2 + 18 = 0$

$x^2 = -18$

$x = \pm\sqrt{(9)(2)(-1)}$

_____

11. $6x^2 + 24 = 0$

$6x^2 = -24$

_____

_____

12. $x^2 + 49 = 0$

_____

_____

_____

13. $x^2 + 100 = 0$

14. $3x^2 + 108 = 0$

15. $x^2 + 12 = 0$

         Holt Algebra 2

Challenge
Imaginary Coefficients

If a quadratic equation with real coefficients has nonreal roots, those roots are complex conjugates. But what if the coefficients of the quadratic equation are also complex or imaginary numbers? Consider the factored equation

$$(x + 3i)(x - i) = 0.$$

The solutions of this equation are i and $-3i$. The expanded polynomial is

$$x^2 + 2ix + 3 = 0.$$

Notice that the coefficients are not all real numbers. That is why the complex solutions are not conjugates of one another. Equations of this type, where the middle term contains an imaginary number, are factored similarly to those with real coefficients except the sign of the constant term will be different due to the presence of the imaginary numbers.

All Real Coefficients	Some Imaginary Coefficients
$x^2 - 11x + 30 = 0$	$x^2 - 11ix - 30 = 0$
$(x - 5)(x - 6) = 0$	$(x - 5i)(x - 6i) = 0$
$x = 5$ or $x = 6$	$x = 5i$ or $x = 6i$

Solve each equation by factoring.

1. $x^2 + 5ix + 14 = 0$ _____

2. $x^2 + 14ix - 48 = 0$ _____

3. $x^2 + 3ix + 108 = 0$ _____

4. $x^2 - 54ix - 245 = 0$ _____

5. $x^2 + 52ix - 576 = 0$ _____

Look at equations of the form $2ix^2 + 5x + 12i = 0$. In this case, both the squared term and the constant contain imaginary coefficients. This equation factors into the binomials $(2ix - 3)$ and $(x - 4i)$ and the

solutions are $4i$ and $\dfrac{3}{2i}$. Multiply the numerator and denominator of the

fraction by $-2i$ to obtain $-\dfrac{3}{2}i$.

Solve each equation by factoring. Write the solutions in $a + bi$ form.

6. $3ix^2 - 7x - 4i = 0$ _____

7. $5ix^2 + 11x - 2i = 0$ _____

8. $2ix^2 - 16x - 30i = 0$ _____

9. $4ix^2 + 7x + 65i = 0$ _____

10. $12ix^2 + 28x - 15i = 0$ _____

LESSON 5-5	**Problem Solving**
	Complex Numbers and Roots

At a carnival, a new attraction allows contestants to jump off a springboard onto a platform to be launched vertically into the air. The object is to ring a bell located 20 feet overhead. The distance from the bell in feet is modeled by the function
$dt = 16t^2 - bt + 20$, **where t is the time in seconds after leaving the platform, and b is the takeoff velocity from the platform.**

1. Kate watches some of the contestants. She theorizes that if the platform launches a contestant with a takeoff velocity of at least 32 feet per second, the contestant can ring the bell.

    a. Find the zeros for the function using 32 feet per second as the takeoff velocity.   _____

    b. Is Kate's theory valid? Explain.

    _____

2. Mirko suggests they vary the value of b and determine for which values of b the roots are real.

    a. Complete the table to show the roots for different values of b.

    b. For which values of b in the table are the roots real?

    _____

    c. What difference does it make if the roots are real?

b	Function	Roots
24	$d(t) = 16t^2 - 24t + 20$	
32	$d(t) = 16t^2 - \_\_t + 20$	
40	$d(t) = 16t^2 - \_\_t + 20$	
48	$d(t) = 16t^2 - \_\_t + 20$	

3. Using the results from the table, and the function, estimate the minimum takeoff velocity needed for a contestant to be able to ring the bell.   _____

Choose the letter for the best answer.

4. Mirko suggests using four bells at heights of 15, 20, 25, and 30 feet from the platform. How many of the bells can a contestant reach if the takeoff velocity is 32 feet per second?

    A 3   C 1

    B 2   D 0

5. At what height must a bell be placed for a contestant to reach it with a takeoff velocity of 48 feet per second?

    A 20 feet or less

    B 25 feet or less

    C 30 feet or less

    D 36 feet or less

Holt Algebra 2

LESSON 5-5 **Reading Strategy**
Understand Symbols

The square root of a real number can be positive or negative. The imaginary number i represents $\sqrt{-1}$. You can use i to find the square roots of imaginary numbers.

$$\sqrt{-3}$$
$$= \sqrt{(-1)3}$$
$$= \sqrt{-1} \cdot \sqrt{3}$$
$$= i\sqrt{3}$$

You can also use i to solve quadratic equations that have no real solutions:

Solve	Check the solution.	

$$x^2 + 49 = 0$$
$$x^2 = -49$$
$$x = \pm\sqrt{-49}$$
$$x = \pm 7i$$

$$(7i)^2 = 7^2 i^2$$
$$= 49(-1)$$
$$= -49$$

$$(-7i)^2 = (-7)^2 i^2$$
$$= 49(-1)$$
$$= -49$$

Both $7i$ and $-7i$ are solutions of $x^2 + 49 = 0$.

Answer each question.

1. Circle the imaginary numbers.

   $-\sqrt{4}$ $i\sqrt{9}$ $3i$ $\sqrt{-8}$ $-\sqrt{3}$ $(-12)^2$

2. Use i to represent a number whose square is -9.

   _____

3. Consider the equation $x^2 + 1 = 0$.

   a. Find the solutions for the equation.

   _____

   b. Why doesn't this equation have real roots?

   _____

4. Show that $i\sqrt{5}$ and $-i\sqrt{5}$ are the solutions of $x^2 = -5$.

   _____

   _____

5. Is $(3i)(5i)$ a real or an imaginary number? Explain.

   _____

   _____

LESSON 5-6

Practice A

The Quadratic Formula

Find the zeros of each function by using the Quadratic Formula,

$$x = \frac{-b \pm \sqrt{b^2 - 4ac}}{2a}.$$

1. $f(x) = x^2 + 4$

   $x^2 + 0x + 4 = 0$

   $x = \dfrac{-0 \pm \sqrt{0^2 - 4 \cdot 1 \cdot 4}}{2 \cdot 1}$

   $x = \dfrac{\pm\sqrt{\underline{\hspace{1cm}}}}{\underline{\hspace{1cm}}}$

   _____

2. $f(x) = 2x^2 - 5x + 3$

   $2x^2 - 5x + 3 = 0$

   $x = \dfrac{-(\underline{\hspace{0.6cm}}) \pm \sqrt{(\underline{\hspace{0.6cm}})^2 - 4 \cdot (\underline{\hspace{0.6cm}}) \cdot (\underline{\hspace{0.6cm}})}}{2 \cdot \underline{\hspace{0.6cm}}}$

   $x = \dfrac{\underline{\hspace{1cm}} \pm \sqrt{\underline{\hspace{0.6cm}} - \underline{\hspace{0.6cm}}}}{\underline{\hspace{1cm}}}$

   _____

3. $f(x) = x^2 + 2x + 4$

   _____

4. $f(x) = x^2 + 2x$

   _____

Find the value of the discriminant for each function.

5. $f(x) = x^2 + x + 4$ 6. $f(x) = -2x^2 + 3x - 1$ 7. $f(x) = 3x^2 + 6x + 3$

_____   _____   _____

Find the type and number of solutions for each equation.

8. $x^2 + 2x + 1 = 0$

   _____

9. $2x^2 + x - 4 = 0$

   _____

10. $2x^2 + 4x + 3 = 0$

   _____

11. $2x^2 - 5x + 3 = 0$

   _____

Solve.

12. The length of a rectangle is 3 feet longer than its width. The area of the rectangle is 270 square feet.

   a. What is the width of the rectangle?   _____

   b. What is the width of the rectangle if the area is only 160 square feet?

   _____

Holt Algebra 2

LESSON
5-6

Practice B
The Quadratic Formula

Find the zeros of each function by using the Quadratic Formula.

1. $f(x) = x^2 + 10x + 9$

2. $g(x) = 2x^2 + 4x - 12$

_____

_____

3. $h(x) = 3x^2 - 3x + \dfrac{3}{4}$

4. $f(x) = x^2 + 2x - 3$

_____

_____

5. $g(x) = 2x^2 + 3x + 1$

6. $g(x) = x^2 + 5x + -3$

_____

_____

Find the type and number of solutions for each equation.

7. $x^2 - 3x = -8$

8. $x^2 + 4x = -3$

9. $2x^2 - 12x = -18$

_____

_____

_____

Solve.

10. A newspaper delivery person in a car is tossing folded newspapers from
    the car window to driveways. The speed of the car is 30 feet per second,
    and the driver does not slow down. The newspapers are tossed horizontally
    from a height of 4 feet above the ground. The height of the papers as they
    are thrown can be modeled by $y = -16t^2 + 4$, and the distance they travel to
    the driveway is $d = 30t$.

   a. How long does it take for a newspaper to land?

   _____

   b. From how many feet before the driveway must the papers be thrown?

   _____

   c. The delivery person starts to throw the newspapers at an angle and the height
      of the papers as they travel can now be modeled by $y = -16t^2 + 12t + 4$.
      How long does it take the papers to reach the ground now?

   _____

LESSON
5-6

Practice C

The Quadratic Formula

Find the zeros of each function by using the Quadratic Formula.

1. $f(x) = x^2 + 8x - 3$

2. $g(x) = 2x^2 - 6x - 1$

3. $h(x) = x^2 - x + 12$

4. $f(x) = -2x^2 - 5x + 20$

5. $f(x) = -2x^2 + 6x - 2$

6. $f(x) = 3x^2 - 10x + 4$

Find the type and number of solutions for each equation.

7. $2x^2 + 7 = -4x$

8. $x^2 - 3 = -6x$

9. $4x^2 + 4 = -8x$

Solve.

10. The height $h(t)$ measured in feet of an object dropped by an astronaut on the moon can be approximated by $h(t) = h_0 - 2.7t^2$, where h_0 is the height from which the object was dropped. About how long would it take an object to fall to the surface of the moon ($h = 0$) if it were dropped by an astronaut from a height of 6 feet?

_____

11. The height in feet, h, of a base jumper jumping off a cliff is given by the equation $h = 3t^2 - 700t + 2000$, where t is the time in seconds. The horizontal distance that he travels from the cliff is given by $d = 13t$.

   a. How long does it take the base jumper from the time he jumps ($t = 0$) until he hits ground ($h = 0$)? _____

   b. When he reaches the ground, how far away is he from the base of the cliff? _____

12. A path of uniform width surrounds a rectangular garden that is 5m wide and 12m long. The area of the path is 168m². Find the width of the path. _____

Holt Algebra 2

Reteach

The Quadratic Formula

The Quadratic Formula is another way to find the roots of a quadratic equation or the zeros of a quadratic function.

Find the zeros of $f(x) = x^2 - 6x - 11$.

Step 1 Set $f(x) = 0$. $\qquad\qquad\qquad x^2 - 6x - 11 = 0$

Step 2 Write the Quadratic Formula. $x = \dfrac{-b \pm \sqrt{b^2 - 4ac}}{2a}$

Step 3 Substitute values for a, b, and c into the Quadratic Formula.

$a = 1,\ b = -6,\ c = -11$

$$x = \frac{-b \pm \sqrt{b^2 - 4ac}}{2a} = \frac{-(-6) \pm \sqrt{(-6)^2 - 4(1)(-11)}}{2(1)}$$

Step 4 Simplify.

$$x = \frac{-(-6) \pm \sqrt{(-6)^2 - 4(1)(-11)}}{2(1)} = \frac{6 \pm \sqrt{36 + 44}}{2} = \frac{6 \pm \sqrt{80}}{2}$$

Step 5 Write in simplest form.

$$x = \frac{6 \pm \sqrt{80}}{2} = 3 \pm \frac{\sqrt{80}}{2} = 3 \pm \frac{\sqrt{(16)(5)}}{2} = 3 \pm \frac{4\sqrt{5}}{2} = 3 \pm 2\sqrt{5}$$

> Remember to divide both terms of the numerator by 2 to simplify.

Find the zeros of each function using the Quadratic Formula.

1. $f(x) = x^2 + x - 1$

$x^2 + x - 1 = 0$

$a = $ _____, $b = $ _____, $c = $ _____

$x = \dfrac{-b \pm \sqrt{b^2 - 4ac}}{2a}$

$x = \dfrac{-(\underline{}) \pm \sqrt{(\underline{})^2 - 4(\underline{})(\underline{})}}{2(\underline{})}$

_____

_____

2. $f(x) = x^2 - 6x + 6$

_____

$a = $ _____, $b = $ _____, $c = $ _____

$x = \dfrac{-b \pm \sqrt{b^2 - 4ac}}{2a}$

_____

_____

_____

LESSON 5-6

Reteach

The Quadratic Formula (continued)

The **discriminant** of $ax^2 + bx + c = 0$ ($a \neq 0$) is $b^2 - 4ac$.

Use the discriminant to determine the number of roots of a quadratic equation. A quadratic equation can have 2 real solutions, 1 real solution, or 2 complex solutions.

Find the type and number of solutions.

$2x^2 - 5x = 3$	$x^2 + 10x = -25$	$3x^2 - 4x = -2$
Write the equation in standard form:	Write the equation in standard form:	Write the equation in standard form:
$2x^2 - 5x - 3 = 0$	$x^2 + 10x + 25 = 0$	$3x^2 - 4x + 2 = 0$
$a = 2, b = -5, c = -3$	$a = 1, b = 10, c = 25$	$a = 3, b = -4, c = 2$
Evaluate the discriminant:	Evaluate the discriminant:	Evaluate the discriminant:
$b^2 - 4ac$	$b^2 - 4ac$	$b^2 - 4ac$
$(-5)^2 - 4(2)(-3)$	$(10)^2 - 4(1)(25)$	$(-4)^2 - 4(3)(2)$
$25 + 24$	$100 - 100$	$16 - 24$
49	0	-8
When $b^2 - 4ac > 0$, the equation has 2 real solutions.	When $b^2 - 4ac = 0$, the equation has 1 real solution.	When $b^2 - 4ac < 0$, the equation has 2 complex solutions.

Find the type and number of solutions for each equation.

3. $x^2 - 12x = -36$

   $x^2 - 12x + 36 = 0$

   $a = $_____, $b = $_____, $c = $_____

   $b^2 - 4ac = $

   _____

   Classify solutions:

   _____

4. $x^2 - 4x = -7$

   _____

   _____

   $b^2 - 4ac = $

   _____

   Classify solutions:

   _____

5. $x^2 - 7x = -3$

   _____

   _____

   $b^2 - 4ac = $

   _____

   Classify solutions:

   _____

Holt Algebra 2

LESSON **Challenge**
5-6

Relating Roots and Coefficients of a Quadratic Equation

The general solution of the quadratic equation $ax^2 + bx + c = 0$ can be written in terms of the coefficients a, b, and c, and this solution is known as the Quadratic Formula. You can explore some other relationships between the roots and the coefficients.

1. Complete the table below.

	Equation	Roots	Sum of the Roots	Product of the Roots
a.	$x^2 - 6x + 8 = 0$			
b.	$x^2 - 7x + 12 = 0$			
c.	$x^2 + 2x - 35 = 0$			
d.	$4x^2 - 8x + 3 = 0$			
e.	$9x^2 + 3x - 2 = 0$			

2. Refer to the table above. Let the roots of the quadratic equation $ax^2 + bx + c = 0$ be represented by r_1 and r_2.

   a. Express the sum of the roots in terms of the coefficients of the equation. $r_1 + r_2 =$ _____

   b. Express the product of the roots in terms of the coefficients of the equation. $r_1 r_2 =$ _____

Use the relationships between roots and coefficients that you wrote in Exercise 2. Verify your answer by solving the equation.

3. Write a quadratic equation whose roots are $2 + \sqrt{5}$ and $2 - \sqrt{5}$. _____

4. The sum of the roots of $5x^2 - kx - 3 = 0$ is equal to the product of the roots. Determine the value of k. _____

5. Without solving, decide which numbers are the roots of $9x^2 - 6x - 1$.

   A. $1 \pm \sqrt{2}$ B. $1 \pm \sqrt{3}$ C. $\dfrac{1 \pm \sqrt{2}}{3}$ D. $\dfrac{1 \pm \sqrt{3}}{2}$ _____

6. Which of these equations has $\dfrac{-5 \pm \sqrt{17}}{2}$ as its solutions?

   A. $x^2 + 5x + 2 = 0$ B. $x^2 + 5x - 2 = 0$

   C. $x^2 - 5x - 2 = 0$ D. $x^2 - 5x + 2 = 0$ _____

LESSON 5-6

Problem Solving

The Quadratic Formula

In a shot-put event, Jenna tosses her last shot from a position of about 6 feet above the ground with an initial vertical and horizontal velocity of 20 feet per second. The height of the shot is modeled by the function $h(t) = -16t^2 + 20t + 6$, where t is the time in seconds after the toss. The horizontal distance traveled after t seconds is modeled by $d(t) = 20t$.

1. Jenna wants to know the exact distance the shot travels at a velocity of 20 feet per second.

   a. Use the Quadratic Formula $t = \dfrac{-b \pm \sqrt{b^2 - 4ac}}{2a}$

   to solve the height function for t. _____

   b. Use the value for t and the distance function to find the distance her shot travels. _____

2. Jenna is working to improve her performance. She makes a table to show how the horizontal distance varies with velocity. Complete the table.

	Velocity (ft/s)	Formula	Time (s)	Distance (ft)
a.	22	$t = \dfrac{-22 \pm \sqrt{(22)^2 - 4(-16)(6)}}{2(-16)}$		
b.	25			
c.	28			

Jenna has not reached her full potential yet. Her goal is to toss the shot from a height of 6 feet 6 inches with a vertical and horizontal velocity of 30 feet per second. Choose the letter for the best answer.

3. If she achieves her goal, how long will her shot stay in the air?

   A 1.65 s

   B 1.87 s

   C 2.07 s

   D 2.27 s

4. If she achieves her goal, what horizontal distance will the shot travel?

   A 41.4 ft

   B 56.1 ft

   C 62.1 ft

   D 68.1 ft

Holt Algebra 2

LESSON 5-6 Reading Strategy
Graphic Organizer

The Quadratic Formula can be used to solve any quadratic equation.

Definition	Facts
When the equation is in the form $$ax^2 + bx + c = 0$$ The quadratic formula is $$x = \frac{-b \pm \sqrt{b^2 - 4ac}}{2a}$$	In a quadratic equation, the expression under the square root sign, $b^2 - 4ac$, is known as the **discriminant**. It tells you about the roots of the equation. $b^2 - 4ac > 0$: two real roots $b^2 - 4ac < 0$: two complex roots $b^2 - 4ac = 0$: one real root
Example $$x^2 - x - 6 = 0$$ $$a = 1, b = -1, c = -6$$ $$x = \frac{-(-1) \pm \sqrt{(-1)^2 - 4(1)(-6)}}{2(1)}$$ $$x = 3, x = -2$$	**Find the number of roots.** $b^2 - 4ac$ $(-1)^2 - 4(1)(-6)$ $1 + 24 = 25$ $25 > 0$ There are two real roots.

Use the equation $2x^2 - 6x - 9 = 0$ to answer the following questions.

1. Write the values of *a*, *b*, and *c*.

   _____

2. Find the value of the discriminant.

   _____

3. Does this quadratic equation have real or complex roots?

   _____

4. Does the graph of the related quadratic function $f(x) = 2x^2 - 6x - 9$ intersect the *x*-axis? Explain how you know.

   _____

5. What are the solutions to this equation?

   _____

   _____

LESSON 5-7

Practice A

Solving Quadratic Inequalities

Graph each inequality and shade the solution region. Use a test point to verify the solution region.

1. $y < x^2 - 2x + 3$

   a. y-intercept is 3.

   b. Vertex is (1, 2).

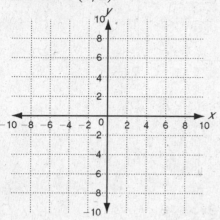

   c. Test point _____

_____

2. $y \geq -x^2 + 4x - 5$

   a. y-intercept is _____

   b. Vertex is _____

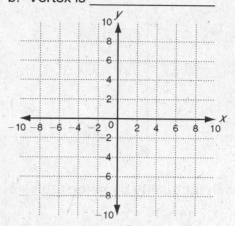

   c. Test point _____

_____

Solve each inequality by using algebra.

3. $x^2 + x - 8 \leq -6$

   a. Write the related equation.

   b. Solve for x to find the critical values.

   c. Test an x-value in each interval.

   d. Write the solution.

_____

_____

_____

_____

4. $x^2 + 10x + 25 > 9$ 5. $x^2 - x < 12$ 6. $x^2 + 2x - 10 \geq 14$

_____   _____   _____

Solve.

7. The annual profit, $p(x)$, in dollars of a small company varies with the number of employees, x, as $p(x) = -40x^2 + 4400x$. What is the range of the number of employees for which the company's annual profit will be at least $112,000?

_____

      Holt Algebra 2

LESSON 5-7

Practice B
Solving Quadratic Inequalities

Graph each inequality.

1. $y < x^2 - 2x + 6$

2. $y > 2x^2 - x - 7$

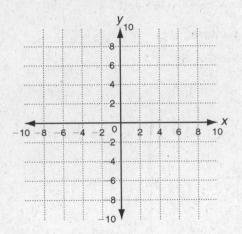

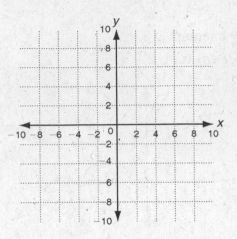

Solve each inequality by using tables or graphs.

3. $x^2 + 3x - 14 \leq 14$

4. $x^2 - 9x > -18$

_____

_____

Solve each inequality by using algebra.

5. $x^2 - x - 3 > x$

6. $x^2 + 6x + 3 < -2$

_____

_____

7. $3 \leq x^2 - 8x + 15$

8. $3x^2 + x + 8 \leq 12$

_____

_____

Solve.

9. An online music service that sells song downloads models its profit using the function $P(d) = -5d^2 + 450d - 1000$, where d is the number of downloads sold and P is the profit. How many downloads does it need to sell to make a profit of more than \$8000?

_____

Holt Algebra 2

Name _____ Date _____ Class_____

Practice C
Solving Quadratic Inequalities

Graph each inequality.

1. $y < -2x^2 - 5x + 6$

2. $y \geq x^2 - 6x + 2$

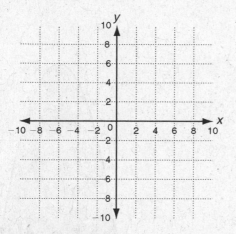
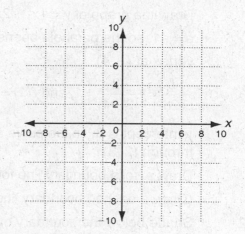

Solve each inequality.

3. $x^2 - 10x + 17 \geq -4$

4. $2x^2 - 7x - 2 < 2$

5. $3x^2 + 5 \leq 53$

6. $x^2 - 6x - 36 > 36$

Solve.

7. Use the Quadratic Formula to find the critical values for the inequality $x^2 - 3x + 8 \geq -2$.

8. The distance, d, in car lengths, that a drag racer travels during the course of a race is given by $d = 0.8t^2 - 3.5t$, where t is time in seconds.

  a. How long does it take for a racer to travel at least 100 car lengths?

  b. During what time period will the racer be more than 50 car lengths but less than 100 car lengths into the race?

  c. During what time period will the racer be less than 50 car lengths from the start?

Holt Algebra 2

LESSON **Reteach**
5-7 *Solving Quadratic Inequalities*

Graphing quadratic inequalities is similar to graphing linear inequalities.

Graph $y \le -x^2 + 2x + 3$.

Step 1 Draw the graph of $y = -x^2 + 2x + 3$.

- $a = -1$, so the parabola opens downward.
- vertex at (1, 4)

$$-\frac{b}{2a} = -\frac{2}{2(-1)} = 1, \text{ and } f(1) = 4$$

- y-intercept is 3, so the curve also passes through (2, 3)

Draw a solid boundary line for $\le$ or $\ge$.

(Draw a dashed boundary line for $<$ or $>$.)

Step 2 Shade below the boundary of the parabola for $<$ or $\le$. (Shade above the boundary for $>$ or $\ge$.)

Step 3 Check using a test point in the shaded region. Use (0, 0).

$$y \le -x^2 + 2x + 3$$

$$?: 0 \le -(0)^2 + 2(0) + 3$$

$$\checkmark : 0 \le 3$$

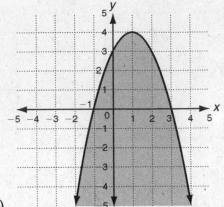

Graph each inequality.

1. $y \ge x^2 - 4x + 3$

Vertex: _____

y-intercept: _____

Boundary: _____

Test point: (1, 1)

_____

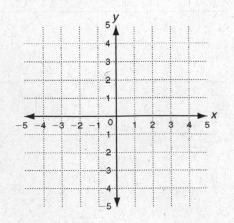

2. $y < -x^2 - 4x - 1$

Vertex: _____

y-intercept: _____

Boundary: _____

Test point: (−1, 0)

_____

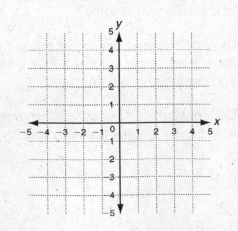

Holt Algebra 2

LESSON 5-7

Reteach

Solving Quadratic Inequalities (continued)

You can use algebra to solve quadratic inequalities.

Solve the inequality $x^2 - 2x - 5 \leq 3$.

Step 1 Write the related equation. $x^2 - 2x - 5 = 3$

Step 2 Solve the equation.

$x^2 - 2x - 8 = 0$

$(x - 4)(x + 2) = 0$

$(x - 4) = 0$ or $(x + 2) = 0$

$x = 4$ or $x = -2$

> Write the equation in standard form. Then factor to solve for x.

> These solutions are called **critical values.**

Step 3 Use the critical values to write three intervals.

Intervals: $x \leq -2$, $-2 \leq x \leq 4$, $x \geq 4$

Step 4 Using the inequality, test a value for x in each interval.

$x^2 - 2x - 5 \leq 3$

$x \leq -2$: Try -3. $(-3)^2 - 2(-3) - 5 \leq 3$?

$10 \leq 3$ False.

$-2 \leq x \leq 4$: Try 0. $(0)^2 - 2(0) - 5 \leq 3$?

$-5 \leq 3$ True.

$x \geq 4$: Try 5. $(5)^2 - 2(5) - 5 \leq 3$?

$10 \leq 3$ False.

Step 5 Shade the solution on a number line.

> Use closed circles when the inequality is $\leq$ or $\geq$.
> Use open circles when the inequality is $<$ or $>$.

Solve each inequality. Graph the solution on the number line.

3. $x^2 - 2x + 1 \geq 4$

Solve: $x^2 - 2x - $ ____ $= $ ____ .

Critical values: _____

Test x-values: _____

_____

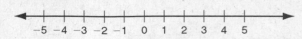

4. $x^2 + x + 4 < 6$

Solve: _____

Critical values: _____

Test x-values: _____

_____

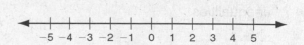

Holt Algebra 2

LESSON 5-7 Challenge

Areas Defined by Inequalities

The area inside a parabola bounded by a horizontal line segment is given

by the formula $A = \dfrac{2}{3}bh$, where b is the length of the line segment and h is

the vertical distance from the vertex of the parabola to the line segment.

Consider the region bounded by the curves
$y = 5 - x^2$ and $y = x^2 - 3$. This region is shown
in the graph at right.

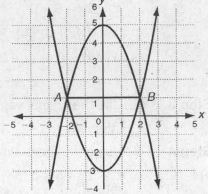

To find the area of the region bounded by the curves,
you need to know the length of the horizontal line
segment AB.

1. Adapt the substitution method for systems of linear
   equations to find the coordinates of the intersection
   points of the parabolas. What are the coordinates of A and B?

   _____

2. What is the length of line segment AB?   _____

3. Find the area enclosed by each parabola and line segment AB. Use this data to find the
   area bounded between the two curves.

   _____

For Exercises 4–6 use this system of inequalities: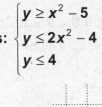

4. Graph the system of inequalities and shade
   the intersection of the three regions.

5. Identify the points of intersection of the
   parabolas and the line $y = 4$.

   _____

6. Find the area enclosed by the three
   inequalities.

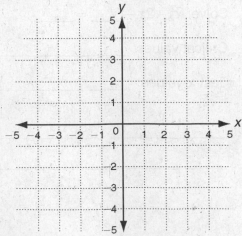

Holt Algebra 2

Name _____ Date _____ Class_____

Problem Solving

Solving Quadratic Inequalities

The manager at Travel Tours is proposing a fall tour to Australia
and New Zealand. He works out the details and finds that the profit
P for x persons is $P(x) = -28x^2 + 1400x - 3496$. The owner of
Travel Tours has decided that the tour will be canceled if the profit is
less than $10,000.

1. a. Write an inequality that you could use to find
    the number of people needed to make the
    tour possible.   _____

    b. Solve the related equation to find the critical
    values.   _____

    c. Test an x-value in each interval.

x-value	Evaluate	$P \geq 10{,}000$?
10	$-28(10)^2 + 1400(10) - 3496$	
30		
40		

    d. How many people will Travel Tours need to make
    the tour possible?   _____

2. A year later, the owner of Travel Tours decides that the
    Australia/New Zealand tour will have to make a profit of at least
    $12,000 for the tour to be possible. What effect will this have on the
    range of people able to take this tour?

_____

The manager plans a tour to the Fiji Islands and determines that the
profit P for x persons is $P(x) = -40x^2 + 1920x - 3200$. Choose the letter
for the best answer.

3. In order to make $10,000 profit, how
    many people will it take for this tour to
    happen?

    A Between 9 and 39 people

    B Between 14 and 36 people

    C At least 22 people

    D At least 30 people

4. The owner thinks the company should
    make at least $15,000 profit on the Fiji
    Islands tour. How many people will it take
    for the tour to happen?

    A Between 9 and 39 people

    B Between 13 and 35 people

    C At least 22 people

    D At least 35 people

Holt Algebra 2

LESSON
5-7

Reading Strategy
Analyze Information

You can graph quadratic inequalities just as you can graph linear
inequalities. The solution of a quadratic inequality is a region in the plane.
The graph of $y = x^2 + 1$ is shown below. Its curve describes the boundary
between two regions.

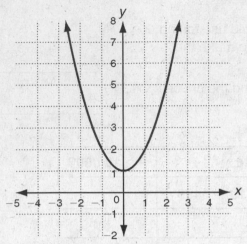

The graph can show four different inequalities:

$$y \geq x^2 + 1$$
$$y > x^2 + 1$$
$$y < x^2 + 1$$
$$y \leq x^2 + 1$$

Analyze the graph using the inequalities shown above.

1. Which inequalities include the boundary as part of their solution?

   _____

2. Which inequality describes just the region outside the parabola?
   Is (0, 1) a solution of this inequality? Explain why or why not.

   _____

3. Describe the region represented by $y > x^2 + 1$.

   _____

4. The points (2, 10) and (3, 10) are in the solution region of which inequality?
   Write another solution of this inequality.

   _____

5. How would you change the graph to show that the boundary line is not
   included in the solution region?

   _____

LESSON
5-8

Practice A

Curve Fitting with Quadratic Models

Use each data set to answer the questions.

1.

x	−2	−1	0	1	2
y	24	12	3	−3	−6

a. What are the first differences for this data set?   _____

b. What are the second differences for this data set?   _____

c. Does this data set represent a quadratic function? Why?

_____

2.

x	−3	0	3	6	9
y	10	4	−1	−5	−8

a. What are the first differences for this data set?   _____

b. What are the second differences for this data set?   _____

c. Does this data set represent a quadratic function? Why?

_____

Write a quadratic function that fits each set of points.

3. (0, −12), (6, 12), (2, −8)

a. Use each ordered pair to write an equation of the form $y = ax^2 + bx + c$.

_____   _____   _____

b. Solve the system of equations using any method you choose.

_____

c. Use the values of *a*, *b*, and *c* to write the quadratic function.

_____

4. (1, 11), (2, 2), (3, −5)   5. (1, 18), (2, 12), (3, 2)

_____   _____

Holt Algebra 2

LESSON 5-8 | **Practice B**

Curve Fitting with Quadratic Models

Determine whether each data set could represent a quadratic function. Explain.

1.

x	−1	0	1	2	3
y	35	22	11	2	−5

_____

2.

x	−2	0	2	4	6
y	18	10	6	2	1

_____

Write a quadratic equation that fits each set of points.

3. (0, −8), (2, 0), and (−3, −5)

4. (−1, −16), (2, 5), and (5, 8)

_____   _____

5. (−2, 6), (0, −6), and (3, −9)

6. (1, 4), (−2, 13), and (0, 3)

_____   _____

Solve.

7. The data table shows the energy, *E,* of a certain object in joules at a given velocity, *v,* in meters per second.

Energy (joules)	4.5	12.5	24.5	40.5
Velocity (m/s)	1.5	2.5	3.5	4.5

a. Find the quadratic relationship between the energy and velocity of the object.

_____

b. What is the energy of an object with a speed of 5 m/s?

_____

c. What is the velocity of the object if the energy is 128 joules?

_____

Holt Algebra 2

LESSON 5-8

Practice C

Curve Fitting with Quadratic Models

The following data sets represent quadratic functions. Find the missing coordinates.

1.

x	−2	−1	0	1	2	3
y	28	14	3		−10	

2.

x	−2	−1	0	1	2	3
y		0		6	12	20

Write a quadratic function that fits each set of points.

3. (1, 0), (−3, 12), and (0, −3)

4. (4, 0), (0, −28), and (6, 2)

_____

5. (3, 0), (2, 3), and (7, 8)

6. (5, −6), (−2, 8), and (−1, 0)

_____

Solve.

7. Do the points (−8, 6), (2, 1), and (6, −1) describe a quadratic function? Explain how you know.

_____

8. Teresa is running a chemical reaction that can be modeled by a quadratic function. When she begins the reaction there are 20 grams of sodium chloride present. At 2 minutes there are 48 grams of sodium chloride. At 5 minutes there are 60 grams of sodium chloride, and at 8 minutes there are 36 grams of sodium chloride.

   a. Write a quadratic function that models her data.

   _____

   b. At what point will all of the sodium chloride be used up in the reaction?

   _____

Holt Algebra 2

LESSON 5-8

Reteach
Curve Fitting with Quadratic Models

When the second differences are constant in a pattern of data, the data could represent a quadratic function.

Data Set 1

x	2	3	4	5	6
y	6	12	20	30	42

> Check that the *x*-values are equally spaced.

Find the first differences. This means the differences between successive *y*-values.

12–6	20–12	30–20	42–30
6	8	10	12

Find the second differences. This means the differences between successive first differences.

8–6	10–8	12–10
2	2	2

> Second differences are constant. They are all 2.

Data Set 1 is a quadratic function.

Data Set 2

x	−1	0	1	2	3
y	0	1	2	9	28

Find the first differences.

1–0	2–1	9–2	28–9
1	1	7	19

> Subtract successive pairs of *y*-values.

Find the second differences.

1–1	7–1	19–7
0	6	12

> Second differences are NOT constant.

Data Set 2 is NOT a quadratic function.

Find the second differences. Determine whether each data set could represent a quadratic function.

1.

x	−2	−1	0	1	2
y	16	1	0	1	16

_____

2.

x	1	2	3	4	5
y	1	3	7	13	21

_____

3.

x	6	4	2	0	−2
y	8	5	2	8	5

_____

4.

x	−4	−2	0	2	4
y	17	12	2	−3	7

_____

Holt Algebra 2

LESSON 5-8

Reteach

Curve Fitting with Quadratic Models (continued)

If you know three points that fit a quadratic function and do not lie on the same line, you can find the quadratic function.

Write a quadratic function that fits the points $(0, -1)$, $(1, 3)$, and $(2, 9)$.

Step 1 Use each point to write an equation in the form $f(x) = ax^2 + bx + c$.

$(0, -1)$ $\qquad$ $-1 = a(0)^2 + b(0) + c$
$\qquad\qquad\qquad$ $-1 = c$

$(1, 3)$ $\qquad$ $3 = a(1)^2 + b(1) + c$
$\qquad\qquad\qquad$ $3 = a + b + c$

$(2, 9)$ $\qquad$ $9 = a(2)^2 + b(2) + c$
$\qquad\qquad\qquad$ $9 = 4a + 2b + c$

Step 2 Substitute $c = -1$ into the other two equations.

$3 = a + b - 1$ $\qquad$ $a + b = 4$

$9 = 4a + 2b - 1$ $\qquad$ $4a + 2b = 10$

Step 3 Use a variable from $a + b = 4$ to solve $4a + 2b = 10$.

$a + b = 4$, so $b = 4 - a$

$\qquad$ $4a + 2b = 10$

$\qquad$ $4a + 2(4 - a) = 10$ $\qquad$ | Substitute $b = 4 - a$.

$\qquad$ $4a + 8 - 2a = 10$

$\qquad\qquad$ $2a = 2$ $\qquad$ | Since $b = 4 - a$,

$\qquad\qquad$ $a = 1$ $\qquad\qquad$ | then $b = 4 - 1 = 3$.

Step 4 Write the function. Use $a = 1$, $b = 3$, and $c = -1$.

$\qquad$ $f(x) = x^2 + 3x - 1$

Use the equations. Write a quadratic function that fits the points $(0, 1)$, $(1, -2)$, and $(2, -3)$.

3. a. $(0, 1)$ $\quad$ _____ $= a($_____$)^2 + b($_____$) + c$ $\qquad$ Simplify: _____

$\quad$ b. $(1, -2)$ $\quad$ _____ $= a($_____$)^2 + b($_____$) + c$ $\qquad$ Simplify: _____

$\quad$ c. $(2, -3)$ $\quad$ _____ $= a($_____$)^2 + b($_____$) + c$ $\qquad$ Simplify: _____

$\quad$ d. Solve the equations to find a, b, and c. $\qquad$ _____

$\quad$ e. Write the quadratic equation. $\qquad$ _____

Holt Algebra 2

LESSON
5-8

Challenge
The Method of Finite Differences

The method of finite differences can be used to determine if a
polynomial function is an appropriate model of a given data set in two
variables.

**Consider the data set
shown in the table at right.**

x	1	2	3	4	5	6
y	6	11	20	33	50	71

1. To construct a *difference table*,
   begin by listing the y-values in order.
   The 1st order differences between
   the y-values are shown. Continue
   by writing the 2nd order and
   3rd order differences.

y-values	6 11 20 33 50 71
1st order differences	5 9 13 17 21
2nd order differences	___ ___ ___ ___
3rd order differences	___ ___ ___

2. For any set of x-values that increases in constant increments, if the
   $(n + 1)$ order differences equal zero, a polynomial of degree n can be
   found to relate the x- and y-values of the data set. Can a polynomial
   function be used to model the given data set? If so, of what
   degree and what general form? _____

To find a quadratic function that will model a sequence in which
the x-values are consecutive integers beginning with 1, first consider
the differences in a general sequence, as shown below.

x-values	1	2	3	4
$y = ax^2 + bx + c$	$a(1)^2 + b(1) + c$	$a(2)^2 + b(2) + c$	$a(3)^2 + b(3) + c$	$a(4)^2 + b(4) + c$
	$a + b + c$	$4a + 2b + c$	$9a + 3b + c$	$16a + 4b + c$
1st order differences	$3a + b$	$5a + b$	$7a + b$	
2nd order differences		$2a$	$2a$	

3. You can write a particular quadratic function by using the general
   differences to determine a, b, and c. Refer to the difference table
   from Exercise 1 to write a quadratic function for the data set.

   a. Use the general 2nd order difference ($2a$) and your 2nd
      order difference to determine a. _____

   b. Use the value of a, the first of the general 1st order
      differences ($3a + b$), and your first 1st order difference to
      determine b. _____

   c. In $y = a + b + c$, use the values of a and b and your first
      y-value to determine c. _____

   d. Write a quadratic function to model the given data set.
      Check the given data points in your function. _____

 Holt Algebra 2

Problem Solving

LESSON 5-8

Curve Fitting with Quadratic Models

Ellen and Kelly test Ellen's new car in an empty parking lot. They mark a braking line where Ellen applies the brakes. Kelly then measures the distance from that line to the place where Ellen stops, for speeds from 5 miles per hour to 25 miles per hour.

Brake Test					
Speed (mi/h)	5	10	15	20	25
Stopping Distance (ft)	7	17	30	46	65

1. Ellen wants to know the stopping distance at 60 miles per hour. She cannot drive the car at this speed in the parking lot, so they decide to try curve fitting, using the data they have collected.

   a. Can you use a quadratic function to represent the data in the table? Explain how you know.

   _____

   b. Use three points to write a system of equations to find a, b, and c in $f(x) = ax^2 + bx + c$. _____

   c. Use any method to solve 3 equations with 3 variables. Find the values for a, b, and c. _____

   d. Write the quadratic function that models the stopping distance of Ellen's car. _____

   e. What is the stopping distance of Ellen's car at 60 miles per hour? _____

The table shows the sizes and prices of decorative square patio tiles. Choose the letter for the best answer.

Patio Tiles Sale					
Side Length (in.)	6	9	12	15	18
Price Each ($)	1.44	3.24	5.76	9.00	12.96

2. What quadratic function models the price of the patio tiles?

   A $P(x) = 0.4x^2$

   B $P(x) = 0.04x^2$

   C $P(x) = 0.04x^2 + 0.4x$

   D $P(x) = 0.04x^2 + x + 0.4$

3. What is the second difference constant for the data in the table?

   A 1.44

   B 1.08

   C 0.72

   D 0.36

Holt Algebra 2

Reading Strategy
Understand Vocabulary

Differences can help you classify a function. To test a function, the
x-values must be evenly spaced. Subtract each *y*-value from the next
y-value. This is referred to as the **first difference.** The difference between
successive first differences is called the **second difference.**

Linear functions have constant first differences. Quadratic functions have
constant nonzero second differences.

Examples

x	−2	−1	0	1	2
y	0	1	2	3	4
1st difference		1	1	1	1

x-values are evenly spaced.

x	−2	−1	0	1	2
y	0	4	10	18	28
1st difference		4	6	8	10
2nd difference			2	2	2

The first difference is constant, so the function is linear.

The second difference values are constant and nonzero, so the function is quadratic.

x	−2	−1	0	1	2
y	2	5	11	17	24
1st difference		3	6	6	17
2nd difference			3	0	1

The second difference values are NOT constant, so the function is NOT quadratic.

Use the data sets A and B to answer the following questions.

Data Set A				
1st difference	4	6	8	10
2nd difference		2	2	2

Data Set B				
1st difference	1	3	6	12
2nd difference		2	3	6

1. Could data set A represent a quadratic function? Explain.

_____

2. Could data set B represent a quadratic function? Explain

_____

3. The first differences of a data set are 9, 18, 27, and 36. Could this data set
   represent a quadratic function? Explain.

_____

_____

Practice A

Operations with Complex Numbers

Graph each complex number.

1. $2i$

2. $-4i$

3. $3 + i$

4. $-3 - 2i$

5. $2 + 3i$

6. $4 - 4i$

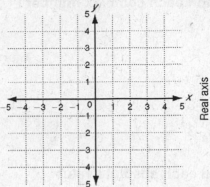

Imaginary axis

Real axis

Find each absolute value.

7. $|6 + 2i|$

8. $|3 + i|$

9. $|3 - 4i|$

_____   _____   _____

Add or subtract. Write the result in the form *a* + *bi*.

10. $6i + 4i$

11. $-i - 3i$

12. $(4i) + (2 + 8i)$

_____   _____   _____

13. $(1 + 2i) + (3 + 4i)$

14. $(2 - 7i) - (5 - 3i)$

15. $(7 - 4i) + (3 - i)$

_____   _____   _____

Multiply. Write the result in the form *a* + *bi*.

16. $2(3i)$

17. $-4(5i)$

18. $2(6 + 8i)$

_____   _____   _____

19. $2i(3 + 5i)$

20. $(3 + i)(1 - 4i)$

21. $(1 + 2i)(2 + 5i)$

_____   _____   _____

Simplify.

22. i^7

23. $\dfrac{2 + 5i}{3i}$

24. $\dfrac{8 + 2i}{1 - 3i}$

_____   _____   _____

Name _____ Date _____ Class_____

Practice B
Operations with Complex Numbers

Graph each complex number.

1. -6

2. $4i$

3. $6 + 7i$

4. $-8 - 5i$

5. $-3i$

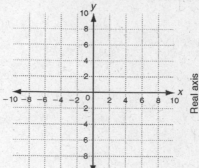

Imaginary axis

Real axis

Find each absolute value.

6. $|4 + 2i|$

7. $|5 - i|$

8. $|-3i|$

_____ _____ _____

Add or subtract. Write the result in the form $a + bi$.

9. $(-1 + 2i) + (6 - 9i)$

10. $(3 - 3i) - (4 + 7i)$

11. $(-5 + 2i) + (-2 + 8i)$

_____ _____ _____

Multiply. Write the result in the form $a + bi$.

12. $3i(2 - 3i)$

13. $(4 + 5i)(2 + i)$

14. $(-1 + 6i)(3 - 2i)$

_____ _____ _____

Simplify.

15. $\dfrac{2 + 4i}{3i}$

16. $\dfrac{3 + 2i}{4 + i}$

17. $2i^{11}$

_____ _____ _____

Solve.

18. In electronics, the total resistance to the flow of electricity in a circuit is called the impedance, Z. Impedance is represented by a complex number. The total impedance in a series circuit is the sum of individual impedances. The impedance in one part of a circuit is $Z_1 = 3 + 4i$. In another part of a circuit, the impedance is $Z_1 = 5 - 2i$. What is the total impedance of the circuit?

_____

Holt Algebra 2

LESSON 5-9 Practice C

Operations with Complex Numbers

Find each absolute value.

1. $|-12 + 6i|$

2. $|-7 - 4i|$

3. $\left|\dfrac{1}{2} + \dfrac{1}{2}i\right|$

_____ _____ _____

Add or subtract. Write the result in the form $a + bi$.

4. $(8 - i) - (-5 - 4i)$

5. $(2 - 11i) - (10 + 6i)$

6. $\left(\dfrac{1}{2} + \dfrac{3}{4}i\right) + \left(-\dfrac{1}{4} - \dfrac{5}{4}i\right)$

_____ _____ _____

Find each sum by graphing on the complex plane.

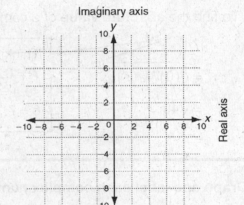

7. $(-6 - i) + (1 + 3i)$

_____

8. $(-2 - 2i) + (8 - 6i)$

_____

Multiply or divide. Write the result in the form $a + bi$.

9. $\dfrac{-3 + 7i}{1 + 8i}$

10. $(-4 - 9i)(8 + 2i)$

11. $\dfrac{5 + i}{2 - i}$

_____ _____ _____

Simplify.

12. $i^{24} - i^{13} + i^{12}$

13. $-4i^{13}$

14. $6 - 4i^{18}$

_____ _____ _____

Solve.

15. In a circuit, the voltage, V, is given by the formula $V = IZ$, where I is the current and Z is the impedance. Both the current and impedance are represented by complex numbers. Find the voltage if the current is $3 + 2i$ and the impedance is $4 - i$.

_____

Holt Algebra 2

LESSON 5-9

Reteach

Operations with Complex Numbers

Graphing complex numbers is like graphing real numbers. The real axis corresponds to the *x*-axis and the imaginary axis corresponds to the *y*-axis.

Imaginary axis

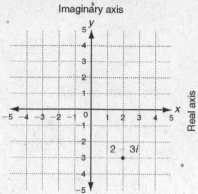

To find the **absolute value** of a complex number, use $|a + bi| = \sqrt{a^2 + b^2}$.

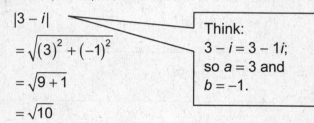

$|7i|$

$= \sqrt{(0)^2 + (7)^2}$

$= \sqrt{49}$

$= 7$

Think:
$7i = 0 + 7i$;
so $a = 0$ and
$b = 7$.

$|3 - i|$

$= \sqrt{(3)^2 + (-1)^2}$

$= \sqrt{9 + 1}$

$= \sqrt{10}$

Think:
$3 - i = 3 - 1i$;
so $a = 3$ and
$b = -1$.

Graph and label each complex number on the complex plane.

1. $1 + i$

2. $4i$

3. $-2 + 0i$

4. $2 - i$

5. $-1 - 3i$

Imaginary axis

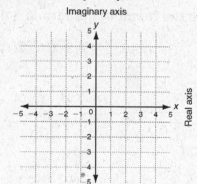

Find each absolute value.

6. $|-8i|$

$|0 - 8i|$

$\sqrt{(0)^2 + (-8)^2}$

7. $|2 + i|$

$|2 + 1i|$

8. $|3|$

$|3 + 0i|$

9. $|5 - 2i|$

10. $|9i|$

11. $|-4 + 3i|$

Holt Algebra 2

LESSON 5-9

Reteach

Operations with Complex Numbers (continued)

To add or subtract complex numbers, add the real parts and then add the imaginary parts.

$(3 - 2i) + (4 + 5i)$

$(3 + 4) + (-2i + 5i)$

$7 + 3i$

> First, group to add the real parts and the imaginary parts. This is similar to adding like terms.

$(4 - i) - (-2 + 6i)$

$(4 - i) + 2 - 6i$

$(4 + 2) + (-i - 6i)$

$6 - 7i$

> Remember to distribute when subtracting. Then group to add the real parts and the imaginary parts.

Use the Distributive Property to multiply complex numbers. Remember that $i^2 = -1$.

$3i(2 - i)$

$6i - 3i^2$ *Distribute.*

$6i - 3(-1)$ *Use $i^2 = -1$.*

$3 + 6i$ *Write in the form $a + bi$.*

$(4 + 2i)(5 - i)$

$20 - 4i + 10i - 2i^2$ *Multiply.*

$20 + 6i - 2(-1)$ *Combine imaginary parts and use $i^2 = -1$.*

$22 + 6i$ *Combine real parts.*

Add, subtract, or multiply. Write the result in the form $a + bi$.

12. $(6 + i) + (3 - 2i)$

   $(6 + 3) + (i - 2i)$

_____

13. $(9 - 3i) - (2 + i)$

   $(9 - 3i) + (-2 - i)$

_____

14. $(3 + i)(2 + 2i)$

   $6 + 6i + 2i + 2i^2$

_____

15. $(2 - 4i) + (1 - 4i)$

_____

16. $(1 - 7i) - (1 - 5i)$

_____

17. $5i(4 + 3i)$

_____

18. $(6 - 5i) + (-5i - 6)$

_____

19. $(2 - i)(3i + 2)$

_____

20. $(2 + 4i)^2$

_____

Challenge

LESSON 5-9

Order of Operations with Complex Numbers

The real number system is a subset of the complex number system and both systems share many properties. However, there are properties of one system that may not apply in the other system.

Exercises 1–3 are performed in the set of real numbers.

1. In the expression $\sqrt{a} \cdot \sqrt{b}$ there are square root operations and multiplication. Which operation should be done first according to the order of operations? _____

2. Evaluate $\sqrt{3} \cdot \sqrt{12}$ and $\sqrt{3 \cdot 12}$. _____

3. What do you notice about the two answers? Will this result always happen? What does that say about the order of operations?

_____

For nonnegative real numbers a and b, $\sqrt{a} \cdot \sqrt{b} = \sqrt{a \cdot b}$.

Is the equation true when a and b are imaginary numbers?

Answer the following questions about complex numbers.

4. Evaluate $\sqrt{-3} \cdot \sqrt{-12}$ and $\sqrt{(-3) \cdot (-12)}$.

_____

5. What do you notice about your two answers? Is this the same as Exercise 3?

_____

6. Write a general rule for the product of radicals when using complex numbers.

_____

Evaluate and simplify.

7. $\sqrt{-8} \cdot \sqrt{-128}$

8. $\sqrt{-3} \cdot \sqrt{-2} \cdot \sqrt{-6} \cdot \sqrt{-4}$

9. $\left(\sqrt{-5}\right)^2$

10. $\sqrt{-2} \cdot \sqrt{-90} \cdot \sqrt{-5}$

11. $\sqrt{-3} \cdot \sqrt{12}$

12. $\left(\sqrt{-2}\right)^5$

Holt Algebra 2

Name _____ Date _____ Class_____

Problem Solving
Operations with Complex Numbers

Hannah and Aoki are designing fractals. Aoki recalls that many
fractals are based on the Julia Set, whose formula is
$Z_{n+1} = (Z_n)^2 + c$, where c is a constant. Hannah suggests they make
their own fractal pattern using this formula, where $c = 1$ and
$Z_1 = 1 + 2i$.

1. Complete the table to show values of n and Z_n.

n	$Z_{n+1} = (Z_n)^2 + c$	Z_n
1	$Z_1 = 1 + 2i$	$Z_1 = 1 + 2i$
2	$Z_2 = (1 + 2i)^2 + 1$	$Z_2 =$
3	$Z_3 = ($_____$)^2 + 1$	$Z_3 =$
4	$Z_4 = ($_____$)^2 + 1$	$Z_4 =$

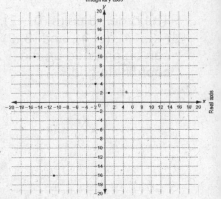

Imaginary axis

Real axis

2. Four points are shown on the complex plane. Which point is not part of
the fractal pattern they have created? Explain.

_____

_____

Choose the letter for the best answer.

3. Aoki creates a second pattern by
changing the value of c to 3. What
happens to Z_n as n increases?

  A The imaginary part is always twice
the real part.

  B The real and imaginary parts become
equal.

  C The real part becomes zero.

  D The imaginary part becomes zero.

4. Hannah changes the formula to
$Z_{n+1} = \dfrac{1}{(Z_n)^2} + c$. Leaving $c = 1$ and

$Z_1 = 1 + 2i$, what is the value of Z_2?

  A $0.48 - 0.16i$

  B $0.88 - 0.16i$

  C $1.2 - 0.4i$

  D $2.2 - 0.4i$

5. Aoki takes Hannah's new formula,

leaves $c = 1$, and sets $Z_1 = \dfrac{1}{1 + 2i}$. What

is the value of Z_3?

  A $Z_3 = -11 - 16i$

  B $Z_3 = 2 + 2i$

  C $Z_3 = 0.48 - 0.16i$

  D $Z_3 = 147.4 + i$

6. Hannah reverts to
$Z_{n+1} = (Z_n)^2 + c$. She sets $Z_1 = i$ and $c = i$.
Which statement is NOT true?

  A Z_n flip-flops between $(-1 + i)$ and $(-i)$.

  B The coefficient of i never reaches 2.

  C The imaginary part becomes zero.

  D On a graph $Z_1 - Z_3$ create a triangle.

Holt Algebra 2

LESSON 5-9

Reading Strategy
Use a Model

Complex numbers can be graphed on a **complex plane.** Use the coordinate plane as a model. In a complex plane, the horizontal axis represents real numbers, and the vertical axis represents imaginary numbers.

The ordered pairs $(0, -2)$, $(-3, -1)$, $(0, 4)$, and $(3, 2)$ can be graphed on the coordinate grid.

The complex numbers $-2i$, $-3 -i$, $4i$, and $3 + 2i$ can be graphed on the complex plane.

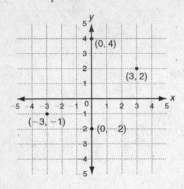

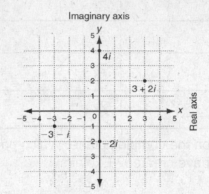

Answer each question.

1. Identify the location of each point on the complex plane below.

   a. *A* _____

   b. *B* _____

   c. *C* _____

   d. *D* _____

   e. *E* _____

   f. *F* _____

   g. *G* _____

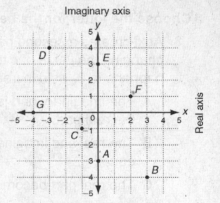

2. Describe the location of the complex number $5 + \sqrt{-4}$ in the complex plane.

   _____

3. How far from the origin is $-1 + i$? Explain how you know.

   _____

4. Explain why the complex numbers $2 + 3i$ and $2 - 3i$ are the same distance from the origin.

   _____

Holt Algebra 2

Date _____

Dear Family,

In Chapter 6, your child will operate (add, subtract, multiply, and divide) with polynomials and apply several theorems about polynomial functions.

A **monomial** is a product of numbers and variables with whole number exponents. A **polynomial** is a single monomial or a sum or difference of several monomials. Each monomial in a polynomial is called a *term*. Polynomials are described by the number of terms that they have.

Classifying Polynomials by Terms

Name	Terms	Example
Monomial	One term	$3x^5$
Binomial	Two terms	$-2x^3 + 6$
Trinomial	Three terms	$2x^2 + x - 5$

Polynomials are also described by their *degree*. The **degree of a monomial** is the sum of the exponents of the variables. The **degree of a polynomial** is the degree of the term with the greatest degree. When the terms are in descending degree, the polynomial is said to be in *standard form*, and the coefficient of the first term is called the **leading coefficient**.

Classifying Polynomials by Degree

Name	Degree	Example
Constant	0	6
Linear	1	$x + 6$
Quadractic	2	$4x^2 + x + 6$
Cubic	3	$-2x^3 + 6$
Quartic	4	x^4
Quintic	5	$3x^5 + x - 1$

Standard Form: $2x^3y - 4x + 1$

degree of terms: 4 1 0

degree of polynomial: 4

> The variable y can be thought of as y^1. So, $2x^3y^1$ has degree $3 + 1 = 4$.

Because this polynomial has degree 4 and 3 terms, you can say it is a "quartic trinomial."

To add or subtract polynomials, you combine like terms.

Add $(x^2 + 5) + (3x^2 - 2x - 8)$.

$(x^2 + 3x^2) + (-2x) + [5 + (-8)]$ *Combine like terms.*

$\quad 4x^2 \qquad -2x \qquad -3$ *Simplify.*

To multiply two polynomials, you distribute each term of the first polynomial to each term of the second polynomial.

Multiply $(x + 2) + (x^2 + 4x - 3)$.

$x(x^2) + x(4x) + x(-3) + 2(x^2) + 2(4x) + 2(-3)$ *Distribute terms.*

$x^3 \qquad +4x^2 \quad -3x \quad +2x^2 \quad +8x \qquad -6$ *Multiply.*

$x^3 + 6x^2 + 5x - 6$ *Combine like terms.*

     Holt Algebra 2

You can divide polynomials using long division. However, if the divisor is a linear binomial with leading coefficient 1, you can use a shorthand method called **synthetic division**.

Divide $(2x^2 + 7x + 9) \div (x + 2)$.

$$
\begin{array}{r|rrr}
-2 & 2 & 7 & 9 \\
   &   & -4 & -6 \\
\hline
   & 2 & 3 & \underline{|3}
\end{array}
$$

$$2x + 3 + \frac{3}{x+2}$$

Step 1: Think of the divisor as $(x - a)$ and put the value of a in the upper left corner. Then write the coefficients of the dividend.

Step 2: In the first column, add down. Multiply the sum by a and put the product in the next column. Repeat, working left to right.

Step 3: Read the quotient from the bottom line. The last number is the remainder.

A polynomial function is a function whose rule is a polynomial.

Polynomial Function: $P(x) = x^3 + 3x^2 + 4$

Your child will learn several important theorems about polynomial functions. These theorems will be used individually and collectively to factor polynomial expressions, to find roots (or solutions) of polynomial equations, and to find zeros (x-intercepts) of polynomial functions.

Remainder Theorem	If the polynomial function $P(x)$ is divided by $(x - a)$, then the remainder r is the same as evaluating $P(a)$.
Factor Theorem	For any polynomial function $P(x)$, $(x - a)$ is a factor of $P(x)$ if and only if $P(a) = 0$.
Rational Root Theorem	If the polynomial $P(x)$ has integer coefficients, then every rational root of the equation $P(x) = 0$ can be written in the form $\frac{P}{q}$, where p is a factor of the constant term and q is a factor of the leading coefficient.
Irrational Root Theorem	If the polynomial $P(x)$ has rational coefficients and $a + b\sqrt{c}$ is a root of the equation $P(x) = 0$, where a and b are rational and $\sqrt{c}$ is irrational, then $a - b\sqrt{c}$ is also a root of $P(x) = 0$.
Complex Conjugate Root Theorem	If $a + bi$ is a root of a polynomial equation with real-number coefficients, then $a - bi$ is also a root.
Fundamental Theorem of Algebra	Every polynomial function of degree $n \geq 1$ has exactly n complex zeros, including multiplicities.

The chapter concludes with an exploration of the graphs of polynomial functions. Special features such as shape, **end behavior**, **local maxima** and **local minima**, and transformations are examined and applied.

For additional resources, visit go.hrw.com and enter the keyword MB7 Parent.

Holt Algebra 2

Practice A
Polynomials

Identify the degree of each monomial.

1. x^2

2. 3

3. a^2b^2

_____   _____   _____

4. $7x$

5. $4x^2y$

6. $2x^5$

_____   _____   _____

Solve.

7. a. Rewrite the polynomial $2x^2 + x^3 + -7x + 1$
   in standard form.   _____

   b. What is the leading coefficient?   _____

   c. What is the degree?   _____

   d. How many terms are in this polynomial?   _____

   e. Name the polynomial.   _____

8. a. Rewrite the polynomial $5 - 3x + 4x^2$ in
   standard form.   _____

   b. What is the leading coefficient?   _____

   c. What is the degree?   _____

   d. How many terms are in this polynomial?   _____

   e. Name the polynomial.   _____

Add or subtract the following polynomials. Write your answer in standard form.

9. $(6x + 7) + (3x + 8)$

10. $(5x - 3) - (3x + 9)$

_____   _____

11. $(2x^2 + 3x + 4) - (x^2 + x + 2)$

12. $(x^2 - 4x + 5) + (-2x^2 + 7x - 10)$

_____   _____

Solve.

13. Britt has 4 full boxes plus 12 extra CDs, and Jim has
    3 full boxes and 5 extra CDs. If the number of CDs in
    each box is represented by c, write an expression that
    shows the total number of CDs that Britt and Jim have.   _____

Holt Algebra 2

LESSON 6-1 Practice B
Polynomials

Identify the degree of each monomial.

1. $6x^2$

2. $3p^3m^4$

3. $2x^8y^3$

_____ _____ _____

Rewrite each polynomial in standard form. Then identify the leading coefficient, degree, and number of terms. Name the polynomial.

4. $6 + 7x - 4x^3 + x^2$

_____

5. $x^2 - 3 + 2x^5 + 7x^4 - 12x$

_____

Add or subtract. Write your answer in standard form.

6. $\left(2x^2 - 2x + 6\right) + \left(11x^3 - x^2 - 2 + 5x\right)$

7. $\left(x^2 - 8\right) - \left(3x^3 - 6x - 4 + 9x^2\right)$

_____ _____

8. $\left(5x^4 + x^2\right) + \left(7 + 9x^2 - 2x^4 + x^3\right)$

9. $\left(12x^2 + x\right) - \left(6 - 9x^2 + x^7 - 8x\right)$

_____ _____

Graph each polynomial function on a calculator. Describe the graph, and identify the number of real zeros.

10. $f(x) = x^3 + 2x^2 - 3$

_____

_____

11. $f(x) = x^4 - 5x^2 + 1$

_____

_____

Solve.

12. The height, h, in feet, of a baseball after being struck by a bat can be approximated by $h(t) = -16t^2 + 100t + 5$, where t is measured in seconds.

a. Evaluate $h(t)$ for $t = 3$ and $t = 5$. _____

b. Describe what the values of the function from part a represent.

_____

Practice C
Polynomials

Rewrite each polynomial in standard form. Then identify the leading coefficient, degree, and number of terms. Name the polynomial.

1. $5x^3 + 2x - 1 - 10x^2 + 9x^5 - 3x^4$

_____

Add or subtract. Write your answer in standard form.

2. $\left(7x^3 + 2x - 1\right) + \left(8x^2 - 6 + 2x - x^3\right)$

_____

3. $\left(12 - 11x - 5x^5\right) - \left(4x^4 + 8x - 4x^5 + 2x^3 - 1\right)$

_____

4. $\left(-3x^4 + x^6 - 9x^5 + 2x^2 - 7\right) - \left(-2x^5 + x - 4x^2 - x^4 + 12\right)$

_____

Solve.

5. What polynomial could you add to $3x^4 - 9x^3 + 5x^2 - x + 7$ to get a sum of $3 + 4x^4 + 3x - x^3 + 3x^2$?

_____

6. What polynomial could you subtract from $5x^3 - 12x - x^2 + 9 - 12x^5 - 6x^4$ to give a difference of $19 + 8x^3 - 18x - 19x^5 - 2x^2 - 8x^4$?

_____

Graph each polynomial function on a calculator. Describe the graph, and identify the number of real zeros.

7. $f(x) = 2x^3 - 6x + 1$

_____

8. $f(x) = 5x^4 + 4x^3 - 5x - 3$

_____

Solve.

9. The profit, P, earned by a small business each year can be modeled to fit the polynomial function $P(y) = 10y^3 - 50y^2 + 20y + 100,000$, where y is the number of years since 1990. Did the company's profits increase or decrease in 1995, compared to 1994?

_____

Holt Algebra 2

LESSON 6-1

Reteach

Polynomials

The **degree** of a polynomial is the value of the exponent of the term of the greatest degree. A polynomial is in **standard form** when the terms are arranged in order with exponents from greatest to least.

Degree	Polynomial in Standard Form
0	8
1	$2x + 3$
2	$-x^2 + 4x - 5$
3	$4x^3 - x$
4	$6x^4 + x^3 - 5x^2 + 3x - 1$
5	$9x^5 + x^3 - 1$

Constants have degree 0.

This third degree polynomial has 2 terms.

This fifth degree polynomial has 3 terms.

To arrange the polynomial $3x^2 + x^4 - 2x + 6x^5 - 7$ in standard form, order the terms from greatest to least exponent.

$$6x^5 + x^4 + 3x^2 - 2x - 7$$

6 is the **leading coefficient** of this polynomial.

Rewrite each polynomial in standard form. Then identify the leading coefficient, degree, and number of terms of each polynomial.

1. $2x + x^3 - x^2 - 5$

   Standard form: $x^3 - x^2 + 2x - 5$

   Leading coefficient: 1

   Degree: _____

   Number of terms: _____

2. $5x^2 + 3x^4 - x$

   Standard form: $3x^4 +$ _____

   Leading coefficient: _____

   Degree: _____

   Number of terms: _____

3. $6x^3 + 7x^5$

   Standard form: _____

   Leading coefficient: _____

   Degree: _____

   Number of terms: _____

4. $-3x^2 + x^4 - x - 2x^3 + 8$

   Standard form: _____

   Leading coefficient: _____

   Degree: _____

   Number of terms: _____

Name _____ Date _____ Class_____

Reteach

Polynomials (continued)

To add polynomials:
- Write each polynomial in standard form.
- Align like terms vertically.
- Add like terms.

Add: $\left(6x + 2x^3 - 5x^2 - 1\right) + \left(4x^2 + 2x + x^3\right)$. ⟵ Standard form: $x^3 + 4x^2 + 2x$

Standard form: $2x^3 - 5x^2 + 6x - 1$

$$\begin{array}{r} 2x^3 - 5x^2 + 6x - 1 \\ + \ x^3 + 4x^2 + 2x \\ \hline 3x^3 - \ x^2 + 8x - 1 \end{array}$$

⟵ Align like terms.

⟵ Add like terms vertically.

To subtract polynomials, **add the opposite** vertically.

Subtract: $\left(6x + 2x^3 - 5x^2 - 1\right) - \left(4x^2 + 2x + x^3\right)$.

Add the opposite: $\left(6x + 2x^3 - 5x^2 - 1\right) + \left(-4x^2 - 2x - x^3\right)$.

$$\begin{array}{r} 2x^3 - 5x^2 + 6x - 1 \\ + \ (-x^3 - 4x^2 - 2x) \\ \hline x^3 - 9x^2 + 4x - 1 \end{array}$$

⟵ Add like terms vertically.

Write each polynomial in standard form. Add or subtract.

5. $\left(3x^2 + 2x^3 - x\right) + \left(6x + 2x^2 + 1\right)$

$$\begin{array}{r} 2x^3 + 3x^2 - x \\ + \ \ \ \ \ 2x^2 + 6x + 1 \\ \hline \end{array}$$

_____

6. $\left(x + 4x^3 - 5\right) + \left(4x^2 - x + 2x^3\right)$

_____

$+$ _____

_____

7. $\left(6x^2 + 4x - 1\right) - \left(2x - x^2 + 1\right)$

Add the opposite:

$\left(6x^2 + 4x - 1\right) + \left(-2x + x^3 - 1\right)$

$$\begin{array}{r} 6x^2 + 4x - 1 \\ + \ x^3 \ \ \ \ \ \ - 2x - 1 \\ \hline \end{array}$$

_____

8. $\left(4x^3 + 6\right) - \left(3x^2 - x^3\right)$

Add the opposite:

_____

_____

$+$ _____

_____

Holt Algebra 2

LESSON	**Challenge**
6-1	***Polynomial Functions Whose Coefficients Are 1***

A *polynomial function in x* is of the form $a_n x^n + a_{n-1} x^{n-1} + \ldots + a_1 x + a_0$, where a_n is a nonzero real number and n is a nonnegative integer.

Explore polynomial functions whose coefficients are all 1.

Consider $Q_n(x) = x^n + x^{n-1} + \ldots + x^3 + x^2 + x + 1$.

1. Write the function when $n = 6$. _____

2. Is $Q_6(x)$ positive or negative

a. when $x > 0$?   b. when $x < 0$?   c. when $x = 0$?

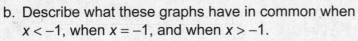

3. Consider $Q_n(x)$ for other even values of n, including 0. When n is even, what can you say

a. about the values of the function $Q_n(x)$?   b. about the graph of the function $Q_n(x)$?

_____   _____

4. Write the function when $n = 3$. _____

5. State a value of x for which $Q_3(x)$

a. is negative.   b. is positive.   c. is 0.

_____ _____ _____

6. a. Use a graphing calculator to graph the function when $n = 1$, 3, 5, and 7. Sketch these graphs on the grid at right.

    b. Describe what these graphs have in common when $x < -1$, when $x = -1$, and when $x > -1$.

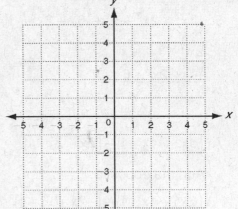

_____

_____

_____

_____

    c. Verify that the function $Q_n(x)$ changes its value from negative to positive at $x = -1$ when n is odd. Show that $Q_n(-1) = 0$, for all odd values of n by evaluating the expression below.

$$Q_n(-1) = (-1)^n + (-1)^{n-1} + \ldots + (-1)^3 + (-1)^2 + (-1)^1 + 1$$

_____

7. When $x = -1$ and n is even, what is the value of $Q_n(-1)$? _____

LESSON
6-1

Problem Solving
Polynomials

As part of a project to build a model castle, Julian wants to find
the surface area of solid towers of various sizes, shaped like the
one shown in the figure below. The diameter of the circular base is
d inches, the height of the cylinder is *d* + 4 inches, and the slant
height of the right circular cone is *d* – 0.6 inch.

1. The general formula for the lateral surface area of a
   cone is $SA = \pi r^2 - \pi rs$, where *r* is the radius of the
   base, and *s* is the slant height of the cone.

   a. Write the formula in terms of *d*.

   _____

   b. What part of the formula will you use to find the
      surface area of the cone part of the model? Why?

   _____

   _____

   _____

2. The general formula for the surface area of a cylinder (with radius *r* and
   height *h*) is $SA = 2\pi r^2 + 2\pi rh$.

   a. Write the formula in terms of *d*.   _____

   b. What part of the formula will you use to find the surface area of the
      cylinder part of the model? Why?

   _____

3. Write a general polynomial expression for the surface area of the model tower.

   _____

Choose the letter for the best answer.

4. What is the approximate surface area in
   square inches of a tower with a
   diameter of 5 inches?

     A 278   C 44

     B 196   D 38

5. What is the approximate surface area in
   square inches of a tower with a diameter
   of 10 inches?

     A 176   C 666

     B 278   D 1174

6. What is the approximate surface area in
   square inches of a tower where the
   height of the cylinder is 12 inches?

     A 931   C 445

     B 716   D 395

7. What is the approximate surface area in
   square inches of a tower where the slant
   height of the cone is 3.4 inches?

     A 103   C 158

     B 134   D 268

LESSON 6-1 Reading Strategy
Understand Vocabulary

A **monomial** is a number or a product of a number and a variable, such as $-2x$ or $3x^2$. A monomial cannot have

- variables in denominators or exponents.

- roots of variables.

- absolute value signs.

- exponents that are not whole numbers.

6^x or $\dfrac{3}{x^2}$

$6\sqrt{x}$

$\left| x^3 \right|$

$x^{0.3}$

These are NOT monomials.

A **polynomial** is a monomial or the sum or difference of monomials. Each monomial in a polynomial is called a **term**. Here are some ways to describe polynomials.

	Standard Form	Degree	Number of Terms	Leading Coefficient
Definition	Terms arranged in descending order by degree	The greatest exponent in a polynomial	The number of monomials	The coefficient of the first term in standard form
Example	$5x^3 - 2x^2 + x + 3$	3	4	5

Answer each question.

1. What is the difference between a monomial and a polynomial?

   _____

2. Circle the polynomials below. Cross out the expressions that are not polynomials.

   $4x^2 - x$ $\left| 2n^2 + 1 \right|$ $3x\sqrt{17}$ $6z^2$ $\dfrac{2}{z^2} + 1$

3. Write the polynomials in standard form. Classify the polynomial based on its degree.

   a. $x - x^5 + 1$ _____ Degree _____

   b. $x^2 + 6 + x^3 - 2x$ _____ Degree _____

Complete the table.

	Polynomial	Degree	Number of Terms	Leading Coefficient
4.	$2y^4 + 3y^3 + y^2 - 7$			
5.	$-6x^5 - x^3 + 2$			

     Holt Algebra 2

LESSON 6-2

Practice A

Multiplying Polynomials

Find each product.

1. $2x(x^2 + 4)$

   $= 2x \cdot$ _____ $+ 2x \cdot$ _____

   _____

2. $3m(2 - m^3)$

   $= 3m \cdot$ _____ $- 3m \cdot$ _____

   _____

3. $6p(p + 7)$

   _____

4. $x(x^2 + 3x - 1)$

   _____

5. $2x(2x^2 - 5x + 6)$

   _____

6. $(x - 3)(x^2 + 2x - 1)$

	x^2	$2x$	-1
x	x^3	$2x^2$	$-x$
-3	D	E	F

   a. $D =$ _____
   b. $E =$ _____
   c. $F =$ _____
   d. $D + E + F =$ _____
   e. $(x^3 + 2x^2 - x) + (D + E + F) =$ _____

7. $(x - 1)(x^2 + 3x - 2)$
   $= x($____$) + x($____$) + x($____$) - 1($____$) - 1($____$) - 1($____$)$

   _____

8. $(x + 3)^3$

   $= (x + 3)($_____$)($_____$)$

   $= (x + 3)($_____$)$

   _____

9. $(x - 5)^3$

   $= (x - 5)($_____$)($_____$)$

   $= (x - 5)($_____$)$

   _____

Solve.

10. Kevin lives on a city block that has a perimeter of $w - 2$ miles. Each day he runs around the block 3 times and then runs to the high school, which is an additional 2 miles. How many miles does Kevin run in d days?

   _____

Holt Algebra 2

LESSON 6-2 Practice B
Multiplying Polynomials

Find each product.

1. $4x^2(3x^2 + 1)$

2. $-9x(x^2 + 2x + 4)$

_____

_____

3. $-6x^2(x^3 + 7x^2 - 4x + 3)$

4. $x^3(-4x^3 + 10x^2 - 7x + 2)$

_____

_____

5. $-5m^3(7n^4 - 2mn^3 + 6)$

6. $(x + 2)(y^2 + 2y - 12)$

_____

_____

7. $(p + q)(4p^2 - p - 8q^2 - q)$

8. $(2x^2 + xy - y)(y^2 + 3x)$

_____

_____

Expand each expression.

9. $(3x - 1)^3$

10. $(x - 4)^4$

_____

_____

11. $3(a - 4b)^2$

12. $5\left(x^2 - 2y^3\right)^3$

_____

_____

Solve.

13. A biologist has found that the number of branches on a certain rare tree
in its first few years of life can be modeled by the polynomial
$b(y) = 4y^2 + y$. The number of leaves on each branch can be modeled
by the polynomial $l(y) = 2y^3 + 3y^2 + y$, where y is the number of years
after the tree reaches a height of 6 feet. Write a polynomial describing
the total number of leaves on the tree.

_____

Holt Algebra 2

LESSON
6-2

Practice C
Multiplying Polynomials

Consider the expansion of $(x + y)^n$.

1. How many terms does the expression contain? _____

2. What is the exponent of x in the first term? _____

3. What is the exponent of y in the first term? _____

4. What is the sum of the exponents in any term
of the expansion? _____

Find each product.

5. $-y^3(10x^2 + 4xy - y^2)$

6. $(2a - b)^3$

7. $5(h - 2)^4$

8. $(2m^2 + n)(3n^2 + 6mn - m^2)$

9. $\left(\dfrac{1}{3}x + 4\right)^3$

10. $(4x - 5)(2x^5 + x^3 - 1)$

11. $(a^3 + a^2b^2)(b^4 + a^2)$

12. $(k^4 + k^3 + 12)(k^2 - k - 9)$

Solve.

13. The momentum of an object is defined as its mass m multiplied by its
velocity. As a certain experimental aircraft burns fuel, its mass decreases
according to the polynomial $m(t) = 3000 - 0.1t^2 - 4t$, where m is in kilograms
and t is measured in minutes since takeoff. Under the force of the engines,
the velocity of the aircraft increases according to the function
$v(t) = 0.001t^3 + 0.01t$, where v is in kilometers per second. What is the
momentum of the rocket?

_____

Holt Algebra 2

LESSON 6-2 Reteach
Multiplying Polynomials

Use the Distributive Property to multiply a monomial and a polynomial.

Think: $k(x + y + z) = kx + ky + kz$

Multiply: $2ab^2(3a^2b - 4ab^2 - b^3)$.

$2ab^2$ is a monomial.

$3a^2b - 4ab^2 - b^3$ is a polynomial.

$2ab^2(3a^2b - 4ab^2 - b^3)$

$2ab^2(3b^2b) + 2ab^2(-4ab^2) + 2ab^2(-b^3)$ *Distribute $2ab^2$.*

$2(3)(a \cdot a^2)(b^2 \cdot b) + 2(-4)(a \bullet a)(b^2 \cdot b^2) + 2(-1)(a)(b^2 \cdot b^3)$ *Group like terms.*

$6a^3b^3 - 8a^2b^4 - 2ab^5$ Multiply.

Remember: Add the exponents of like bases to multiply.

Find each product.

1. $4x^2(x^2 + 2x - 3)$

   $4x^2(x^2) + 4x^2(2x) + 4x^2(-3)$

   $4x^2(x^2) + 4(2)(x^2 \cdot x) + 4(-3)x^2$

2. $c^2d^2(3c^2 - cd + 7d^2)$

   $c^2d^2(3c^2) + c^2d^2(-cd) + c^2d^2(7d^2)$

   $3(c^2 \cdot c^2)(d^2) - (c^2 \cdot c)(d^2 \cdot d)$
   $+ 7c^2(d^2 \bullet d^2)$

_____

3. $5xy^2(x^3 + 4x^2 + 2)$

   $5xy^2(x^3) + 4xy^2(4x^2) + 5xy^2(2)$

4. $3a^2b^2(8a^2 - 2ab - b^2)$

   $3a^2b^2(8a^2) + 3a^2b^2(-2ab)$
   $+ 3a^2b^2(-b^2)$

_____

5. $2y^3(y^2 - 9y + 4)$

6. $x^2y^2(4x^2 + 7y)$

_____

_____

_____

     Holt Algebra 2

LESSON	**Reteach**
6-2	*Multiplying Polynomials* (continued)

Use the Distributive Property to multiply two polynomials.

Distribute each term of the first polynomial to each term of the second polynomial.

Multiply: $(x + 2)(4x^2 - 3x - 1)$.

Horizontal Method: $(x + 2)(4x^2 - 3x - 1)$

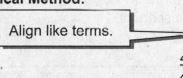
Distribute x to each term of $(4x^2 - 3x - 1)$.

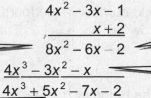
Distribute 2 to each term of $(4x^2 - 3x - 1)$.

$[x(4x^2) + x(-3x) + x(-1)] + [2(4x^2) + 2(-3x) + 2(-1)]$

$4x^3 - 3x^2 - x + 8x^2 - 6x - 2$ *Multiply.*

$4x^3 - 3x^2 + 8x^2 - x - 6x - 2$ *Group like terms.*

$4x^3 + 5x^2 - 7x - 2$ *Combine like terms.*

Vertical Method:

Align like terms.

Combine like terms.

$$
\begin{array}{r}
4x^2 - 3x - 1 \\
x + 2 \\
\hline
8x^2 - 6x - 2 \\
4x^3 - 3x^2 - x \\
\hline
4x^3 + 5x^2 - 7x - 2
\end{array}
$$

Multiply $4x^2 - 3x - 1$ by 1.

Multiply $4x^2 - 3x - 1$ by x.

Use the horizontal method to find each product.

7. $(x - 3)(x^2 - 2x + 2)$

$x(x^2) + x(-2x) + x(2) - 3(x^2) - 3(-2x)$
$-3(2)$

_____

_____

8. $(a + b)(a^2 + ab - 4b)$

_____

_____

_____

Use the vertical method to find each product.

9. $x^2 + 4x - 6$
       $x + 2$

_____

10. $y^2 - 3y + 1$
       $y - 1$

_____

LESSON
6-2

Challenge
Triangular Coefficients

Pascal's triangle can be used to raise a binomial to a power. What if you wanted to raise a trinomial of the form $x^2 + x + 1$ to a power, like the fifth power? This can be done with normal expansion techniques using the distributive laws, but it is very tedious.

Consider the products of $x^2 + x + 1$ and the triangle of coefficients.

$(x^2 + x + 1)^0 = 1$ 1

$(x^2 + x + 1)^1 = x^2 + x + 1$ 1   1   1

$(x^2 + x + 1)^2 = x^4 + 2x^3 + 3x^2 + 2x + 1$ 1   2   3   2   1

$(x^2 + x + 1)^3 = x^6 + 3x^5 + 6x^4 + 7x^3 + 6x^2 + 3x + 1$ 1   3   6   7   6   3   1

Each row of this triangle, let's call it Pascal[3], starts and ends with 1 and reads the same forward and backward. Each of the numbers is the sum of the 3 numbers above it if we consider the numbers before and after the ones to be zeros. For instance, the second number in the fourth row is $3 = 0 + 1 + 2$. The fourth number in this row is $7 = 2 + 3 + 2$. Subsequent rows follow the same pattern.

1.   a. Find the numbers in the fifth row of Pascal[3]. _____

     b. Use these numbers to expand the trinomial
       $x^2 + x + 1$ to the fourth power. _____

2.   a. Find the numbers in the sixth row of Pascal[3].

     b. Expand the expression $(x^2 + x + 1)^5$. _____

3. What is the eighth term in the expansion of $(x^2 + x + 1)^6$?

_____

Look for and use an analogous pattern in the triangle Pascal[4].

4. Write the first 5 rows of this triangle.

5. What is the sixth term in the expansion of
   $(x^3 + x^2 + x + 1)^3$? _____

6. What is the fifth term in the expansion of
   $(x^3 + x^2 + x + 1)^4$? _____

Holt Algebra 2

LESSON 6-2
Problem Solving
Multiplying Polynomials

Latesha is making an open wooden toy box to hold the building blocks at her day care center. She has a square panel of cedar with side length of 24 inches. The first step is to cut out congruent squares from each corner. She needs to know what the side length of the cutout square should be in order for the finished toy box to have the greatest volume possible.

1. Draw a sketch to help solve the problem.

2. The toy box will be square and x inches deep. Write an expression for the side length of the finished box.

   _____

3. Write an equation to represent the volume. _____

4. Express the volume as the sum of monomials. _____

5. Latesha decides to try some possible values for x. She knows that x must be less than 12. Explain why.

   _____

6. Complete the table for each value of x. Round each volume to the nearest square inch.

x (in.)	2	3	4	5	6
Volume (sq in.)					

7. Latesha decides that she will use an integer value for x, so that she does not have to cut fractions of an inch.

   a. What value for x should she choose? _____

   b. Explain why this is the best choice.

   _____

   c. What are the dimensions of her finished toy box?

   _____

LESSON 6-2

Reading Strategy
Use a Graphic Organizer

You can multiply a polynomial by a monomial. Use the Distributive Property to multiply each term of the polynomial by the monomial.

Definition	Facts
Distributive Property: $a(b + c + d) = ab + ac + ad$	The product of a polynomial and a monomial is a polynomial. Use Properties of Exponents to multiply monomials.
Example $4x(x^2 + 2x - 3)$ $= 4x(x^2) + 4x(2x) + 4x(-3)$ $= 4x^3 + 8x^2 - 12x$	**Useful Hints** Make sure that the polynomial is in standard form before multiplying. Combine like terms before multiplying.

Use the information in the table to answer each question.

A	B
$5x^2 - 2x^2$	$x + 2x^2 - 3$

1. Expression A has 2 terms. Can you simplify it so it is a monomial? If yes, write A as a monomial. _____

2. Is B in standard form? If not, write it in standard form. _____

3. a. Multiply A × B. Write your answer in standard form.

   _____

   b. How many terms does the product have? _____

   c. What is the degree of the product? _____

4. Which Property of Exponents did you use to multiply the variables?

   _____

Practice A
Dividing Polynomials

Divide by using long division.

1. $x - 3\overline{)x^2 + 2x + 6}$

2. $x + 2\overline{)3x^2 + 3x - 12}$

3. $2x + 1\overline{)4x^3 + 6x^2 + 3x}$

4. $5x^2\overline{)10x^4 - 20x^3 + 25x^2}$

Complete using synthetic division.

5. $(x^2 + 4x + 1) \div (x - 5)$

$$\begin{array}{r|rrr} 5 & 1 & 4 & 1 \\ & & 5 & 45 \\ \hline & A & B & C \end{array}$$

a. $A = $ _____

b. $B = $ _____

c. $C = $ _____

d. What is the remainder? _____

e. Write the quotient. _____

Divide by using synthetic division.

6. $(x^2 - 8x + 6) \div (x + 2)$

7. $(x^2 + 4x - 2) \div (x - 3)$

Use synthetic substitution to evaluate the polynomial for the given value.

8. $P(x) = x^2 - 4x + 5$ for $x = 4$

9. $P(x) = 2x^2 + 7x - 1$ for $x = -3$

Holt Algebra 2

LESSON **Practice B**
6-3
Dividing Polynomials

Divide by using long division.

1. $(x^2 - x - 6) \div (x - 3)$

2. $(2x^3 - 10x^2 + x - 5) \div (x - 5)$

_____

3. $(-3x^2 + 20x - 12) \div (x - 6)$

4. $(3x^3 + 9x^2 - 14) \div (x + 3)$

_____

Divide by using synthetic division.

5. $(3x^2 - 8x + 4) \div (x - 2)$

6. $(5x^2 - 4x + 12) \div (x + 3)$

_____

7. $(9x^2 - 7x + 3) \div (x - 1)$

8. $(-6x^2 + 5x - 10) \div (x + 7)$

_____

Use synthetic substitution to evaluate the polynomial for the given value.

9. $P(x) = 4x^2 - 9x + 2$ for $x = 3$

10. $P(x) = -3x^2 + 10x - 4$ for $x = -2$

_____

Solve.

11. The total number of dollars donated each year to a small charitable organization has followed the trend $d(t) = 2t^3 + 10t^2 + 2000t + 10{,}000$, where d is dollars and t is the number of years since 1990. The total number of donors each year has followed the trend $p(t) = t^2 + 1000$. Write an expression describing the average number of dollars per donor.

_____

Holt Algebra 2

Practice C

LESSON 6-3

Dividing Polynomials

Divide by using long division.

1. $(2x^3 + 14x^2 - 4x - 48) \div (2x + 4)$

2. $(x^3 + 12x^2 - 4) \div (x - 3)$

3. $(12x^4 + 23x^3 - 9x^2 + 15x + 4) \div (3x - 1)$

4. $(-2x^3 + 11x^2 - 8x - 7) \div (2x + 1)$

Divide by using synthetic division.

5. $(9x^2 - 3x + 11) \div (x - 6)$

6. $(3x^4 - 2x^2 + 1) \div (x + 2)$

7. $(6x^5 - 3x^2 + x - 2) \div (x - 1)$

8. $(-x^4 - 7x^3 + 6x^2 - 1) \div (x - 3)$

Use synthetic substitution to evaluate the polynomial for the given value.

9. $P(x) = 4x^3 - 12x - 2$ for $x = 5$

10. $P(x) = -3x^4 + 5x^3 - x + 7$ for $x = -2$

Solve.

11. The total weight of the cargo entering a seaport each year can be modeled by the function $C(t) = 0.2t^3 + 1000t^2 + 10t + 50{,}000$, where t is the number of years since the port was opened. The average weight of cargo delivered by each ship is modeled by the function $A(t) = 0.1t + 500$. Write an expression describing the number of ships entering the port each year.

Holt Algebra 2

LESSON 6-3

Reteach
Dividing Polynomials

In arithmetic long division, you follow these steps: divide, multiply, subtract, and bring down. Follow these same steps to use long division to divide polynomials.

Divide: $(6x^2 + x + 8) \div (2x - 1)$.

Step 1 Divide the first term of the dividend, $6x^2$, by the first term of the divisor, $2x$.

$$
\begin{array}{r}
3x \\
2x-1{\overline{\smash{\big)}\,6x^2 + x + 8}} \\
\underline{-(6x^2 - 3x)} \\
4x + 8
\end{array}
$$

Divide: $6x^2 \div 2x = 3x$.

Multiply the complete divisor: $3x(2x - 1) = 6x^2 - 3x$.

Subtract and bring down.

> Remember to use the Distributive Property when you subtract.

Step 2 Divide the first term of the difference, $4x$, by the first term of the divisor, $2x$.

$$
\begin{array}{r}
3x + 2 \\
2x-1{\overline{\smash{\big)}\,6x^2 + x + 8}} \\
\underline{-(6x^2 - 3x)} \\
4x + 8 \\
\underline{-(4x - 2)} \\
10
\end{array}
$$

Multiply: $3x(2x - 1) = 6x^2 - 3x$.

Divide: $4x \div 2x = 2$.

Multiply the complete divisor: $2(2x - 1) = 4x - 2$.

Subtract. Use the Distributive Property.

Step 3 Write the quotient including the remainder.

$$\left(6x^2 + x + 8\right) \div \left(2x - 1\right) = 3x + 2 + \frac{10}{2x - 1}$$

Use long division to divide.

1.
$$
\begin{array}{r}
4x \\
x+2{\overline{\smash{\big)}\,4x^2 + 7x + 6}} \\
\underline{-\left(4x^2 + 8x\right)} \\
-x + 6
\end{array}
$$

2. $x+4{\overline{\smash{\big)}\,2x^2 + 9x + 9}}$

3. $x-5{\overline{\smash{\big)}\,3x^2 - 5x - 50}}$

4. $3x+2{\overline{\smash{\big)}\,6x^2 + 7x - 6}}$

LESSON
6-3

Reteach

Dividing Polynomials (continued)

When the divisor is in the form $(x - a)$, use **synthetic division** to divide.

Divide: $(2x^2 - x - 10) \div (x - 3)$.

Step 1 Find a. The divisor is $(x - 3)$. So, $a = 3$.

Step 2 Write a in the upper left corner.

Then write the coefficients of the dividend.

$$3\underline{|\quad 2 \quad -1 \quad -10}$$

> 2, –1, and –10 are the coefficients of $2x^2 - x - 10$.

Step 3 Draw a horizontal line. Copy the first coefficient below the line.

$$\begin{array}{r} 3\underline{|\quad 2 \quad -1 \quad -10} \\ 2 \end{array}$$

Step 4 Multiply the first coefficient by a, or 3. Write the product in the second column. Add the numbers in the column.

$$\begin{array}{r} 3\underline{|\quad 2 \quad -1 \quad -10} \\ \underline{\quad\quad 6\quad\quad} \\ 2 \quad 5 \end{array}$$

> $2a = 2(3) = 6$

Step 5 Multiply that sum by a, or 3. Write the product in the third column.

Add the numbers in the column.

Draw a box around the last number. It is the remainder.

$$\begin{array}{r} 3\underline{|\quad 2 \quad -1 \quad -10} \\ \underline{\quad\quad 6 \quad 15} \\ 2 \quad 5 \quad \boxed{5} \end{array}$$

> $5a = 5(3) = 15$

> The numbers in the bottom row are the coefficients of the quotient.

Step 6 Write the quotient. $2x + 5 + \dfrac{5}{x - 3}$

Use synthetic division to divide.

5. $(4x^2 + 7x + 10) \div (x + 2)$

$a = -2$

$$\begin{array}{r} -2\underline{|\quad 4 \quad 7 \quad 10} \\ \underline{\quad\quad -8 \quad\quad} \\ 4 \quad \boxed{} \end{array}$$

6. $(2x^2 - 6x - 12) \div (x - 5)$

$a = \underline{}$

$$\begin{array}{r} \underline{|\quad 2 \quad -6 \quad -12} \\ \underline{\quad\quad\quad\quad} \\ \boxed{} \end{array}$$

LESSON
6-3

Challenge
Fractional Synthetic Division

Synthetic division is an efficient tool for dividing a polynomial by a binomial and also for evaluating a polynomial for a given constant. However, the process works only when the divisor is a binomial of the form $(x - a)$, where the coefficient of x is 1. How could the process be used to divide the polynomial $3x^2 + 8x - 12$ by $2x - 6$?

Write the division as a fraction and then multiply both the numerator and denominator by $\dfrac{1}{2}$ to get the divisor in the form for synthetic division.

$$\frac{3x^2 - 8x - 12}{2x - 6} \cdot \frac{\frac{1}{2}}{\frac{1}{2}} = \frac{\frac{3}{2}x^2 - 4x - 6}{x - 3}$$

Now use synthetic division to find the quotient.

$$\begin{array}{r|rrr} 3 & \frac{3}{2} & -4 & -6 \\ & & \frac{9}{2} & \frac{3}{2} \\ \hline & \frac{3}{2} & \frac{1}{2} & -\frac{9}{2} \end{array}$$

Read the quotient from the bottom line.

$\dfrac{3}{2}x + \dfrac{1}{2} - \dfrac{\frac{9}{2}}{2x - 6}$, which simplifies to $\dfrac{3}{2}x + \dfrac{1}{2} - \dfrac{9}{4x - 12}$

Divide using synthetic division.

1. $(4x^2 + 8x - 10) \div (2x + 6)$

2. $(3x^3 + 12x^2 - 15x + 15) \div (3x - 9)$

3. $(25x^3 + 30x + 40) \div (5x + 10)$

4. $\left(x^4 - \dfrac{1}{16}\right) \div (2x - 1)$

5. $(2x^2 - 5x + 7) \div (2x - 1)$

6. $(3x^2 + 7x - 13) \div (3x + 5)$

7. $(4x^5 - 129) \div (4x - 8)$

8. $(x^6 - 729) \div [(x + 3)(x - 3)]$

Holt Algebra 2

LESSON
6-3

Problem Solving
Dividing Polynomials

An art class is making pedestals in the shape of regular prisms to display sculptures in an art show. Blake is in charge of the mirrors for the tops of the pedestals. He needs to estimate the total area of the mirrored surfaces. He will use that total to help determine the amount of mirrored product to purchase.

The figures below show the shape of the bases for each of the three kinds of prisms that will be used for pedestals. Each regular polygon has a side length of *x*. Recall that, for a prism, $V = Bh$.

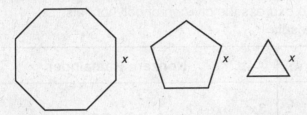

1. The triangular prism has a height of $2x + 1$ and its volume can be modeled by $V(x) = \dfrac{\sqrt{3}}{2}x^3 + \dfrac{\sqrt{3}}{4}x^2$. What is the area of the top of the pedestal?

_____

Choose the letter for the best answer.

2. The volume of the pentagonal prism can be modeled by $V = 6.88x^3 - 1.72x^2$. Which expression represents the area of the top of the prism if the height is $4x - 1$?

   A $0.57x^2$

   B $1.72x^2$

   C $2.28x^2$

   D $6.88x^2$

3. The volume of the octagonal prism can be modeled by $V = 4.83x^3 - 24.15x^2$. Which expression represents the area of the top of the prism if the height is $x - 5$?

   A $48.3x^2$

   B $38.64x^2$

   C $4.83x^2$

   D $3.86x^2$

4. Which expression represents the total area that will be mirrored?

   A $A = x^2\left(\dfrac{\sqrt{3}}{4} + 6.55\right)$

   B $A = 6.98x$

   C $A = 12.58\,x^3 + 22.86\,x^2$

   D $A = \sqrt{6.98x}$

5. If $x = 5$, what is the total mirrored area in square units?

   A 6.98

   B 34.9

   C 69.8

   D 174.5

LESSON 6-3

Reading Strategy
Compare and Contrast

Two polynomials can be divided as long as the divisor has a lower degree. Think about division with numbers and the relationships of the dividend, divisor, quotient, and remainder. When 465 (dividend) is divided by 7 (divisor), the quotient is 66 and the remainder is 3. You can write this division in different ways.

Form 1	Form 2	Form 3	Form 4
$\dfrac{465}{7} = 66 + \dfrac{3}{7}$	$465 \div 7 = 66 \text{ R3}$	$7\overline{)465}\ \ ^{66}\text{ R3}$	$465 = 66 \times 7 + 3$

You can use the same relationships to express the division of polynomials.
Form 4 is a good way to check your result.

No Remainder, or R = 0	Nonzero Remainder
$\dfrac{x^2 - 1}{x + 1} = x - 1$ This can also be written as $x + 1\overline{)x^2 - 1}\ \ ^{x-1}$ or $(x^2 - 1) \div (x + 1) = x - 1.$	$\dfrac{3x^2 + 6x + 2}{x} = (3x + 6)\ \text{R2}$ This can also be written as $x\overline{)3x^2 + 6x + 2}\ \ ^{3x+6}\ \text{R2}$ or $(3x^2 + 6x + 2) \div x = (3x + 6)\ \text{R2}.$

Answer each question.

1. How can you check that $\dfrac{3x^2 + 6x + 2}{x}$ gives quotient $3x + 6$ and remainder 2?

   _____

2. When $x^2 + 4x + 4$ is divided by $x + 1$, the quotient is $x + 3$ and the remainder is 1. Write the result of this division in the four different forms.

   a. Form 1   _____

   b. Form 2   _____

   c. Form 3   _____

   d. Form 4   _____

3. Can you divide $3x + 7$ by x^2? Explain why or why not.

   _____

4. Describe the relationship between the dividend, divisor, and quotient when the remainder is 0.

   _____

LESSON 6-4

Practice A
Factoring Polynomials

Tell whether each statement is true or false.

A is $(x + 1)$ and B is $P(x) = x^2 - 2x - 3$

1. If $P(1) = 0$, then A is a factor of B. _____

2. If $P(-1) = 0$, then A is a factor of B. _____

3. If $P(0) = 0$, then B is in perfect square form. _____

4. Synthetic substitution can be used to determine if A is a factor of B. _____

Determine whether the given binomial is a factor of the polynomial $P(x)$.

5. $(x + 1)$; $P(x) = 5x^2 + 11x + 6$

6. $(x - 3)$; $P(x) = 3x^4 + 3x^3 - 2x^2 - 2x$

_____

_____

Factor each expression.

7. $2x^2 + 8x + 2x + 8$

8. $x^3 + 2x^2 - x - 2$

_____

_____

9. $x^3 + x^2 + 7x + 7$

10. $x^3 - 2x^2 - 4x + 8$

_____

_____

11. $g^2 + 8$

12. $128m - 2m^4$

_____

_____

Solve.

13. June factored the polynomial $c^9 - d^{12}$ into $(c^3 + d^4)(c^6 - c^3d^4 + d^8)$. Is she correct? How do you know?

_____

Holt Algebra 2

Practice B

Factoring Polynomials

Determine whether the given binomial is a factor of the polynomial
$P(x)$.

1. $(x - 4); P(x) = x^2 + 8x - 48$

2. $(x + 5); P(x) = 2x^2 - 6x - 1$

3. $(x - 6); P(x) = -2x^2 + 15x - 18$

4. $(x + 3); P(x) = 2x^2 - x + 7$

Factor each expression.

5. $2x^4 + 2x^3 - x^2 - x$

6. $4x^3 + x^2 - 8x - 2$

7. $5x^6 - 5x^4 + x^3 - x$

8. $2x^4 + 54x$

9. $64x^3 - 1$

10. $3x^4 + 24x$

Solve.

11. Since 2006, the water level in a certain pond
has been modeled by the polynomial
$d(x) = -x^3 + 16x^2 - 74x + 140$, where the depth
d, is measured in feet over x years. Identify the
year that the pond will dry up. Use the graph to
factor $d(x)$.

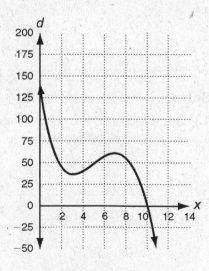

Holt Algebra 2

Practice C
Factoring Polynomials

**Use the Factor Theorem to verify that each linear binomial is a factor
of the given polynomial. Then use synthetic division to write the
polynomial as a product.**

1. $(x + 5)$; $P(x) = 2x^2 + 6x - 20$

2. $(x - 1)$; $P(x) = x^4 - 6x^3 + 4x^2 + 1$

_____   _____

3. $(x + 2)$; $P(x) = 3x^3 + 12x^2 + 17x + 10$

4. $(x - 8)$; $P(x) = x^4 - 8x^3 - 4x^2 + 33x - 8$

_____   _____

Factor each expression.

5. $16x^3 - 12x^2 + 20x - 15$

6. $3x^6 + 54x^4 + 243x^2$

_____   _____

7. $x^6 - 10x^5 + 25x^4$

8. $6x^3 + 12x^2 + 4x + 8$

_____   _____

9. $250x^4 + 54x$

10. $-3x^5 + 24x^2$

_____   _____

Solve.

11. The voltage generated by an electrical circuit changes over time according
    to the polynomial $V(t) = t^3 - 4t^2 - 25t + 100$, where V is in volts and t is in
    seconds. Factor the polynomial to find the times when the voltage is equal
    to zero.

_____

Holt Algebra 2

LESSON	**Reteach**
6-4	*Factoring Polynomials*

Sometimes you can use grouping to factor a third degree polynomial. To **factor by grouping** means to group terms with common factors. Then factor the common factors. Continue to factor until the expression can no longer be factored.

Factor: $x^3 + 4x^2 - 9x - 36$.

Start by grouping terms to factor out the greatest possible power of x.

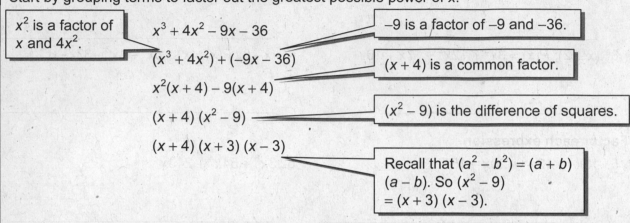

x^2 is a factor of x and $4x^2$.

$x^3 + 4x^2 - 9x - 36$

$(x^3 + 4x^2) + (-9x - 36)$

$x^2(x + 4) - 9(x + 4)$

$(x + 4)(x^2 - 9)$

$(x + 4)(x + 3)(x - 3)$

−9 is a factor of −9 and −36.

$(x + 4)$ is a common factor.

$(x^2 - 9)$ is the difference of squares.

Recall that $(a^2 - b^2) = (a + b)(a - b)$. So $(x^2 - 9) = (x + 3)(x - 3)$.

Factor each expression.

1. $x^3 - 3x^2 - 4x + 12$

   $(x^3 - 3x^2) + (-4x + 12)$

   $x^2(x - 3) - 4(x - 3)$

   _____

   _____

2. $x^3 + 6x^2 - x - 6$

   $(x^3 + 6x^2) + (-x - 6)$

   _____

   _____

3. $x^3 + x^2 - 9x - 9$

   _____

   _____

   _____

4. $x^3 + 2x^2 - 16x - 32$

   _____

   _____

   _____

LESSON
6-4

Reteach
Factoring Polynomials (continued)

Use special rules to factor the sum or difference of two cubes.

Recognizing these common cubes can help you factor the sum or difference of cubes.

$1^3 = 1$, $2^3 = 8$, $3^3 = 27$, $4^3 = 64$, $5^3 = 125$, and $6^3 = 216$

Rule for the Sum of Two Cubes: $a^3 + b^3 = (a + b)(a^2 - ab + b^2)$.

Factor: $y^3 + 64$.

$y^3 + 64$	*Identify the cubes: y^3 and $64 = 4^3$.*
$y^3 + 4^3$	*Write the expression as the sum of two cubes.*
$(y + 4)(y^2 - 4y + 16)$	*Use the rule to factor.*

Using the rule: $a = y$ and $b = 4$.
So $a^2 = y^2$, $ab = 4y$, and $b^2 = 16$.

Rule for the Difference of Two Cubes: $a^3 - b^3 = (a - b)(a^2 + ab + b^2)$.

Factor: $8x^3 - 125$.

$8x^3 - 125$	*Identify the cubes: $(2x)^3$ and $125 = 5^3$.*
$(2x)^3 - 5^3$	*Write the expression as the difference of two cubes.*
$(2x - 5)(4x^2 + 10x + 25)$	*Use the rule to factor.*

Using the rule: $a = 2x$ and $b = 5$.
So $a^2 = (2x)^2 = 4x^2$, $ab = (2x)(5) = 10x$, and $b^2 = 25$.

Factor each expression.

5. $27x^3 + 8$
   $(3x)^3 + 2^3$

6. $y^3 - 216$
   $y^3 - 6^3$

_____

7. $y^3 + 27$

8. $x^3 - 1$

_____

_____

Holt Algebra 2

LESSON 6-4

Challenge

The Nested Form of a Polynomial

Polynomials in one variable are usually written in descending order of the exponents of the variable. Another useful way to write a polynomial is called *nested form*, in which the variable is factored out until the innermost nest contains only the leading coefficient.

- **Example** To write $4x^3 - 3x^2 + 5x - 8$ in nested form:

  Factor out an x. $(4x^2 - 3x + 5)x - 8$

  Factor out x again. $[(4x - 3)x + 5]x - 8$

  Factor out x again. $\{[(4)x - 3]x + 5\}x - 8$

  Thus, $4x^3 - 3x^2 + 5x - 8 = \{[(4)x - 3]x + 5\}x - 8$

Write the polynomial in nested form.

1. $6x^3 + 8x^2 - 5x + 1$

2. $-2x^4 + 5x^3 - x^2 + 3x - 4$

_____   _____

Nested form is convenient for evaluating a polynomial.

In Exercises 3–6, use $N(x) = \{[(5)x - 3]x + 7\}x - 1$.

3. Find the value of $N(3)$ mentally.
   Remember to follow the order of operations.   _____

4. Find $N(3)$ using a calculator.   _____

5. Write the expanded form of $N(x)$.   _____

6. Use the expanded form to find the value of $N(3)$.
   Match this result with those from Exercises 3 and 4.   _____

7. Show how the nested form could be used to divide $2x^3 - 6x^2 - 2x - 30$ by
   $x - 4$. Write the quotient and the remainder.

_____

_____

_____

_____

8. Use synthetic division to verify your result of Exercise 7.

_____

LESSON 6-4 Problem Solving

Factoring Polynomials

Paulo is drawing plans for a set of three proportional nesting baskets, in the shape of open rectangular prisms.

1. The volume for the middle-sized basket (B) can be modeled by the function $V_B(x) = x^3 - 8x^2 + 4x + 48$. Use the graph to factor V_B.

   a. What are the values of x where $V_B = 0$?

   _____

   b. Use these zeros to write the factors.

   _____

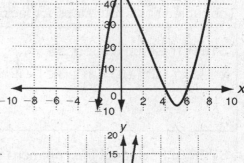

2. The volume for the largest basket (C) can be modeled by the function $V_C(x) = 2x^3 + 10x^2 + 8x$. Use the graph to factor V_C.

   a. What are the values of x where $V_C = 0$?

   _____

   b. Use these zeros to write the factors.

   _____

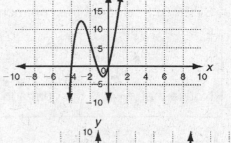

3. The volume for the smallest basket (A) can be modeled by the function $V_A(x) = x^3 - 22x^2 + 157x - 360$. Use the graph to factor V_A.

   a. What are the values of x where $V_A = 0$?

   _____

   b. Use these zeros to write the factors.

   _____

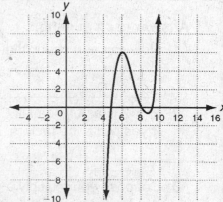

4. Complete the table. Use $x = 12$ units to find the actual dimensions and volume.

Basket	Dimensions (in terms of x)	Actual Dimensions	Volume
A			
B			
C			

5. Are the actual dimensions of the three baskets proportional? Explain.

_____

6. Are the volumes of the three baskets proportional? Explain.

_____

Holt Algebra 2

LESSON 6-4

Reading Strategy
Identify Relationships

You already know how to factor linear and quadratic functions, which are polynomials. Higher-degree polynomials can also be factored. One method is to group the terms in the polynomial and find common factors.

The table shows four steps for factoring $x^3 + 3x^2 + 2x + 6$.

STEP 1: Group the terms. $x^3 + 3x^2 + 2x + 6 = (x^3 + 3x^2) + (2x + 6)$	**STEP 2:** Find the common factors of each group. Common factor of $(x^3 + 3x^2)$ is x^2 Common factor of $(2x + 6)$ is 2
STEP 3: Factor out the common factors in each group. $(x^3 + 3x^2) + (2x + 6)$ $= x^2(x + 3) + 2(x + 3)$ Notice that $x + 3$ is the common factor.	**STEP 4:** Factor out $x + 3$. $x^2(x + 3) + 2(x + 3) = (x + 3)(x^2 + 2)$ The factors of $x^3 + 3x^2 + 2x + 6$ are $(x + 3)$ and $(x^2 + 2)$

Answer each question.

1. How can you check that $x + 3$ and $x^2 + 2$ are factors of $x^3 + 3x^2 + 2x + 6$?

   _____

2. $x^2 + 2$ is a polynomial. Can you factor $x^2 + 2$ into two linear factors? If yes, write the factors. If no, explain.

   _____

3. Suppose you multiply a polynomial of degree 3 by a polynomial of degree 2. What is the degree of the product of the two polynomials? _____

Use $x^3 - 8x^2 - x + 8$ to answer the following questions.

4. a. How would you group this polynomial to factor it? _____

   b. What is the common factor of the first group? _____

   c. What is the common factor of the second group? _____

   d. Find the common binomial factor in both groups and write the factors.

   _____

   e. Which of the two factors can also be factored? Write its factors. _____

   f. What are the factors of $x^3 - 8x^2 - x + 8$? _____

Holt Algebra 2

LESSON 6-5 Practice A
Finding Real Roots of Polynomial Equations

Solve each polynomial equation by factoring.

1. $5x^3 + 10x^2 + 5x = 0$

   $= 5x(\underline{})$

   _____

2. $x^3 + 2x^2 - 9x - 18 = 0$

   $= (x^3 - 9x) + (\underline{})$

   _____

3. $4x^3 + 40x^2 + 100x = 0$

   _____

4. $8x^4 - 48x^3 = 56x^2$

   _____

Identify the roots of each equation. State the multiplicity of each root.

5. $x^3 + 2x^2 - 3x = 0$

   _____

6. $2x^3 - 4x^2 + 2x = 0$

   _____

7. $x^3 - 7x^2 + 11x - 5 = 0$

   _____

8. $x^3 + 12x^2 + 36x = 0$

   _____

Use the Rational Root Theorem to identify all *possible* rational roots.

9. $3x^3 + 2x^2 - 1 = 0$

   _____

10. $x^4 - 3x^2 + 12 = 0$

   _____

11. $2x^3 - x - 10 = 0$

   _____

12. $x^4 + 6x - 9 = 0$

   _____

Solve.

13. Kim and Stefan both factor the equation $x^2 - 4 = 0$. Kim thinks that the root 2 has multiplicity 2, but Stefan thinks the root 2 has multiplicity 1. Who is correct? How do you know?

   _____

   _____

Holt Algebra 2

LESSON 6-5 Practice B
Finding Real Roots of Polynomial Equations

Solve each polynomial equation by factoring.

1. $9x^3 - 3x^2 - 3x + 1 = 0$

2. $x^5 - 2x^4 - 24x^3 = 0$

_____

_____

3. $3x^5 + 18x^4 - 21x^3 = 0$

4. $-x^4 + 2x^3 + 8x^2 = 0$

_____

_____

Identify the roots of each equation. State the multiplicity of each root.

5. $x^3 + 3x^2 + 3x + 1 = 0$

6. $x^3 + 5x^2 - 8x - 48 = 0$

_____

_____

Identify all the real roots of each equation.

7. $x^3 + 10x^2 + 17x = 28$

8. $3x^3 + 10x^2 - 27x = 10$

_____

_____

Solve.

9. An engineer is designing a storage compartment in a spacecraft. The compartment must be 2 meters longer than it is wide and its depth must be 1 meter less than its width. The volume of the compartment must be 8 cubic meters.

   a. Write an equation to model the volume of the compartment.

   _____

   b. List all possible rational roots.   _____

   c. Use synthetic division to find the roots of the polynomial equation. Are the roots all rational numbers?

   _____

   d. What are the dimensions of the storage compartment?   _____

Holt Algebra 2

LESSON	**Practice C**
6-5	*Finding Real Roots of Polynomial Equations*

Solve each polynomial equation by factoring.

1. $-3x^4 + 6x^3 + 105x^2 = 0$

2. $8x^7 - 56x^6 + 96x^5 = 0$

_____ _____

Identify the roots of each equation. State the multiplicity of each root.

3. $x^3 + 6x^2 + 12x - 8 = 0$

4. $x^3 + 10x^2 + 32x + 32 = 0$

_____ _____

Identify all the real roots of each equation.

5. $x^3 + 2x^2 - 48x = 0$

6. $x^4 - 13x^3 + 55x^2 - 81x + 18 = 0$

_____ _____

7. $6x^3 + 12x^2 - 18x = 0$

8. $x^4 + 8x^3 + 7x^2 - 22x + 6 = 0$

_____ _____

Solve.

9. A jewelry box is designed such that its length is twice its width and its depth is 2 inches less than its width. The volume of the box is 64 cubic inches.

    a. Write an equation to model the volume of the box.

_____

    b. List all possible rational roots. _____

    c. Use synthetic division to find the roots of the polynomial equation. Are the roots all rational numbers?

_____

    d. What are the dimensions of the box? _____

Holt Algebra 2

LESSON 6-5

Reteach

Finding Real Roots of Polynomial Equations

To find the roots of a polynomial equation, set the equation equal to zero. Factor the polynomial expression completely. Then set each factor equal to zero to solve for the variable.

Solve the equation: $2x^5 + 6x^4 = 8x^3$.

Step 1 To set the equation equal to 0, rearrange the equation so that all the terms are on one side.

$$2x^5 + 6x^4 = 8x^3$$
$$2x^5 + 6x^4 - 8x^3 = 0$$

Step 2 Look for the greatest number and the greatest power of x that can be factored from each term.

$$2x^5 + 6x^4 - 8x^3 = 0 \longleftarrow \boxed{\text{The GCF is } 2x^3.}$$
$$2x^3(x^2 + 3x - 4) = 0$$

Step 3. Factor the quadratic.

$$2x^3(x^2 + 3x - 4) = 0$$
$$2x^3(x + 4)(x - 1) = 0$$

Step 4 Set each factor equal to 0.

$$2x^3 = 0 \qquad x + 4 = 0 \qquad x - 1 = 0$$

Step 5 Solve each equation.

$$2x^3 = 0 \qquad x + 4 = 0 \qquad x - 1 = 0$$
$$x = 0 \qquad\quad x = -4 \qquad\quad x = 1$$

The solutions of the equation are called the roots.

The roots are –4, 0, and 1.

Solve each polynomial equation.

1. $3x^6 - 9x^5 = 30x^4$

   $3x^6 - 9x^5 - 30x^4 = 0$

   $3x^4(x^2 - 3x - 10) = 0$

   _____

   _____

2. $x^4 + 6x^2 = 5x^3$

   $x^4 - 5x^3 + 6x^2 = 0$

   _____

   _____

   _____

3. $2x^3 - 6x^2 - 36x = 0$

   _____

   _____

   _____

4. $2x^6 - 32x^4 = 0$

   _____

   _____

   _____

LESSON 6-5

Reteach

Finding Real Roots of Polynomial Equations (continued)

You can use the Rational Root Theorem to find rational roots.

Rational Root Theorem

If a polynomial has integer coefficients, then every rational root can be written in the form $\frac{p}{q}$, where p is a factor of the constant term and q is a factor of the leading coefficient.

Use the Rational Root Theorem. Solve the equation: $x^3 + 3x^2 - 6x - 8 = 0$.

The constant term is –8. The leading coefficient is 1.

    p: factors of –8 are ±1, ±2, ±4, ±8

    q: factors of 1 are ±1

    Possible roots, $\frac{p}{q}$: ±1, ±2, ±4, ±8

Test some possible roots to find an actual root. Use a synthetic substitution table. The first column lists possible roots. The last column represents the remainders. A root has a remainder of 0.

2 is a root, so $x - 2$ is a factor. Use the coefficients from the table to write the other factor.

$\frac{p}{q}$	Coefficients of the Equation			
	1	3	–6	–8
1	1	4	–2	–10
2	1	5	4	0
4	1	7	22	80

    $(x - 2)(x^2 + 5x + 4) = 0$

    $(x - 2)(x + 4)(x + 1) = 0$ ← Factor the quadratic to find the other factors.

    $x = 2$ or $x = -4$ or $x = -1$

The roots of the equation are –4, –1, and 2.

Use the Rational Root Theorem. Solve $x^3 - 7x^2 + 7x + 15 = 0$.

5. a. Identify possible roots. _____

   b. Use the synthetic substitution table to identify an actual root. _____

$\frac{p}{q}$	Coefficients of the Equation		
	1	–7	7	15

   c. Write the factors of the equation.

_____

   d. Identify the roots of the equation.

_____

Holt Algebra 2

LESSON
6-5

Challenge
Writing Polynomial Functions

Solving a polynomial equation means to find the roots of the equation.
The multiplicity of each root determines whether the graph of the equation
crosses the *x*-axis or just touches the *x*-axis.

The graph at left below shows *x*-intercepts of –5, 0, 2, and 6. The curve
just touches the *x*-axis at 2, indicating an even multiplicity, and passes
through the *x*-axis at –5, 0, and 6, indicating an odd multiplicity.

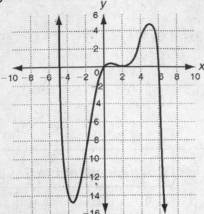 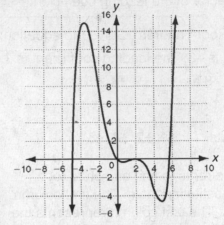

An equation for this polynomial function is

$$y = 0.01(x + 5)(x)(x - 2)^2(x - 6).$$

Graphing this function gives the graph at right above. It is the reflection
across the *x*-axis of the graph at left. To reflect a graph across the *x*-axis,
replace each *y* with –*y*, which gives the polynomial function

$$y = -[0.01(x + 5)(x)(x - 2)^2(x - 6)].$$

Write a possible polynomial function whose graph fits the given conditions.

1. Crosses the *x*-axis at –3, 0, and 4; lies above the
   x-axis between –3 and 0; and lies below the *x*-axis
   between 0 and 4 _____

2. Touches the *x*-axis at –1, crosses the *x*-axis at 1
   and 3, and lies above the *x*-axis between 1 and 3 _____

3. Has *x*-intercepts of –5, –2, $\frac{1}{2}$, and 3; lies above

   the *x*-axis between –5 and –2 and also between

   –2 and $\frac{1}{2}$ but lies below the *x*-axis between $\frac{1}{2}$ and 3 _____

4. Has *x*-intercepts of –6, 0, 1, 3, and 4; lies above
   the *x*-axis at all points between the *x*-intercepts
   except on the interval from 0 to 1 _____

5. Real coefficients, roots –3*i*, 1, and $1 + \sqrt{3}$;
   and touches the *x*-axis at 1 _____

Holt Algebra 2

LESSON 6-5

Problem Solving

Finding Real Roots of Polynomial Equations

Most airlines have rules concerning the size of checked baggage. The rules for Budget Airline are such that the dimensions of the largest bag cannot exceed 45 in. by 55 in. by 62 in. A designer is drawing plans for a piece of luggage that athletes can use to carry their equipment. It will have a volume of 76,725 cubic inches. The length is 10 in. greater than the width and the depth is 14 in. less than the width. What are the dimensions of this piece of luggage?

1. Write an equation in factored form to model the volume of the piece of luggage.

   _____

2. Multiply and set the equation equal to zero.

   _____

3. Think about possible roots of the equation. Could a root be a multiple

   of 4? _____ a multiple of 5? _____

   a multiple of 10? _____. How do you know?

   _____

4. Use synthetic substitution to test possible roots. Choose positive integers that are factors of the constant term and reasonable in the context of the problem.

Possible Root	1	−4	−140	−76,725

Choose the letter for the best answer.

5. Which equation represents the factored polynomial?

   A $(w + 55)(w^2 + 25w + 1550) = 0$

   B $(w − 35)(w^2 + 60w + 1405) = 0$

   C $(w − 45)(w^2 + 41w + 1705) = 0$

   D $(w − 4)(w^2 − 140w + 76{,}725) = 0$

6. Which could be the dimensions of this piece of luggage?

   A 31 in. by 45 in. by 55 in.

   B 45 in. by 55 in. by 55 in.

   C 45 in. by 45 in. by 55 in.

   D 45 in. by 55 in. by 62 in.

Holt Algebra 2

Name _____ Date _____ Class_____

Reading Strategy
Understand Operations

To find an equation's roots, you must perform two operations: First, factor
the expression. Second, set the factors equal to zero. When a linear
factor, such as $x - 3$, appears more than once, then 3 is a multiple root
of the equation. You can find the multiplicity of any root, r, by counting the
number of times the factor $x - r$ appears in the polynomial.

Polynomial Equation	Step 1: Factor.	Step 2: Set factors equal to 0.	Multiplicity
$x^3 + 8x^2 + 16x = 0$	$x(x + 4)(x + 4)$	**Root 1:** $x + 4 = 0$; $x = -4$ **Root 2:** $x = 0$	2 1

If -4 and 0 are real roots of the polynomial $P(x) = x^3 + 8x^2 + 16x$, then
$P(-4) = 0$ and $P(0) = 0$. From the roots of a polynomial function, you
can find its factors.

Answer each question.

1. How can you check if a number is a root of a polynomial function?

_____

2. In a polynomial function, $P(3) = 0$ and $P(-2) = 0$. Find two factors of
   the polynomial.

_____

3. A polynomial equation has a multiple root -4. Its multiplicity is 3.
   a. Write the factor that corresponds to this root. _____
   b. How many times is this a factor of the polynomial? _____

Complete the table.

	Polynomial Equation	Factors	Roots
4.	$4x(x^2 - 9) = 0$		
5.	$-x(x^2 - 6x + 5) = 0$		
6.	$(x + 2)(x^2 - 4) = 0$		

Holt Algebra 2

Name _____ Date _____ Class_____

Practice A

Fundamental Theorem of Algebra

Identify the number of zeros for each function.

1. $P(x) = x^3 + 2x^2 - 12x + 1$ 2. $P(x) = 2x^5 - 5x + 10$ 3. $P(x) = 3x^4 + 2x$

_____   _____   _____

Write the simplest polynomial function with the given zeros.

4. −1, 0, and 2

    a. Write the factored expression.   _____

    b. Multiply the first two factors.   _____

    c. Multiply the result by the remaining factor. _____

    d. Combine like terms.   _____

5. −3, 1, and 5   6. −4, −1, and 1

_____   _____

7. 2*i*

    a. How many zeros does this function have?   _____

    b. Write the conjugate pair for the complex root. _____

    c. Write the factored expression.   _____

    d. Multiply the binomials.   _____

8. −2 and $\sqrt{3}$ 9. 3 and 2 + *i*

_____   _____

Solve the equation by finding all roots.

10. $x^3 - 6x^2 - 2x + 12 = 0$

_____

Holt Algebra 2

LESSON
6-6

Practice B

Fundamental Theorem of Algebra

Write the simplest polynomial function with the given roots.

1. 1, 4, and −3

2. $\frac{1}{2}$, 5, and −2

_____

3. $2i$, $\sqrt{3}$, and 4

4. $\sqrt{2}$, −5, and −3i

_____

Solve each equation by finding all roots.

5. $x^4 - 2x^3 - 14x^2 - 2x - 15 = 0$

6. $x^4 - 16 = 0$

_____

7. $x^4 + 4x^3 + 4x^2 + 64x - 192 = 0$

8. $x^3 + 3x^2 + 9x + 27 = 0$

_____

Solve.

9. An electrical circuit is designed such that its output voltage, V, measured in volts, can be either positive or negative. The voltage of the circuit passes through zero at $t = 1$, 2, and 7 seconds. Write the simplest polynomial describing the voltage $V(t)$.

_____

LESSON 6-6

Practice C

Fundamental Theorem of Algebra

Write the simplest polynomial function with the given roots.

1. $-\dfrac{3}{4}$, 6, and -1

_____

2. $-5i$, 2, and 7

_____

3. $-i$, -3, and -1

_____

4. $2i$, 4, and $\sqrt{6}$

_____

Solve each equation by finding all roots.

5. $4x^4 - 8x^3 - 3x^2 - 18x - 27 = 0$

_____

6. $x^4 + 3x^3 - x^2 + 9x - 12 = 0$

_____

7. $x^4 - 3x^3 - 8x^2 + 22x - 24 = 0$

_____

8. $x^3 + 6x^2 + 4x + 24 = 0$

_____

Solve.

9. For a scientific experiment, Tony needs a glass bell jar in the shape of a cylinder with a hemisphere on top. The height of the cylinder must be 3 inches longer than its radius and the volume must be 72π cubic inches. What should the radius of the cylinder be?

_____

Holt Algebra 2

LESSON 6-6 Reteach
Fundamental Theorem of Algebra

If r is a root of a polynomial function, then $(x - r)$ is a factor of the polynomial, $P(x)$. So, you can use the roots to write the simplest form of a polynomial function.

Write the simplest polynomial function with roots -4, -2, and 3.

Step 1 Write the factors of the polynomial, $P(x) = 0$.

$(x + 4)(x + 2)(x - 3) = 0$

Root (a)	-4	-2	3
Factor $(x - a)$	$x + 4$	$x + 2$	$x - 3$

Step 2 Multiply the first two factors, $(x + 4)(x + 2)$.

$(x^2 + 6x + 8)(x - 3) = 0$

Step 3 Multiply $(x^2 + 6x + 8)(x - 3)$. Then simplify.

$x^3 - 3x^2 + 6x^2 - 18x + 8x - 24 = 0$

$x^3 + 3x^2 - 10x - 24 = 0$

The function is $P(x) = x^3 + 3x^2 - 10x - 24 = 0$.

Write the simplest polynomial function with the given roots.

1. -5, 1, and 2

$(x + 5)(x - 1)(x - 2) = 0$

$(\underline{\hspace{3cm}})(x - 2) = 0$

_____

_____

2. -3, -1, and 0

$x(x + 3)(x + 1) = 0$

_____

_____

3. 1, 4, and 5

_____

_____

_____

4. -2, 3, and 6

_____

_____

_____

5. 2, 4, and 6

_____

_____

_____

6. -5, 0, and 5

_____

_____

_____

LESSON
6-6

Reteach

Fundamental Theorem of Algebra (continued)

To solve $x^4 + x^3 - 5x^2 + x - 6 = 0$ means to find all the roots of the equation. A fourth degree equation has 4 roots.

Step 1   Identify possible real roots.

Possible roots, $\dfrac{p}{q}$: ±1, ±2, ±3, ±6

> The factors, p, of –6 are ±1, ±2, ±3, ±6. The factors, q, of 1 are ±1.

Step 2   Graph $y = x^4 + x^3 - 5x^2 + x - 6$.

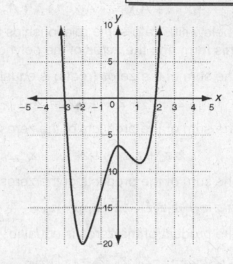

Step 3   Test 2 as a root using synthetic substitution.

```
2| 1   1  -5   1  -6
       2   6   2   6
   ─────────────────
   1   3   1   3  |0
```

> The remainder is 0, so 2 is a root.
> $(x - 2)(x^3 + 3x^2 + x + 3) = 0$

Test –3 as a root using synthetic substitution.

```
-3| 1   3   1   3
       -3   0  -3
    ────────────────
    1   0   1  |0
```

> The remainder is 0, so –3 is a root.
> $(x - 2)(x + 3)(x^2 + 1) = 0$

Step 4   Find the remaining roots.

$x^2 + 1 = 0$

$x = \pm i$

The roots of the equation are 2, –3, i, and –i.

Find the roots of the equation $x^4 - 3x^3 + 6x^2 - 12x + 8 = 0$.

7. Possible roots: ±1, ±2, ±4, ±8

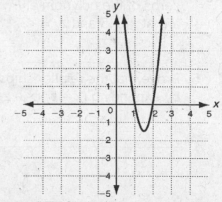

Test: _____ and _____.

_____ and _____ are real roots.

Solve _____ to find the remaining roots.

Remaining roots: _____ and _____.

Holt Algebra 2

Challenge
Polynomial Function Coefficients

A polynomial function may be written in standard form.

$$P(x) = a_n x^n + a_{n-1}x^{n-1} + a_{n-2}x^{n-2} + \ldots + a_2 x^2 + a_1 x + a_0$$

Dividing by the leading coefficient, a_n, does not change the zeros of the polynomial. This produces a new polynomial that can also be written in descending order.

$$Q(x) = x^n + A_1 x^{n-1} + A_2 x^{n-2} + A_3 x^{n-3} + \ldots + A_{n-1}x + A_n$$

The properties below illustrate some relationships that occur between the coefficients in this form and the zeros of the polynomial.

i) The sum of the zeros (roots) is equal to $-A_1$.

$$z_1 + z_2 + z_3 + \ldots + z_n = -A_1$$

ii) The sum of the products of the zeros taken two at a time is equal to A_2.

$$z_1 z_2 + z_1 z_3 + z_1 z_4 + \ldots + z_{n-2}z_n + z_{n-1}z_n = A_2$$

iii) The sum of the products of the zeros taken three at a time is equal to $-A_3$.

$$z_1 z_2 z_3 + z_1 z_2 z_4 + \ldots + z_{n-2}z_{n-1}z_n = -A_3$$

iv) The product of the zeros is equal to A_n or $-A_n$.

$$z_1 z_2 z_3 z_4 - \ldots - z_{n-2}z_{n-1}z_n = (-1)^n A_n$$

Solve.

1. Show that the relationships *i*) and *ii*) hold true for the polynomial function $P(x) = x^2 + 2x - 15$, which has zeros at $z_1 = 3$ and $z_2 = -5$.

_____

2. Show that the relationships *i*), *ii*), and *iii*) hold true for the polynomial function $P(x) = x^3 - 3x^2 - 6x + 8$, which has zeros at $z_1 = 1$, $z_2 = 4$, and $z_3 = -2$.

_____

3. Use the relationships to find the final zero of the polynomial $P(x) = x^3 - 8x^2 - 5x + 84$ given that two of the zeros are at $z_1 = 7$ and $z_2 = -3$.

_____

4. Use the relationships and solve a system of equations to find the remaining zeros of the polynomial $P(x) = x^4 - x^3 - 19x^2 - 11x + 30$ given that two zeros are at $z_1 = 5$ and $z_2 = -2$.

_____

5. Prove that the relationships above are true for a polynomial with three zeros by expanding $(x - z_1)(x - z_2)(x - z_3)$.

_____

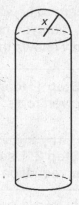

LESSON 6-6 Problem Solving
Fundamental Theorem of Algebra

A company that makes accessories for cars needs a container like that shown at the right to hold touch-up paint. The hemispherical top will be fitted with a brush applicator. The cylindrical part of the container should be 4 inches tall. The volume of the entire container is $\frac{13}{12}\pi$ cubic inches. Find the value of *x*, the radius of the hemisphere.

1. a. Write a formula for the volume of the cylindrical part
    of the container.

    _____

    b. Write a formula for the volume of the hemispherical
    part of the container.

    _____

2. Write an equation to represent the total volume of the container.

   _____

3. Write the equation in standard form.

   _____

4. Graph the equation with a graphing calculator.
   Hint: Use a window with *x*-values from –8 to 5
   with a scale of 1, and *y*-values from –20 to 250
   with a scale of 30 to see the general shape of
   the graph. Sketch the graph.
   Then focus on the area of the positive root by
   using a window of –8 to 3 on the *x*-axis and
   –20 to 20 on the *y*-axis. Use Trace to help you
   find a possible positive root.

5. Verify the root using synthetic substitution.
   What is the positive root?

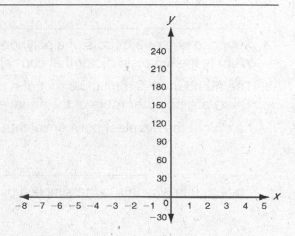

   _____

6. Use the Quadratic Formula to find approximate values for the other two roots.
   Explain why these two roots cannot also be solutions to the problem.

   _____

7. What is the value of *x*, the radius of the hemisphere,
   for this paint container?   _____

Holt Algebra 2

LESSON
6-6

Reading Strategy
Use a Model

You've learned how to find the roots of a polynomial equation. If you know the roots, then you can find a polynomial function that has those roots. The table below shows the method for a polynomial function that has two roots.

Step 1: Identify factors from the given roots.	**Root** $x = 2$ $x = -5$	➜ ➜	**Factor** $x - 2$ $x + 5$
Step 2: Use the factors to write an equation.	$(x - 2)(x + 5) = 0$		
Step 3: Multiply the factors to find the polynomial with the given roots.	$x^2 + 5x - 2x - 10 = 0$ $x^2 + 3x - 10 = 0$		

$x^2 + 3x - 10 = 0$ is the simplest polynomial with roots 2 and –5. If you multiply this equation by any nonzero number, the new equation will also have the same roots.

Answer each question.

1. How can you use the method described above if you know all three roots of a polynomial equation?

   _____

2. Suppose one of the roots of a polynomial is 0.
   What is the simplest factor that corresponds to 0? _____

3. The number –2 is a multiple root of a polynomial. The multiplicity of –2 is 3. There are no other roots of the equation.

   a. Write the simplest polynomial that has the given roots.

   _____

   b. Explain why this is the simplest polynomial.

   _____

4. a. Write the simplest polynomial function
      with roots 0, 0, 0, and 2.   _____

   b. What is the degree of this polynomial?   _____

LESSON 6-7 Practice A
Investigating Graphs of Polynomial Functions

Complete the table to identify the leading coefficient, degree, and end behavior of each polynomial function.

	Polynomial	Leading Coefficient	Degree	End Behavior
1.	$P(x) = x^2 + 3x + 6$			As $x \to -\infty$, $P(x) \to +\infty$ As $x \to +\infty$, $P(x) \to +\infty$
2.	$P(x) = -3x^3 + 2x - 5$			As $x \to -\infty$, $P(x) \to$ _____ As $x \to +\infty$, $P(x) \to$ _____
3.	$P(x) = 2x^4 + 2x^3 + 3$			As As
4.	$P(x) = -6x^5 + 3x^3 + 1$			As As

Graph the function $P(x) = x^3 + 4x^2 - x - 4$.

5. Identify possible rational roots.

_____

6. Test the roots using synthetic division to find a zero.

_____

7. Use your results from the synthetic division to factor the polynomial to find all zeros.

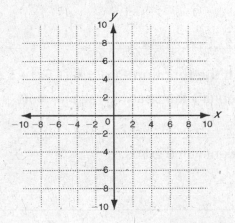

_____

8. Find other points to use to draw the graph, such as the *y*-intercept and points between the zeros such as $P(-2)$ and $P(-3)$.

_____

9. Identify the end behavior of the graph.

_____

10. Sketch the graph of the function.

Holt Algebra 2

LESSON	**Practice B**
6-7	*Investigating Graphs of Polynomial Functions*

Identify the leading coefficient, degree, and end behavior.

1. $P(x) = 2x^5 - 6x^3 + x^2 - 2$

_____

2. $Q(x) = -4x^2 + x - 1$

_____

Identify whether the function graphed has an odd or even degree and a positive or negative leading coefficient.

3.
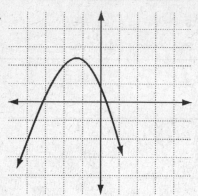

4.
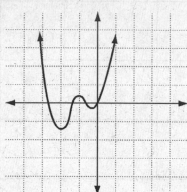

5.
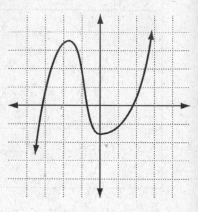

_____   _____   _____

Graph the function $P(x) = x^3 + 6x^2 + 5x - 12$.

6. Identify the possible rational roots.

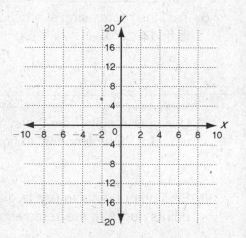

_____

7. Identify the zeros.

_____

8. Describe the end behavior of the function.

_____

9. Sketch the graph of the function.

Solve.

10. The number, $N(y)$, of subscribers to a local magazine can be modeled by the function $N(y) = 0.1y^4 - 3y^3 + 10y^2 - 30y + 10,000$, where y is the number of years since the magazine was founded. Graph the polynomial on a graphing calculator and find the minimum number of subscribers and the year in which this occurs.

_____

Practice C
Investigating Graphs of Polynomial Functions

Identify the leading coefficient, degree, and end behavior.

1. $R(x) = -6x^4 + 4x^3 - x^2 + 1$

_____

2. $Q(x) = 12 + 8x - 16x^3 - x^2$

_____

Identify whether the function graphed has an odd or even degree and a positive or negative leading coefficient.

3.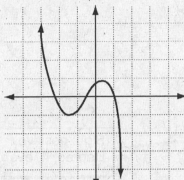

4.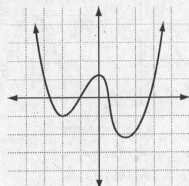

5.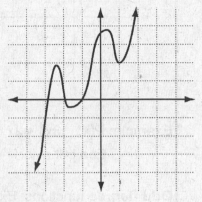

_____   _____   _____

Graph the function.

6. $P(x) = x^3 + 2x^2 - 4x - 8$

Graph each function on a calculator, and estimate the local maxima and minima.

7. $P(x) = -x^4 + 4x^3 - 2x^2 - x + 5$

_____

8. $P(x) = x^5 - x^4 - 5x^2$

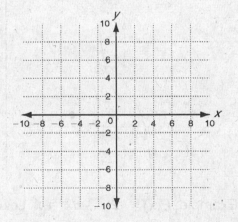

_____

Solve.

9. An engineer needs a metal box to shield sensitive electronic devices from external electric fields. One side of the box should be open so that it can be placed over the components. The box can be made from a 3 m by 4 m sheet of metal by cutting squares from the corners and folding up the sides.

a. What is the maximum volume of the box? _____

b. What dimensions of the box result in the
   maximum volume? _____

LESSON 6-7

Reteach

Investigating Graphs of Polynomial Functions

Examine the sign and the exponent of the leading term (term of greatest degree) of a polynomial $P(x)$ to determine the **end behavior** of the function.

Even degree functions: Exponent of leading term is even.

Positive leading coefficient
As $x \to -\infty$, $P(x) \to +\infty$.
As $x \to +\infty$, $P(x) \to +\infty$.

Negative leading coefficient
As $x \to -\infty$, $P(x) \to -\infty$.
As $x \to +\infty$, $P(x) \to -\infty$.

> *Read:*
> As x approaches positive infinity, $P(x)$ approaches negative infinity.

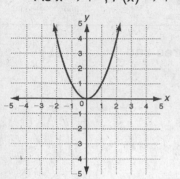

Example: $P(x) = 3x^4 + 2x^3 - 5$ Leading term: $3x^4$

End behavior: As $x \to -\infty$, $P(x) \to +\infty$.
As $x \to +\infty$, $P(x) \to +\infty$.

> Sign: positive
> Degree: 4, even

Odd degree functions: Exponent of leading term is odd.

Positive leading coefficient
As $x \to +\infty$, $P(x) \to +\infty$.
As $x \to -\infty$, $P(x) \to -\infty$.

Negative leading coefficient
As $x \to -\infty$, $P(x) \to +\infty$.
As $x \to +\infty$, $P(x) \to -\infty$.

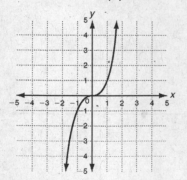

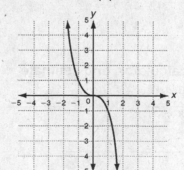

Example: $P(x) = -2x^5 - 6x^2 + x$ Leading term: $-2x^5$

End behavior: As $x \to -\infty$, $P(x) \to +\infty$.
As $x \to +\infty$, $P(x) \to -\infty$.

> Sign: negative
> Degree: 5, odd

Identify the end behavior of each function.

1. $P(x) = 4x^3 + 8x^2 - 5$
   Leading term: $4x^3$
   Sign and degree: _____
   End behavior: _____

2. $P(x) = -9x^6 + 2x^3 - x + 7$
   Leading term: _____
   Sign and degree: _____
   End behavior:_____

_____   _____

LESSON 6-7

Reteach

Investigating Graphs of Polynomial Functions *(continued)*

You can use the graph of a polynomial function to analyze the function.

$P(x)$: odd degree and positive leading coefficient if: As $x \to -\infty$, $P(x) \to -\infty$ and as $x \to +\infty$, $P(x) \, x \to +\infty$.	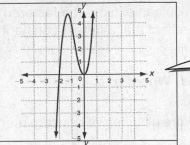	Notice the graph increases, then decreases, and then increases again.
$P(x)$: odd degree and negative leading coefficient if: As $x \to -\infty$, $P(x) \, x \to +\infty$ and as $x \to +\infty$, $P(x) \, x \to -\infty$.		Notice this graph is the reverse. It decreases, then increases, and then decreases again.
$P(x)$: even degree and positive leading coefficient if: As $x \to -\infty$, $P(x) \, x \to +\infty$ and as $x \to +\infty$, $P(x) \, x \to +\infty$.	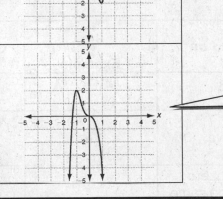	Look at the end behavior. The graph increases at both ends.
$P(x)$: even degree and negative leading coefficient if: As $x \to -\infty$, $P(x) \to -\infty$ and as $x \to +\infty$, $P(x) \to -\infty$.		This is the reverse. The graph decreases at both ends.

Identify whether each function has an odd or even degree and a positive or negative leading coefficient.

3.

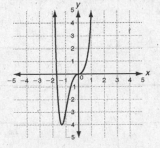

4.

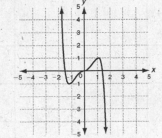

5.

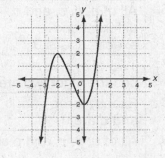

_____   _____   _____

Holt Algebra 2

LESSON
6-7

Challenge
Polynomial Functions in Factored Form

In general, the graph of a polynomial equation of degree n contains $(n − 1)$ or fewer turning points. You can explore the factored form of a polynomial equation to note the effect that different constant values have on the shape of the curve.

$P(x) = (x − a)(x − b)(x − c)(x − d)$ Where a, b, c, and d are real numbers.

1. Suppose that a, b, c, and d are all different nonzero numbers.

    a. Make a conjecture about the number of turning points. _____

    b. Write a particular function that satisfies the conditions.

        _____

    c. Use a graphing calculator to obtain a graph of the function you wrote in part **b**. Sketch the graph on the grid at right.

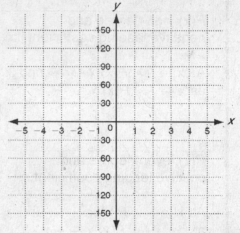

Follow the steps outlined in Exercise 1 to explore different conditions placed on a, b, c, and d. Summarize your results in the table shown below.

	Conditions Placed on a, b, c, and d	Example	Number of Turning Points	Other Observations
2.	All of a, b, c, and d are different and nonzero			
3.	All of a, b, c, and d nonzero and exactly two are the same			
4.	All of a, b, c, and d nonzero and exactly three are the same			
5.	All of a, b, c, and d nonzero and all are equal			
6.	All of a, b, c, and d different and exactly one is 0			
7.	Two of a, b, c, and d are 0 and the other two are different			
8.	Exactly three of a, b, c, and d are 0			
9.	All of a, b, c, and d are 0			

LESSON 6-7 Problem Solving
Investigating Graphs of Polynomial Functions

The Spanish Club members are baking and selling fruit bars to raise money for a trip. They are going to make open boxes to display the bars from sheets of cardboard that are 11 inches by 17 inches. They will cut a square from each corner and fold up the sides and tape them. Find the maximum value for the volume of the box and find its dimensions.

1. Write a formula to represent the volume of the box. _____

2.   a. Write the equation in standard form.   _____

    b. Is the leading coefficient positive or negative? _____

    c. Is the degree of the polynomial even or odd? _____

    d. Describe the end behavior of the graph.

    _____

3. Use a graphing calculator to graph the equation. Hint: Try a window from −10 to 10 on the x-axis, with a scale of 1, and from −500 to 500 on the y-axis, with a scale of 100.

    a. How many turning points does the graph have? _____

    b. Estimate the local maxima and minima from
       the graph.   _____

4. What values of x are excluded as solutions because they do not make sense for this problem? _____

5. Use the CALC menu on your graphing calculator to find the approximate values of x and y at the local maximum for the graph.   _____

6. What is the maximum volume of the box?   _____

7. What are the dimensions of the box to the nearest tenth of an inch?

    _____

Choose the letter for the best answer.

8. Arturo is going to build a dog run using one side of his house and 100 feet of fencing. His design has an area that can be modeled by $A(x) = 100x - 7x^2$. What is the maximum area he can enclose?

    A 357 ft^2 C 100 ft^2

    B 204 ft^2 D 70 ft^2

9. In order to eliminate some choices on a standardized test, Ruth identifies which of these functions could NOT have a local maximum.

    A $F(x) = -7x^2 + 5x + 2$

    B $F(x) = -7x^3 + 5x - 11$

    C $F(x) = 7x^3 - 5x^2 - 2$

    D $F(x) = 7x^2 - 3x - 18$

     Holt Algebra 2

LESSON
6-7
Reading Strategy
Analyze Information

The **end behavior** of a function tells you how the function behaves as its x value approaches positive or negative infinity. You can find the end behavior of a function by looking at its degree and its leading coefficient.

	Degree of Polynomial Is ODD	Degree of Polynomial Is EVEN
Leading Coefficient: $a > 0$	As $x \to +\infty$, $P(x) \to +\infty$ As $x \to -\infty$, $P(x) \to -\infty$	As $x \to +\infty$, $P(x) \to +\infty$ As $x \to -\infty$, $P(x) \to +\infty$
Leading Coefficient: $a < 0$	As $x \to +\infty$, $P(x) \to -\infty$ As $x \to -\infty$, $P(x) \to +\infty$	As $x \to +\infty$, $P(x) \to -\infty$ As $x \to -\infty$, $P(x) \to -\infty$

Use the function $f(x) = -2x^2 + 3x + 1$.

1. a. What information about this function will help you find its end behavior?

_____

   b. Explain how this function behaves as $x \to +\infty$.

_____

   c. Explain how this function behaves as $x \to -\infty$.

_____

Use the graph to answer the questions.

2. Explain the end behavior of the function shown in the graph.

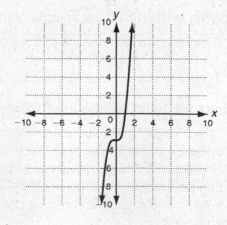

_____

3. What conclusion can you draw about the degree of this polynomial function?

_____

4. What conclusion can you draw about the leading coefficient of this polynomial function?

_____

Holt Algebra 2

LESSON 6-8

Practice A

Transforming Polynomial Functions

Describe how each function is transformed.

1. $g(x) = f(x) + 5$

_____

2. $g(x) = f(x + 10)$

_____

3. $g(x) = f(x - 1)$

_____

4. $g(x) = f(x) - 6$

_____

Write the rule for function g(x).

5. $g(x)$ reflects $f(x) = x^3 + 2x + 3$ across the x-axis.   _____

6. $g(x)$ reflects $f(x) = x^3 - x + 1$ across the y-axis.   _____

7. $g(x)$ compresses $f(x) = x^4 + 2$ vertically by $\dfrac{1}{2}$.   _____

8. $g(x)$ stretches $f(x) = x^3 + x^2 - 6$ horizontally by 3.   _____

For $f(x) = x^3 - 3x$, write a rule and sketch its graph.

9. Translate 3 units up

_____

10. Stretch vertically by a factor of 2

_____

11. Reflect across the y-axis

_____

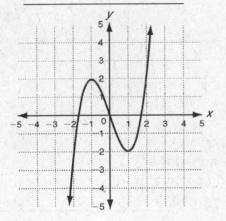

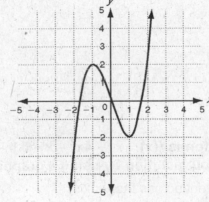

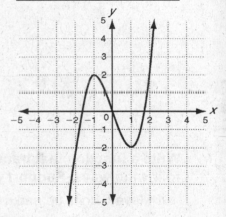

Solve.

12. The profits of Watson's Manufacturing can be modeled by the function $P(y) = -0.01y^2 + 40y + 500,000$, where y is the number of years since the company was founded. If the function modeling the company's profits changes to $R(y) = -0.01y^2 + 40y + 400,000$, how are the company's profits affected?

_____

_____

Holt Algebra 2

LESSON 6-8

Practice B

Transforming Polynomial Functions

For $f(x) = x^3 + 1$, write the rule for each function and sketch its graph.

1. $g(x) = f(x + 4)$

   _____

2. $g(x) = 3f(x)$

   _____

3. $g(x) = f\left(\dfrac{1}{2}x\right)$

   _____

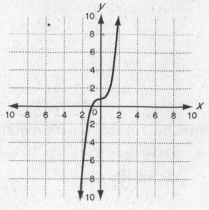

Let $f(x) = -x^3 + 4x^2 - 5x + 12$. Write a function $g(x)$ that performs each transformation.

4. Reflect $f(x)$ across the y-axis

5. Reflect $f(x)$ across the x-axis

_____   _____

Let $f(x) = x^3 + 2x^2 - 3x - 6$. Describe $g(x)$ as a transformation of $f(x)$ and graph.

6. $g(x) = \dfrac{1}{4}f(x)$

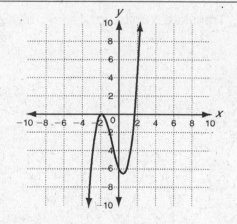

7. $g(x) = f(x - 6)$

_____

Write a function that transforms $f(x) = x^3 + 4x^2 - x + 5$ in each of the following ways. Support your solution by using a graphing calculator.

8. Move 6 units up and reflect across the y-axis.

   _____

9. Compress vertically by a factor of 0.25 and move 3 units right.

   _____

Solve.

10. The number of participants, N, in a new Internet political forum during each month of the first year can be modeled by $N(t) = 4t^2 - t + 2000$, where t is the number of months since January. In the second year, the number of forum participants doubled compared to the same month in the previous year. Write a function that describes the number of forum participants in the second year.

   _____

Holt Algebra 2

LESSON 6-8 **Practice C**

Transforming Polynomial Functions

For $f(x) = -2x^4 + 7x^2 - 4$, write the rule for each function and sketch its graph below.

1. a. $g(x) = f(x - 5)$

    b. $g(x) = 0.25f(x)$

2. a. $g(x) = f(0.25x)$

    b. $g(x) = 4f(x)$

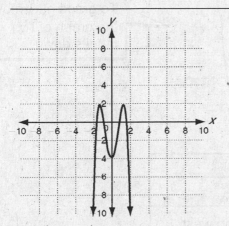

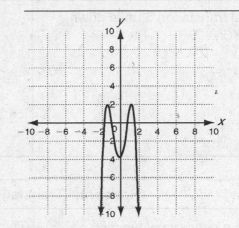

Write a function $g(x)$ that transforms $f(x) = 4x^3 - 5$ in each of the following ways.

3. Move 2 units left and reflect across the x-axis.

4. Compress horizontally by a factor of $\frac{1}{5}$ and move 1 unit up.

5. Stretch vertically by a factor of 3 and move 3 units right.

Solve.

6. Many mathematical functions can be written in the form of a long polynomial. This technique is known as the Taylor expansion. For example, the trigonometric sine function can be approximated by $\sin(x) \approx x - \frac{x^3}{6} + \frac{x^5}{20}$. Using this polynomial approximation of $\sin(x)$, write the corresponding polynomial approximation of $6 \sin(x) + 1$.

LESSON 6-8

Reteach

Transforming Polynomial Functions

Translations of polynomial functions shift the graph of the function right, left, up, or down.

Vertical Translation	
If $f(x)$ is a polynomial function, $g(x) = f(x) + k$ is a vertical translation of $f(x)$. *Example:* $f(x) = x^3 + 2$	Think: Add to y, go high. $f(x)$ shifts up for $k > 0$. $f(x)$ shifts down for $k < 0$.
Vertical translation 5 units down $g(x) = f(x) - 5$ $g(x) = x^3 + 2 - 5$ $g(x) = x^3 - 3$	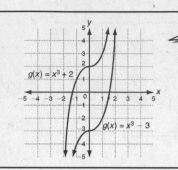

To graph $g(x)$, move the graph of $f(x)$ 5 units down.

Horizontal Translation	
If $f(x)$ is a polynomial function, $g(x) = f(x - h)$ is a horizontal translation of $f(x)$. *Example:* $f(x) = x^3 + 2$	Think: Add to x, go west. $f(x)$ shifts right for $h > 0$. $f(x)$ shifts left for $h < 0$.
Horizontal translation 4 units left $g(x) = f\left(x - (-4)\right)$ $g(x) = (x + 4)^3 + 2$	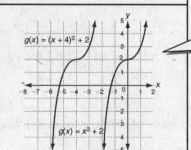

To graph $g(x)$, move the graph of $f(x)$ 4 units left.

For $f(x) = x^3 + 2$, write the rule for each function and sketch its graph.

1. $g(x) = f(x) + 1$

   Translate $f(x)$ 1 unit _____.

   $g(x) = $ _____

   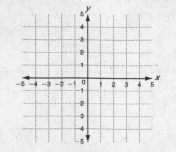

2. $g(x) = f(x - 3)$

   Translate $f(x)$ 3 units _____.

   $g(x) = $ _____

   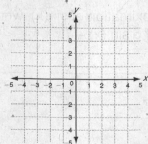

LESSON 6-8

Reteach

Transforming Polynomial Functions *(continued)*

Stretches and compressions are transformations of polynomial functions.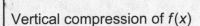

Vertical Stretch or Compression	
If $f(x)$ is a polynomial function, $g(x) = af(x)$ is a vertical stretch or compression of $f(x)$. *Example*: $f(x) = 2x^4 - 6x^2 + 4$	Vertical stretch if $a > 1$ Vertical compression if $0 < a < 1$
Vertical compression of $f(x)$ $g(x) = \dfrac{1}{2}f(x)$ $g(x) = \dfrac{1}{2}(2x^4 - 6x^2 + 4)$ $g(x) = x^4 - 3x^2 + 2$	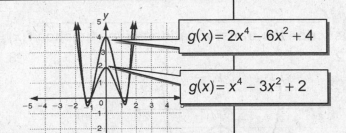 $g(x) = 2x^4 - 6x^2 + 4$ $g(x) = x^4 - 3x^2 + 2$

Horizontal Stretch or Compression	
If $f(x)$ is a polynomial function, $g(x) = f\left(\dfrac{1}{b}x\right)$ is a horizontal stretch or compression of $f(x)$ *Example*: $f(x) = 2x^4 - 6x^2 + 4$	Horizontal stretch if $b > 1$ Horizontal compression if $0 < b < 1$
Horizontal stretch of $f(x)$ $g(x) = f\left(\dfrac{1}{2}x\right)$ $g(x) = 2\left(\dfrac{1}{2}x\right)^4 - 6\left(\dfrac{1}{2}x\right)^2 + 4$ $g(x) = \dfrac{1}{8}x^4 - \dfrac{3}{2}x^2 + 4$	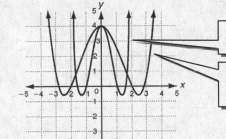 $g(x) = 2x^4 - 6x^2 + 4$ $g(x) = \dfrac{1}{8}x^4 - \dfrac{3}{2}x^2 + 4$

Let $f(x) = 2x^4 - 6x^2 + 4$. Describe $g(x)$ as a transformation of $f(x)$ and write the rule for $g(x)$.

3. $g(x) = 2f(x)$

4. $g(x) = f(2x)$

_____   _____

_____   _____

Holt Algebra 2

LESSON
6-8

Challenge

Polynomial Transformations

Graphs can be transformed by translations, dilations, reflections, and rotations. The graph represents the function $f(x) = x^4 - 8x^2 - 9$.

1. Describe three different transformations that could be performed on this graph to give a function with a *y*-intercept of 2.

_____

_____

_____

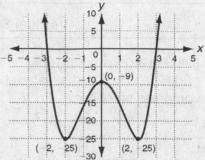

Describe the transformations of the function $f(x) = x^4 - 8x^2 - 9$.

2.

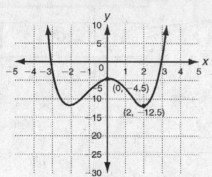

3.

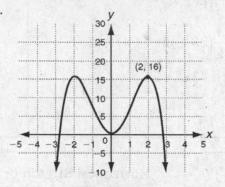

_____

4.

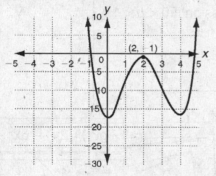

5.

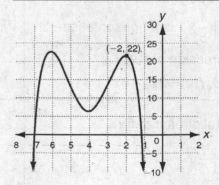

_____

_____

6.

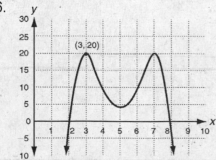

7.

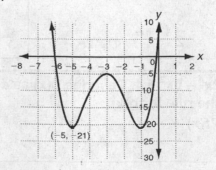

_____

_____

Holt Algebra 2

LESSON
6-8

Problem Solving
Transforming Polynomial Functions

A traffic engineer determines that the number of cars passing
through a certain intersection each week can be modeled by
$C(x) = 0.02x^3 + 0.4x^2 + 0.2x + 35$, where x is the number of weeks
since the survey began. A new road has just opened that affects the
traffic at that intersection. Let $N(x) = C(x) + 200$.

1. Find the rule for $N(x)$.

   _____

2. What transformation of $C(x)$ is represented by $N(x)$?

   _____

3. On the graph of $C(x)$, sketch the graph for $N(x)$.

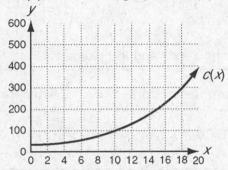

4. Use a graphing calculator to graph $N(x)$. Use a window from 0 to 20 with a
   scale of 1 on the x-axis and from 0 to 500 with a scale of 1 on the y-axis.
   Compare it to your sketch. Explain why only the values in Quadrant 1 are
   considered for this problem.

   _____

5. Explain the meaning of the transformation of $C(x)$ into $N(x)$ in terms of the
   weekly number of cars passing through the intersection.

   _____

6. Emergency roadwork temporarily closes off most of the traffic to this
   intersection. Write a function $R(x)$ that could model the effect on $C(x)$
   Explain how the graph of $C(x)$ might be transformed into $R(x)$.

   _____

7. Describe the transformation $2C(x)$ by writing the new rule and explaining
   the change in the context of the problem.

   _____

Name _____ Date _____ Class_____

Reading Strategy
Use a Model

Just like quadratic and linear functions, polynomial functions can be transformed. One type of transformation is reflection across the *x*- or *y*-axis. You can reflect a graph by making its "mirror" image across the axis. Look at the graph of $f(x) = x^3 + x^2 - 4$, which is reflected across the *y*-axis.

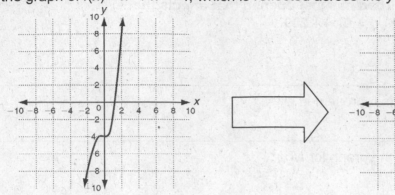

The table shows rules for reflecting across the *x*-axis and the *y*-axis.

Transformation	Rule	Before Reflection	After Reflection
Reflection across the *x*-axis	$-f(x)$	$f(x) = x^3 + x^2 - 4$	$-f(x) = -(x^3 + x^2 - 4)$ $= x^3 - x^2 + 4$
Reflection across the *y*-axis	$f(-x)$	$f(x) = x^3 + x^2 - 4$	$f(-x) = (-x)^3 + (-x)^2 - 4$ $= -x^3 + x^2 - 4$

Answer each question.

1. a. Draw the graph of the polynomial $f(x) = x^3 + x^2 - 4$ reflected across the *x*-axis.

   b. The point $\left(x, f(x)\right)$ is mapped to $\left(x, -f(x)\right)$ after reflection across the *x*-axis. Find the point that is mapped to (1, 2) after reflection across the *x*-axis.

   _____

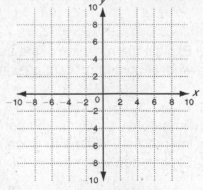

2. Write the function for each transformation of the polynomial.

	Polynomial	Reflect across *x*-axis	Reflect across *y*-axis
a.	$f(x) = x^3 + 4$		
b.	$g(x) = -6x^5 - x^3 + 2$		
c.	$h(x) = x^2 - 3x + 5$		

Holt Algebra 2

LESSON 6-9

Practice A

Curve Fitting with Polynomial Models

Complete each statement.

1. Linear functions have constant _____ differences.

2. Cubic functions have constant _____ differences.

3. Quadratic functions have constant _____ differences.

4. Quadratic functions are _____ degree functions.

5. Linear functions are _____ degree functions.

6. Cubic functions are _____ degree functions.

Use finite differences to determine the degree of the polynomial that best describes the data.

7.

x	0	1	2	3	4	5
y	−5	1	12	29	53	85

a. Which differences are constant? _____

b. Identify the degree of the polynomial of best fit. _____

8.

x	−2	−1	0	1	2	3
y	32	22	15	15	24	42

a. Which differences are constant? _____

b. Identify the degree of the polynomial of best fit. _____

9.

x	5	7	9	11	13	15
y	26	40	45	44	40	36

a. Which differences are constant? _____

b. Identify the degree of the polynomial of best fit. _____

10. Use a graphing calculator to find a polynomial function for the data in Exercise 7.

_____

11. Use a graphing calculator to find a polynomial function for the data in Exercise 9.

_____

Holt Algebra 2

LESSON 6-9 Practice B
Curve Fitting with Polynomial Models

Use finite differences to determine the degree of the polynomial that best describes the data.

1. _____

x	y
0	4
1	14
2	24
3	30
4	30
5	24

2. _____

x	y
−2	70
−1	35
0	15
1	7
2	8
3	15

3. _____

x	y
2	1
1	7
0	12
−1	16
−2	19
−3	21

4. _____

x	y
−6	−31
−5	0
−4	16
−3	19
−2	11
−1	−6

Solve.

5. The data set shows the average price for a luxury commodity for the years since 1998.

Year	1998	1999	2000	2001	2002	2003	2004	2005
Price ($)	1000	2027	4472	7507	10,472	12,875	14,392	14,867

a. Write a polynomial function for the data.

_____

b. Predict the price of the item in 2008.

_____

Holt Algebra 2

LESSON 6-9

Practice C

Curve Fitting with Polynomial Models

Use finite differences to determine the degree of the polynomial that best describes the data.

1. _____

x	y
−3	0
−2	104
−1	164
0	186
1	178
2	150
3	114

2. _____

x	y
7	28
8	15
9	−1
10	−20
11	−42
12	−67
13	−95

3. _____

x	y
−10	12
−7	90
−4	153
−1	211
2	274
5	352
8	455

4. _____

x	y
50	−100
55	−200
60	−290
65	−364
70	−420
75	−460
80	−490

Solve.

5. The data set represents the population of a rare turtle species on an island for the years since 1980.

Year	1980	1984	1988	1990	1995	2000	2001	2005
Population	1000	736	1208	1600	2650	3200	3184	2500

   a. Write a polynomial function for the data.

   _____

   b. Predict when the species will become extinct. _____

Holt Algebra 2

LESSON 6-9

Reteach

Curve Fitting with Polynomial Models

To use finite differences to determine the degree of a polynomial,

- check that the x-values increase by a constant value, and

- find successive differences of the y-values until the differences are constant.

Finite Differences					
Function Type	Linear	Quadratic	Cubic	Quartic	Quintic
Degree	1	2	3	4	5
Constant Finite Differences	First	Second	Third	Fourth	Fifth

Example:

x	−3	−2	−1	0	1	2	The x-values increase by 1.
y	78	14	0	0	2	18	

First Differences	14 − 78	0 − 14	0 − 0	2 − 0	18 − 2	First differences are not constant.
	−64	−14	0	2	16	

Second Differences	−14 − (−64)	0 − (−14)	2 − 0	16 − 2	Second differences are not constant.
	50	14	2	14	

Third Differences	14 − 50	2 − 14	14 − 2	Third differences are not constant.
	−36	−12	12	

Fourth Differences	−12 − (−36)	12 − (−12)	Fourth differences are constant.
	24	24	

A fourth degree polynomial best describes the data.

Use finite differences to determine the degree of the polynomial that best describes the data.

1.

x	−2	−1	0	1	2
y	−5	2	3	4	11
First Differences					
Second Differences					
Third Differences					

2. Identify the degree of the polynomial. _____

Holt Algebra 2

LESSON	**Reteach**
6-9	*Curve Fitting with Polynomial Models (continued)*

Use finite differences that are close to select a polynomial model to fit a data set. Then use your calculator to write the function.

x	10	20	30	40	50
y	2633	3812	4862	6529	9552
First Differences	3812 − 2633	4862 − 3812	6529 − 4862		9552 − 6529
	1179	1050	1667		3023
Second Differences	1050 − 1179		1667 − 1050		3023 − 1667
	−129		617		1356
Third Differences	617 − (−129)			1356 − 617	
	746			739	

Since the third differences are reasonably close, you can use a cubic function to model the data.

Use the cubic regression feature on your calculator.

Use the coefficients a, b, c, and d to write the function.

$$f(x) \approx 0.12x^3 - 8.06x^2 + 273.1x + 584.6$$

CubicReg
$y = ax^3 + bx^2 + cx + d$
$a = .12375$
$b = -8.0625$
$c = 273.1$
$d = 584.6$
$R^2 = .9999999758$

Write a polynomial function for the data.

3.

x	2	4	6	8	10	12
y	−12	−15	38	190	446	773
First Differences						
Second Differences						
Third Differences						
Fourth Differences						

4. Write a polynomial function that best describes the data set.

Holt Algebra 2

Challenge

Polynomial Models

LESSON
6-9

Polynomials can be fit to any finite number of points if no two points lie on the same vertical line. For instance, one form of a linear equation frequently used is the slope-intercept form, $y = mx + b$. Given two points on a line, $(3, 12)$ and $(-1, 4)$, these values may be substituted for x and y in the slope-intercept form to obtain the system of linear equations below.

$$\begin{cases} 12 = 3m + b \\ 4 = -m + b \end{cases}$$

Solving this system by eliminating b yields $m = 2$ and $b = 6$ to give the linear equation $y = 2x + 6$ that passes through the two points given.

This process works equally well for quadratic equations. Every quadratic equation can be written in the form $y = ax^2 + bx + c$. Given three points, you can write a system of three linear equations in the variables a, b, and c. Solving this system yields values for a, b, and c to write a quadratic equation.

Use a polynomial model to represent the data given.

1. Quadratic polynomial $y = ax^2 + bx + c$

x	5	10	15	20	25
y	30	34	36	36	34

2. Quadratic polynomial $y = ax^2 + bx + c$

x	0	1	2	3	4	5	6	7	8
y	45	24	11	1	-2	1	9	26	47

3. Cubic polynomial $y = ax^3 + bx^2 + cx + d$

x	-3	2	5	8
y	0	0	24	264

4. Quartic polynomial $y = ax^4 + bx^3 + cx^2 + dx + e$

x	-3	-1	1	3	5
y	0	0	24	-24	-144

Holt Algebra 2

LESSON 6-9

Problem Solving

Curve Fitting with Polynomial Models

Carla has been making a "wild scape" in her backyard. The table shows the number of birds visiting her feeder at the same hour on the first day of each month since she began her project. Use a polynomial model to make a reasonable estimate of the number of birds there might be in July.

Birds at Feeder from 7:00 to 8:00 A.M.					
Jan	Feb	Mar	Apr	May	Jun
3	8	18	36	65	108

1. Use finite differences to determine the degree of the polynomial that best fits the data.

   a. First differences _____

   b. Second differences _____

   c. Third differences _____

   d. Fourth differences _____

   e. Which degree polynomial best describes the data? _____

2. Use your graphing calculator to find values for R^2.

   a. For LinReg, $R^2 =$ _____.

   b. For QuadReg, $R^2 =$ _____.

   c. For CubicReg, $R^2 =$ _____.

3. Write the polynomial model for this data. _____

4. Use your polynomial model to make a reasonable estimate of the number of birds there might be in July. _____

The table below shows the number of travel insurance policies sold by a travel agency over a six-year period. Choose the letter for the best answer.

Year	2001	2002	2003	2004	2005	2006
Policies Sold	73	126	163	185	192	184

5. Which function best models the data?

   A $f(x) \approx -0.926x^2 - 6.88x + 6.3$

   B $f(x) \approx -7.59x^2 + 75.27x + 5.5$

   C $f(x) \approx 0.05x^3 + 8.06x^2 + 76.74x + 4.3$

   D $f(x) \approx -0.02x^3 + 0.34x^2 - 9.47x + 2.8$

6. Use the polynomial model to estimate the number of policies that may be sold in 2008.

   A About 150   C About 130

   B About 140   D About 120

LESSON 6-9 Reading Strategy
Draw Conclusions

You can find the degree of a polynomial by finding the differences in its data set.

Degree	1	2	3	4
Type	Linear	Quadratic	Cubic	Quartic
Constant Differences	First differences	Second differences	Third differences	Fourth differences

Look at the first and second differences of the following data set.

x	0	1	2	3	4	5
y	1	6	17	34	57	86

First Differences	6 – 1 5	17 – 6 11	34 – 17 17	57 – 34 23	86 – 57 29

Second Differences	11 – 5 6	17 – 11 6	23 – 17 6	29 – 23 6

The first differences are not constant, but the second differences all equal 6. The data set represents a polynomial of degree 2, or a quadratic function.

Answer each question.

1. In a data set, the third differences all equal –2. What type of function is represented by this data set? _____

2. The ordered pairs (1, 3), (2, 5), and (3, 7) represent a linear function. Use the constant finite difference to find the value of the function at $x = 6$. _____

Use the following data set for Exercise 3.

x	–2	–1	0	1	2	3
y	–9	–2	–1	0	7	26

3. a. What are the first differences of this data set? _____

   b. What are the second differences? _____

   c. Do you need to find the third differences? If so, what are they? _____

   d. What kind of function does this data set represent? _____

Holt Algebra 2

Date _____

Dear Family,

In Chapter 7, your child will study exponential and logarithmic functions, and use the properties of exponents and logarithms to simplify expressions and solve equations.

A parent **exponential function** has the form $f(x) = b^x$.

The defining features of an exponential function are that the **base** b is a constant and the exponent x is a variable.

An exponential function will have an **asymptote**, or a line that the graph approaches but never reaches. In the graph of $y = 5^x$ at right, as x continues in the negative direction, the value of y gets smaller and smaller, approaching zero. So, the x-axis, or the line $y = 0$, is a horizontal asymptote for $y = 5^x$.

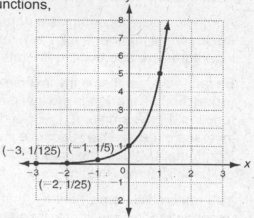

Two of the most common applications of exponential functions are **exponential growth** and **exponential decay**. Topics such as the interest on a savings account, the depreciation of an automobile, or the growth of a population can all be modeled by an exponential function in the form:

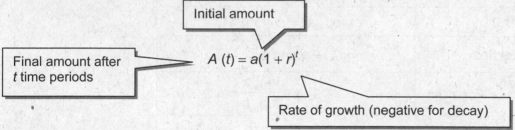

Initial amount

Final amount after t time periods

$$A(t) = a(1 + r)^t$$

Rate of growth (negative for decay)

Relations that "undo" each other are called **inverse relations**. When both relations happen to be functions, you have **inverse functions**. The inverse function of $f(x)$ is written as $f^{-1}(x)$. (*Note:* The superscript -1 means "inverse"; it does not mean an exponent of -1.) For example, the functions below are inverses because they "switch" input and output values.

$f(x) = 2x - 8$	
x (input)	y (output)
2	−4
10	12
0	−8

inverse functions

$\longleftrightarrow$

inputs and outputs switch

$f^{-1}(x) = \dfrac{1}{2}x + 4$	
x (input)	y (output)
−4	2
12	6
−8	0

An exponential equation gives you the amount that results from raising a base to an exponent. The inverse, a **logarithm**, gives you the exponent to which a base must be raised to result in a given amount.

exponent: $5^2 = 25$ **logarithm:** $\log_5 25 = 2$

Think: What is 5 raised to an exponent of 2?

Think: To what exponent do you raise 5 to get 25?

A logarithm with base 10 is called a **common logarithm**. If no base is written on a logarithm, it is assumed to be 10. For example, log 1000 means the same thing as $\log_{10} 1000$.

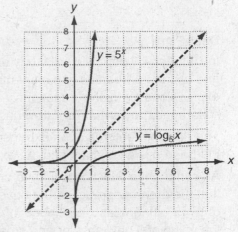

Another special logarithm is a **natural logarithm**, which has the irrational number $e \approx 2.718\ldots$ as a base. Natural logarithms are abbreviated "ln" rather than "log."

Because a logarithm is the inverse of an exponent, a **logarithmic function** is the inverse of an exponential function. For example, $f(x) = 5^x$ and $f^{-1}(x) = \log_5 x$ are inverses of each other. Because inverse functions switch input/output values, the graph of $f^{-1}(x) = \log_5 x$ is a reflection of $f(x) = 5^x$ across the line $y = x$.

You may recall from Chapter 1 that there are several special properties for exponents. Similarly, there are special properties for logarithms:

Product Property	$\log_b (m \cdot n) = \log_b m + \log_b n$
Quotient Property	$\log_b \dfrac{m}{n} = \log_b m - \log_b n$
Power Property	$\log_b a^p = p \cdot \log_b a$
Inverse Properties	$\log_b b^x = x$ and $b^{\log_b x} = x$
Change of Base Formula	$\log_b x = \dfrac{\log_a x}{\log_a b}$

By applying the properties of exponents and logarithms, your child will learn to solve a variety of exponential and logarithmic equations. These types of equations have many applications. Exponents or logarithms are necessary to determine the age of fossils (carbon dating), to determine whether a substance is an acid or base (the pH scale), to measure perceived loudness (decibels), and to rate earthquakes (the Richter scale).

You may also recall from earlier chapters that parent functions can be transformed by translations (left, right, up, or down), stretches, compressions, and reflections. These same transformations will now be applied to exponential and logarithmic functions.

The chapter concludes with a section on **exponential regression** and **logarithmic regression**. By using a graphing calculator, your child will be able to fit an exponential or logarithmic model to a set of real-world data, and use the model to make future predictions.

For additional resources, visit go.hrw.com and enter the keyword MB7 Parent.

Holt Algebra 2

Practice A

Exponential Functions, Growth, and Decay

Complete each statement.

1. A function of the form $f(x) = ab^x$ is called an exponential _____ function when b is greater than 1.

2. A function of the form $f(x) = ab^x$ is called an exponential _____ function when b is a number between 0 and 1.

Tell whether the function shows growth or decay. Then graph.

3. $f(x) = 3(2.5)^x$

   a. Find the value of the base.

   b. Does the function show growth or decay?

   c. Make a table of values for the function.

x	−2	−1	0	1	2	3
$f(x)$						

   d. Graph the function.

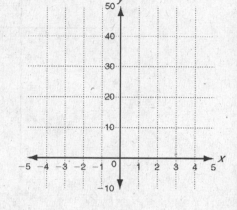

4. $g(x) = 2(0.2)^x$

5. $j(x) = -(1.5)^x$

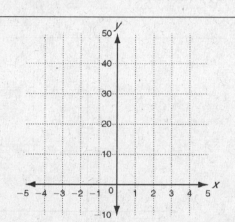

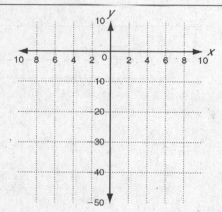

Solve.

6. Some real estate agents estimate that the value of a house could increase about 4% each year.

   a. Write a function to model the growth in value for a house valued at $100,000.

   _____

   b. Graph the function.

   c. A house is valued at $100,000 in 2005. Predict the year its value will be at least $130,000.

   _____

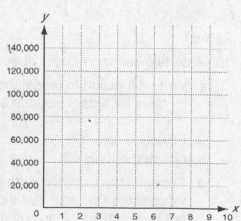

Holt Algebra 2

LESSON 7-1

Practice B

Exponential Functions, Growth, and Decay

Tell whether the function shows growth or decay. Then graph.

1. $g(x) = -(2)^x$

2. $h(x) = -0.5(0.2)^x$

_____

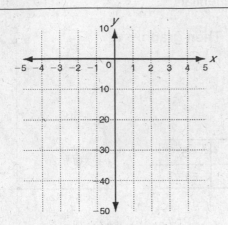

_____

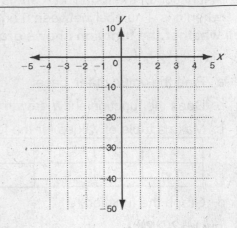

3. $j(x) = -2(0.5)^x$

4. $p(x) = 4(1.4)^x$

_____

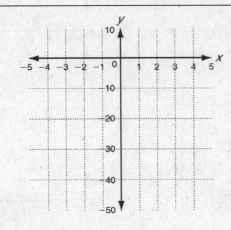

_____

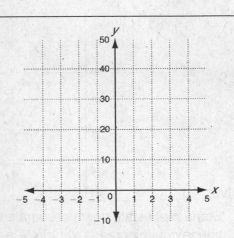

Solve.

5. A certain car depreciates about 15% each year.

   a. Write a function to model the depreciation in value for a car valued at $20,000.

_____

   b. Graph the function.

   c. Suppose the car was worth $20,000 in 2005. What is the first year that the value of this car will be worth less than half of that value?

_____

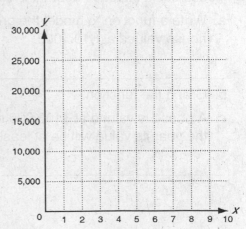

· Holt Algebra 2

Name _____   Date _____   Class_____

Practice C
Exponential Functions, Growth, and Decay

Tell whether the function shows growth or decay. Then graph.

1. $j(x) = -3(0.04)^x$ 2. $k(x) = 5(1.4)^x$ 3. $p(x) = 0.25(6)^x$

_____   _____   _____

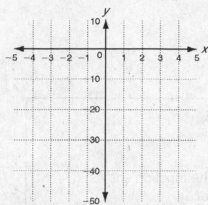 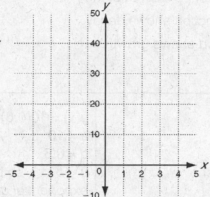 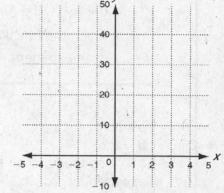

Tell whether the function is an exponential function.
Write *yes* or *no*.

4. $f(x) = -2x^5 - 9$ 5. $g(x) = -0.2(5)^x$ 6. $h(x) = 10(2.2)^x$

_____   _____   _____

Solve.

7. Colleen's station wagon is depreciating at a rate of
   9% per year. She paid $24,500 for it in 2002. What
   will the car be worth in 2008 to the nearest hundred dollars?   _____

8. Kyle estimates that his business is growing at a rate
   of 5% per year. His profits in 2005 were $67,000.
   Estimate his profits for 2010 to the nearest hundred dollars.   _____

9. A parcel of land Jason bought in 2000 for
   $100,000 is appreciating in value at a rate of
   about 4% each year.

   a. Write a function to model the appreciation
      of the value of the land.

   _____

   b. Graph the function.

   c. In what year will the land double its value?

   _____

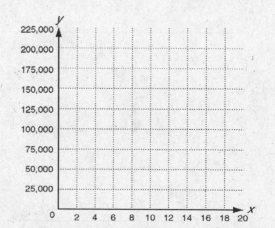

LESSON 7-1

Reteach
Exponential Functions, Growth, and Decay

The **base** of an exponential function indicates whether the function shows growth or decay.

Exponential function: $f(x) = ab^x$

- a is a constant.
- b is the base. The base is a constant.
  If $0 < b < 1$, the function shows decay.
  If $b > 1$, the function shows growth.
- x is an exponent.

$f(x) = 1.2^x$
$a = 1$
$b = 1.2$
$b > 1$, so the function shows *exponential growth*.

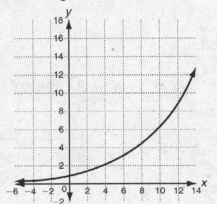

$g(x) = 10(0.6)^x$
$a = 10$
$b = 0.6$
$0 < b < 1$, so the function shows *exponential decay*.

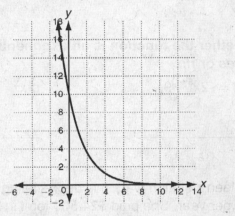

Tell whether each function shows growth or decay. Then graph.

1. $h(x) = 0.8(1.6)^x$

   $a = $ _____ $b = $ _____

   _____

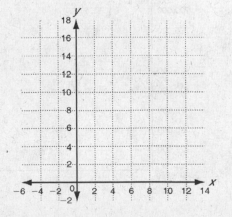

2. $p(x) = 12(0.7)^x$

   $a = $ _____ $b = $ _____

   _____

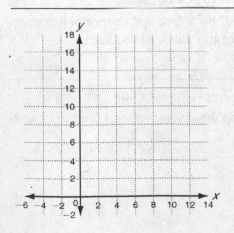

Holt Algebra 2

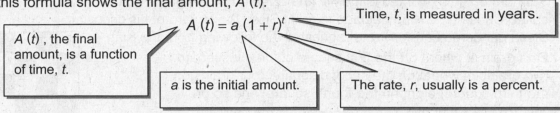

LESSON 7-1

Reteach

Exponential Functions, Growth, and Decay (continued)

When an initial amount, *a*, increases or decreases by a constant rate, *r*, over a number of time periods, *t*, this formula shows the final amount, *A* (*t*).

$$A(t) = a(1 + r)^t$$

Time, *t*, is measured in years.

A (*t*) , the final amount, is a function of time, *t*.

a is the initial amount.

The rate, *r*, usually is a percent.

An initial amount of $15,000 increases by 12% per year. In how many years will the amount reach $25,000?

Step 1 Identify values for *a* and *r*.

$a = \$15{,}000 \qquad r = 12\% = 0.12$

Step 2 Substitute values for *a* and *r* into the formula.

$f(t) = a(1 + r)^t$

$f(t) = 15{,}000(1 + 0.12)^t$

$f(t) = 15{,}000(1.12)^t \qquad$ *Simplify*.

Remember:
On the graph, *x* corresponds to *t* and *y* corresponds to *f*(*t*).

Step 3 Graph the function using a graphing calculator. Modify the scales: [0, 10] and [0, 30,000].

Step 4 Use the graph and the [TRACE] feature on the calculator to find *f* (*t*) = 25,000.

Step 5 Use the graph to approximate the value of *t* when *f*(*t*) = 25,000.

$t \approx 4.5$ when $f(t) - 25{,}000$

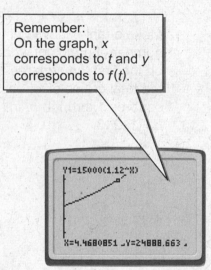

The amount will reach $25,000 in about 4.5 years.

Write an exponential function and graph the function to solve.

3. An initial amount of $40,000 increases by 8% per year. In how many years will the amount reach $60,000?

a. $a = $ _____

b. $r = $ _____

c. $f(t) = $ _____

d. Approximate *t* when $f(t) = 60{,}000$

$t \approx $ _____

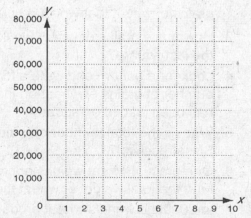

Holt Algebra 2

Challenge

The Vizier and His Wheat

According to legend, Sissa Ben Dahir, the Vizier of the court of King Shirham of India, worked diligently and invented a new game that was called Chess. The King decided to grant Sissa the reward of his choosing. Sissa pondered carefully and requested the following from the King.

One grain of wheat on the first square of the chessboard, two grains of wheat on the second square, four grains on the third square, eight on the fourth square, and so on.

The King thought this was a very modest request and said that he would grant the Vizier's request.

At right is a chessboard with 64 squares.

1. Make a table showing the number of grains of wheat on the first ten squares and the total grains of wheat on squares 1 through n, for $n = 1, 2, 3, \ldots, 10$.

2. Using the information from the table, look for a pattern and write an expression for the number of grains of wheat that would be placed on square n.

   _____

3. How many grains of wheat would be placed on the last square?

   _____

4. Look for a pattern and write a formula for the total number of grains of wheat on the board after wheat has been placed on square n.

   _____

5. What is the total number of grains of wheat that Sissa received?

   _____

6. One grain of wheat weighs approximately 0.000008 kilogram. Find the total weight of wheat the Vizier requested.

   _____

7. In 2000 the world's wheat production was approximately 580 million metric tons. At this rate how many years would it take to fill Sissa's request? One metric ton is 1000 kilograms.

   _____

Name _____ Date _____ Class_____

Problem Solving

Exponential Functions, Growth, and Decay

Justin drove his pickup truck about 22,000 miles in 2004. He read that in 1988 the average residential vehicle traveled about 10,200 miles, which increased by about 2.9% per year through 2004.

1. Write a function for the average mileage, $m(t)$, as a function of t, the time in years since 1988. _____

2. Assume that the 2.9% increase is valid through 2008 and use your function to complete the table to show the average annual miles driven.

Year	1988	1992	1996	2000	2004	2008
t	0	4				
m (t)	10,200					

3. Did Justin drive more or fewer miles than the average residential vehicle driver in 2004? by how much (to the nearest 100 miles)?

_____

4. Later Justin read that the annual mileage for light trucks increased by 7.8% per year from 1988 to 2004.

   a. Write a function for the average miles driven for a light truck, $n(t)$, as a function of t, the time in years since 1988. He assumes that the average number of miles driven in 1988 was 10,200. _____

   b. Graph the function. Then use your graph to estimate the average number of miles driven (to the nearest 1000) for a light truck in 2004.

   _____

   c. Did Justin drive more or fewer miles than the average light truck driver in 2004? by how much?

   _____

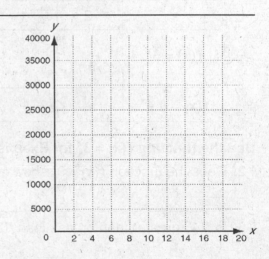

Justin bought his truck new for $32,000. Its value decreases 9.0% each year. Choose the letter for the best answer.

5. Which function represents the yearly value of Justin's truck?

   A $f(t) = 32,000(1 + 0.9)^t$

   B $f(t) = 32,000(1 - 0.9)^t$

   C $f(t) = 32,000(1 + 0.09)^t$

   D $f(t) = 32,000(1 - 0.09)^t$

6. When will the value of Justin's truck fall below half of what he paid for it?

   F In 6 years

   G In 8 years

   H In 10 years

   J In 12 years

Holt Algebra 2

<table>
<tr><td>LESSON
7-1</td></tr>
</table>

Reading Strategy
Drawing Conclusions

In an exponential function, the variable appears as an exponent: $f(x) = ab^x$, where a is a constant and b is the base. Depending on the value of b, the function either increases (grows) or decreases (decays). You can draw conclusions about the function and its graph based on the value of b.

Exponential Growth	Exponential Decay
An exponential function shows growth if $a > 0$ and $b > 1$.	An exponential function shows decay if $a > 0$ and $0 < b < 1$.

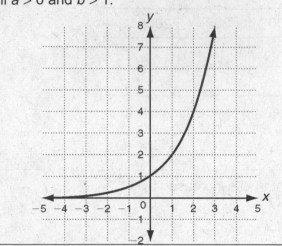 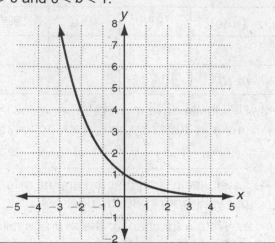

1. Complete the table.

x	–2	–1	0	1	2	3
$f(x) = 3^x$	$\dfrac{1}{9}$					
$f(x) = 0.4^x$						

Use the function $f(x) = 3^x$ for Exercises 2 and 3.

2. Does the function $f(x) = 3^x$ show exponential growth or decay? Explain.

_____

3. Is $f(4)$ greater than or less than $f(3)$? Explain how you can draw this conclusion.

_____

Use the function $f(x) = 0.4^x$ for Exercises 4 and 5.

4. Does the function $f(x) = 0.4^x$ show exponential growth or decay? Explain.

_____

5. Is $f(-3)$ greater than or less than $f(-2)$? Explain how you can draw this conclusion.

_____

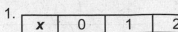

Practice A

Inverses of Relations and Functions

Graph the relation and connect the points. Then graph the inverse. Identify the domain and range of each relation.

1.

x	0	1	2	4	6
y	3	4	5	6	7

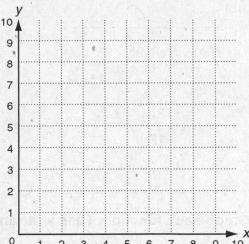

  a. Plot the ordered pairs and draw a curve through the points.

  b. Identify the domain and range for the relation.

  _____

  c. Switch the *x*- and *y*-values for each ordered pair and plot those points. Draw a curve through the points.

  d. Identify the domain and range for the inverse.

_____

Use inverse operations to write the inverse of each function.

2. $f(x) = 2x - 9$

  a. Undo the subtraction by _____

  b. Undo the multiplication by _____

  c. $f^{-1}(x) =$ _____

3. $f(x) = -4x$ 4. $f(x) = x + 6$ 5. $f(x) = 3x - 12$

_____   _____   _____

6. $f(x) = 6 - 10x$ 7. $f(x) = 7x + 1$ 8. $f(x) = 22x$

_____   _____   _____

Solve.

9. Holly paid $9.89 for lunch, including a 15% tip. What was the cost of her food?

  a. Write an equation for the total cost, *c*, as a function of the cost of the food, *x*.   _____

  b. Find the inverse function that models the cost of the food as a function of the total cost.   _____

  c. Evaluate the inverse function for $c = 9.89$.   _____

Name _____ Date _____ Class _____

Practice B
Inverses of Relations and Functions

Use inverse operations to write the inverse of each function.

1. $f(x) = 15x - 10$

2. $f(x) = 10 - 4x$

3. $f(x) = 12 - 9x$

_____

_____

_____

4. $f(x) = 5x + 2$

5. $f(x) = x + 6$

6. $f(x) = x + \dfrac{1}{2}$

_____

_____

_____

7. $f(x) = -\dfrac{x}{12}$

8. $f(x) = \dfrac{x - 12}{4}$

9. $f(x) = \dfrac{3x + 1}{6}$

_____

_____

_____

Graph each function. Then write and graph its inverse.

10. $f(x) = 2x - 4$

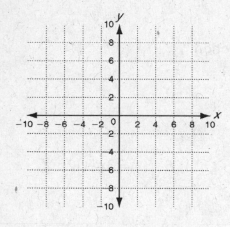

11. $f(x) = \dfrac{5}{2}x - 2$

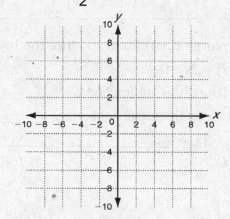

_____

_____

Solve.

12. Dan works at a hardware store. The employee discount is determined by the formula $d = 0.15(c - 10)$. Use the inverse of this function to find the cost of the item for which Dan received an $18.00 discount.

a. Find the inverse function that models cost as a function of the discount.

_____

b. Evaluate the inverse function for $d = 18$.

_____

c. What was Dan's final cost for this item?

_____

LESSON 7-2 **Practice C**

Inverses of Relations and Functions

Use inverse operations to write the inverse of each function.

1. $f(x) = 0.2x + 1$

2. $f(x) = x^2 + 9$

3. $f(x) = 7 - 4x$

_____

4. $f(x) = -\dfrac{x+2}{8}$

5. $f(x) = \dfrac{x^2}{16}$

6. $f(x) = \dfrac{5x-2}{6}$

_____

Graph each function. Then write and graph its inverse.

7. $f(x) = \dfrac{x-4}{3}$

8. $f(x) = 3 + 0.3x$

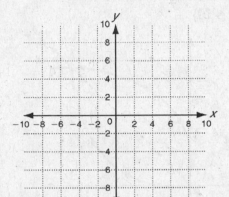

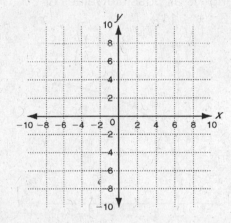

_____

Solve.

9. Frank wants to take out a home equity credit line. The maximum credit line he can get is equal to 80% of the equity he has in his home. Equity is the difference between the home's market value, v, and the mortgage balance, m.

   a. Write an equation for the amount of the credit line, c, as a function of the market value, v, and the mortgage balance, m.

   b. Find the inverse function that models the market value as a function of the amount of the credit line and the mortgage balance.

   c. What is the market value of Frank's home if he qualifies for a credit line of $72,000 and $m = \$150,000$?

Holt Algebra 2

LESSON 7-2

Reteach

Inverses of Relations and Functions

To graph an **inverse** relation, reflect each point across the line $y = x$.
Or you can switch the *x*- and *y*-values in each ordered pair of the relation to find the ordered pairs of the inverse.

Remember, a relation is a set of ordered pairs.

x	0	1	4	6	10
y	3	6	9	10	11

The domain is all possible values of x: $\{x \mid 0 \le x \le 10\}$.

The range is all possible values of y: $\{y \mid 3 \le y \le 11\}$.

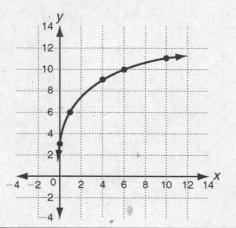

To write the **inverse** of the relation, switch the places of *x* and *y* in each ordered pair.

x	3	6	9	10	11
y	0	1	4	6	10

The domain of the inverse corresponds to the range of the original relation: $\{x \mid 3 \le x \le 11\}$.
The range of the inverse corresponds to the domain of the original relation: $\{y \mid 0 \le y \le 10\}$.

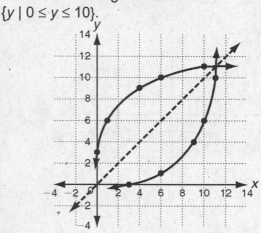

Complete the table to find the ordered pairs of the inverse. Graph the relation and its inverse. Identify the domain and range of each relation.

1. Relation

x	0	2	5	8	10
y	6	10	12	13	13

Inverse

x	6				
y	0				

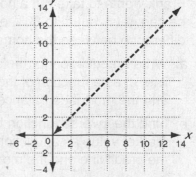

Relation: Domain: _____

Range: _____

Inverse: Domain: _____

Range: _____

Holt Algebra 2

LESSON 7-2 Reteach

Inverses of Relations and Functions (continued)

Inverse operations undo each other, like addition and subtraction, or multiplication and division.

In a similar way, **inverse functions** undo each other.

The inverse of a function $f(x)$ is denoted $f^{-1}(x)$.

Use inverse operations to write inverse functions.

Function: $f(x) = x + 8$	**Function:** $f(x) = 5x$
Subtraction is the opposite of addition. Use subtraction to write the inverse.	Division is the opposite of multiplication. Use division to write the inverse.
Inverse: $f^{-1}(x) = x - 8$	**Inverse:** $f^{-1}(x) = \dfrac{x}{5}$
Choose a value for x to check in the original function. Try $x = 1$.	Choose a value for x to check in the original function. Try $x = 2$.
$f(x) = x + 8 \rightarrow f(1) = 1 + 8 = 9$	$f(x) = 5x \rightarrow f(2) = 5(2) = 10$
Substitute 9, into $f^{-1}(x)$. The output of the inverse should be 1.	Substitute 10 into $f^{-1}(x)$. The output of the inverse should be 2.
$f^{-1}(x) = x - 8 \rightarrow f^{-1}(9) = 9 - 8 = 1$	$f^{-1}(x) = \dfrac{x}{5} \rightarrow f^{-1}(10) = \dfrac{10}{5} = 2$
Think: (1, 9) in the original function should be (9, 1) in the inverse. √	*Think:* (2, 10) in the original function should be (10, 2) in the inverse. √

Use inverse operations to write the inverse of each function.

2. $f(x) = x - 4$

3. $f(x) = \dfrac{x}{6}$

_____

_____

Use $x = 5$ to check.

Use $x = 12$ to check.

_____

_____

_____

_____

4. $f(x) = x + 3$

5. $f(x) = 14x$

_____

_____

LESSON
7-2

Challenge
One-to-One Functions

Every function $f(x)$ has an inverse, but not every inverse is a function. Consider the function $f(x) = x^2$. You can also write this function as $y = x^2$. One way to find the inverse of a function is to switch y and x in the original function. Switching variables gives the equation $x = y^2$. Notice that the graph of $x = y^2$ does not satisfy the function definition since the x-value of 4 has both 2 and –2 as y-values.

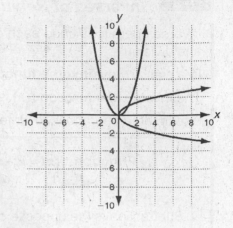

If a function meets the requirement that each element of the range is paired with exactly one element in the domain, then it is called a one-to-one function. In the graph of a one-to-one function, no horizontal line intersects the graph at more than one point.

1. Examine the graph of $y = x^2$ above. Tell why it does not pass the horizontal line test.

   _____

2. Graph the function $f(x) = 3x - 4$. Is this a one-to-one function? Find the inverse. Is the inverse a one-to-one function?

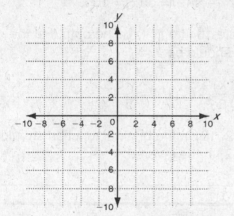

3. Graph the function $f(x) = \dfrac{1}{x}$. Is this a one-to-one function? Find the inverse. Is the inverse a one-to-one function?

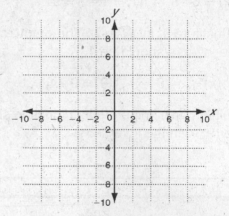

4. Graph the function $f(x) = x^3$. Is this a one-to-one function? Find the inverse. Is the inverse a one-to-one function?

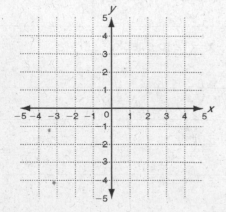

5. Graph the function $f(x) = x^2 + 3x + 2$. Is this a one-to-one function? Is the inverse a function and a one-to-one function?

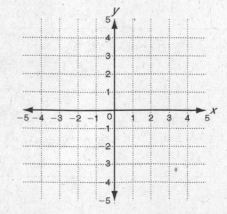

Holt Algebra 2

LESSON	**Problem Solving**
7-2	*Inverses of Relations and Functions*

Sally and Janelle pay a total of $47.96 to camp for three nights at a state park. This includes a one-time park entrance fee of $5 and 9% sales tax. They paid $12 per night to stay for three nights last year, and the one-time park entrance fee was $5.

1. By how much per night has the price changed since last year?

   a. Write an equation for the total price, *p*, as a
      function of the price per night, *n*.   _____

   b. Find the inverse function that models the price
      per night as a function of the total price.   _____

   c. Evaluate the inverse function to find *n*, the price
      per night.   _____

   d. By how much has the price per night changed
      since last year?   _____

2. Sally is thinking about whether they want to stay at the park next year.
   Assume that the entrance fee and the sales tax rate will not change.

   a. If the price per night does not increase from this year's price, how much
      will it cost to stay for five nights next year?

      _____

   b. If the park management quotes them a price of $87.20 for five nights next
      year, what is the increase in the price per night?

      _____

Choose the letter for the best answer.

3. If Sally and Janelle decide that they
   want to spend five nights at this same
   park in the future and spend no more
   than $100, what is the maximum price
   per night that they can pay?

   A $16.00

   B $16.50

   C $17.00

   D $17.50

4. If the price of a camping vacation can
   be expressed as a function of the number
   of nights, what does the inverse function
   represent?

   F Number of nights as a function of the
     price per night

   G Number of nights as a function of the
     price of the vacation

   H Price of the vacation as a function of
     the price per night

   J Price of the vacation as a function of
     the number of nights

LESSON 7-2 Reading Strategy
Understand Operations

Every function has an inverse. But the inverse may or may not be a function. Remember that a function is a relation in which each value of x has only one value of y. You can find the inverse of a function by switching the x-values (domain) and y-values (range) in each ordered pair.

Function	Domain and Range	Inverse Function
$f(x) = \{(1, 2), (2, 2), (3, 4)\}$	Domain: $\{1, 2, 3\}$ Range: $\{2, 4\}$	Switch the x-values and y-values. $\{(2, 1), (2, 2), (4, 3)\}$ The inverse is not a function because the number 2 is mapped to two y-values, 1 and 2.
$f(x) = \{(1, 3), (2, 5), (3, 7)\}$	Domain: $\{1, 2, 3\}$ Range: $\{3, 5, 7\}$	Switch the x and y values. $f^{-1}(x) = \{(3, 1), (5, 2), (7, 3)\}$
$f(x) = 2x - 3$	Domain: all real numbers Range: all real numbers	Use inverse operations to find the inverse. $f^{-1}(x) = \dfrac{x+3}{2}$

Answer each question.

1. a. Describe how you find the inverse of the relation
   $R = \{(-1, 1), (1, 1), (-2, 4), (2, 4)\}$.

   _____

   b. Write the inverse of R.

   _____

   c. Is R^{-1} a function? Explain.

   _____

2. A function $g(x)$ has an inverse $g^{-1}(x)$. Find the value of the function and its inverse. Use the fact that the inverse can be used to undo the original function.

   a. $g(3) = 4$; $g^{-1}(4) = ?$ b. $g^{-1}(2) = 1$; $g(1) = ?$ c. $g^{-1}(8) = 7$; $g(7) = ?$

   _____   _____   _____

3. Describe the inverse operations you could use to find the inverse of $f(x) = \dfrac{x}{2} + 1$.

   _____

Holt Algebra 2

Practice A
Logarithmic Functions

Write each exponential equation in logarithmic form.

1. $7^3 = 343$

   $\log_{base} 343 = \text{exponent}$

   $\log_7 343 = $ _____

2. $2^6 = 64$

   $\log_{base} 64 = \text{exponent}$

   $\log_2 64 = $ _____

3. $15^2 = 225$

   $\log_{base} 225 = \text{exponent}$

   $\log_{15} 225 = $ _____

4. $2^3 = 8$

5. $17^0 = 1$

6. $1^{12} = 1$

_____

7. $4^5 = 1024$

_____

8. $3^6 = 729$

9. $5^4 = 625$

_____

Write each logarithmic equation in exponential form.

10. $\log_4 64 = 3$

    $\log_{base} 64 = \text{exponent}$

    _____ $= 64$

11. $\log_8 512 = 3$

    $\log_{base} 512 = \text{exponent}$

    _____ $= 512$

12. $\log_6 36 = 2$

    $\log_{base} 36 = \text{exponent}$

    _____ $= 36$

13. $\log_{10} 100 = 2$

14. $\log_5 125 = 3$

15. $\log_9 1 = 0$

_____

16. $\log_2 128 = 7$

_____

17. $\log_3 243 = 5$

18. $\log_{100} 1{,}000{,}000 = 3$

_____

Evaluate by using mental math.

19. log 10,000

    $10^4 = 10{,}000$

    log 10,000 = _____

20. log 100,000

    $10^5 = 100{,}000$

    log 100,000 = _____

21. log 1

    $10^0 = 1$

    log 1 = _____

22. $\log_2 16$

23. $\log_4 1$

24. $\log_9 81$

_____

25. $\log_{100} 100{,}000{,}000$

_____

26. log 1,000,000,000

27. $\log_3 81$

_____

28. $\log_4 64$

_____

29. $\log_5 25$

30. log 1000

_____

Holt Algebra 2

LESSON 7-3

Practice B
Logarithmic Functions

Write each exponential equation in logarithmic form.

1. $3^7 = 2187$

2. $12^2 = 144$

3. $5^3 = 125$

_____   _____   _____

Write each logarithmic equation in exponential form.

4. $\log_{10} 100{,}000 = 5$

5. $\log_4 1024 = 5$

6. $\log_9 729 = 3$

_____   _____   _____

Evaluate by using mental math.

7. $\log 1{,}000{,}000$

8. $\log 10$

9. $\log 1$

_____   _____   _____

10. $\log_4 16$

11. $\log_8 1$

12. $\log_5 625$

_____   _____   _____

Use the given x-values to graph each function. Then graph its inverse. Describe the domain and range of the inverse function.

13. $f(x) = 2^x$; $x = -2, -1, 0, 1, 2, 3, 4$

14. $f(x) = \left(\dfrac{1}{2}\right)^x$; $x = -3, -2, -1, 0, 1, 2, 3$

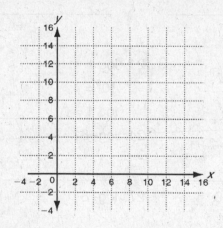   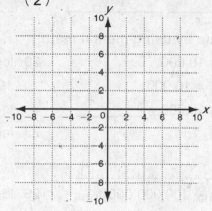

_____   _____

Solve.

15. The hydrogen ion concentration in moles per liter for a certain brand of tomato-vegetable juice is 0.000316.

   a. Write a logarithmic equation for the pH of the juice.   _____

   b. What is the pH of the juice?   _____

Name _____ Date _____ Class_____

Practice C
Logarithmic Functions

Write each exponential equation in logarithmic form.

1. $20^3 = 8000$

2. $11^4 = 14{,}641$

3. $a^b = c$

_____

_____

_____

Write each logarithmic equation in exponential form.

4. $\log_{10} 10{,}000{,}000 = 7$

5. $\log_6 216 = 3$

6. $\log_p q = r$

_____

_____

_____

Evaluate by using mental math.

7. $\log 1$

8. $\log 10{,}000$

9. $\log 1{,}000$

_____

_____

_____

10. $\log_5 3125$

11. $\log_{15} 1$

12. $\log_4 256$

_____

_____

_____

Use the given *x*-values to graph each function. Then graph its inverse. Describe the domain and range of the inverse function.

13. $f(x) = 0.1^x$; $x = -1, 0, 1, 2$

14. $f(x) = \left(\dfrac{5}{2}\right)^x$; $x = -3, -2, -1, 0, 1, 2, 3$

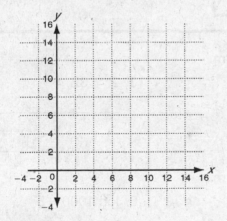

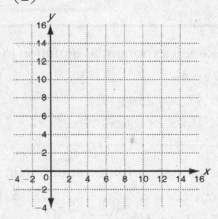

_____

_____

Solve.

15. The hydrogen ion concentration in moles per liter of a certain solvent is 0.00794.

   a. Write a logarithmic equation for the pH of the solvent. _____

   b. What is the pH of the solvent? _____

Holt Algebra 2

LESSON 7-3	**Reteach**
	Logarithmic Functions

A **logarithm** is another way to work with exponents in equations.

If $b^x = a$, then $\log_b a = x$.

> If b to the x power equals a, then x is the logarithm of a in base b.

Use the definition of the logarithm to write exponential equations in logarithmic form and to write logarithmic equations in exponential form.

Exponential Form		**Logarithmic Form**
$3^4 = 81$	base, $b = 3$ exponent, $x = 4$ value, $a = 81$	$\log_3 81 = 4$

Logarithmic Form		**Exponential Form**
$\log_5 125 = 3$	base, $b = 5$ exponent, $x = 3$ value, $a = 125$	$5^3 = 125$

If no base is written for a logarithm, the base is assumed to be 10.

Example: $\log 100 = 2$ because $10^2 = 100$.

> Assume the base is 10.

Write each exponential equation in logarithmic form.

1. $7^2 = 49$

    $b = 7, x = 2, a = 49$

    _____

2. $6^3 = 216$

    $b = $ ___, $x = $ ___, $a = $ _____

    _____

3. $2^5 = 32$

    _____

    _____

Write each logarithmic equation in exponential form.

4. $\log_9 729 = 3$

    $b = 9, x = 3, a = 729$

    _____

5. $\log_2 64 = 6$

    $b = $ ___, $x = $ ___, $a = $ _____

    _____

6. $\log 1000 = 3$

    _____

    _____

LESSON 7-3

Reteach
Logarithmic Functions (continued)

The logarithmic function is the inverse of the exponential function. Use this fact to graph the logarithmic function.

Graph *a* function and its inverse.
Graph $f(x) = 0.5^x$ using a table of values.

x	−2	−1	0	1	2
f(x)	4	2	1	0.5	0.25

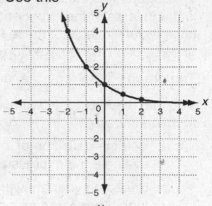

Write the inverse function.

$$f^{-1}(x) = \log_{0.5} x$$

The base is 0.5.

x and *f*(*x*) switch places in the function and its inverse.

x	4	2	1	0.5	0.25
f⁻¹(x)	−2	−1	0	1	2

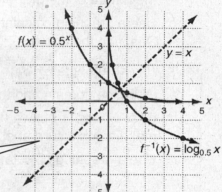

Remember, the graph of the inverse is the reflection of the original function across the line $y = x$.

Complete the tables. Graph the functions.

7. $f(x) = 4^x$

x	−2	−1	0	1	2
f(x)	$\frac{1}{16}$	$\frac{1}{4}$			

$f^{-1}(x) = \log_4 x$

x	$\frac{1}{16}$	$\frac{1}{4}$			
f⁻¹(x)					

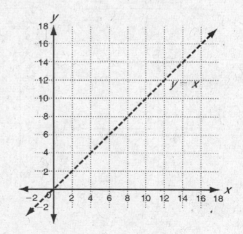

Holt Algebra 2

Name _____ Date _____ Class_____

Challenge

Variations of a Logarithmic Function

The logarithmic function $y = \log_b x$, where $b > 0$ and $b \neq 1$, is the inverse of the exponential function $y = b^x$. The inverse relationship of these functions can be seen in their graphs; each is the reflection of the other across the line $y = x$.

The graphs of $y = \log_{10} x$ and $y = 10^x$ are shown at right.

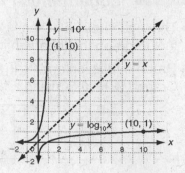

You can explore some variations of the graph of the logarithmic function in base 10.

1. a. Use the definition of logarithm to
    evaluate the expression $y = \log_{10} 10^x$. _____

   b. Based on your answer to part **a**, make a conjecture about
      the nature of the graph of the function $y = \log_{10} 10^x$. _____

   c. Use a graphing calculator to graph $y = \log_{10} 10^x$.
      Describe the graph. _____

2. Consider the function $y = 10^{\log_{10} x}$.

   a. Write the domain and the range of the function. _____

   b. Based on your answer to part **a** and the result of Exercise 1,
      make a conjecture about the graph of the function. _____

   c. Use a graphing calculator to graph. Describe the graph.

_____

**For each function write the domain and the range. Then use a
graphing calculator to graph. Draw the graph on the grid provided.**

3. $y = \log_{10} x^2$ _____

4. $y = (\log_{10} x)^2$ _____

5. $y = \log_{10} |x|$ _____

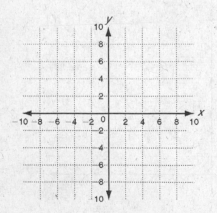

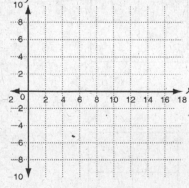

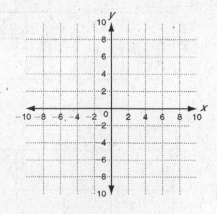

Holt Algebra 2

LESSON
7-3

Problem Solving
Logarithmic Functions

The acidity of rainwater varies from location to location. Acidity is measured in pH and is given by the function pH = −log[H⁺], where [H⁺] represents the hydrogen ion concentration in moles per liter. The table gives the [H⁺] of rainwater in different locations.

1. Find the acidity of rainwater in eastern Ohio.

   a. Substitute the hydrogen ion concentration for rainwater in eastern Ohio in the function for pH.

   _____

   b. Evaluate the function. What is the acidity of rainwater in eastern Ohio to the nearest tenth of a unit?

   _____

Hydrogen Ion Concentration of Rainwater	
Location	[H⁺] (moles per liter)
Central California	0.0000032
Eastern Texas	0.0000192
Eastern Ohio	0.0000629

2. Find how the acidity of rainwater in central California compares to the acidity of rainwater in eastern Ohio.

   a. Write a function for the acidity of rainwater in central California.

   _____

   b. Evaluate the function. What is the acidity of rainwater in central California to the nearest tenth of a unit?

   _____

   c. Compare the pH of rainwater in the two locations. Is the pH of rainwater in eastern Ohio greater than or less than that in central California? By how much?

   _____

Choose the letter for the best answer.

3. What is the pH of rainwater in eastern Texas?

   A pH = 3.7 C pH = 4.4

   B pH = 4.0 D pH = 4.7

5. What is the pH of a sample of irrigation water with a hydrogen ion concentration of 8.3×10^{-7} moles per liter?

   A pH = 6.1 C pH = 6.3

   B pH = 6.2 D pH = 6.4

4. Nick makes his own vegetable juice. It has a hydrogen ion concentration of 5.9×10^{-6} moles per liter. What is the pH of his vegetable juice?

   F pH = 4.9 H pH = 5.1

   G pH = 5.0 J pH = 5.2

6. What is the pH of a shampoo sample with a hydrogen ion concentration of 1.7×10^{-8} moles per liter?

   F pH = 7.4 H pH = 7.8

   G pH = 7.6 J pH = 8.0

LESSON 7-3

Reading Strategy

Understand Vocabulary

Exponential equations can also be written as logarithmic equations. The logarithm is equal to the exponent in the exponential equation.

$$b^x = a \qquad \log_b a = x$$

1. Complete the table.

Exponential Equation	$3^3 = 27$	$5^{-1} = 0.2$		$8^0 = 1$
Logarithmic Equation	$\log_3 27 = 3$		$\log_4 16 = 2$	

2. Explain why the logarithm of 1 with base b is always 0.

_____

A logarithmic function is the inverse of an exponential function. You can identify an inverse function by comparing its graph to the graph of the original function. The two graphs are a reflection of each other across the line $y = x$.

Exponential function: $f(x) = b^x$
The base b is any number greater than 1.
Example: $g(x) = 3^x$
The domain is all real numbers.
The range is all positive numbers.

Logarithm function: $f^{-1}(x) = \log_b x$
Use the same base to find the inverse function.
The inverse of $g(x)$ is $g^{-1}(x) = \log_3 x$.
In the inverse function, the domain and range are switched.

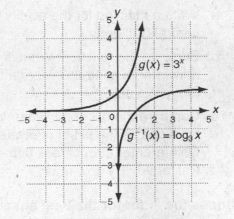

3. Find the inverse function of $f(x) = 4^x$.   _____

4. a. Find the inverse function of $g(x) = \left(\dfrac{1}{2}\right)^x$.   _____

   b. What are the domain and range of $g(x)$ and $g^{-1}(x)$?

   Domain of $g(x)$: _____   Range of $g(x)$: _____

   Domain of $g^{-1}(x)$: _____   Range of $g^{-1}(x)$: _____

Holt Algebra 2

LESSON 7-4

Practice A
Properties of Logarithms

Express as a single logarithm. Simplify, if possible.

1. $\log_3 9 + \log_3 27$

    $\log_3 (9 \cdot 27) = \log_3 243$

    $3^x = 243$, so $x =$ _____

2. $\log_2 16 + \log_2 4$

    $\log_2 (16 \cdot 4) = \log_2$ ____

    $2^x =$ ____, so $x =$ _____

3. $\log_5 125 + \log_5 25$

    $\log_5 (125 \cdot 25) = \log_5$ _____

    $5^x =$ ____, so $x =$ ____

4. $\log_{10} 250 + \log_{10} 40$

5. $\log_6 3 + \log_6 2$

6. $\log_8 16 + \log_8 4$

Express as a single logarithm. Simplify, if possible.

7. $\log_5 250 - \log_5 10$

8. $\log_3 21 - \log_3 7$

9. $\log_2 160 - \log_2 5$

10. $\log_4 128 - \log_4 8$

11. $\log_6 72 - \log_6 2$

12. $\log_5 1000 - \log_5 8$

Simplify, if possible.

13. $\log_6 36^2$

    $2 \log_6 36$

    $2 \cdot 2 =$ _____

14. $\log_5 5^4$

    $4 \log_5 5$

15. $\log_2 8^3$

    $3 \log_2 8$

16. $\log_3 3^4$

17. $\log_4 64^4$

18. $\log_8 8^2$

Evaluate. Round to the nearest hundredth.

19. $\log_5 13$

20. $\log_3 7$

21. $\log_8 21$

Solve.

22. The Richter magnitude of an earthquake, M, is related to the

    energy released in ergs, E, by the formula $M = \dfrac{2}{3}\log\left(\dfrac{E}{10^{11.8}}\right)$.

    Find the energy released by an earthquake of magnitude 6.8. _____

Holt Algebra 2

LESSON
7-4

Practice B
Properties of Logarithms

Express as a single logarithm. Simplify, if possible.

1. $\log_3 9 + \log_3 27$

2. $\log_2 8 + \log_2 16$

3. $\log_{10} 80 + \log_{10} 125$

_____

4. $\log_6 8 + \log_6 27$

5. $\log_3 6 + \log_3 13.5$

6. $\log_4 32 + \log_4 128$

Express as a single logarithm. Simplify, if possible.

7. $\log_2 80 - \log_2 10$

8. $\log_{10} 4000 - \log_{10} 40$

9. $\log_4 384 - \log_4 6$

_____

10. $\log_2 1920 - \log_2 30$

11. $\log_3 486 - \log_3 2$

12. $\log_6 180 - \log_6 5$

Simplify, if possible.

13. $\log_4 4^6$

14. $\log_5 5^{x-5}$

15. $7^{\log_7 30}$

_____

16. $12^{\log_{12} 1}$

17. $\log_8 8^5$

18. $\log_3 9^4$

Evaluate. Round to the nearest hundredth.

19. $\log_{12} 1$

20. $\log_3 30$

21. $\log_5 10$

_____

Solve.

22. The Richter magnitude of an earthquake, M, is related to the
    energy released in ergs, E, by the formula $M = \dfrac{2}{3}\log\left(\dfrac{E}{10^{11.8}}\right)$.
    Find the energy released by an earthquake of magnitude 4.2. _____

Holt Algebra 2

LESSON 7-4
Practice C
Properties of Logarithms

Express as a single logarithm. Simplify, if possible.

1. $\log_6 12 + \log_6 18$

2. $\log_3 81 - \log_3 27$

3. $\log_4 128 - \log_4 8$

_____

4. $\log_6 18 + \log_6 72$

5. $\log_5 3125 - \log_5 25$

6. $\log_8 128 + \log_8 256$

_____

7. $\log_5 5 + \log_5 125$

8. $\log_2 256 - \log_2 64$

9. $\log_3 8019 - \log_3 99$

_____

10. $\log_8 80 + \log_8 51.2$

11. $\log_7 13.3 - \log_7 1.9$

12. $\log_{10} 125 + \log_{10} 80$

_____

Evaluate. Round to the nearest hundredth.

13. $\log_8 8^6$

14. $2^{\log_2 8^x}$

15. $\log_2 16^5$

_____

16. $\log_3 3^{(2x + 1)}$

17. $\log_4 16^{(x - 1)}$

18. $5^{\log_5 17}$

_____

19. $\log_3 5^2$

20. $\log_5 \left(\dfrac{1}{125} \right)^2$

21. $\log_6 \left(\dfrac{1}{6^4} \right)^3$

_____

22. $\log_4 20^2$

23. $\log_9 27^4$

24. $\log_2 10$

_____

Solve.

25. Carmen has a painting presently valued at $5000. An art dealer told her the painting would appreciate at a rate of 6% per year. In how many years will the painting be worth $8,000?

   a. Write a logarithmic expression.   _____

   b. Simplify your expression.   _____

Holt Algebra 2

LESSON 7-4

Reteach
Properties of Logarithms

Use properties of logarithms to simplify logarithms.

The Product Property uses addition instead of multiplication.

Product Property

The logarithm of a product can be written as the sum of the logarithm of the numbers.

$$\log_b mn = \log_b m + \log_b n$$

where m, n, and b are all positive numbers and $b \neq 1$

Simplify: $\log_8 4 + \log_8 16 = \log_8 (4 \cdot 16) = \log_8 64 = 2$

The bases must be the same for both logarithms.

Think: 8 to what power is equal to 64, or $8^? = 64$.

The Quotient Property uses subtraction instead of division.

Quotient Property

The logarithm of a quotient can be written as the logarithm of the numerator minus the logarithm of the denominator.

$$\log_b \frac{m}{n} = \log_b m - \log_b n$$

where m, n, and b are all positive numbers and $b \neq 1$

Simplify: $\log_3 243 - \log_3 9 = \log_3 \left(\frac{243}{9}\right) = \log_3 27 = 3$

The bases must be the same for both logarithms.

Think: 3 to what power is equal to 27, or $3^? = 27$.

Complete the steps to simplify each expression.

1. $\log_6 54 + \log_6 4$

   $\log_6 (54 \cdot 4)$

   $\log_6 216$

   _____

2. $\log_2 128 - \log_2 8$

   $\log_2 \left(\frac{128}{8}\right)$

   _____

   _____

3. $\log_9 3 + \log_9 27$

   _____

   _____

   _____

LESSON 7-4	**Reteach**

Properties of Logarithms (continued)

The Power Property uses multiplication instead of exponentiation.

Power Property

The logarithm of a power can be written as the product of the exponent and the logarithm of the base.

$$\log_b a^p = p \log_b a$$

for any real number p

where a and b are positive numbers and $b \neq 1$

Simplify: $\log_4 64^5 = 5 \log_4 64 = 5(3) = 15$

"Bring down" the exponent to multiply.

Think: 4 to what power is equal to 64, or $4^? = 64$.

Logarithms and exponents undo each other when their bases are the same.

Inverse Properties

The logarithm of b^x to the base b is equal to x.	b raised to the logarithm of x to the base b is equal to x.
$$\log_b b^x = x$$	$$b^{\log_b x} = x$$
The logarithm undoes the exponent when the bases are the same.	The exponent undoes the logarithm when the bases are the same.
Simplify: $\log_7 7^{4x} = 4x$	Simplify: $3^{\log_3 64} = 64$
The base of the log is 7 and the base of the exponent is 7.	The base of the exponent is 3 and the base of the log is 3.

Simplify each expression.

4. $\log_5 125^2$

  $2 \log_5 125$

  _____

5. $\log_2 16^4$

  $4 \log_2 16$

  _____

6. $\log_9 81^3$

  _____

7. $\log_6 6^{5y}$

  _____

8. $4^{\log_4 75}$

  _____

9. $2^{\log_2 3x}$

  _____

LESSON 7-4

Challenge

Some Other Properties of Logarithms

Logarithmic properties allow simplification of expressions that otherwise would be difficult to compute. One such property is

$$\log_b \sqrt[r]{x} = \frac{\log_b x}{r}$$

which shows that the logarithm of a root is equal to the logarithm of the radicand divided by the index of the radical.

1. Evaluate $\log_{10} \sqrt{1000}$ on your calculator and then evaluate $\frac{\log_{10} 1000}{2}$ without a calculator. How do your answers compare?

   _____

2. Evaluate $\log_2 \sqrt[4]{64}$ with your calculator and with the above formula. Which is easier to compute? (Hint: You will need the Change of Base Formula for one of the calculations.)

   _____

3. Evaluate $\log_3 \sqrt[5]{729}$ with your calculator and with the above formula. Which is easier to compute?

   _____

Another useful property of logarithms is called the Chain Rule for Logarithms.

$$\log_a b \cdot \log_b c = \log_a c$$

4. Prove this formula by changing all the logarithms to base 10.

   _____

   _____

   _____

5. Evaluate $\log_2 3 \cdot \log_3 5 \cdot \log_5 8 \cdot \log_8 13$ using your calculator and the Change of Base Formula both with and without using the above formula.

   _____

6. Evaluate $\log_2 3 \cdot \log_3 4 \cdot \log_4 5 \cdot \log_5 6 \cdot \cdots \cdot \log_{31} 32$ both with and without using the above formula. Which is easier to compute?

   _____

Problem Solving
Properties of Logarithms

Trina and Willow are researching information on earthquakes. One of the largest earthquakes in the United States, centered at San Francisco, occurred in 1906 and registered 7.8 on the Richter scale. The Richter magnitude of an earthquake, *M*, is related to the energy released in ergs, *E*, by the formula $M = \dfrac{2}{3}\log\left(\dfrac{E}{10^{11.8}}\right)$.

1. Find the amount of energy released by the earthquake in 1906.

   a. Substitute 7.8 for magnitude, *M*, in the equation. _____

   b. Solve for the value of log *E*.   _____

   c. Willow says that *E* is equal to 10 to the power of the value of log *E*. Is she correct? What property or definition can be used to find the value of *E*? Explain.

   _____

   d. Trina says the energy of the 1906 earthquake was 3.16×10^{23} ergs. Willow says the energy was $10^{23.5}$ ergs. Who is correct? How do you know?

   _____

Choose the letter for the best answer.

2. An earthquake in 1811 in Missouri measured 8.1 on the Richter scale. About how many times as much energy was released by this earthquake as by the California earthquake of 1906?

   A 2.8

   B 3.0

   C 3.6

   D 5.7

3. Another large earthquake in California measured 7.9 on the Richter scale. Which statement is true?

   F 0.1 times as much energy was released by the larger earthquake.

   G The difference in energy released is 1.31×10^{23} ergs.

   H The energy released by the second earthquake was 3.26×10^{23} ergs.

   J The total energy released by the two earthquakes is equal to the energy released by an 8.0 earthquake.

4. Larry wrote the following: $\log 10^{0.0038} = 3.8 \times 10^{-3}$. Which property of logarithms did he use?

   A Product Property

   B Quotient Property

   C Inverse Property

   D Power Property

5. Vijay wants to change $\log_5 7$ to base 10. Which expression should he use?

   F $\dfrac{\log_{10} 7}{\log_{10} 5}$ H $\dfrac{\log_{10} 7}{\log_5 5}$

   G $\dfrac{\log_{10} 5}{\log_{10} 7}$ J $\dfrac{\log_7 5}{\log_{10} 7}$

Holt Algebra 2

Name _____ Date _____ Class_____

Reading Strategy
Identify Relationships

The inverse relationship between logarithmic and exponential functions can be used to find all the properties of logarithms. For example, to find the logarithm of a product, add the logarithms of its factors. Remember, when the base of the logarithm is not given, it is assumed to be base 10.

	Property of Exponent	Property of Logarithm
Product Property	$b^x b^y = b^{x+y}$	$\log_b (xy) = \log_b x + \log_b y$
Quotient Property	$\dfrac{b^x}{b^y} = b^{x-y}$	$\log_b \left(\dfrac{x}{y}\right) = \log_b x - \log_b y$
Power Property	$(b^x)^y = b^{x \cdot y} = b^{xy}$	$\log_b x^y = y \log_b x$
Inverse Property	$b^{\log_b x} = x$	$\log_b b^x = x$

Write true or false for each. Explain your answer using a property.

1. $\log 5 + \log 2 = 1$

2. $\log_2 40 - \log_2 5 = 3$

3. $\log_2 25^2 = 3$

4. $4^{\log_4 18} = 16$

Simplify each expression. Tell which property or properties you used.

5. $\log x^5$

6. $\log x^2 - \log x$

7. $\log x + \log \left(\dfrac{10}{x}\right)$

8. $\dfrac{1}{2}(x^{-2}x^3)(\log x^2)$

9. $\log x^3 y^5 - \log xy^3$

10. $7 (\log 0.2 + \log 50)$

Solve.

11. $64^x = 2^{(x+5)}$

Holt Algebra 2

LESSON 7-5 Practice A

Exponential and Logarithmic Equations and Inequalities

Solve and check.

1. $4^{2x} = 6$

   $\log 4^{2x} = \log 6$

   $2x \log 4 = \log 6$

   $2x = \dfrac{\log 6}{\log 4} \approx$ _____

2. $8^{2x-5} = 48$

   $\log 8^{2x-5} = \log 48$

   $(2x - 5) \log 8 = \log 48$

3. $4^{x+2} = 20$

   $\log 4^{x+2} = \log 20$

4. $3^{5x} = 27^{2x+1}$

5. $36^{x+2} = 6^{4x}$

6. $5^{5x-6} = 50$

7. $16^{3x} = 64^{x+9}$

8. $81^x = 243^{x+2}$

9. $\left(\dfrac{1}{2}\right)^{3x} = 8^2$

Solve.

10. $\log_2 x^7 = 21$

    $7\log_2 x = 21$

    $\log_2 x = 3$

11. $\log_5 x^3 = 15$

12. $\log_6 (x-4)^2 = 2$

13. $\log x - \log 9 = 3$

14. $\log x + \log 4 = 1$

15. $\log (x + 6) = \log (5x - 2)$

Solve.

16. Halle deposited $4000 into an account that earns 5% interest each year. The growth of her investment can be expressed by the exponential equation $A = 4000 (1 + 0.05)^t$, where A is the amount in the account after t years. In how many years will her account exceed $10,000?

_____

Holt Algebra 2

LESSON 7-5 Practice B

Exponential and Logarithmic Equations and Inequalities

Solve and check.

1. $5^{2x} = 20$

2. $12^{2x-8} = 15$

3. $2^{x+6} = 4$

_____

4. $16^{5x} = 64^{x+7}$

5. $243^{0.2x} = 81^{x+5}$

6. $25^x = 125^{x-2}$

_____

7. $\left(\dfrac{1}{2}\right)^x = 16^2$

8. $\left(\dfrac{1}{32}\right)^{2x} = 64$

9. $\left(\dfrac{1}{27}\right)^{x-6} = 27$

_____

Solve.

10. $\log_4 x^5 = 20$

11. $\log_3 x^6 = 12$

12. $\log_4 (x-6)^3 = 6$

_____

13. $\log x - \log 10 = 14$

14. $\log x + \log 5 = 2$

15. $\log (x+9) = \log (2x-7)$

_____

16. $\log (x+4) - \log 6 = 1$

17. $\log x^2 + \log 25 = 2$

18. $\log (x-1)^2 = \log (-5x-1)$

_____

Use a table and graph to solve.

19. $2^{x-5} < 64$

20. $\log x^3 = 12$

21. $2^x 3^x = 1296$

_____

Solve.

22. The population of a small farming community is declining at a rate of 7% per year. The decline can be expressed by the exponential equation $P = C(1 - 0.07)^t$, where P is the population after t years and C is the current population. If the population was 8,500 in 2004, when will the population be less than 6,000?

_____

Holt Algebra 2

LESSON 7-5 Practice C
Exponential and Logarithmic Equations and Inequalities

Solve.

1. $16^{3x} = 8^{x+6}$

2. $\log_2 x^6 = 3$

3. $12^{x-1} = 20^2$

4. $9^{2x} = 27^{x+4}$

5. $256^{0.5x} = 64^{2x+5}$

6. $216^{\frac{x}{3}} = 36^{2x+3}$

7. $\left(\frac{1}{9}\right)^{3x} = 27$

8. $\left(\frac{1}{16}\right)^{x+5} = 8^2$

9. $\left(\frac{2}{5}\right)^{8x} = \left(\frac{25}{4}\right)^2$

10. $\log_5 (4x - 5)^2 = 6$

11. $\log_4 (3x + 4)^5 = 15$

12. $\log_3 (10x - 1)^5 = 10$

13. $\log x - \log 8 = 3$

14. $\log 5x + \log 2 = 10$

15. $\log (x^2 - 9) = \log (5x + 5)$

16. $\log (x^2 - 1) - \log 12 = 1$

17. $\log x^3 + \log 8 = 3$

18. $\log (9x + 1) - \log x^2 = 1$

Use a table and graph to solve.

19. $\log x^2 - \log 200 = \log 2$

20. $4^{x^2} \cdot 2^{5x} = 8$

21. $3^{x^2 - 4x} \geq \frac{1}{27}$

Solve.

22. Lorena deposited $9000 into an account that earns 4.25% interest each year.

a. Write an equation for the amount, A, in the account after t years. _____

b. In how many years will her account exceed $20,000? _____

c. If she waits for 50 years, how much will be in her account? _____

Holt Algebra 2

LESSON 7-5 Reteach
Exponential and Logarithmic Equations and Inequalities

An **exponential equation** contains an expression that has a variable as an exponent.

$5^x = 25$ is an exponential equation.

$x = 2$, since $5(2) = 25$.

Remember: You can take the logarithm of both sides of an exponential equation. Then use other properties of logarithms to solve.

> If $x = y$, then
> $\log x = \log y$
> $(x > 0$ and $y > 0)$.

Solve $6^{x+2} = 500$.

Step 1   Since the variable is in the exponent, take the log of both sides.

$6^{x+2} = 500$
$\log 6^{x+2} = \log 500$

Step 2   Use the Power Property of Logarithms: $\log a^p = p \log a$.

$\log 6^{x+2} = \log 500$

$(x + 2) \log 6 = \log 500$ *"Bring down" the exponent to multiply.*

Step 3   Isolate the variable. Divide both sides by log 6.

$(x + 2) \log 6 = \log 500$

$$x + 2 = \frac{\log 500}{\log 6}$$

Step 4   Solve for x. Subtract 2 from both sides.

$$x = \frac{\log 500}{\log 6} - 2$$

Step 5   Use a calculator to approximate x.

$x \approx 1.468$

Step 6   Use a calculator to check.

$6^{1.468 + 2} \approx 499.607$

Solve and check.

1. $4^{-x} = 32$

   $\log 4^{-x} = \log 32$

   $-x \log 4 = \log 32$

   _____

   _____

2. $3^{4x} = 90$

   $\log 3^{4x} = \log 90$

   $4x \log 3 = \log 90$

   _____

   _____

3. $5^{x-3} = 600$

   _____

   _____

   _____

   _____

Holt Algebra 2

LESSON
7-5

Reteach
Exponential and Logarithmic Equations and Inequalities (continued)

A **logarithmic equation** contains a logarithmic expression that has a variable.

$\log_5 x = 2$ is a logarithmic equation.

$x = 25$, since $5^2 = 25$.

Combine and use properties of logarithms to solve logarithmic equations.

Solve: $\log 80x - \log 4 = 1$

Step 1   Use the Quotient Property of Logarithms.

$\log 80x - \log 4 = 1$

$\log \dfrac{80x}{4} = 1$

> $\log x - \log y = \log \dfrac{x}{y}$

Step 2   Simplify.

$\log \dfrac{80x}{4} = 1$

$\log 20x = 1$

Step 3   Use the definition of the logarithm:
if $b^x = a$, then $\log_b a = x$.

$\log_{10} 20x = 1$

$10^1 = 20x$

> Remember: Use 10 as the base when the base is not given.

Step 4   Solve for x. Divide both sides by 20.

$10 = 20x$

$\dfrac{1}{2} = x$

Solve and check.

4. $\log_3 x^4 = 8$

    $4 \log_3 x = 8$

    $\log_3 x = \dfrac{8}{4}$

5. $\log 4 + \log (x + 2) = 2$

    $\log 4 (x + 2) = 2$

    $\log_{10} (4x + 8) = 2$

    $4x + 8 = 10^2$

6. $\log 75x - \log 3 = 1$

_____   _____   _____

_____   _____   _____

LESSON 7-5

Challenge

Exponential Heating and Cooling

Newton's Law of Cooling states that the rate of heat loss of an object is proportional to the difference in temperatures between the object and its surrounding ambient temperature. This phenomenon is modeled with a differential equation and that equation may be solved to give

$$T(t) = T_A + [T_0 - T_A]b^t$$

where $T(t)$ is the varying temperature of the object at a given time, t, T_A is the surrounding ambient temperature, T_0 is the initial temperature of the object, and b is a constant that depends on the material the object is composed of and how fast it heats or cools.

Suppose you decided to make a cup of hot chocolate heated to 180 °F in the kitchen that is at 72 °F.

1. Solve the above equation for the constant b. _____

2. If the cup of hot chocolate cooled to 150 °F in 15 minutes, find the value of the constant b in the above equation. Express your answer to five decimal places. _____

3. Solve the above equation for t. _____

4. Suppose you like your hot chocolate at the tepid temperature of 120 °F. How long, to the nearest minute, will you have to wait until it cools to this temperature? _____

To go along with your hot chocolate, you take a frozen cherry pie from the freezer and place it in the oven preheated to 350 °F. Assume the freezer is at 32 °F.

5. If the cherry pie comes to a temperature of 120 °F in 20 minutes, find the value of the constant b in the above equation. Express your answer to 5 decimal places. _____

6. How long will it take for the pie to reach its final temperature of 220 °F? _____

7. The pie is taken out of the oven and set on a table in a room at 80 °F. In 10 minutes it has cooled to 185 °F. However, the pie must cool to 125 °F before it is ready to eat. How much longer will you have to wait? _____

Problem Solving

Exponential and Logarithmic Equations and Inequalities

While John and Cody play their favorite video game, John drinks 4 cups of coffee and a cola, and Cody drinks 2 cups of brewed tea and a cup of iced tea. John recalls reading that up to 300 mg of caffeine is considered a moderate level of consumption per day. The rate at which caffeine is eliminated from the bloodstream is about 15% per hour.

Caffeine Content of Some Beverages	
Beverage	**Caffeine (mg per serving)**
Brewed coffee	103
Brewed tea	36
Iced tea	30
Cola	25

1. John wants to know how long it will take for the caffeine in his bloodstream to drop to a moderate level.

   a. How much caffeine did John consume?

   _____

   b. Write an equation showing the amount of caffeine in the bloodstream as a function of time.

   _____

   c. How long, to the nearest tenth of an hour, will it take for the caffeine in John's system to reach a moderate level?

   _____

2. a. Cody thinks that it will take at least 8 hours for the level of caffeine in John's system to drop to the same level of caffeine that Cody consumed. Explain how he can use his graphing calculator to prove that.

   _____

   b. What equations did Cody enter into his calculator?

   _____

   c. Sketch the resulting graph.

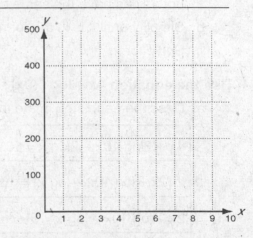

Choose the letter for the best answer.

3. About how long would it take for the level of caffeine in Cody's system to drop by a factor of 2?

   A 0.2 hour

   B 1.6 hours

   C 2.7 hours

   D 4.3 hours

4. If John drank 6 cups of coffee and a cola, about how long would it take for the level of caffeine in his system to drop to a moderate level?

   F 0.5 hour

   G 1.6 hours

   H 4.7 hours

   J 5.3 hours

Holt Algebra 2

Reading Strategy

LESSON
7-5

Use Relationships

In solving equations with logarithms and exponents, first use the properties
of logarithms and exponential functions to simplify equations. Here are two
additional properties that are useful for solving equations.

- If $x = y$, then $b^x = b^y$.
- If $x = y$, then $\log_b x = \log_b y$.

Use the equation $2^x = 16$ for Exercise 1.

1. a. Express 16 as a power of 2. _____

   b. Rewrite the equation so both sides have
      the same base. What is the value of x? _____

   c. Show how you can check your solution.

   _____

Use the equation $\log_{10} x = 2$ for Exercise 2.

2. a. Rewrite the equation using the definition of logarithm. _____

   b. What is the solution of the equation? _____

   c. What is the value of $\log_{10} 100$? _____

Use the equation $243^x = 3^x \cdot 9^2$ for Exercise 3.

3. a. Rewrite the equation so that the exponents on
      both sides have the same base. _____

   b. Simplify until it is in the form $3^x = 3^y$. _____

   c. Solve for x. _____

Use the equation $4x + \log(10x)^2 - 2\log x = 10$ for Exercise 4.

4. a. Describe each step in the table to solve the equation.

$4x + 2\log 10x - 2\log x = 10$	Use of the Power Property
$2(2x + \log 10x - \log x) = 10$	
$2x + \log 10x - \log x = 5$	
$2x + \log\left(\dfrac{10x}{x}\right) = 5$	

   b. Simplify and solve the resulting equation. _____

   _____

Holt Algebra 2

LESSON 7-6

Practice A

The Natural Base, *e*

Graph each exponential function.

1. $f(x) = e^{-x}$

   a. Complete the table.

x	−2	−1	0	1	2	3
f(x)	7.4					

   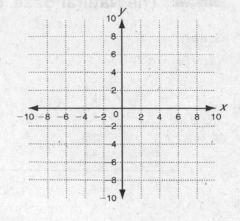

   b. Graph the ordered pairs and draw a curve through the points.

2. $f(x) = 2 - e^x$

   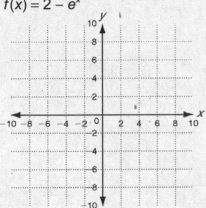

3. $f(x) = e^{2-x}$

   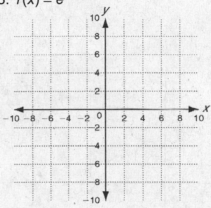

Simplify.

4. $\ln e^{7x}$

5. $\ln e^{x+4}$

6. $e^{\ln x}$

_____

7. $e^{3 \ln x}$

8. $e^{5 \ln (x+1)}$

9. $\ln e^{x-1}$

_____

10. $x \cdot \ln e^3$

11. $e^{-1 \cdot \ln 5x}$

12. $2 \ln e^x$

_____

Solve.

13. Use the formula $A = P e^{rt}$ to find the total amount of an investment of $5000 at 6% interest compounded continuously for 8 years.

_____

Holt Algebra 2

LESSON 7-6

Practice B
The Natural Base, e

Graph.

1. $f(x) = e^{2x}$

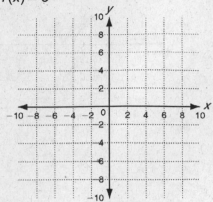

2. $f(x) = e^{0.5x}$

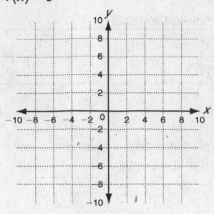

3. $f(x) = e^{1+x}$

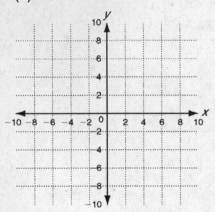

4. $f(x) = e^{2-x}$

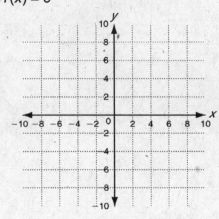

Simplify.

5. $\ln e^{x+2}$

6. $e^{\ln 2x}$

7. $e^{7 \ln x}$

8. $\ln e^{3x+1}$

9. $\ln e$

10. $\ln e^{2x+y}$

Solve.

11. Use the formula $A = P e^{rt}$ to compute the total amount for an investment of $4500 at 5% interest compounded continuously for 6 years.

12. Use the natural decay function, $N(t) = N_0 e^{-kt}$, to find the decay constant for a substance that has a half-life of 1000 years.

Holt Algebra 2

LESSON 7-6 Practice C
The Natural Base, e

Graph.

1. $f(x) = -e^{x+2}$

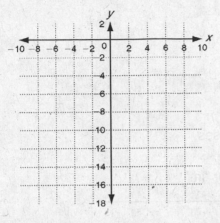

2. $f(x) = -e^{x-2}$

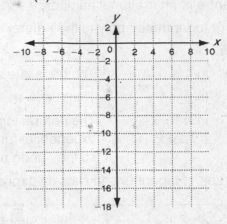

Simplify.

3. $\ln e^{5x-3}$

_____

4. $\ln e^{2 \ln 8x}$

_____

5. $e^{4 \ln (x-2)}$

_____

6. $e^{-\ln 4 - x}$

_____

7. $\ln e^{\sqrt{x}}$

_____

8. $\ln e^{\frac{4}{x}}$

_____

Solve.

9. Ariana has a choice of two investments. She can invest $12,000 at 5% for 8 years, or she can invest $9000 at 6.5% for 7 years. Both accounts are compounded continuously. Which investment will result in the greater amount of interest earned?

_____

_____

10. Use the natural decay function, $N(t) = N_0 e^{-kt}$, to find the age of a fossil containing 35% of the original amount of a particular substance. This substance has a half-life of 2450 years.

a. Find the decay constant.

_____

b. Find the age of the fossil.

_____

Holt Algebra 2

LESSON 7-6 Reteach

The Natural Base, e

The **natural logarithmic function**, $f(x) = \ln x$, is the inverse of the exponential function with the natural base e, $f(x) = e^x$.

The constant e is an irrational number. $e \approx 2.71828....$

Properties of logarithms apply to the natural logarithm.

In particular:

$\ln 1 = 0$	The base is e and $e^0 = 1$.
$\ln e = 1$	Think: $e^1 = e$.
$\ln e^x = x$	The natural logarithm and the
$e^{\ln x} = x$	exponential function are inverses, so they undo each other.

Use properties of logarithms to simplify expressions with e or "ln."

Simplify: $\ln e^{x+2}$
Step 1 Use the Power Property. "Bring down" the exponent to multiply.
$\ln e^{x+2}$
$(x + 2) \ln e$

Step 2 Simplify.
$(x + 2) \ln e$
$x + 2$

$\boxed{\ln e = 1}$

Simplify: $e^{4 \ln x}$
Step 1 Use the Power Property. Write the exponent.
$e^{4 \ln x}$
$e^{\ln x^4}$

Step 2 Simplify.
$e^{\ln x^4}$
x^4

$\boxed{e^{\ln x} = x}$

Simplify each expression.

1. $\ln e^{-6x}$

$-6x \ln e$

_____

2. $\ln e^{t-3}$

$(t - 3) \ln e$

_____

3. $e^{2 \ln x}$

$e^{\ln x^2}$

_____

4. $\ln e^{1.8}$

_____

_____

5. $\ln e^{x+1}$

_____

_____

6. $e^{7 \ln x}$

_____

_____

Holt Algebra 2

Reteach

The Natural Base, e (continued)

The natural base, e, appears in the formula for interest compounded continuously.

$A = Pe^{rt}$

A = total amount

P = principal, or initial amount

r = annual interest rate

t = time in years

What is the total amount for an investment of $2000 invested at 3% and compounded continuously for 5 years?

Step 1   Identify the values that correspond to the variables in the formula.

P = initial investment = $2000

r = 3% = 0.03

$t = 5$

Step 2   Substitute the known values into the formula.

$A = Pe^{rt}$

$A = 2000\, e^{0.03\,(5)}$

Step 3   Use a calculator to solve for A, the total amount.

$A = 2000\, e^{0.03\,(5)}$

$A \approx 2323.67$

Use the e^x key on a calculator:
$2000e^{(.03*5)} = 2323.668485$

The total amount is $2323.67.

Use the formula $A = Pe^{rt}$ to solve.

7. What is the total amount for an investment of $500 invested at 4.5% and compounded continuously for 10 years?

$P =$ _____ $r =$ _____ $t =$ _____

_____

8. Randy deposited $1000 into an account that paid 2.8% with continuous compounding. What was her balance after 6 years?   _____

9. a. Martin borrows $5500. The rate is set at 6% with continuous compounding. How much does he owe at the end of 2 years?   _____

   b. Martin found a bank with a better interest rate of 5.5%. How much less does he owe at the end of 2 years?   _____

LESSON 7-6

Challenge

Exploring the Number e

John Napier, the inventor of logarithms in 1614, based his work on a number the Swiss mathematician Leonard Euler later called *e*. The value of *e* is the irrational number 2.71828 . . ..

As you have seen, one way to approximate the value of *e* is to let the value of *n* become very large in the sequence of numbers obtained from

the expression $1\left(1+\dfrac{1}{n}\right)^n$. You can explore some other methods for

evaluating *e*.

Consider the sequence $1, \dfrac{1}{1}, \dfrac{1}{2\cdot 1}, \dfrac{1}{3\cdot 2\cdot 1}, \dots$

1. Write the 9th term of the sequence.   _____

2. Using a calculator, determine

   a. the sum of the first 5 terms of the sequence.   _____

   b. the sum of the first 7 terms of the sequence.   _____

   c. the sum of the first 10 terms of the sequence.   _____

3. Use what you know about the value of *e* and the
   results of Exercise 2 to write an expression for *e*
   in terms of the given sequence of numbers.   _____

A *continued fraction* is formed by a number added to a fraction whose denominator is a fraction added to a fraction whose denominator is a fraction, and so on, forming a pattern.

• **Example** To evaluate, start with the last denominator.

$$1+\cfrac{1}{2+\cfrac{1}{3+\cfrac{1}{4}}} = 1+\cfrac{1}{2+\cfrac{1}{\frac{13}{4}}} = 1+\cfrac{1}{2+\cfrac{4}{13}} = 1+\cfrac{1}{\frac{30}{13}} = 1+\frac{13}{30} = \frac{43}{30}$$

Start.

Complete the continued fraction by finding the missing denominator. Then evaluate.

4. $2+\cfrac{1}{1+\cfrac{1}{2+\cfrac{2}{3+\cfrac{3}{4+4}}}}$

5. $1+\cfrac{2}{1+\cfrac{1}{6+\cfrac{1}{10+\cfrac{1}{14+1}}}}$

_____   _____

6. Continue the pattern further in the fractions above and make an observation.

_____

Name _____ Date _____ Class_____

Problem Solving
The Natural Base, e

Irene reads that the 2004 census of whooping cranes tallied
213 birds at one wildlife refuge in Texas. This number exceeded
the 2003 record by 19. If the population of whooping cranes can
be modeled using the exponential growth function $P_t = P_0\, e^{kt}$,
the population, P_t, at time t can be found, where P_0 is the initial
population and k is the growth factor. Predict the population of
whooping cranes over the next few years.

1. What was the size of the population of whooping cranes in 2003? _____

2. Use the population figures for 2003 and 2004 to find the growth factor, k.

_____

3. Complete the table to predict the population of whooping cranes through 2010.

Year	2006	2007	2008	2009	2010
t	3				
Population, P_t					

Choose the letter for the best answer.

4. Irene wants to know when the population
   of whooping cranes will exceed 1000.
   Using the 2003 population as P_0, which
   year is the best prediction?

   A 2017

   B 2019

   C 2021

   D 2023

5. Irene wonders how the 2010 whooping
   crane population would change if the
   growth factor doubled. Which statement
   is true?

   F The population would increase by a
   factor of e^2.

   G The population would increase by a
   factor of $e^{0.0934}$.

   H The population would increase by a
   factor of $e^{(0.0934)\,(7)}$.

   J The population would increase by a
   factor of $7e^2$.

6. How long will it take for an investment in
   an account paying 6% compounded
   continuously to double?

   A 10.2 years

   B 10.8 years

   C 11.6 years

   D 12.4 years

7. Darlene has a sample of a fossil that has
   33% of its original carbon-14. Carbon-14
   has a half-life of 5730 years. The decay
   constant for carbon-14 is
   1.2×10^{-4}. Find the age of the fossil.

   F About 7820 years

   G About 8450 years

   H About 8980 years

   J About 9240 years

Holt Algebra 2

Reading Strategies

LESSON 7-6

Use a Graphic Organizer

Definition The number *e* is an irrational constant like π. You can estimate *e* by using very large values of *n* in the formula. $f(n) = \left(1 + \dfrac{1}{n}\right)^n$ $\approx 2.7182818...$ $e \approx 2.7182818...$	**Facts** A logarithm with base *e* is called a natural logarithm (ln *x*). The functions e^x and ln *x* have the same properties as the other exponential and logarithmic functions you have studied.
Example (compound interest) For a **principal** investment of $100 with a growth **rate** of 5% for 10 **years** compounded continuously, the total **amount** will be: $A = Pe^{rt}$ $= 100 \cdot e^{0.05 \times 10}$ $= \$164.87$	**Useful Hints** You can use the property of inverse functions to solve many problems containing *e* and ln. For example: ln $e^3 = 3$ and $e^{\ln 3} = 3$

Answer each question.

1. a. Rewrite $e^{3\ln x}$ using the Power Property of logarithms. _____

   b. Now simplify. _____

2. The graph shows $g(x) = e^x$ and $g^{-1}(x) = \ln x$.

   a. Label each curve with the correct function.

   b. What transformation is represented by the 2 curves?

   _____

   c. Explain how you can tell that they are inverse functions.

   _____

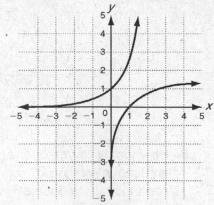

3. $A = Pe^{rt}$ is a formula used for continuously compounded interest.

   a. Which variable represents the principal or starting amount? _____

   b. Which variable represents the time length of the investment? _____

   c. Which variable represents the rate of interest paid on the investment? _____

Holt Algebra 2

Name _____ Date _____ Class_____

Practice A

Transforming Exponential and Logarithmic Functions

Graph each function. Find the asymptote. Tell how the graph is transformed from the graph of $f(x) = 4^x$.

1. $f(x) = 4^{x+1}$

   a. Complete the table.

x	−3	−2	−1	0	1
f(x)					16

   b. Graph the ordered pairs and draw a curve through the points.

   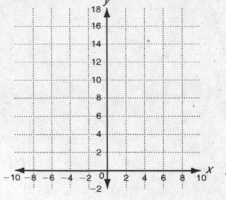

   c. Describe the asymptote. _____

   d. How is the graph transformed from the graph of $f(x) = 4^x$?

   _____

2. $f(x) = -4^x$

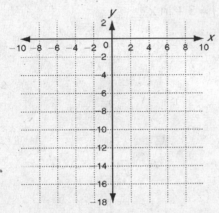

3. $f(x) = 4^{\frac{x}{2}}$

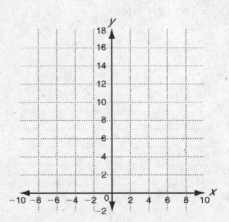

Write each transformed function.

4. The function $f(x) = \ln x$ is reflected across the y-axis. _____

5. The function $f(x) = 8^x$ is horizontally compressed by a factor of 2. _____

6. The function $f(x) = 3^x$ is vertically stretched by a factor of 4. _____

7. The function $f(x) = \log x$ is shifted 3 units left and reflected across the y-axis.

   a. Write the function that is shifted 3 units left. _____

   b. Take your answer to part a and write a function that reflects it across the x-axis. _____

Holt Algebra 2

LESSON	**Practice B**
7-7	*Transforming Exponential and Logarithmic Functions*

**Graph each function. Find the asymptote. Tell how the graph is
transformed from the graph of its parent function.**

1. $f(x) = 5(2^x)$

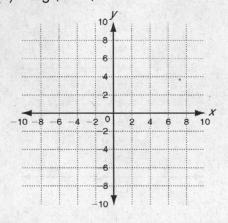

2. $f(x) = 5^{\frac{x}{4}}$

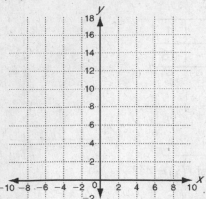

_____

3. $f(x) = \log (x + 5)$

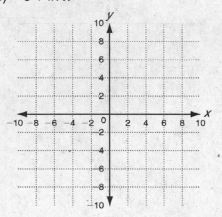

4. $f(x) = 3 + \ln x$

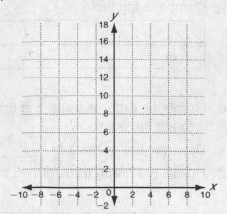

_____

Write each transformed function.

5. The function $f(x) = \log (x + 1)$ is reflected across the y-axis
   and translated down 4 units.

   _____

6. The function $f(x) = -8^{x-3}$ is reflected across the x-axis,
   compressed horizontally by a factor of 0.2, and stretched
   vertically by a factor of 2.

   _____

Solve.

7. The function $A(t) = Pe^{rt}$ can be used to calculate the growth of an investment
   in which the interest is compounded continuously at an annual rate, r, over
   t years. What annual rate would double an investment in 8 years?

_____

Holt Algebra 2

LESSON 7-7

Practice C

Transforming Exponential and Logarithmic Functions

Graph each function. Find the asymptote. Tell how the graph is transformed from the graph of the parent function.

1. $f(x) = 3^{2x}$

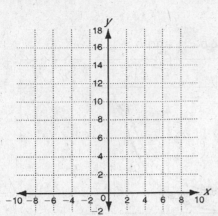

2. $f(x) = -\ln x$

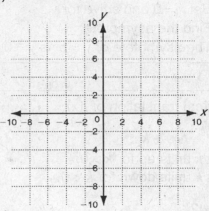

_____   _____

Write each transformed function.

3. The function $f(x) = -9^{(x+4)}$ is translated 4 units right and
   1 unit down, and vertically stretched by a factor of 7.   _____

4. The function $f(x) = 3 \ln (2x + 8)$ is horizontally stretched by
   a factor of 3, translated 7 units up, and reflected
   across the x-axis.   _____

5. The function $f(x) = -\log (5 - x) - 2$ is translated 6 units left,
   horizontally compressed by a factor of $\frac{1}{3}$, and reflected
   across the y-axis.   _____

6. The function $f(x) = 8 \cdot 7^{2x} - 5$ is horizontally stretched by
   a factor of 2, vertically compressed by a factor of 0.5,
   translated 1 unit right, and reflected across the x-axis.   _____

7. What transformations does the function $f(x) = -\ln (x + 1) - 2$
   undergo to become the function $g(x) = \ln (x - 1)$?

_____

Solve.

8. The function $A(t) = Pe^{rt}$ can be used to calculate the growth of an investment
   where the interest is compounded continuously at an annual rate, r, over t years.
   How much should the Blakes deposit at 3.95% if they want to have $50,000
   in 15 years?

_____

Holt Algebra 2

LESSON
7-7

Reteach

Transforming Exponential and Logarithmic Functions

You can transform exponential functions just like polynomial functions.

To graph the transformations:

- Find the *y*-intercept.
  Set $x = 0$ and solve for *y*.
- Find the asymptote.
  The asymptote of $y = b^x$ is $y = 0$ (or the *x*-axis) for $0 < b < 1$ and $b > 1$.

Translations

Vertical translation of $f(x)$ $f(x) + k$ Shift *k* units up for $k > 0$. Shift *k* units down for $k < 0$. $f(x) = 2^x$ $g(x) = 2^x - 1$ *Think*: $k = -1$ *y*-intercept: $y = 2^0 - 1 = 1 - 1 = 0$ Asymptote shifts down 1 unit: $y = -1$	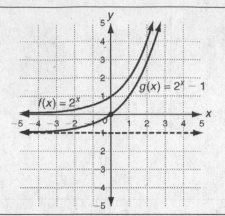
Horizontal translation of $f(x)$ $f(x - h)$ Shift *h* units right for $h > 0$. Shift *h* units left for $h < 0$. $f(x) = 2^x$ $g(x) = 2^{(x-1)}$ *Think*: $h = 1$ *y*-intercept: $y = 2^{0-1} = 2^{-1} = \dfrac{1}{2}$ Asymptote does not shift: $y = 0$	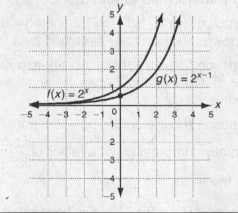

Find the *y*-intercept and asymptote for each function. Then graph
each function and $f(x) = 2^x$ on the same plane.

1. $g(x) = 2^x + 2$

   y-intercept: _____ asymptote: $y = 2$

   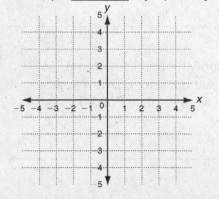

2. $g(x) = 2^{x+2}$

   y-intercept: _____ asymptote: _____

   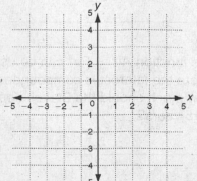

    Holt Algebra 2

LESSON 7-7

Reteach

Transforming Exponential and Logarithmic Functions (continued)

Transformations of logarithmic functions are like transformations of exponential and polynomial functions. Remember to find the asymptote to graph the transformation.

The asymptote of $y = \ln x$ is $x = 0$ (or the y-axis).

Translations	
Vertical translation of $f(x)$ $\qquad f(x) + k$ Shift k units up for $k > 0$. Shift k units down for $k < 0$. $f(x) = \ln x$ $g(x) = \ln x + 1$ $\qquad$ *Think: k = 1* Asymptote does not shift: $x = 0$. $\ln 1 = 0$, so $(1, 1)$ lies on the graph.	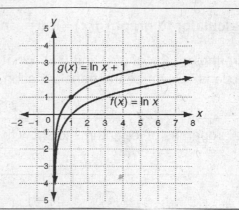
Horizontal translation of $f(x)$ $\qquad f(x - h)$ Shift h units right for $h > 0$. Shift h units left for $h < 0$. $f(x) = \ln x$ $g(x) = \ln(x + 1)$ *Think: h = −1* Asymptote shifts left 1 unit: $x = -1$. When $x = 0$, $y = 0$. So, $(0, 0)$ lies on the graph.	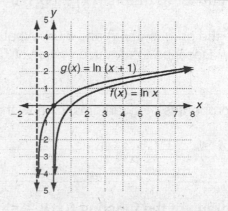

Find the asymptote for each function. Then graph each function and $f(x) = \ln x$ on the same plane.

3. $g(x) = \ln x - 2$

Asymptote: _____

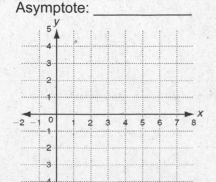

4. $g(x) = \ln(x - 1)$

Asymptote: _____

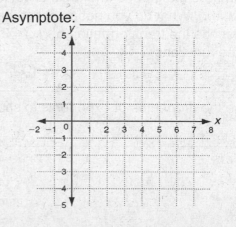

LESSON
7-7

Challenge
Functions That Look Alike

Transformations of exponential and logarithmic functions
may appear in several forms due to the properties of
exponents and logarithms. In other words, functions that have
equations that look different may produce equivalent graphs.
Consider the function $f(x) = \log x$ shown at right.

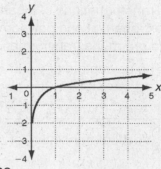

Use your calculator to graph $g(x) = \log \dfrac{1}{x}$ and $h(x) = -\log x$.

1. Compare the graphs of $g(x)$ and $h(x)$. What do you notice about the
   two functions? Describe the transformation of $f(x) = \log x$ to $g(x)$ and $h(x)$.

   _____

2. Use the properties of logarithms to show that $g(x)$ and $h(x)$ are equivalent.

   _____

Use your calculator to graph $j(x) = \log(100\sqrt{x})$ and $k(x) = \dfrac{\log x}{2} + 2$.

3. Compare the graphs of $j(x)$ and $k(x)$. What do you notice about the two
   functions? Describe the transformation of $f(x) = \log x$ to $j(x)$ and $k(x)$.

   _____

4. Use the properties of logarithms to show that $j(x)$ and $k(x)$ are equivalent.

   _____

   _____

Look at the graph of the function $f(x) = 2^x$ shown at right.

Use your calculator to graph $g(x) = 2^{2x-3}$, $h(x) = 4^{x-1.5}$,

and $k(x) = \dfrac{4^x}{8}$.

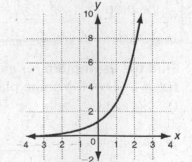

5. Compare the graphs and table of values for $g(x)$, $h(x)$,
   and $k(x)$. What do you notice about the three functions?
   Describe the transformation of $f(x) = 2^x$ to each of these
   three functions.

   _____

6. Use the properties of exponents to show that $g(x)$, $h(x)$, and $k(x)$ are equivalent.

   _____

   _____

Holt Algebra 2

LESSON 7-7

Problem Solving

Transforming Exponential and Logarithmic Functions

Alex is studying a new species of hybrid plant. The average height of the plant can be modeled by the function $h(t) = 2 \ln (t + 1.25)$, where h is the height in feet and t is the number of weeks after planting.

1. Alex graphs the function to see the rate an average plant grows.

   a. About how tall can he expect the plant to be after 3 weeks?

   _____

   b. What is the y-intercept? What does it tell Alex about the plant?

   _____

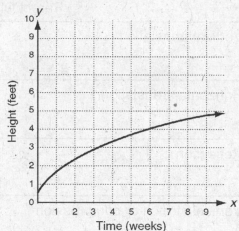

2. Alex plants seeds and finds that the height is now modeled by the parent function.

   a. Give the parent function $g(t)$. _____

   b. Describe how the function $h(t)$ is transformed from the parent function.

   _____

   c. Choose the letter of the graph that represents the parent function.

   _____

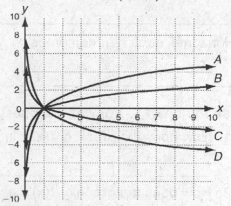

Alex experiments with different fertilizers and finds that he can change the growth curve of the hybrid plant. Choose the letter for the best answer.

3. Alex finds that the height of the plants can now be modeled by the function $f(t) = 1.5 \ln (t + 1) + 0.4$. Which statement describes the transformation from the parent function?

   A Translation 0.4 unit up and 1 unit left; vertical stretch by 1.5

   B Translation 1 unit up and 0.4 unit right; vertical stretch by 1.5

   C Translation 0.4 unit down and 1 unit left; horizontal stretch by 1.5

   D Translation 1 unit down and 0.4 unit right; horizontal stretch by 1.5

4. Alex looks at the graph of the growth of his plants after trying a different fertilizer. The graph is transformed from the parent function by a vertical compression by a factor of 0.5 and a translation 1 unit right. Which function describes this transformation?

   F $k(t) = 2 \ln (t + 1)$

   G $k(t) = 2 \ln (t - 1)$

   H $k(t) = 0.5 \ln (t - 1)$

   J $k(t) = 0.5 \ln (t + 1)$

Holt Algebra 2

Reading Strategies
Read a Table

Exponential and logarithmic functions as well as linear, quadratic, and polynomial functions can all undergo the same types of transformations.

Parent function: $f(x)$

Vertical translation	$f(x) + k$	$k > 0$ up
		$k < 0$ down
Horizontal translation	$f(x - h)$	$h > 0$ right
		$h < 0$ left
Reflection	$-f(x)$	across x-axis
	$f(-x)$	across y-axis
Vertical stretch or compression	$af(x)$	$a > 1$ stretch
		$0 < a < 1$ compression
Horizontal stretch or compression	$f\left(\dfrac{1}{b}x\right)$	$b > 1$ stretch
		$0 < b < 1$ compression

Use the chart to answer the questions below.

1. How does the graph of $f(x) = \ln x$ compare to the graph of $g(x) = \ln x - 4$?

_____

2. How does the graph of $f(x) = e^x$ compare to the graph of $g(x) = e^{(x - 5)}$?

_____

3. Describe the transformation of $g(x) = 8\, e^x$ from the parent function.

_____

4. How does the graph of $g(x) = -\ln x$ compare to the graph of $f(x) = \ln x$?

_____

5. Write the transformed function, $g(x)$, if $f(x) = \ln x$ is translated 7 units left. _____

6. Write the transformed function, $g(x)$, if $f(x) = e^x$ is reflected over the y-axis. _____

7. Write the transformed function, $g(x)$, if $f(x) = \log x$ is horizontally compressed by a factor of $\dfrac{1}{6}$. _____

Holt Algebra 2

LESSON 7-8 Practice A

Curve Fitting with Exponential and Logarithmic Models

Is *f* an exponential function of *x*? If so, find the constant ratio.

1.

x	−1	0	1	2	3	4
f(x)	2.75	3	4	8	24	88

a. Find the first differences. _____

b. Find the ratios between consecutive first differences.

_____

c. Is the ratio constant? If so, identify the ratio. _____

d. Does the data set represent an exponential function? _____

2.

x	−1	0	1	2	3
f(x)	$\frac{4}{5}$	1	2	7	32

_____

3.

x	−1	0	1	2	3
f(x)	$\frac{1}{6}$	1	6	12	18

_____

Use exponential regression to find a function that models the data.

4.

x	−1	0	1	2	3
f(x)	48	24	12	6	3

a. Enter the data into two lists in your graphing calculator.
   Use the exponential regression feature and write
   the constants *a* and *b*. _____

b. Write the function in the form $f(x) = ab^x$. _____

c. Graph the data and your function to verify that the function fits the data.

5. Use the data from Exercise 1.

a. Enter the data into two lists in your graphing calculator.
   Use the exponential regression feature and write
   the constants *a* and *b*. _____

b. Write the function in the form $f(x) = ab^x$. _____

Holt Algebra 2

LESSON 7-8 Practice B
Curve Fitting with Exponential and Logarithmic Models

Determine whether f is an exponential function of x. If so, find the constant ratio.

1.

x	−1	0	1	2	3
f(x)	9	3	1	0.3	0.9

2.

x	−1	0	1	2	3
f(x)	0.01	0.03	0.15	0.87	5.19

_____

_____

3.

x	−1	0	1	2	3
f(x)	$\frac{5}{6}$	$\frac{5}{2}$	7.5	22.5	67.5

4.

x	−1	0	1	2	3
f(x)	1	0.5	0.33	0.25	0.2

_____

_____

Use exponential regression to find a function that models the data.

5.

x	1	2	3	4	5
f(x)	14	7.1	3.4	1.8	0.8

6.

x	2	12	22	32	42
f(x)	5	20	80	320	1280

_____

_____

Solve.

7. a. Bernice is selling seashells she has found at the beach. The price of each shell depends on its length. Find an exponential model for the data.

Length of Shell (cm)	5	8	12	20	25
Price ($)	2	3.5	5	18	40

_____

b. What is the length of a shell selling for $9.00? _____

c. If Bernice found a 40 cm Conch shell. How much could she sell it for? _____

8. a. Use logarithmic regression to find a function that models this data.

Time (min)	1	2	3	4	5
Speed (m/s)	1.5	6.2	10.6	12.9	14.8

_____

b. When will the speed exceed 20 m/s? _____

c. What will the speed be after 1 hour? _____

Holt Algebra 2

LESSON 7-8

Practice C
Curve Fitting with Exponential and Logarithmic Models

Determine whether f is an exponential function of x. If so, find the constant ratio.

1.

x	−1	0	1	2	3
f(x)	3.28	8.4	14.8	22.8	32.8

_____

2.

x	−1	0	1	2	3
f(x)	3.5	7	14	21	28

_____

3.

x	−1	0	1	2	3
f(x)	$\frac{8}{3}$	4	6	9	$\frac{27}{2}$

_____

4.

x	−1	0	1	2	3
f(x)	$\frac{243}{4}$	$\frac{81}{2}$	27	18	12

_____

Use exponential regression to find a function that models the data.

5.

x	1	2	3	4	5
f(x)	9.3	21.8	50.8	118.6	276.6

_____

6.

x	2	4	6	8	10
f(x)	413.2	45.5	4.9	0.6	0.1

_____

Use logarithmic regression to find a function that models the data.

7.

x	1	2	3	4	5
f(x)	−4	−3.7	−3.5	−3.3	−3.2

_____

8.

x	2	4	6	8	10
f(x)	1.5	1	0.7	0.5	0.4

_____

Solve.

9. a. Use exponential regression to find a function that models this data.

Time (min)	1	3	6	8	10
Bacteria	413	575	945	1316	1832

_____

   b. When will the number of bacteria reach 2500? _____

   c. How many bacteria will exist after 1 hour? _____

LESSON
7-8

Reteach

Curve Fitting with Exponential and Logarithmic Models

To use finite differences to determine if a function is exponential:

- check that the *x*-values increase by a constant value.
- find successive differences of the *y*-values.
- check the *ratios* of the first differences. If the ratios are constant, the data is exponential.

> The *x*-values increase by 1.

Data Set 1

x	−1	0	1	2	3
y	2.2	3	7	27	127
First Difference	$3 - 2.2$ 0.8	$7 - 3$ 4	$27 - 7$ 20	$127 - 27$ 100	

> The first differences seem to increase by a constant factor.

Check the ratios of the first differences.

$$\frac{4}{0.8} = 5 \qquad \frac{20}{4} = 5 \qquad \frac{100}{20} = 5$$

The data set is exponential, with a constant ratio of 5.

Data Set 2

x	−1	0	1	2	3
y	−4	−1	2	5	8
First Difference	$-1 - (-4)$ 3	$2 - (-1)$ 3	$5 - 2$ 3	$8 - 5$ 3	

> The *x*-values increase by 1.

First differences are constant. The data set is linear, not exponential.

For each data set, determine whether *y* is an exponential function of *x*. If so, find the constant ratio.

1.

x	−1	0	1	2	3
y	0.375	1.5	6	24	96

2.

x	−1	0	1	2	3
y	9	17	41	113	329

First differences:

First differences:

1.125, 4.5, _____

_____

Ratios:

Ratios:

_____

_____

_____

_____

LESSON
7-8

Reteach

Curve Fitting with Exponential and Logarithmic Models (continued)

You can use the exponential regression feature on a graphing calculator to model exponential data.

The data in the table below can be modeled by an exponential function. When will the number of bacteria reach 3700?

Time, t (min)	0	1	2	3	4	5
Bacteria, $B(t)$	120	205	369	640	1132	1972

Step 1 Enter the data into two lists.

Enter the time data into L_1 and the number of bacteria into L_2.

Step 2 Use the exponential regression feature.

Look for **ExpReg** in the STAT CALC menu.

> Select ExpReg [ENTER].
> Then enter the lists: L_1, L_2 [ENTER].

Exp Reg

$y = a* b^x$

$a = 118.902912$

$b = 1.754348983$

$r^2 = .9999104934$

$r = .9999552457$

> The calculator displays the constants a and b for the exponential equation: $y = ab^x$.

The number of bacteria $B(t)$ at time t is modeled by:

$B(t) \approx 118.9\,(1.75)^t$.

Step 3 Graph the data and the function model.

Enter $118.9\,(1.75)^t$ as Y1.

Enter 3700 as Y2.

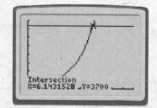

Use the intersection feature to find x when Y1 = 3700: $x \approx 6.1432$.

The number of bacteria will reach 3700 in about 6.14 minutes.

Solve.

3. a. Use exponential regression to find a function that models this data.

Time, t (min)	0	1	2	3	4	5
Bacteria, $B(t)$	250	360	485	686	964	1348

$B(t) \approx$ _____

b. When will the number of bacteria reach 1800?

_____

Holt Algebra 2

Challenge

Fitting the Prediction

According to the CTIA Semi-Annual Wireless Survey, the number of wireless
telephone customers has been growing since its founding in 1985.

Estimated Wireless Subscribers								
Years Since 1984	3	5	7	9	11	13	15	17
Subscribers (millions)	1.23	3.51	7.56	16.01	33.76	55.31	86.05	128.37

1. Plot the data in the table. Which is the independent
   and which is the dependent variable? Which model,
   exponential or logarithmic, would best fit the data?

   _____

   _____

   _____

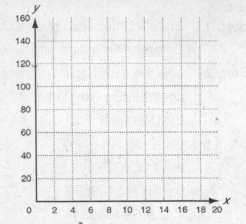

2. Use your calculator to fit an appropriate regression
   curve to this set of data. Are the data highly
   correlated? How do you know?

   _____

3. Use your model to make a prediction about the number of wireless
   subscribers in 1998. The estimated number of wireless subscribers in 1998
   was 69,209,321. How does your prediction compare?

   _____

4. Use your model to make a prediction about the number of wireless
   subscribers in 2000. The estimated number of wireless subscribers in 2000
   was 109,478,031. How does your prediction compare?

   _____

A common problem in regression analysis involves using data to make
predictions outside the realm of the data. This process is called extrapolation
and is not recommended. For instance, to use your regression equation to
make predictions far in the future would be questionable. Without supporting
evidence, the trend observed may or may not continue into the future.

5. Use your model to make a prediction about the number of wireless subscribers
   in the year 2004. The estimated number of subscribers was 182,140,362.
   How does your prediction compare?

   _____

6. Graph your model equation on top of the scatter plot of the data.
   Comment on the position of your 2004 prediction.

   _____

Problem Solving
LESSON 7-8

Curve Fitting with Exponential and Logarithmic Models

Solve.

1. A small group of farmers joined together to grow and sell wheat in 1985. The table shows how their production of wheat increased over 20 years.

Wheat Produced by Growers Co-op						
Years After 1985	3	6	10	13	16	20
Wheat (tons)	70	105	150	210	340	580

a. Find an exponential model for the data. _____

b. Use the model to predict when their wheat production will exceed 2000 tons. _____

2. The table shows the U.S. production of tobacco from 1997 to 2002.

Tobacco Production						
Years After 1996	1	2	3	4	5	6
Tobacco (× 100,000 pounds)	1787	1480	1293	1053	992	890

a. Find a logarithmic model for the data. _____

b. Use the model to predict when tobacco production could fall below 50,000,000 pounds. _____

Robert recently discovered a forgotten student loan bill. The amount due after 10 years is now $10,819.33. He found some old statements and determined that after 7 years the bill was $8831.80 and after 5 years he owed $7714.03. Choose the letter for the best answer.

3. Which function models the data?

A $S(x) = 5000(1.07)^x$

B $S(x) = 1.07(5000)^x$

C $S(x) = 5500(1.07)^x$

D $S(x) = 1.07(5500)^x$

4. How much did Robert borrow initially?

F $5750

G $5500

H $5250

J $5000

5. Robert is planning to pay the loan in full next year. How much will he owe then?

A $12,092.14

B $11,925.07

C $11,869.33

D $11,576.69

6. What is the interest rate on Robert's student loan?

F 7%

G 6%

H 5%

J 4%

Holt Algebra 2

Reading Strategies

LESSON 7-8

Compare and Contrast

Like an exponential function, a linear function can either increase or
decrease. But exponential functions grow (or decay) extremely quickly. The
tables below compare a linear and an exponential function.

You can also identify what type of curve or function best fits a data set by
looking at how the data change.

Linear Function: $f(x) = 2x$

x	−1	0	1	2	3	4
f(x)	4	6	8	10	12	14

In a linear function, the first differences
between y-values are constant.

Exponential Function: $g(x) = 2^x$

x	−1	0	1	2	3	4
g(x)	0.5	1	2	4	8	16

In an exponential function, the ratios between
two consecutive y-values or between
consecutive first differences are constant.

Use the data sets above for Exercises 1–3.

1. a. Find the first differences for the y-values
   of the linear function.

   _____

   b. How do you know these data represent a
   linear function?

   _____

2. a. Find the first differences for the y-values
   of the exponential function.

   _____

   b. Find the ratios between consecutive first
   differences.

   _____

   c. How do you know these data represent
   an exponential function?

   _____

3. Compare the graphs of $f(x)$ and $g(x)$. How are they different?

   _____

   _____

x	−1	0	1	2
f(x)	$\frac{4}{3}$	1	$\frac{3}{4}$	$\frac{9}{16}$

4. Can the data set above be modeled by an exponential function or a linear
   function? How do you know?

   _____

Holt Algebra 2

Answer Key

Practice A

1. a. 5.29; 0.75

   b. –2.6, 0.75, $1.\overline{8}$, 5.29

   c. –2.6, $\dfrac{3}{4}$, $1.\overline{8}$, $2\sqrt{7}$

2. $\dfrac{2}{11}$, $\dfrac{9}{7}$, 2.8, $\sqrt{10}$

3. –5.916, $-\sqrt{2}$, $\dfrac{-6}{11}$, $\dfrac{1}{8}$

4. $\dfrac{-7}{5}$, $\dfrac{-\pi}{4}$, $3.\overline{14}$, $\sqrt{23}$

5. –6.5, $-6\dfrac{1}{8}$, π, 6.159

6. Real, rational   7. Real, rational

8. Real, rational, integer

9. $\{x \mid -6 < x \le -4\}$

10. All real numbers between 4 and 6 including 4 but not including 6

11. $[10, \infty)$

12. $\{-5, -3, -1, 1, 3, 5\}$

Practice B

1. $-4.9, -3\dfrac{1}{8}, \dfrac{2}{3}, \sqrt{28}, 6.1\overline{7}; -4.9, -3\dfrac{1}{8}, \dfrac{2}{3}$,

   and $6.1\overline{7}$ are rational numbers, and $\sqrt{28}$ is an irrational number.

2. $-6\sqrt{3}, \dfrac{-8}{3}, 0, 4.\overline{615}, 5\pi$; 0 is a whole

   number and an integer; 0, $\dfrac{-8}{3}$, and

   $4.\overline{615}$ are rational numbers; 5π and $-6\sqrt{3}$ are irrational numbers.

3. $\{x \mid x = -3n$ and n is a natural number$\}$

4. All real numbers between –4 and 0 and between 10 and 21 including –4 but excluding 0, 10, and 21

5. $\{-3, 1, 5\}$

6. $\{x \mid x \le -1$ or $2 < x < 5\}$

7. $\{52, 53, 54, 55, 56, 57, 58\}$

8. $\{x \mid 2.75 \le x \le 3.5\}$

Practice C

1. 1.68, $2\dfrac{1}{100}$, 2.16, $3\dfrac{7}{40}$, 3.86, $4\dfrac{2}{5}$

2. Rational numbers

3. Possible answer: There is no pattern to the numbers so they cannot be described in set-builder notation.

4. Possible answer: 1, 5

5. Irrational numbers, integers, whole numbers, and natural numbers

6. False; possible answer: π

7. False; possible answer: 3.3

8. $(-\infty, -5)$, $[-2, 1]$, and $[4, \infty)$

9. Possible answer: –7 and $\sqrt{2}$

Reteach

1. $-1.\overline{9}, -0.456, \sqrt{3}, 2\dfrac{2}{3}, \pi$

2. 0.2; –2.24; $-\sqrt{5}, -1.75, \dfrac{1}{5}, 1, 1.55$

3. 2.45; 3.46; –0.17;

   $-4.36, -2.\overline{63}, -\dfrac{1}{6}, \sqrt{6}, 2\sqrt{3}$

4. –1, 0, 1, 2, 3, …

5. Whole number multiples of 4

6. –5, 12]   7. , 0)

8. $\{-1 < x \le 6\}$

Challenge

1. 2   2. 4

3. 8   4. 16

5. For each additional element in the set, the number of subsets doubles.

6. 256; Possible answer: I kept doubling the number of subsets from 4 elements to 8 elements.

7. 2^n 8. 1

9. 5   10. 10

Holt Algebra 2

11. 10

12. 5

13. 1

14. Pascal's Triangle

Problem Solving

1. 0.09; $\frac{9}{50}$; $1\frac{3}{10}$; 8.9; 900; 1030

2. roster notation; cannot be written in interval or set-builder notation

3. $\mathbb{Q}$

4. D

5. H

6. True; number of people must be a whole number and all whole numbers are integers.

7. False; possible answer: $C = \pi(5)$

Reading Strategies

1. x is greater than or equal to -3.

2. x is between -6 and 4.

3. x is less than or equal to -1.

4. x is any real number except 0.

5. x is any number from -10 to -5 or x is greater than or equal to -2.

LESSON 1-2

Practice A

1. 5

2. -6.1

3. $-\frac{1}{2}$

4. $\frac{1}{11}$

5. $\frac{2}{7}$

6. $-\frac{3}{2}$

7. 2

8. -4

9. Commutative

10. Distributive

11. Associative

12. Additive Inverse

13. $16.70

14. $43.40

15. $18.80

16. $40.20

17. Sometimes; if $a = b = c$

18. Always; Associative Property

19. Never; Additive Inverse Property

Practice B

1. 6; $\frac{-1}{6}$

2. $-3\frac{1}{4}$; $\frac{4}{13}$

3. 0.7; $\frac{-10}{7}$

4. Distributive

5. Commutative

6. Associative

7. Multiplicative Inverse

8. $7.50

9. $103.84

10. Always; Additive Inverse

11. Never; $1 + (2 \cdot 3) \neq (1 + 2) \cdot (1 + 3)$

12. $2(\$2.89) + 3(\$1.79) = \$11.15$

13. $5(\$1.79) + \$3.19 = \$12.14$

14. $3(1.79 - 0.36) + (3.19 - 0.80) + 2(2.89) = \$12.46$

Practice C

1. y; x; Commutative

2. 0; Additive Identity

3. t; s; Distributive

4. $\frac{1}{m}$; Multiplicative Inverse

5. Distributive

6. Multiplicative Identity and Associative

7. 2 more times

8. $19.49 (0.7) = \$13.64$

9. Possible answer: 10% of $25.59 is $2.56. Half of that, or 5% of $25.59, is $1.28. Add $25.59, $2.56, and $1.28 to find the total cost of $29.43.

10. Possible answer: 40% off $10.00 is $10 − 0.4($10) = $6.00. 15% off $10.00 is $10 − 0.15($10) = $8.50; 25% off $8.50 is $8.50 − 0.25($8.50) = $6.38. $6.00 ≠ $6.38; 40% off is a greater discount.

Reteach

1. -20

2. 36

3. 7.9

4. $-\frac{2}{3}$

5. $-\sqrt{3}$

6. $\frac{3}{4}$

7. Additive Identity

8. Associative Property

9. Commutative Property

10. Additive Inverse

11. Commutative

12. Additive Identity

13. $\dfrac{1}{25}$

14. $-\dfrac{5}{3}$

15. –8

16. 3

17. $-\dfrac{1}{4}$

18. $\dfrac{1}{\pi}$

19. Distributive Property

20. Commutative Property

21. Associative Property

Challenge

1. No, $1 + 1 = 2$ and 2 is not in set A; yes, multiplication table contains only 0 and 1.

2. Yes, 0, any number $+ 0 =$ itself; yes, 1, any number $\times 1 =$ itself.

3. Yes, the only values in the table are a, b, and c.

4. Yes; identity $= b$, anything § $b =$ itself

5. Yes; table is symmetric about the diagonal.

6. a § $c = b$; b § $b = b$; c § $a = b$

Problem Solving

1. $5.75

2. $0.68

3. $1.11

4. Possible answer: Take 10% of the subtotal, which is $1.95. Then double it to get 20%, $3.90.

5. A

6. H

7. C

8. G

Reading Strategies

1. Always true; possible answer: Additive Inverse Property

2. Sometimes true; possible answer: true: $a = b$; false: $a \neq b$

3. Never true; possible answer: the multiplicative identity is 1 and $a \neq 1$.

4. Sometimes true; possible answer: true: $a = c$, $a \neq 0$, $c \neq 0$; false: $a \neq c$

LESSON 1-3

Practice A

1. 36; 49

2. 100; 121

3. 7

4. 10

5. 12

6. 6.5

7. 8.7

8. 9.5

9. $4\sqrt{3}$

10. $5\sqrt{3}$

11. –24

12. $3\sqrt{5}$

13. $6\sqrt{2}$

14. $10\sqrt{2}$

15. 6

16. 8

17. $\dfrac{-8\sqrt{2}}{3}$

18. $7\sqrt{5}$

19. $6 - 2\sqrt{2}$

20. $4\sqrt{15n}$

Practice B

1. 8.8

2. –7.5

3. 6.2

4. $9\sqrt{3}$

5. $\dfrac{3}{2}$

6. $3\sqrt{14}$

7. $-\dfrac{1}{3}$

8. 5

9. $-8\sqrt{5}$

10. $6\dfrac{\sqrt{5}}{5}$

11. $-3\sqrt{5}$

12. $\dfrac{\sqrt{78}}{24}$

13. $-3\sqrt{5}$

14. $18\sqrt{3}$

15. $-14\sqrt{2}$

16. 120 ft

Practice C

1. 170.8 m

2. 199.8 ft

3. 242.7 in.

4. $\dfrac{\sqrt{15}}{2}$; 2

5. $\dfrac{26}{5}$; –5

6. $-84\sqrt{165}$; –1079

7. $\dfrac{3\sqrt{11}}{11}$; 1

8. $\dfrac{-9\sqrt{10}}{2}$; –14

9. $\dfrac{-5}{6}$; –1

10. 78 ft

Reteach

1. $\sqrt{5}$; $2\sqrt{5}$

2. 7; $\sqrt{7}$; $3\sqrt{7}$

Holt Algebra 2

3. 5; $\sqrt{5}$; $4\sqrt{5}$

4. 3; 12; $\sqrt{36}$; 6

5. 64; 25; $\dfrac{8}{5}$

6. 200; 8; $\sqrt{25}$; 5

7. $\sqrt{144}$; 12

8. $\sqrt{64}$; 8

9. $\dfrac{\sqrt{49}}{\sqrt{100}}$; $\dfrac{7}{10}$

10. $\dfrac{4\sqrt{5}}{5}$

11. $\dfrac{\sqrt{6}}{\sqrt{6}}$; $\dfrac{\sqrt{6}}{\sqrt{6}}$

12. $\dfrac{3\sqrt{16}}{\sqrt{8}}$; $\dfrac{12}{8} = \dfrac{3}{2}$

13. $8\sqrt{7}$

14. $2\sqrt{3}$

15. $3\sqrt{5}$; $9\sqrt{5}$

Challenge

1. $\dfrac{s\sqrt{3}}{2}$ units

2. $\dfrac{s^2\sqrt{3}}{4}$ square units

3. $\dfrac{81\sqrt{3}}{4}$ square units

4. 3 units

5. $\dfrac{108\sqrt{3}}{4}$ square units

6. 1 unit

7. $\dfrac{120\sqrt{3}}{4}$ square units

8. $3\sqrt{3}$ units

Problem Solving

1. 6 yd

2. The side length of the smallest fountain is $\dfrac{1}{2}$ the side length of the largest fountain.

3. 9 yd

4. A

5. H

6. C

7. J

Reading Strategies

1. 1, 4, 9, 16, 25, 36, 49, 64, 81, 100

2. Possible answer: 100 is a factor of 500 and $500 = 100 \cdot 5$, so $\sqrt{500} = \sqrt{100} \cdot \sqrt{5} = 10\sqrt{5}$

3. Multiply the factors to look for a perfect square; $\sqrt{75} \cdot \sqrt{3} = \sqrt{225} = \sqrt{15}$.

4. Write the expression as the square root of the quotient. Then divide under the square root; $\dfrac{\sqrt{48}}{\sqrt{16}} = \sqrt{\dfrac{48}{16}} = \sqrt{3}$

LESSON 1-4

Practice A

1. $g + 7$

2. $2w - 10$

3. $3m$

4. 7

5. 11

6. -4

7. 12

8. $15 + 7y$

9. $2s + 13t$

10. $11a - 5ab$

11. $10v - 12 + 7w$

12. $8x - 3y$

13. $-9fg + 3g - 4f$

14. $8x - 6y$

15. $21c + 5d - 6cd$

16. $28j - 3k$

17. $3h + 2k$

Practice B

1. $90 - w$

2. $12d$

3. -62

4. -1

5. $2r + 2t$

6. $-7a - 13b$

7. -14

8. 28

9. a. $0.15(5s)$

   b. $37.50

   c. $0.15(260s)$

10. a. $500 - 10m$

    b. $500 - 8m$

Practice C

1.

x	$(x-9)^2$	$x^2 - 81$	$x^2 - 18x + 81$
22	121	-77	121
21	100	-80	100
1	64	-80	64
2	49	-77	49

2. $3x^2 + 6x - 1$

3. $4a^2 + 8a + 36b$

4. a. $5 + 0.75c$

   b. $5 + 0.75c + 1.25d$ c. $148.75

Reteach

1. $3(5)$; $2(5)(4) - 3(5)$; $25 + 40 - 15$; 50
2. $7^2 - 7(6) + 3(6)$; $49 - 7(6) + 3(6)$; $49 - 42 + 18$; 25
3. $\dfrac{(5(4) - 2^3)}{3(2)}$; $\dfrac{(5(4) - 8)}{3(2)}$; $\dfrac{(20 - 8)}{3(2)}$; $\dfrac{12}{3(2)}$; $\dfrac{12}{6}$; 2
4. $-6x - 2x + 4x + 3$; $-4x + 3$
5. $4c^2 + cd - c^2 + cd$; $4c^2 - c^2 + cd + cd$; $3c^2 + 2cd$
6. $3ab - 7$
7. $6s - 13t$

Challenge

1. b
2. a
3. c
4. a
5. § yes, Ω no; Ω table not symmetric about the diagonal
6. No; because Ω is not commutative

Problem Solving

1. $\dfrac{t}{6}$
2. 10 c
3. 96 min or 1.6 h
4. $240d$ cups or $15d$ gallons
5. A
6. H
7. B
8. J

Reading Strategies

1. Substitute -1 for b and 6 for c.
2. -1
3. g^2, $-3g^2$, and $6g^2$; $-4h^2$ and $8h^2$; $5g^2h$ and $7g^2h$
4. Substitute 2 for m and -5 for n; evaluate exponent; multiply; add and subtract; 64.
5. No; possible answer: he did not simplify the expression correctly. It simplifies to $2a^2 + 2a$. For $a = 4$, the result is 24.

LESSON 1-5

Practice A

1. 4; 4; 4
2. a; a; a; a; a

3. $3d$; $3d$; $3d$; $3d$
4. $\dfrac{x}{7}$; $\dfrac{x}{7}$; $\dfrac{x}{7}$
5. $\dfrac{1}{3}$; $\dfrac{1}{3}$; $\dfrac{1}{3}$; $\dfrac{1}{3}$; $\dfrac{1}{27}$
6. $\dfrac{6}{-5}$; $\dfrac{6}{-5}$; $\dfrac{6}{-5}$; $\dfrac{36}{25}$
7. $3r^5(-3)$; $-9r^5$
8. $(16f^{10}g^2)(2fg^3)$; $(16f^{11}g^5)(2)$; $32f^{11}g^5$
9. $\dfrac{9m^6}{3k^2}$; $\dfrac{3m^6}{k^2}$
10. $\dfrac{16p^5q^4}{2p^2q^3}$; $\dfrac{16p^3q}{2}$; $8p^3q$
11. 8.4×10^5
12. 2.0×10^3
13. 5.0×10^{-4}
14. 2.03×10^3

Practice B

1. $-3 \cdot x \cdot x \cdot x \cdot x \cdot x$
2. $((j - 3k)(j - 3k)(j - 3k)$
3. $7 \cdot t \cdot t \, (-4r)(-4r)(-4r)(-4r)$
4. $\dfrac{-1}{16}$
5. $\dfrac{64}{25}$
6. $\dfrac{-8}{27}$
7. $\dfrac{17f^8}{g^9}$
8. $\dfrac{1}{16a^6b^{14}}$
9. $\dfrac{2n^3}{3}$
10. 3.24×10^{-1}
11. 5.0×10^{-5}
12. 2.184×10^{20}
13. x^3y^3 cubic units
14. 43 million; 79 million; 3.6×10^7
15. 2.68×10^5

Practice C

1. $\dfrac{1}{2}a^5b^4c^4$ cubic units
2. $\dfrac{175p^{13}q^8}{3}$ cubic units
3. $-\dfrac{125x^{16}z^{24}}{y^9}$
4. $-\dfrac{7g^2}{8h^{12}}$
5. $\dfrac{1}{36m^{12}n^{16}}$
6. 1.8×10^{12}
7. 5.3×10^7 ft^3
8. 1.0×10^{18}

Holt Algebra 2

Reteach

1. $c \cdot c$

2. $(3xy)(3xy)(3xy)(3xy)$

3. $a \cdot a \cdot a(b - c)(b - c)$

4. $\dfrac{1}{6}$ 5. 1

6. $\dfrac{1}{144}$ 7. $-\dfrac{1}{64}$

•8. 49 9. $\dfrac{64}{27}$

10. -1 11. $\dfrac{4}{25}$

12. -9 13. $25a^2b^6$

14. w^6x^8 15. y^2z^5

16. $\dfrac{2s^2}{t}$ 17. $\dfrac{a^{12}}{b^6}$

18. $\dfrac{-27y^8}{x^3}$

Challenge

1. -125 and -125 2. -16 and 16

3. Possible answer: $-a^n$ is always negative; $(-a^n)$ is negative if n is odd and positive if n is even.

4. True as written

5. $(-3)^2 + 81 - 3^4 - 3^2 = 0$

6. $4x^2 + 36x^4y^4 - (6(x^2y^2))^2 - (2x)^2 = 0$

7. $-(12a)^3 + (2b)^2 + 1728a^3 - 2b^2 - 2b^2 = 0$

8. $(2g^2 + 2h^3 - 4)^0 + 24 = 25$

9. True as written

10. $(-12abc)^0 - 25d^2 + (34ab)^0 + (5d)^2 = 2$

Problem Solving

1. 101 million   2. 1998 to 1999

3. 1995   4. 1995

5. 1994, 1996   6. 36.4

7. B   8. H

Reading Strategies

1. g; 5   2. 6^8

3. $k^u \cdot k^v = k^{u+v}$; $2^2 \cdot 2^4 = 2^6$

4. $h^{-7}, \dfrac{1}{h^7}$ 5. xx^5

6. $-2p^3(3s^3)$

7. $\dfrac{2a^5}{a^2}$ is not simplified because a is a like term; $2a^3$.

8. Use the Negative Exponent and Power of a Quotient Properties: $\left(\dfrac{x}{y}\right)^{-2} = \left(\dfrac{y}{x}\right)^2 = \dfrac{y^2}{x^2}$.

LESSON 1-6

Practice A

1. x 2. y

3. Domain: {Mon, Tue, Wed, Thu, Fri}; Range: {287, 395, 128, 326, 649}

4. Domain: {−2, −1, 0, 1}; Range: {1, −2}

5. This is a function.

6. This is not a function.

7. yes   8. yes

9. no

Practice B

1. Domain: {Jun, Jul, Aug, Sep}; Range: {82°, 88°, 93°}; this is a function.

2. Domain: {−4, −2, 0, 2, 4}; Range: {−3, −2, 4}; this is a function.

3.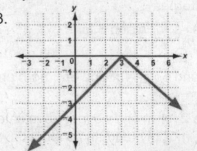

This is a function.

4. This is not a function; (1, 1) (1, −4)

5.

This is a function.

6. Yes, each value of x is associated with only 1 value of y.

7. No, each car model is manufactured as many individual cars.

8. Yes, there is only 1 score associated with each test date.

Practice C

1. Domain: {−2, 1, 3, 6}; Range: {−3 , 4}

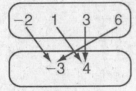

2. Domain: {0, 2, 3}; Range: {−2, −1, 1, 2}

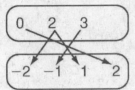

3. Domain: {1, 2, 3, 4};
   Range: {37, 38, 44, 59}

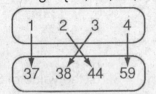

4. Domain: {−2, −1, 0, 1, 2};
   Range: {−3, −2, −1, 0, 2, 3}

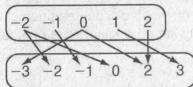

5. not a function; function

6. function; not a function

7. function; not a function

8. not a function; not a function

9. function; not a function

10. not a function; function

Reteach

1. 2002, 2003, 2004, 2005}; 28, 35, 42, 46}

2. −3, −2, −1, 0}; −1, 0, 1, 2}

3. Function

4. Not a function; possible answer: (1, 0), (1, −2)

Challenge

1. V, W, X, Z; Y: (3, 3) does not exist because 3 is not greater than 3.

2. W, Z; V: 10 is a factor of 20, but 20 is not a factor of 10; X: 8 is a multiple of 4 but 4 is not a multiple of 8; Y: 3 > 2 but 2 is not greater than 3.

3. V, W, X, Y, Z   4. W, Z

Problem Solving

1. Yes; each calorie value has only one fat value.

2. Yes; each calorie value has only one carbohydrate value.

3. No; the carbohydrate value 12.2 has two calorie values, 102 and 83.

4. D   5. G

6. B   7. H

Reading Strategies

1. −2, 0, 1, 2; domain is the set of x values.

2. 4, 2, 0, −4, −6; range is the set of y values.

3. Not a function because the x value −2 is repeated

4. The relation is a function because no input values are repeated.

LESSON 1-7

Practice A

1. 3; 15; −6

2. 1; 0; 1

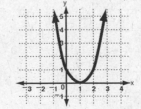

3. −2; −3; −4

4. 1; 3; 4

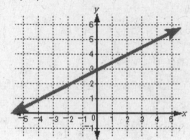

5.

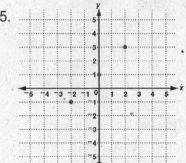

6.

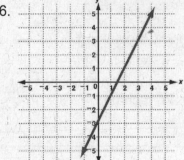

7. $2.30

Calling Card Costs

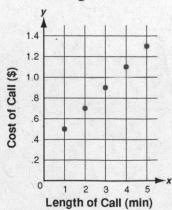

Length of Call (min)

1. 6, 2, −4

.2. −2, −3, $-\dfrac{3}{4}$

3. 2, 0, $8\dfrac{1}{4}$

4. $-\dfrac{3}{4}$ −1, $-\dfrac{1}{4}$

5. 0, −4

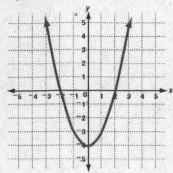

6. 4, 1

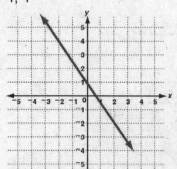

7. $f(c) = \dfrac{0.77c}{1.24}; f(5) = 3.10$; the value of $5 Canadian is equivalent to 3.10 euros.

8. $f(p) = 0.85p - 200$; $f(2500) = 1925$; $1925 is the final, discounted price of a computer with an original price of $2500.

Practice C

1. $8, 5\dfrac{7}{8}, 5.6, 5\dfrac{1}{4}$

2. $-54, -\dfrac{11}{9}, -9, 54$

3. $-2\dfrac{3}{4}, -2, -\dfrac{1}{2} - 2\dfrac{3}{4}$

4. $-1, \dfrac{1}{4}, 1\dfrac{1}{4}, 2$

5. Possible answer: The domain is a positive whole number, x, representing the number of people at a party; the range is a positive whole number, $\dfrac{3x}{8}$, representing the number of pizzas needed.

6. Possible answer: The domain is a positive rational number, m, representing

the number of miles traveled; the range is a positive rational number, $\frac{m}{15}$, representing the time required.

7. $f(a) = 30a$

8. $f(t) = \$1.49(80t)$

Reteach

1. −2; 7; 2

2. 10; 7; 12

3. 0; $\frac{45}{4}$; −5

4.

5.

x	2x − 4	g (x)
0	2(0) − 4	−4
1	2(1) − 4	−2
2	2(2) − 4	0
3	2(3) − 4	2
4	2(4) − 4	4

Challenge

1. *f* takes a number, doubles it, and subtracts 3; *g* squares a number, adds the same number, and subtracts 5.

2. $10x^2 − 3$

3. $4x^2 + 2x − 5$

4. *g*

5. $2x^2 + 2x − 13$

6. $4x^2 − 10x + 1$

7. No

8. 2

9. $2x + h + 1$

Problem Solving

1. Plan A, 100 min; plan B, 0 min

2. Possible answer: For 150 min the two plans cost the same amount.

3. Plan A, $55; plan B, $50

4. Plan B; costs less than plan A for 300 minutes

5. A

6. G

7. C

8. F

Reading Strategies

1. $f(x) = x^3 − x^2$

2. f of x is equal to 5 times x squared plus 4 times x minus 3.

3. Substitute −1 for x in $x^3 + 6x$; $(−1)^3 + 6(−1)$; $f(−1) = −7$

4. Find $x = 2$ on the *x*-axis. Then find the corresponding *y*-value on the graph; $f(2) = 1$.

LESSON 1-8

Practice A

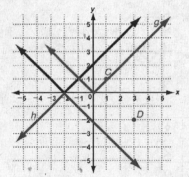

1. (−1, 3)

2. (3, −2)

3. *x*-coordinate

4. *y*-coordinate

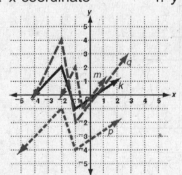

5. *x*-coordinate

6. It is 3 less than the original *y*-coordinate.

7. *y*-coordinate

8. (x, y) becomes (x − 2, y + 4).

9. (x, y) becomes $\left(x, \frac{2}{3}y\right)$.

Practice B

1. (−1, 5)

2. (2, −1)

Holt Algebra 2

3. (6, 7)

4.

x − 1	x	y	y − 5
−4	−3	3	−2
−2	−1	1	−4
0	1	2	−3
1	2	1	−4
2	3	2	−3

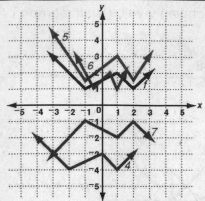

5.

x	y	$\frac{3}{2}y$
−3	3	$\frac{9}{2}$
−1	1	$\frac{3}{2}$
1	2	3
2	1	$\frac{3}{2}$
3	2	3

6.

$\frac{1}{2}x$	x	y
$-\frac{3}{2}$	−3	3
$-\frac{1}{2}$	−1	1
$\frac{1}{2}$	1	2
1	2	1
$\frac{3}{2}$	3	2

7.

x	y	−y
−3	3	−3
−1	1	−1
1	2	−2
2	1	−1
3	2	−2

8. Profits are reduced by 10%; vertical compression; (x, 0.9y).

Practice C

1. Areas are equal.

2. Area is $\frac{1}{2}$ of original trapezoid.

3. Area is doubled.

4. Area is $\frac{1}{2}$ of original trapezoid.

5. Area is $\frac{3}{2}$ of original trapezoid.

6. **Music Rentals**

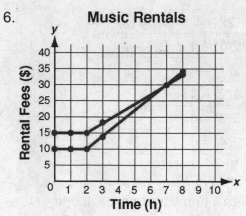

7. Translation

8. Vertical compression

9. Horizontal stretch and translation

Reteach

1.

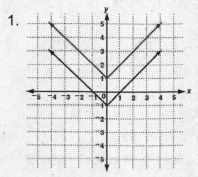

2.

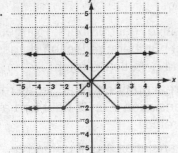

3.

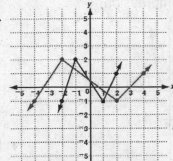

4.

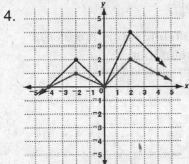

Challenge

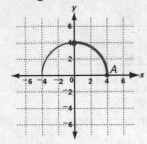

1. (4, –2), (0, –2), (–1, –6), (3, –6)
2. $(x, y) \rightarrow (y, -x)$ 3. $(x, y) \rightarrow (-y, x)$
4. (0, 4), (0, 0), (4, –1), (4, 3)
5. (–4, 0), (0, 0), (1, 4), (–3, 4)
6. (–2, 0), (2, 0), (3, 4), (–1, 4)

Problem Solving

1. $120; $160; $220; $240
2. $40 per hour   3. $20 per hour
4. Translated down 15 units

5. Possible answers: A line would go from (0, 160) to (3, 160) with no open circle; the range would not include any numbers less than 160.

6. He would have to pay more to rent the Art Center.

7. A   8. J

Reading Strategies

1. The shape of the figure does not change, only the position changes.

2. Add 3 to each x-coordinate; y-coordinates do not change.

3. x-coordinates do not change; subtract 5 from each y-coordinate.

4. x-coordinates do not change; multiply each y-coordinate by –1.

5. Subtract 4 from each x-coordinate and add 2 to each y-coordinate.

LESSON 1-9

Practice A

1. Quadratic   2. Cubic
3. Linear
4. Quadratic; translation left
5. Linear; translation down
6. Cubic; reflection across the y-axis
7. Quadratic; translation 2 units up

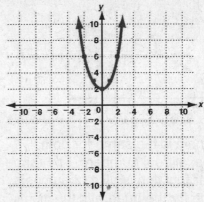

8. Cubic; horizontal stretch by factor of 2

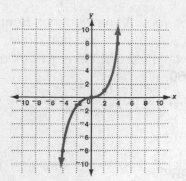

Practice B

1. Square root; translation 4 units left

2. Cubic; translation 4 units right

3. Quadratic; horizontal compression

4. Cubic; translation 1 unit down

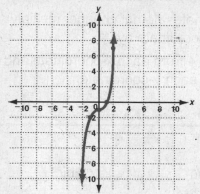

5. Square root; vertical compression

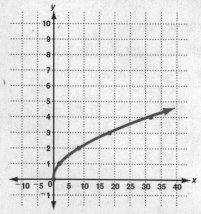

6. The domain is the same for both functions, all real numbers. The range for the linear function is all real numbers, but the range for the quadratic function is all real numbers greater than or equal to 0.

7. The domain and the range for the cubic function are all real numbers. The domain and the range for the square-root function are all real numbers greater than or equal to 0.

Practice C

1. Domain: positive real numbers; Range: negative real numbers; reflection across the x-axis and a vertical stretch

2. Domain: all real numbers; Range: all real numbers; translation 2 units right and a horizontal stretch

3. Quadratic; translation 1 unit up and a horizontal compression

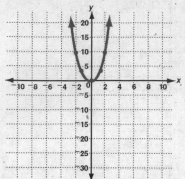

4. Linear; domain and range are all real numbers greater than 0.

Distance Traveled at 55 mi/h

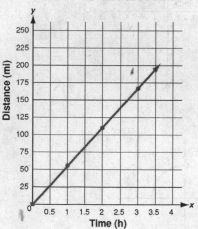

5. Quadratic; domain and range are all real numbers greater than 0.

Surface Area of a Cube

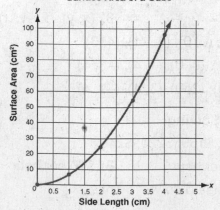

Reteach

1. Quadratic; reflection across x-axis

2. Square root; horizontal translation left 2 units

3. Quadratic function $f(x) = x^2$; vertical shift down 3 units

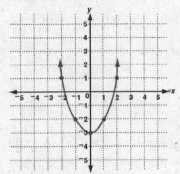

4. Linear function $f(x) = x$; reflection across y-axis

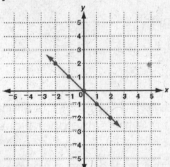

Challenge

1. a. third differences

   b. 3rd degree or cubic

2. a. fourth differences

   b. 4th degree

3. Every set of differences is the same (i.e., 2, 4, 8, 16, 32, 64, ...).

4. The second difference is the same pattern as the differences for $y = 2^x$, so this must be an exponential function.

Problem Solving

1. The graph of $f(x) = 7x + 2$ is translated up 2 units and the line is steeper by a factor of 7.

2. 44; yes; Possible answer: I tried points (3, 23), (4, 30), (5, 37), (7, 51), (8, 58); when x has a value greater than 6, the points do not match well.

3. The graph of $f(x) = x^2 + 5$ is translated up 5 units.

4. 41; not exactly; Possible answer: I tried points (2, 9), (4, 21), (5, 30), (8, 69), (10, 105), and (12, 149), and they match reasonably well.

5. Possible answer: The quadratic parent function translated up 5 units best models these data.

Reading Strategies

1. Possible answer: It has the same shape as the quadratic function above; It is not in exactly the same position on the graph.

2. Translation 1 unit left

3. Possible answer: It has the same shape and it also starts at the origin; It is in a different quadrant of the coordinate plane.

4. Reflection across the x-axis

LESSON 2-1

Practice A

1. Addition   2. Division

3. Subtraction and multiplication

4. 19; 19; 63   5. 7; 7; 17

6. 3; 3; $w \le 18$ 7. $x = 1$

8. $r > 3$ 9. $g = 4$

10. $n = -4$ 11. $d > \dfrac{1}{3}$

12. $z > 5$ 13. $s < -3$

14. $h \le -4$ 15. $m \le 3$

16. $k > 2$ 17. $y \ge -3$

Practice B

1. $x = 1$ 2. $w = -8$

3. $p = 1$ 4. $y = \varnothing$

5. $t = 7$ 6. $c = -4\dfrac{1}{8}$

7. $x \le 2$ 8. $k < 5$

9. $d \ge 4$

10. a. 28

    b. 3 minutes

11. $v \le 17$

Practice C

1. 83.2°; 69.8°; 135.2°; 71.8°
2. 61.2°; 117.1°; 73.4°; 108.1°
3. 82.1°; 82.1°; 97.9°; 97.9°
4. a. $50 + 39.95 + 0.015s = 95.95$; $s = 400$; Harriet made $400 in sales the first month.

   b. $f \geq 39.95 + 0.015 \cdot 500$; $f \geq 47.45$; Harriet will pay a minimum of $47.45.

   c. $39.95 + 0.015s \leq 0.05s$; $s \geq 1141.43$; Harriet's total sales for the month must be at least $1141.43.

5. $k = \dfrac{-3x}{11} - 1$

6. Any value for q other than $\dfrac{1}{2}$

Reteach

1. 27; 36; 12
2. 28; 126; 18
3. $8w - 48$; $8w = 216$; 27
4. 9; 6; 2
5. $9y$; $6y$; 5
6. $4x + 5$; $4x = 24$; 6
7. $-6x$; $\dfrac{\boxed{-6}\,x}{\boxed{-6}} < \dfrac{-24}{\boxed{-6}}$; 4
8. $-3w + 2$; $-3w < 21$; $\dfrac{\boxed{-3}\,w}{\boxed{-3}} > \dfrac{\boxed{21}}{\boxed{-3}}$; -7
9. $-12y$; $-12y$; $-5y - 1$; $-5y \geq 30$; $\dfrac{\boxed{-5}\,y}{\boxed{-5}} \leq \dfrac{\boxed{30}}{\boxed{-5}}$; -6

Challenge

1. a. $\dfrac{10 - 0}{2} = 5$ b. 2.5

   c. 1.25, 0.625, 0.3125

   d. 7.5, 6.25, 5.625

   e. Infinitely many points

2. Possible answer: midpoint: 0.015; three points in the left half of the interval: 0.0125, 0.01125, 0.011125; three points in the right half of the interval: 0.0175, 0.01625, 0.015625

3. Possible answer: midpoint: $\dfrac{5}{12}$; three points in the left half of the interval:

$\dfrac{3}{8}, \dfrac{17}{48},$ and $\dfrac{11}{32}$; three points in the right half of the interval: $\dfrac{11}{24}, \dfrac{7}{16},$ and $\dfrac{41}{96}$

4. a. Infinitely many points

   b. Both contain infinitely many points.

Problem Solving

1. 4.5 cm
2. $y = 4.5x + 3.5$
3. 11 days
4. C
5. D
6. No; she forgot to reverse the inequality sign when multiplying by a negative number.
7. Yes

Reading Strategies

1. 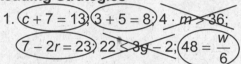 $c + 7 = 13$; $3 + 5 = 8$; $4 \cdot m > 36$; $7 - 2r = 23$; $22 < 3g - 2$; $48 = \dfrac{w}{6}$

2. Possible answer: The process is similar because you use the same operations on both sides.
3. The number that makes the equation true
4. Substitute 11 for x. $11 - 3 = 8$, so 11 is the solution.
5. The numbers that make the inequality true
6. Possible answer: Choose some numbers that are less than 11 and substitute them for x to see if the results are true.
7. Possible answer: The solution of the equation is one number, 11, but the solution set of the inequality is all the numbers less than 11.

LESSON 2-2

Practice A

1. $2 \times 126 = 252$

   $3 \times 84 = 252$; proportion

2. $2 \times 5.2 = 10.4$

   $2.6 \times 4 = 10.4$; proportion

Holt Algebra 2

3. $3.5 \times 44 = 154$

   $8 \times 19 = 152$; not a proportion

4. $c = 15$ 5. $a = 3.5$

6. $x = 2\dfrac{1}{3}$ 7. $f = -48$

8. $k = \dfrac{2}{7}$ 9. $w = -27$

10. $\dfrac{15}{100} = \dfrac{a}{1360}$; $a = 204$

11. $\dfrac{1}{1.62} = \dfrac{10}{m}$; $m = 6.2$ 12. $\dfrac{20}{8} = \dfrac{b}{31}$; $b = 78$

Practice B

1. $g = 63$ 2. $z = 5\dfrac{1}{3}$

3. $h = 0.21$ 4. $f = 36$

5. $y = 0.003$ 6. $v = 9$

7.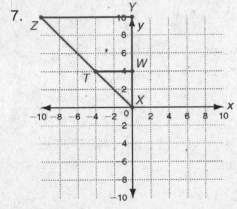

8. 7.5 ft   9. 9 students

10. $22\dfrac{2}{3}$ yd

Practice C

1. $n = 7.5$ 2. $w = 6.5$

3. $a = 7$ 4. $d = -8$

5. $m = 4$ 6. $c = 2$

7. $1,485,200   8. $714,548

9. $1,234,567   10. 750 students

11. 6 ft 9 in.   12. 42 rupees

Reteach

1. 78; $\dfrac{26n}{26} = \dfrac{\boxed{234}}{26}$; 9

2. $9 \cdot 9$; $\dfrac{40.5x}{\boxed{40.5}} = \dfrac{\boxed{81}}{\boxed{40.5}}$; 2

3. $4t = 17 \cdot 32$; $\dfrac{4t}{\boxed{4}} = \dfrac{\boxed{544}}{\boxed{4}}$; 136

4. $x = 126$

5. $\dfrac{\boxed{15}}{100} = \dfrac{x}{680}$; $15 \cdot 680$; $x = 102$

6. $\dfrac{\boxed{72}}{100} = \dfrac{x}{\boxed{5000}}$; $100x = 72 \cdot 5000$; $x = 3600$

7. $\dfrac{40}{104} = \dfrac{h}{\boxed{169}}$; $40 \cdot 169$; 6760;

   $\dfrac{104h}{104} = \dfrac{\boxed{6760}}{\boxed{104}}$; 65; 65

Challenge

1. a. 17 to 16

   b. 629

   c. 391

2. $\dfrac{5}{3}$ 3. 729

4. 1095 born, 657 died   5. $1\dfrac{2}{3}$

Problem Solving

1. 0.125 inch or $\dfrac{1}{8}$ inch

2. 0.17 feet or about 2 inches

3. $8\dfrac{1}{3}$ inches

4. No; possible answer: the caterpillar would have a radius of about 7.5 ft so it wouldn't fit in a shoe box.

5. A   6. B

7. B   8. D

Reading Stategies

1. $\dfrac{50}{75}$ 2. $\dfrac{75}{50}$

3. $\dfrac{30}{y}$ 4. $\dfrac{15}{10} = \dfrac{y}{30}$

5. Multiply 15 times 30 and multiply y times 10.

       Holt Algebra 2

6. Multiply 15 times 30 and then divide the product by 10.

7. 45 boys

LESSON 2-3

Practice A

1. +2; +2; +5; +5; linear

2. +3; +3; +3; +2; +4; +3; nonlinear

3.

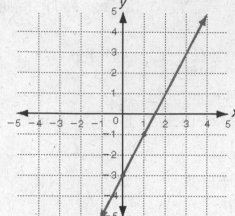

4.

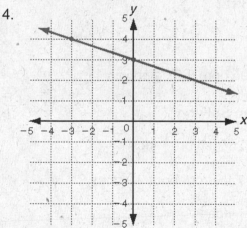

5. 2; 8

6. −2; −3

7. 4; $\dfrac{-8}{5}$

8. 5x + 7

9. y = 2x − 6

10. $y = \dfrac{4x}{3} + \dfrac{1}{3}$

Practice B

1. Nonlinear

2. Linear

3, 4, 5, 6.

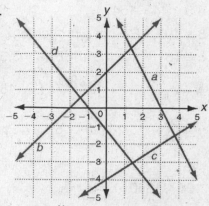

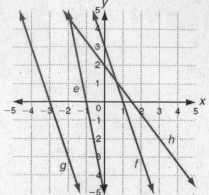

7. x-intercept = −1; y-intercept = −5

8. x-intercept = 1; y-intercept = 3

9. y = −3x − 9

10. $y = \dfrac{-4x}{3} + 2$

11. Vertical

12. Horizontal

13. Vertical

Practice C

1. a. No, the data set is nonlinear. Possible answer: The difference between the data items is not consistent or proportional.

   b. Possible answer: It is appropriate for the data to be nonlinear since a car uses gas differently depending on where and how it is being driven.

2. a. Yes, the data set is linear. Possible answer: The difference between ordered pairs is proportional.

   $\dfrac{20}{5} = \dfrac{6}{1.5} = \dfrac{8}{2}$

   b. c-intercept = −156; T-intercept = 39

   c. 148

3. Trapezoid; (−6, 4), (0, 4), (−4, 0), (4, −4)

Holt Algebra 2

Reteach

1. a. 0; 2

   b. 0; 3

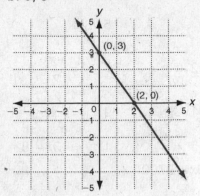

2. a. 0; −2

   b. 0; 4

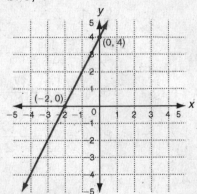

3. a. 2; 1

   b. 2

   c. −1

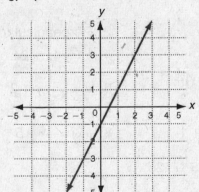

4. a. $\dfrac{1}{2}x + 1$

   b. $\dfrac{1}{2}$

   c. 1

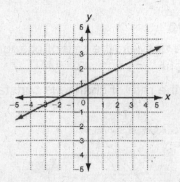

Challenge

1. To find the x-intercept, let $y = 0$.

   $$ax + by = c$$

   $$ax + b(0) = c$$

   $$ax = c$$

   $$x = \dfrac{c}{a}$$

   To find the y-intercept, let $x = 0$.

   $$ax + by = c$$

   $$a(0) + by = c$$

   $$by = c$$

   $$y = \dfrac{c}{b}$$

2. Possible answer: If any of a, b, or c are 0, then there is no triangle since the lengths of two of the sides are $\dfrac{c}{b}$ and $\dfrac{c}{a}$.

3. a. $A = \dfrac{c^2}{2ab}$

   b. 10 square units

4. Possible answer: $2x + y = 20$

5. a.

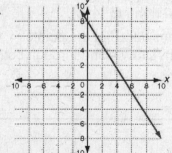

   b. $a = 8$, $b = 5$, $c = 40$

   c. $8x + 5y = 40$

   d. $y = \dfrac{-8}{5}x + 8$; $\dfrac{-8}{5}$

   e. 20 square units

Holt Algebra 2

Problem Solving

1. No; Possible answer: the rate of change is not constant.

2. a. Because the rate of change is constant
   b. 6
   c.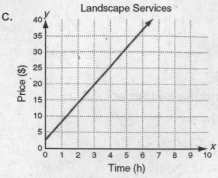

   Landscape Services

   d. $56

3. D   4. B

Reading Strategies

1.

	Linear Function	Slope-Intercept Form	Slope	y-intercept
1.	$4x + y = 7$	$y = -4x + 7$	-4	7
2.	$3y - 3x = -9$	$y = x - 3$	1	-3
3.	$-6x + 2y = 12$	$y = 3x + 6$	3	6

4. Possible answer: The x-intercept is the point where the line crosses the x-axis. The y-intercept is the point where the line crosses the y-axis.

5. Possible answer: Plot (2, –1). The slope of the line is $\frac{1}{2}$, so move 1 unit up and 2 units to the right, to (4, 0).

6. Possible answer: Plot the points (4, 0) and (0, –2). Draw a line through both points.

LESSON 2-4

Practice A

1. Slope = 3

   y-intercept = 2

2. Slope = $\frac{1}{2}$

   y-intercept = –7

3. Slope = $\frac{5}{2}$

   y-intercept = –2

4. $\frac{-1}{3}$ 5. 3

6. $y = 3x + 2$ 7. $y = \frac{-x}{2} - 1$

8. $y = 2x - 1$ 9. $y = \frac{2}{3}x - \frac{11}{3}$

10. $y = -x + 5$ 11. $y = -3x - 8$

12. a. $y = 40x + 9700$
    b. 12,460 feet

Practice B

1. 2   2. $\frac{1}{2}$

3. $y = 2x - 4$ 4. $y = -3x + 1$

5. $y = -\frac{2}{5}x - 1$ 6. $y = \frac{1}{5}x - \frac{17}{5}$

7. $y = \frac{1}{2}x$ 8. $y = -\frac{3}{2}x + \frac{13}{2}$

9. $y = \frac{1}{2}x - 4$

10. a. $T = 2t + 56$
    b. 80°F

Practice C

1. Neither   2. Perpendicular

3. Parallel   4. $y = -4x + 24$

5. $y = \frac{2}{3}x + \frac{14}{3}$ 6. $y = -\frac{1}{2}x + 2$

7. $y = \frac{1}{3}x + 1$ 8. $f(x) = -x + 5$

9. $f(x) = -\frac{5}{2}x - \frac{25}{3}$

10. a. $y = 3x + 172$
    b. 196 cm
    c. Possible answer: No, Michelle will not continue to improve at this rate forever. She will reach a point where she will improve only slightly each week.

Holt Algebra 2

Reteach

1. 3; 1; 1; 3

2. -2; $\boxed{-1}$; -1; $-x-2$

3. -1; $\dfrac{\boxed{1}}{\boxed{2}}$; $\dfrac{1}{2}$; $\dfrac{1}{2}x-1$

4. 4; -1, 2; 2; 4; -1; $4x+6$

5. 2; 1, -1; -1; 2; 1; $2x-3$

Challenge

1. a. 2

   b. $-\dfrac{1}{2}$

2. $y_Q = 2x_Q - 4$

3. $m = \dfrac{2x_Q - 12}{x_Q + 4}$

4. $x_Q = 4$, $y_Q = 4$

5. $4\sqrt{5}$

6. 5

7. 10

8. 17

9. 25

Problem Solving

1. a. $y = 75x + 125$

   b. A flat fee of \$125 charged in addition to the hourly rate.

   c. \$3125

2. a. $y = \dfrac{1}{4}x + 3.5$

   b.

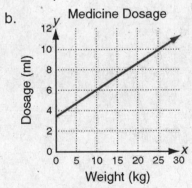

Medicine Dosage

   c. 9 ml

3. D

4. B

Reading Strategies

1. Perpendicular; because the slopes are $\dfrac{2}{3}$ and $-\dfrac{3}{2}$ and their product is -1.

2. a. Possible answer: $y = -x + 5$

   b. Yes; possible answer: because all three lines have the same slope (-1)

3. Because they both have a slope of 3

4. It's slope must be $\dfrac{1}{2}$.

5. Lines A and C are parallel, so their slopes are equal.

LESSON 2-5

Practice A

1. Correct

2. Incorrect

3. Correct

4.

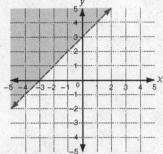

5.

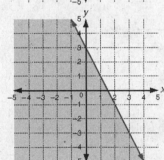

6.

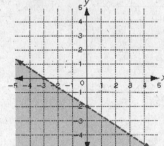

7.

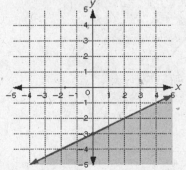

Holt Algebra 2

Practice B

1.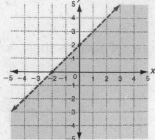

2.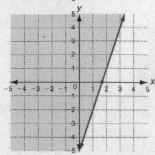

3.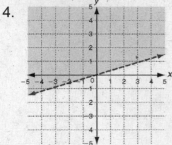

4.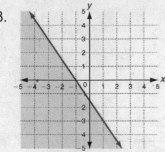

5. a. $2x + \dfrac{5y}{3} \geq 250$

   b. 60 tickets

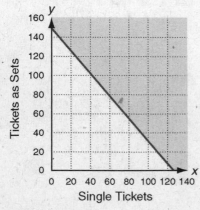

Practice C

1. a. $25x + 35y \geq 2400$

   b. 61 tickets

2. a. $15x + 10.75y \leq 137.25$

   b. $4 \leq x \leq 7$; $3 \leq y \leq 6$

   c. Possible answer: Depending on when you start the 10-day period, the number of weekdays and weekend days will vary.

   d. Possible answer: Pick up the car on a Friday and return it the following Sunday. This gives you 6 weekend days at the lower rate and 4 weekdays at the higher rate.

3. $y \geq 2x - 6$

4. $y < -\dfrac{1}{3}x + 2$

5. $y > \dfrac{3}{4}x - 3$

Reteach

1. a. 1

   b. 2

   c. Solid

   d. Below

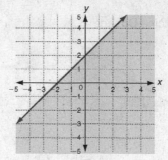

2. a. –2

   b. 1

   c. Dashed

   d. Above

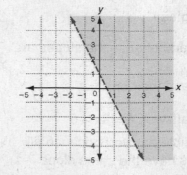

Holt Algebra 2

3. a. 4

   b. 2

   c. Dashed

   d. False

   e. Above

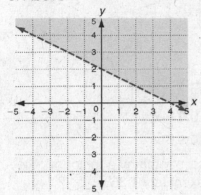

4. a. $\dfrac{1}{3}$

   b. −1

   c. Solid

   d. False

   e. Below

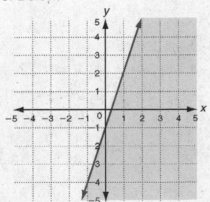

Challenge

1. Yes; point J lies in the solution region.

2. Yes; point K lies in the solution region.

3. $y = -\dfrac{1}{2}x$

4. Yes; all points on the line segment JK lie in the solution region.

5. $-4 \le x \le 4$

6. a. $3x + 4\left(-\dfrac{1}{2}x\right) < 12, \; x < 12$

   b. Possible answer: All the points on line R where the domain is limited to $x < 12$

---

are in the shaded half-plane and therefore in the solution region.

Problem Solving

1. $12n + 8.5p \le 200$ 2. 16.7; 23.5

3.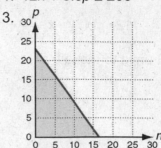

4. Positive whole numbers

5. Solid, because the total cost could be equal to $200

6. The solution region is the area below the line, because they cannot spend any more than $200.

7. No; Possible answer: because the point (10, 15) is not in the shaded region of the graph, so it is not a solution.

8. 13   9. 9 of each type.

10. D   11. A

Reading Strategies

1. a. $y \ge x + 1$

   b. Possible answer: (0, 6) and (−4, 4)

   c. Yes

2. $y > x + 1$

3. Change the solid boundary line to a dashed line.

4. The boundary line and the shaded area below it

5. $y < x + 1$ 6. $y \le x + 1$

LESSON 2-6

Practice A

1. 3   2. $f\left(\dfrac{1}{4}x\right)$

3. $\dfrac{1}{4}f(x)$ 4. $f(x + 5)$

5. $f\left(\dfrac{3}{2}x\right)$ 6. $f(-x)$

Holt Algebra 2

7. $g(x) = 2x + 2$

8. $g(x) = \left(\dfrac{1}{3}\right)x - 1$

9. $g(x) = \dfrac{3}{16}x$

10. $g(x) = \dfrac{1}{5}x - \dfrac{2}{5}$

11. $g(x) = \dfrac{1}{8}x - \dfrac{3}{8}$

12. $g(x) = -x + 4$

13. Horizontal shift 3 units to the left

Practice B

1. $g(x) = 2x + 3$

2. $g(x) = -\dfrac{1}{10}x + \dfrac{1}{5}$

3. $g(x) = -x - 3$

4. $g(x) = 4.6x + 7$

5. $g(x) = 1.19x - 2.1$

6. $g(x) = \dfrac{5}{2}x - 2$

7. $g(x) = 3.2x - 9.6$

8. a. $g(x) = 1.5[1 + 0.75(5x - 1)] = 5.625x + 0.375$

   b. Vertical stretch by a factor of 1.5

Practice C

1.

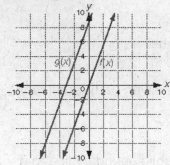

$g(x) = 3x + 9$

2.

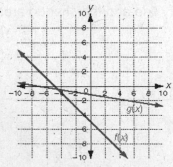

$g(x) = -\dfrac{1}{5}x - 1$

3.

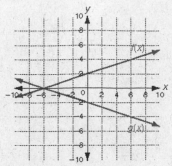

$g(x) = -\dfrac{1}{3}x - 2$

4. a. $f(x) = 0.014x$

   b. $f(x) = 0.019x$

   c. Vertical stretch by a factor of approximately 1.36

   d. 42,500,000

5. a. $g(x) = -x - 1$

   b. $f(x) = x + 1$

   c. Vertical shift 2 units down or horizontal shift 2 units right

Reteach

1. 5; 5; $2x - 11$

2. 4; $2x - 1 - 4$; $2x - 5$

3. 3; $2x - 1 + 3$; $2x + 2$ 4. 1; $x + 1$; $2x + 1$

5. $g(x) = 2x - 8$ 6. $g(x) = 2x - 19$

7. $g(x) = 2x$ 8. $g(x) = 2x$

9. $\dfrac{1}{4}$; $\dfrac{1}{4}$; $\dfrac{1}{2}x + \dfrac{1}{4}$ 10. $\dfrac{1}{3}x$; $\dfrac{1}{3}x$; $\dfrac{2}{3}x + 1$

11. $f\dfrac{1}{\left(\dfrac{1}{3}\right)}x = f(3x)$; $6x + 1$

12. $g(x) = 10x + 5$

Challenge

1. 2, 2, –4   2. (4, 4)

4. $\dfrac{1}{2}$, –4, 2

5. The slope is the reciprocal of the slope of the original line; the x- and y-intercept values are interchanged.

6. $y = \dfrac{1}{2}x + 2$ 8. $y = \dfrac{1}{2}x - 2$

Holt Algebra 2

9. Possible answer: The lines are parallel. The intercepts have the same values but opposite signs.

Problem Solving

1. $C(p) = 0.55p + 2.25$

2. $J(p) = 0.55p + 3.5$

3. Possible answer: The slopes are the same so the lines are parallel.

4. y-intercept of $C(p)$ is 2.25; y-intercept of $J(p)$ is 3.5; the cost of the cover.

5. The line is shifted up.

6. $1000

7. B   8. D

Reading Strategies

1. The line is shifted up 2 units.

2. The line is shifted down 1 unit.

3. No; the two lines are parallel because their slopes are the same.

4. The line is shifted 2 units to the left.

5. The line is shifted 1 unit to the right.

LESSON 2-7

Practice A

1.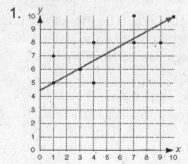

Positive

2.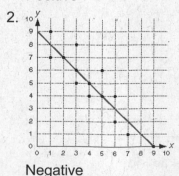

Negative

3.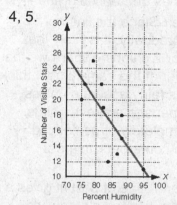

Positive

4, 5.

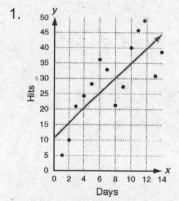

6. -0.55 7. Possible answer: $f(x) = -0.55x + 63.8$

8. Between -1 and 0, because the scatter plot shows a negative correlation

9. As the percent humidity increases, the number of stars visible decreases.

Practice B

1.

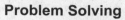

$y = 2.5x + 11$

2. b. $r = 0.848$

   c. $y = 0.33x - 11.33$

   d. Possible answer: about 50 photos

3. Possible answer: If the slope is negative, the correlation coefficient is negative. If the slope is positive, the correlation coefficient is positive.

Holt Algebra 2

Practice C

1. Possible answer: $r = 0.9$
2. Possible answer: $r = -0.75$
3. $r = 0$
4. Possible answer: The slope of the line of best fit is negative and close to zero. This means that, over time, the number of chipping sparrows visiting a bird feeder at the same time has decreased gradually.
5. Possible answer: Since the line is dropping very gradually, it is likely that there will be 1 or 2 chipping sparrows that visit a bird feeder at the same time. I think this prediction is fairly accurate unless something happens to make the birds stop visiting completely or something causes them to come back in great numbers.
6. Possible answer: A line of best fit gives a ballpark estimate. It gives a prediction that is close, but it will not account for instances outside of the norm.

Reteach

1. Positive
2. (4, 8) and (6, 11); $m = \dfrac{3}{2}$
3. $y = \dfrac{3}{2}x + 2$
4. 0.965
5. $y \approx 1.38x + 2.29$
6. $y \approx 5.878$
7. $y \approx 9.604$

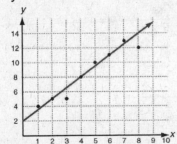

Challenge

1.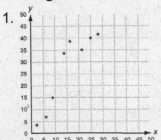

2. Slope: 1.568; y-intercept: 2.787; $r = 0.925$
3. a. Each point would shift 10 units to the right.
   b. The relationship between points would not change.
   c. The slope would not change; the y-intercept would change.
   d. No; Possible answer: because the relationship between points has not changed, the correlation is the same.
4. a. Each y-value is reduced by half, so the points are closer to the x-axis.
   b. The relationship between points would not change.
   c. I would expect a change in the slope and the y-intercept
   d. No; Possible answer: because the relationship between points has not changed, the correlation is the same.
5. a. The x-coordinates are the same, but the y-coordinates are multiplied by -1.
   b. The relationship between points would not change.
   c. The slope and the y-intercept of the line of best fit are numerically the same, but both are now negative.
   d. The value of r should be the same, but it is now negative since the data now shows a negative correlation.

Problem Solving

1. Negative correlation
2.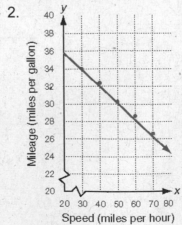
3. Slope ≈ -0.15

4. Possible answer: $y \approx -0.15x + 38$

5. $r \approx -0.98$

6. Possible answer: There is a strong negative correlation.

7. $y \approx -0.175x + 39.85$

8. A   9. C

Reading Strategies

1. The slope and r have the same sign.

2. No; possible answer: a value close to 0 means that the two variables have relatively no correlation.

3. Possible answer: the correlation coefficient would be positive; the more hours I spend studying, the higher my grade will be.

4. Possible answer: the correlation coefficient would be negative; the more rain there is, the fewer people want to go to the beach.

LESSON 2-8

Practice A

1. $x < 4$ and $x > 0$ 2. $x \geq -2$ or $x < -3$

3. $x \geq -4$ and $x \leq -1$ 4. 36; –36; 12; –12

5. $x = 6$ or $x = -6$ 6. $x = 3$ or $x = -3$

7. Disjunction, or   8. Conjunction, and

9. Disjunction, or   10. $-\dfrac{5}{3} \leq x \leq \dfrac{7}{3}$

11. $x < -1$ or $x > 1$ 12. 9 or 15

Practice B

1. $x = 3$ or $x = -4$ 2. $x = \pm 4$

3. $x = \pm 1$ 4. $x = 0$ or $x = 5$

5. $x = 6$ or $x = -8$ 6. $x = -3$ or $x = 11$

7. $x < 4$ 8. $x \geq 4$ or $x < -4$

9. $x \leq -2$ or $x \geq 2$ 10. $x < -\dfrac{1}{3}$ or $x > 5$

11. $x < -\dfrac{10}{3}$ or $x > \dfrac{10}{3}$

12. $x \geq -3$ and $x \leq 3$ 13. $|m - 4.4| \leq 0.05$

Practice C

1. $x = -6$ or $x = 9$ 2. $x = -11$ or $x = -7$

3. $x = -3$ or $x = 11$ 4. $\dfrac{-1}{2} < x < 2$

5. $x < 5$ 6. $x \leq -\dfrac{5}{4}$ or $x \geq \dfrac{7}{4}$

7. $x < -\dfrac{2}{5}$ or $x > \dfrac{6}{5}$ 8. $x \leq -1$ or $x \geq 5$

9. $x > -1$ and $x < \dfrac{7}{9}$

10. Possible answer: Ben is correct. There is no solution. When the inequality is simplified, the result is an inequality that sets the absolute value of an expression less than a negative number. Since absolute values are always positive, this is never true.

Reteach

1. –1; 2   2. –3; 0

3. $x < -3$; $x \geq -1$ 4. $x \geq -2$; $x < 3$

5. $x < 4$ and $x > -4$

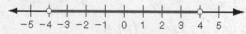

6. $x \leq 4$ or $x \geq 5$

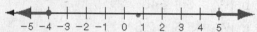

7. –2; 2; –5; –1

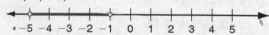

8. 3; –3; 2; –4; 1; –2

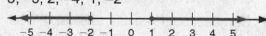

Challenge

1. a. $\dfrac{-c - b}{a} \leq x \leq \dfrac{c - b}{a}$

b. Possible answer: The solution of the absolute-value inequality gives $x \leq \dfrac{c - b}{a}$ and $x \geq \dfrac{-c - b}{a}$. Read the second inequality from right to left and combine the two inequalities into a single inequality.

2. $-4 \leq x \leq 1$ 3. $-2 \leq x \leq \dfrac{1}{2}$

Holt Algebra 2

4. a. The values of *b* and *c* are the same in both inequalities. The value of *a* has increased from the first inequality to the second.

   b. As *a* increases, the length of the solution interval decreases.

   c. $-1 \le x \le \dfrac{1}{4}$

   d. $\dfrac{-5-3}{8} \le x \le \dfrac{5-3}{8} = \dfrac{-8}{8} \le x \le \dfrac{2}{8} = -1 \le x \le \dfrac{1}{4}$

   e. Possible answer: When the coefficient of *x* is doubled, the solution interval is reduced by $\dfrac{1}{2}$ of the units.

5. a. $\dfrac{-21+6}{3} = -5 \le x \le \dfrac{21+6}{3} = 9$

   b. $-2.5 \le x \le 4.5$

   c. $-1.25 \le x \le 2.25$

Problem Solving

1. a. 292.5

   b. 50

   c. 5.5

2. a. $|W_1 - 292.5| \le 157.5$

   b. $|W_2 - 50| \le 40$

   c. $|W_3 - 5.5| \le 2.5$

3. a. $f \ge 3.9$ and $f \le 10.5$

   b. $f \ge 0.8$ and $f \le 2.8$

   c. $f \ge 0.18$ and $f \le 0.38$

4. Conjunction; Possible answer: the compound statement uses the term *and*.

5. $3.9 \le f \le 10.5$ 6. $|g - b| \le 315$

Reading Strategies

1. a. Yes; since $x = 6$ makes the first inequality in the disjunction true, the compound statement is also true.

   b. No; $x = 0$ makes both inequalities false, so the compound statement is also false.

   c. $-2 < x \le 1$; all *x*-values within this range make both inequalities false.

2. a. The conjunction is true for all numbers greater than 0 and less than or equal to 6.

   b. The conjunction is false for all numbers less than or equal to 0 and all numbers greater than 6.

3. a. All number greater than 5 or all numbers less than –5; $x > 5$ or $x < -5$

   b. $x \ge -5$ and $x \le 5$

LESSON 2-9

Practice A

1. $g(x) = |x| + 3$ 2. $g(x) = |x - 3|$

3. $g(x) = |-x|$ 4. $g(x) = \left|\dfrac{1}{3}x\right|$

5. $g(x) = -|x$ 6. $g(x) = 0.1|x|$

7. $f(x) = |x - 6| + 4$ 8. $f(x) = |x + 1| + 5$

9. $f(x) = |x - 3| - 3$

10. $f(x) = |x - 1| + 3$

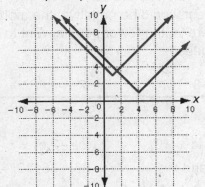

11. $f(x) = 2\left|\dfrac{1}{5}x - 1\right|$

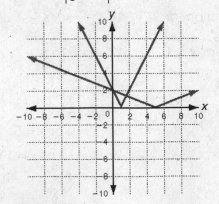

Practice B

1. $g(x) = |2x| - 4$ 2. $g(x) = |-2x| + 3$

3. $g(x) = |2x + 5| + 3$ 4. $f(x) = |x - 6| - 3$

5. $f(x) = |x + 8| - 1$ 6. $f(x) = |x + 7| + 2$

Holt Algebra 2

7. $f(x) = \dfrac{|3x - 4|}{3}$

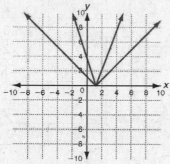

8. a. $y = |x - 5|$

b.

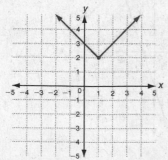

c. Translation 5 units to the right

Practice C

1. Translation 2 units left

2. Horizontal compression by a factor of $\dfrac{1}{2}$

3. Translation 5 units right and 3 units up, then vertical stretch by a factor of 4

4. $(3, 7)$

5. $(0, -4)$

6. $(-8, -1)$

7. $f(x) = |x - 7| + 2$

8. $f(x) = |2x| - 3$

9. $f(x) = -|x + 1| + 4$

10. a. $g(x) = -|x| - 2$

b. $h(x) = -2|x| - 4$

c. Vertical stretch by a factor of 2

Reteach

1. 1; 2

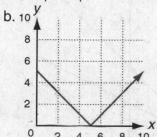

2. $x + 3$; 1

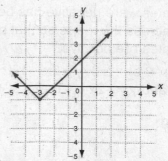

3. $|x| - 1$; $3|x| - 3$

4. $\dfrac{1}{2}$; $\dfrac{1}{2}$; 1; $|2x + 1|$

5. $\dfrac{1}{2}$; $|4x| - 2$; $|2x| - 1$

Challenge

1. a.

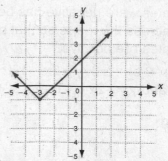

b. Domain is all real numbers; range is all positive real numbers.

c. The part of the graph where the y-coordinates were negative has been reflected across the x-axis so that all y-coordinates are positive.

2. a.

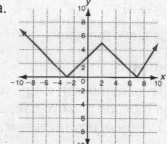

b. $y = 5$ if $x \geq 3$ and $y = 2x - 1$ if $-2 < x < 3$

3. a.

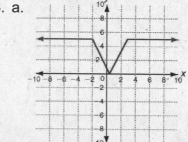

Holt Algebra 2

b. The part of the graph where the
   y-coordinates were negative has been
   reflected across the x-axis so that all
   y-coordinates are positive.

c. $y = 5$ if $x \le -2$ or $x \ge 3$, $y = 2x - 1$ if
   $1 \le x < 3$, and $y = -2x + 1$ if $-2 < x < 1$

Problem Solving

1. $D(t) = |t|$

2. 3, 3; Possible answer: a person who is 3
   minutes away from the exhibit is 3 blocks
   from the exhibit.

3. All real numbers

4. All positive real numbers

5. a. $C(t) = 5|t|$

   b. Vertical stretch

   c. The vertex stays the same.

Reading Strategies

1. Domain: {all real numbers}; range: $(0 \le y)$; the range must be positive because
   the absolute value of any number is
   positive.

2. Possible answer: Shifting the function
   down means changing the y-coordinates
   so I would subtract 3 from the function
   value; shifting to the right means
   changing the x-coordinates, so I would
   subtract 3 from the x-value.

4. a. $f(x) = |x + 2| + 1$

   b. $(-2, 1)$

5. No; the values of $f(x) = |x| - 2$ are positive
   only for x greater than 2 or x less than −2.

LESSON 3-1

Practice A

1. No   2. Yes

3. No

4. a.

x	y
−2	−1
−1	0
0	1
1	2
2	3

x	y
−2	−2
−1	$-\frac{3}{2}$
0	−1
1	$-\frac{1}{2}$
2	0

b.

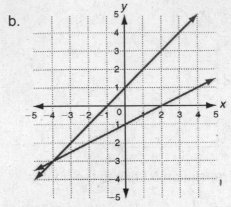

c. $(-4, -3)$

5. $(3, -1)$

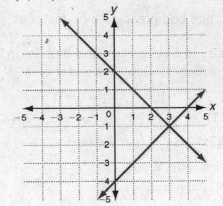

6. $(2, 4)$

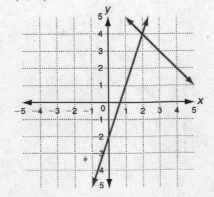

Holt Algebra 2

Practice B

1. Consistent, dependent; infinitely many solutions

2. Inconsistent; no solutions

3. Consistent, independent; one solution

4. It is the solution.

5. (6, –2)   6. (1, 4)

7. (5, 5)   8. (–1, –2)

9. It is the solution.

10. 126 square feet

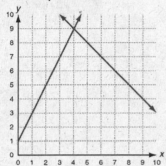

11. 35 quarters + 25 dimes = 60 coins

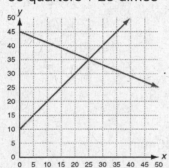

Practice C

1. Matches 2nd graph.

2. Matches 3rd graph.

3. Matches 1st graph.

4. a. $\begin{cases} y = -x + 16 \\ y = -\dfrac{1}{6}x + 3.5 \end{cases}$

   b. 15 h

   c. 1 gallon

5. a. 15 months

   b. $1950

Reteach

1.

$y = -x + 1$	
x	y
0	1
1	0
2	–1
3	–2

$y = 2x - 5$	
x	y
0	–5
1	–3
2	–1
3	1

(2, –1)

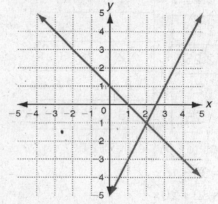

2. $y = -x + 2$, $m = -1$, $b = 2$

   $y = -x - 1$, $m = -1$, $b = -1$

   none inconsistent

3. $y = 3x - 1$, $m = 3$, $b = -1$

   $y = 3x - 1$, $m = 3$, $b = -1$

   infinitely many dependent

Challenge

1. $b = -9$, $c = 36$ 2. $b = -9$, $c \neq 36$

3. $b \neq -9$

4. 3 lines intersect at a single point

5. 3 lines that coincide   6. 3 parallel lines

7. Possible answer: In order to be inconsistent, the equations must be parallel and have different y-intercepts. If the constant terms are equal to 0, then all y-intercepts are 0, therefore there are no parallel lines and the system must be consistent.

8. Possible answer: To be independent, the slopes cannot be equal. This can be

Holt Algebra 2

stated as $\dfrac{-a}{b} \neq \dfrac{-c}{d}$, $-ad \neq -bc$, or $-ad + bc \neq 0$.

Problem Solving

1. a. $\begin{cases} 4x + 8y = 26 \\ x + 1 = y \end{cases}$

   b.

4x + 8y = 26	
x	y
1	2.75
1.5	2.50
2	2.25
2.5	2
3	1.75

x + 1 = y	
x	y
1	2
1.5	2.5
2	3
2.5	3.5
3	4

   c. Small: $1.50; large: $2.50

2. a. $\begin{cases} y = 95 + 15x \\ y = 80 + 20x \end{cases}$

   b.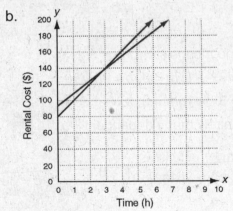

   c. 3 h

   d. $140

3. B

Reading Strategies

1. a; d

2. b

3. a; c

4. 5

5. 4

6. 6

Practice A

1. a. $x = 4$

   b. $y = 1$

   c. (4, 1)

2. (3, 2)

3. (1, 5)

4. (−1, −3)

5. a. $\begin{cases} -12x + 15y = -21 \\ 12x - 16y = 24 \end{cases}$

   b. $y = -3$

   c. (−2, −3)

6. (4, −1)

7. (−3, 3)

8. (−1, 2)

Practice B

1. (10, 2)

2. (−3, −4)

3. (−4, −8)

4. (−5, 1)

5. (6, −3)

6. (−3, −2)

7. (8, 5)

8. (−1, 7)

9. (2, −3)

10. (16, −2)

11. (−12, 9)

12. (−3, −7)

13. a. $\begin{cases} d = 8.25 - 8h \\ d = 3h \end{cases}$

   b. 0.75 h or 45 min

Practice C

1. (−1.2, 4)

2. $\left(-3, -3\dfrac{1}{2}\right)$

3. $\left(8\dfrac{1}{4}, -2\right)$

4. $\left(-8\dfrac{1}{2}, 1\right)$

5. (−6, 11)

6. $\left(7, 3\dfrac{1}{2}\right)$

7. $\left(6, 7\dfrac{1}{2}\right)$

8. $\left(\dfrac{2}{5}, -\dfrac{4}{5}\right)$

9. $\left(9, -\dfrac{3}{4}\right)$

10. a. $\begin{cases} 4n + 2r = 23.5 \\ 2n + 4r = 18.5 \end{cases}$

   b. $7.00

Holt Algebra 2

11. a. 102

b. 96

Reteach

1. $2x - 5$; $5x - 5 = 10$; $x = 3$; $y = 2(3) - 5 = 1$; (3, 1)

2. $y + 2$; $y + 2$; $y = -1$; $x = -1 + 2 = 1$; (1, −1)

3. 6; −3; $x = 2$; (2, −3)

4. $8x = -8$; −1; $y = 4$; (−1, 4)

Challenge

1. $y = -3x + 22$

2. $y = x + 6$

3. $y = 3x - 14$

4. $y = -2.5x + 3.5$

5. $y = -8x$

6. $y = x^2 - 2x + 1$

7. $y = x^2 - 4x + 8$

Problem Solving

1. a. $\begin{cases} 0.18x + 0.10y = (0.15)50 \\ x + y = 50 \end{cases}$

   b. 31.25 lb of Feed X and 18.75 lb of Feed Y

2. a. $\begin{cases} 0.18x + (0.10)(15) = (0.12)z \\ x + 15 = z \end{cases}$

   b. 5 lb of Feed X

   c. 20 lb of the mixture

3. A   4. B

5. D   6. C

Reading Strategies

1. Possible answer: substitution because I can easily solve the first equation for y

2. Possible answer: elimination because I can eliminate x from the system by adding the two equations together

3. Possible answer: substitution because I can easily solve the second equation for x

4. Possible answer: elimination because I can eliminate y from the system by multiplying the second equation by 2, then adding the equations

Practice A

1.

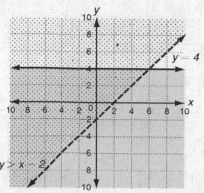

Possible answer: The solution region is the area where the two shading patterns overlap.

2.

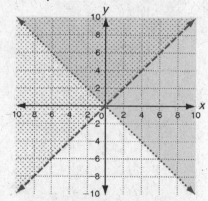

3.

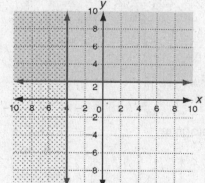

4.

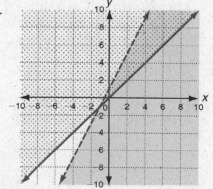

Holt Algebra 2

5.

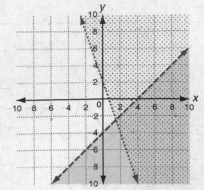

Practice B

1.

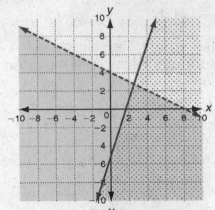

2.

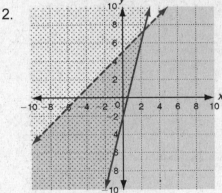

3. Parallelogram

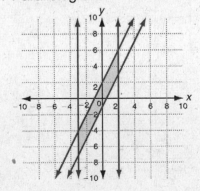

4. Trapezoid

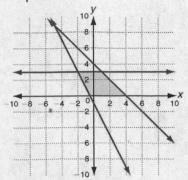

5. $\begin{cases} 8x + 4y \geq 1000 \\ x + y \leq 240 \end{cases}$

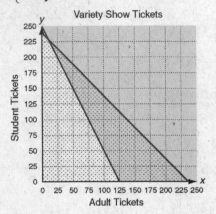

Variety Show Tickets

Practice C

1. Square

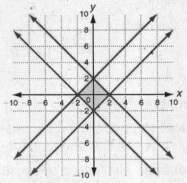

2. Quadrilateral

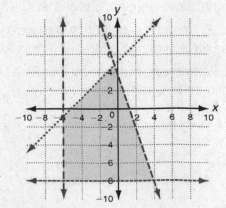

Holt Algebra 2

3. Trapezoid

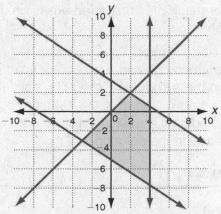

4. $\begin{cases} x + y \leq 20{,}000 \\ 0.06x + 0.075y \geq 1300 \end{cases}$

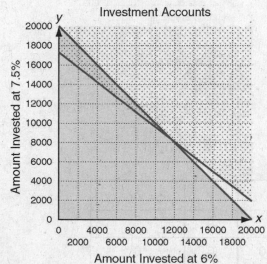

Investment Accounts

Reteach

1. a. Above

   b. below

   c. possible answer: (1, 3)

   d. possible answer: (4, 0)

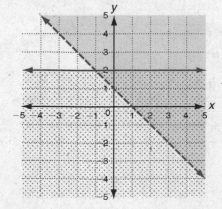

2. a. Below

   b. above

   c. left

   d. triangle

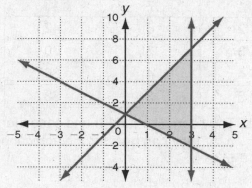

Challenge

1.

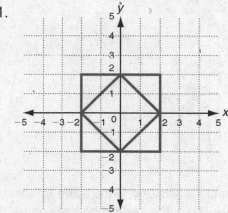

2. square

3. Possible answer: The original square is rotated 45°.

4. rectangle

5. a. horizontal translation 3 units to the right

   b. vertical translation 3 units down

   c. horizontal compression by a factor of $\frac{1}{2}$

6. (−1, 0), (−1, −4), (7, −4), (7, 0)

7. (−5, −2), (−5, 6), (−1, 6), (−1, −2)

8. (−2, ±4), (2, ±4)

9. $\begin{cases} |x| \leq 5 \\ |y| \leq 5 \end{cases}$

10. $\begin{cases} |x + 3| \leq 5 \\ |y - 5| \leq 1 \end{cases}$

11. $\begin{cases} |2x| \leq 1 \\ |y - 1| \leq 1 \end{cases}$

Holt Algebra 2

Problem Solving

1. a.

Hiking Time (m)	Canoeing Time (n)	Total Miles per day
1	7	45
2	6	42
3	5	39
4	4	36
5	3	33

b. They can hike for 1 h and canoe for 7 h, or they can hike for 2 h and canoe for 6 h.

2. a. $\begin{cases} 3m + 6n \geq 40 \\ m + n \leq 8 \end{cases}$

b.

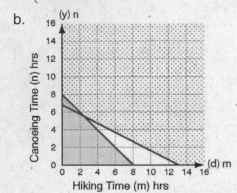

c. Possible answer: Where the shadings over lap is the region containing all possible solutions of the inequalities.

d. Possible answer: (0, 8)

3. A   4. D

Reading Strategies

1. Possible answer: Substitute the x- and y-coordinates for x and y in the two inequalities. Both inequalities must be satisfied for that ordered pair to be a solution of the system.

2. Substitute 3 for x and 2 for y in both inequalities; no, it is not a solution.

3. Possible answer: In both cases, you are finding the ordered pair or pairs that satisfy the equations or inequalities by graphing.

4. Possible answer: The lines in a system of inequalities can be solid or dashed, and it is also necessary to shade areas above or below the lines.

5. Possible answer: It is the region of intersection of two shaded areas on the graph.

6. Possible answer: You use a dashed line when the symbol is < or > but a solid line when the symbol is ≤ or ≥. The solid line has points included in the solution, but the points on a dashed line are not included in the solution.

LESSON 3-4

Practice A

1. a.

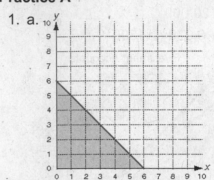

b. (0, 6), (6, 0), (0, 0)

c.

x	y	$P = 2x + y$
0	0	0
0	6	6
6	0	12

d. (6, 0)

2. (1, 6)

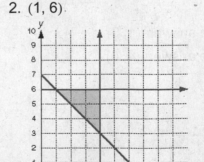

3. a. $\begin{cases} x \geq 0 \\ y \geq 0 \\ x + y \leq 40 \\ y < x \end{cases}$

Holt Algebra 2

b.

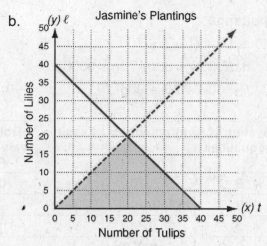

Jasmine's Plantings

c. 19

d. 1

b.

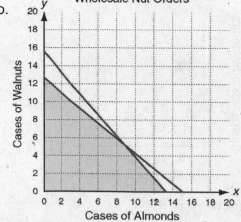

Wholesale Nut Orders

c. $P = 17x + 15y$

d. 9 cases of almonds, 5 cases of walnuts

Practice B

1. (10, 0)

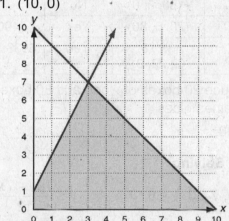

2. (3, 1)

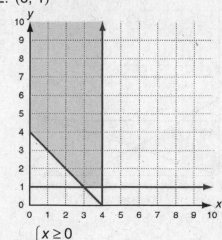

3. a. $\begin{cases} x \geq 0 \\ y \geq 0 \\ 20x + 24y \leq 300 \\ 30x + 26y \leq 400 \end{cases}$

Practice C

1. (0, 9)

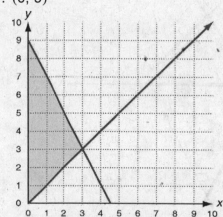

2. 30 of Model B and 5 of Model D

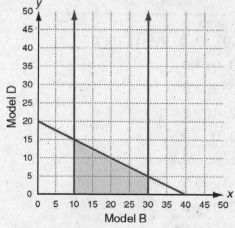

3. 20 experienced, 0 inexperienced

Holt Algebra 2

Tent Sale Workers

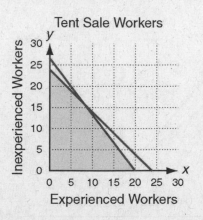

Reteach

1.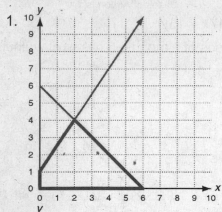

2.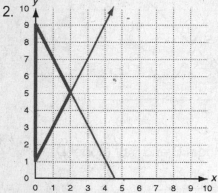

3. (0, 0), (0, 1), (2, 4), (6, 0)

$P(0, 0) = 0$

$P(0, 1) = 5$

$P(2, 4) = 24$

$P(6, 0) = 12$

max at (2, 4)

4. (0, 1), (0, 9), (2, 5)

$P(0, 1) = 6$

$P(0, 9) = 54$

$P(2, 5) = 36$

min at (0, 1)

Challenge

1. a. $D: w + i + g \leq 100$

   b. $E: 35w + 80i + 70g \leq 6300$

2. $P = 60w + 75i + 90g$

3.

System of inequalities	Intersection	Feasible	Dollar value of P
A, B, C	(0, 0, 0)	Yes	0
A, B, D	(0, 0, 100)	No	—
A, B, E	(0, 0, 90)	Yes	8100
A, C, D	(0, 100, 0)	No	—
A, C, E	(0, 78.75, 0)	Yes	5906.25
A, D, E	(0, −70, 170)	No	—
B, C, D	(100, 0, 0)	Yes	6000
B, C, E	(180, 0, 0)	No	—
B, D, E	(20, 0, 80)	Yes	8400
C, D, E	(37.78, 62.22, 0)	Yes	6933.33

4. Produce 20 boxes of wood and 80 boxes of stained glass

5. $8400

Problem Solving

1. $x \geq 0$, $y \geq 0$, $y \leq 6$, $y \geq \frac{1}{3}x$, $y \leq \frac{100 - 7x}{12}$

2.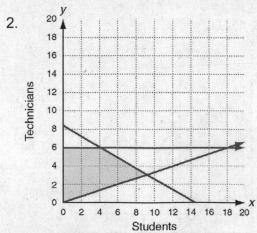

3. (0, 0), (0, 6), (4, 6), (9, 3)

4. $C = x + 2y$ 5. (4, 6)

6. 6 technicians and 4 students

7. D   8. C

Holt Algebra 2

Reading Strategies

1.-4.

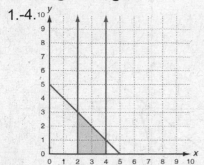

5. Yes; trapezoid

6.

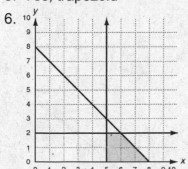

7.

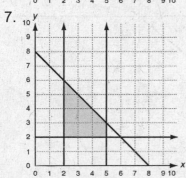

8.

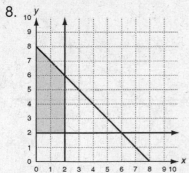

9.

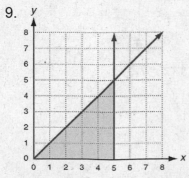

Practice A

1-3.

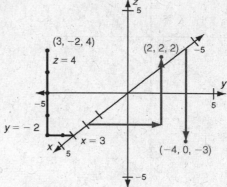

4. 6; –2; –4   **5.** 2; 6; –3

6. 5; –3; 1.5

7. a. (2, 0, 0); (0, 5, 0); (0, 0, 4)

b, c.

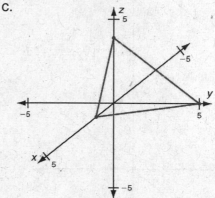

8. a. $2x + 5y + 3z = 30$

b.

Corydoras	Angelfish	Guppies
4	2	4
8	1	3
5	1	5
2	4	2

Practice B

1.

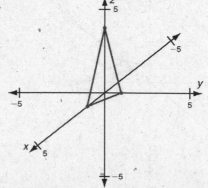

Holt Algebra 2

2.

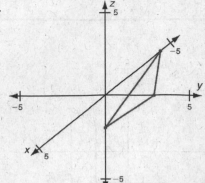

2.

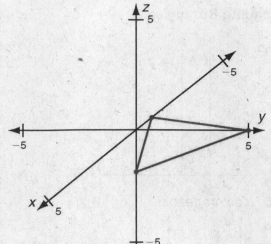

3.

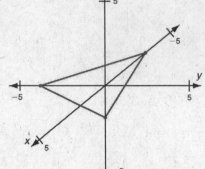

3.

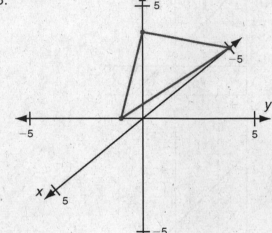

4.

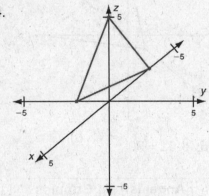

4.

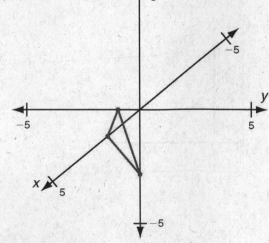

5. a. $4x + 3y + 2z = 24$

b. 2 bags

c. 2 bags of each

Practice C

1.

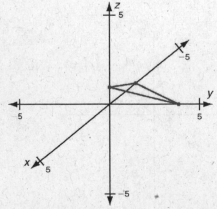

5. a. $5x + 7y + 14z = 72$

b. 5 vans

c. 6 cars

Holt Algebra 2

Reteach

1.

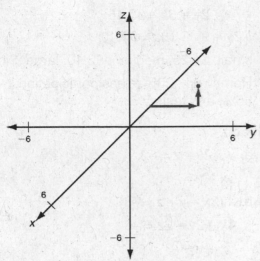

2.

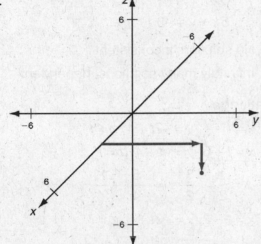

3. x-intercept is at $(4, 0, 0)$

y-intercept is at $(0, 3, 0)$

z-intercept is at $(0, 0, 2)$

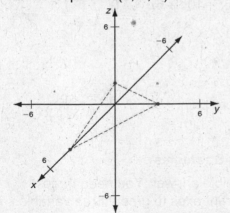

4. x-intercept is at $(5, 0, 0)$

y-intercept is at $(0, -5, 0)$

z-intercept is at $(0, 0, 2)$

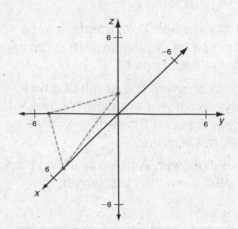

Challenge

1. $2x + y - z = 0$

2. $22x + 32y + 8z = 228$

3. $31x + 20y - 7z = 57$

Problem Solving

1. a. $5x + 4y + 10z = 60$

   b.

Starting Positions		
	x	y	z
Alicia	12	0	0
Lily	0	15	0
Van	0	0	6

2.

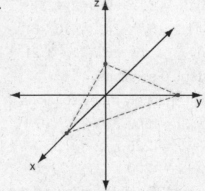

3. a. $(10, 1, 0.6)$

   b. $(4, 5, 2)$

   c. $(1, 3.75, 4)$

4. C   5. B

Reading Strategies

1. Possible answer: the surface of a table; a room

Holt Algebra 2

2. Possible answer: Both graphs can be determined by finding the intercepts of the linear equations.

3. Possible answer: The graph of a two-dimensional linear equation is a line, whereas that of a three-dimensional equation is a plane.

4. Possible answer: A plane has length and width, but a line has just length.

LESSON 3-6

Practice A

1. a. $-2x + y = 2$

   b. $-3x + 3y = 3$

   c. $x = -1, y = 0$

   d. $z = 5$

   e. $(-1, 0, 5)$

2. $(2, 3, -1)$

3. $(1, -4, 0)$

4. $(-3, 2, -2)$

5. $(1, 1, -2)$

6. $\begin{cases} 2x + z = 28 \\ 3y + 2z = 56 \\ x + y + z = 30; \end{cases}$ large: \$16, small: \$6,

   medium: \$8

Practice B

1. $(0, 0, -5)$

2. $(-2, 1, 3)$

3. $(8, -7, -1)$

4. $(-4, 0, -6)$

5. $(2, -2, 5)$

6. $(-1, -3, 2)$

7. Inconsistent; 0 solutions

8. Consistent; infinitely many solutions

9. $\begin{cases} 2b + y + 3r = 1500 \\ b + 2y + 2r = 1225 \\ 2b + 3y + r = 1200 \end{cases}$

   blue tickets: 125 points; yellow tickets: 200 points; red tickets: 350 points

Practice C

1. $(-7, 9, -9)$

2. $(4, 2.5, -7)$

3. Inconsistent; 0 solutions

4. Consistent; 1 solution

5. $\begin{cases} 4x + 2y + 8z = 45.20 \\ 7x + 2y + 5z = 35.45 \\ 2x + 9y + 16z = 93.40; \end{cases}$

   small: \$1.25, medium: \$2.10, large: \$4.50

6. Homework: 20%, class participation: 35%, and tests: 45%

Reteach

1. a. $x + 2y - z = -2$

      $3x + y = -1$

   b. $2 (2x - y + z = -3)$

      $4x - 2y + 2z = -6$

      $5x + y = -3$

   c. $\begin{cases} 3x + y = -1 \\ 5x + y = -3 \end{cases}$

2. No solution; inconsistent

3. Infinitely many solutions; dependent

Challenge

1. $x = t + 4; y = -2t + 1; z = t$

2. $x = t + 6; y = -t - 4; z = t$

3. $x = \dfrac{1}{2}t + \dfrac{3}{2}; y = -\dfrac{5}{4}t + \dfrac{11}{4}; z = t$

4. $x = t - 2; y = -2t + 8; z = t$

Problem Solving

1. a. $\begin{cases} 7t + 8c + 8p = 7.6 \\ 9t + 4c + 8p = 7.4 \\ 6t + 10c + 6p = 7.0 \end{cases}$

   b. 40%

   c. 25%

   d. 35%

2. 1 more point

3. 5 points

4. D

5. B

Reading Strategies

1. Possible answer: You need three different axes to graph three variables. A plane contains only two axes.

2. Possible answer: $2x + 4y - 2z = 6$ and $5x + 10y - 5z = 15$

Holt Algebra 2

3. The planes intersect in one point, so there is one solution.

4. Possible answer: The value of x is the same in all three equations, so you can substitute a value of x from one equation into any other equation in the system.

LESSON 4-1

Practice A

1. 3

2. 5

3. 3×5

4. 2.5

5. Row 2; column 4; k_{24}

6. Only other 3×5 matrices

7.
$$A + B = \begin{bmatrix} 3+12 & 6+7 \\ 5+5 & 0+9 \end{bmatrix} = \begin{bmatrix} 15 & 13 \\ 10 & 9 \end{bmatrix}$$

8. Not Possible

9. $\begin{bmatrix} 9 & 1 \\ 0 & 9 \end{bmatrix}$

10.
$$3D = 3 \cdot \begin{bmatrix} 7 & 0 \\ 3 & 14 \\ 4 & 6 \end{bmatrix} = \begin{bmatrix} 3(7) & 3(0) \\ 3(3) & 3(14) \\ 3(4) & 3(6) \end{bmatrix} = \begin{bmatrix} 21 & 0 \\ 9 & 42 \\ 12 & 18 \end{bmatrix}$$

11. $\begin{bmatrix} 4 & 8 \\ 6 & 10 \\ 12 & 18 \end{bmatrix}$

12. $\begin{bmatrix} 25 & 8 \\ 15 & 52 \\ 24 & 36 \end{bmatrix}$

Practice B

1. $P = \begin{bmatrix} 40 & 75 & 100 & 120 \\ 70 & 95 & 120 & 140 \\ 80 & 105 & 130 & 150 \end{bmatrix}$

2. 3×4

3. $80; the cost of a 1-day deluxe pass

4. p_{23}

5. $4P$

6. Not possible

7. $\begin{bmatrix} -1 & 21 \\ -3 & 0 \\ 19 & 20 \end{bmatrix}$

8. $\begin{bmatrix} 9 & 3 \\ 3 & -12 \\ -1 & 10 \end{bmatrix}$

9. $\begin{bmatrix} 15 & -6 & 0 & 27 \\ 12 & 48 & -15 & 18 \end{bmatrix}$

10. $\begin{bmatrix} 2 & 4 & 30 & 60 \\ 55 & 82 & -20 & 18 \end{bmatrix}$

11. $\begin{bmatrix} 27 & -14 & -20 & 11 \\ -14 & 36 & -15 & 22 \end{bmatrix}$

12. $F = \begin{bmatrix} -2 & 3 \\ -5 & -4 \end{bmatrix}$

Practice C

1. $\begin{bmatrix} -7 & -4 & 17 \\ 22 & 26 & 9 \end{bmatrix}$

2. $\begin{bmatrix} -30 & 90 & 20 \\ 100 & -50 & 40 \\ 10 & 20 & 30 \end{bmatrix}$

3. $\begin{bmatrix} 25 & -15 & 0 \\ -9 & 6 & 21 \end{bmatrix}$

4. $\begin{bmatrix} -\dfrac{3}{2} & \dfrac{9}{2} & 1 \\ 5 & -\dfrac{5}{2} & 2 \\ \dfrac{1}{2} & 1 & \dfrac{3}{2} \end{bmatrix}$

5. $\begin{bmatrix} 83 & -35 & -32 \\ -25 & -17 & 21 \end{bmatrix}$

6. $\begin{bmatrix} 124 & -176 & 220 \\ -88 & 280 & 444 \end{bmatrix}$

7. $\begin{bmatrix} -3 & 6 \\ 4 & -1 \end{bmatrix}$

8. $Z = \begin{bmatrix} -1 & -2 \\ -6 & 6 \end{bmatrix}$

9. 4; 3

10. $\begin{bmatrix} 150 & 225 & 300 \\ 200 & 300 & 400 \end{bmatrix}$

11. $\begin{bmatrix} 108 & 162 & 216 \\ 144 & 216 & 288 \end{bmatrix}$

Reteach

1. a. 3
   b. 5
   c. 3×5

2. 2

3. 7

4. -2

5. 0

6. m_{12} and m_{33}

7. $\begin{bmatrix} -2 & -2 \\ -1 & -6 \end{bmatrix}$

8. $[4 \quad 5]$

9. $[6 \quad 1]$

Holt Algebra 2

10. $\begin{bmatrix} -1 & 0 \\ 2 & -2 \end{bmatrix} + \begin{bmatrix} 1 & 2 \\ 3 & 4 \end{bmatrix} = \begin{bmatrix} 0 & 2 \\ 5 & 2 \end{bmatrix}$

11. $\begin{bmatrix} 1 & 0 \\ -2 & 2 \end{bmatrix}$

12. $\begin{bmatrix} 1 & 2 \\ 3 & 4 \end{bmatrix}; \begin{bmatrix} 4 & 8 \\ 12 & 16 \end{bmatrix}$

Challenge

1. Matrix G must have dimensions $m \times n$.

2. Matrix H must have dimensions $m \times n$.

3. Yes

4. They have the same dimensions. There are nonzero entries along the main diagonal.

5. $S = \begin{bmatrix} a+d & 0 & 0 \\ 0 & b+e & 0 \\ 0 & 0 & c+f \end{bmatrix}$

6. Matrix S has the same dimensions as matrices A and B.

7. Yes; the sum of A and B is S, which is another diagonal matrix.

8. Yes; $C + D = \begin{bmatrix} a+r & b+s & c+t \\ 0 & d+u & e+v \\ 0 & 0 & f+w \end{bmatrix}$,

which is another upper triangular matrix.

9. $C = \begin{bmatrix} a & 0 & 0 \\ b & c & 0 \\ d & e & f \end{bmatrix}$, $D = \begin{bmatrix} r & 0 & 0 \\ s & t & 0 \\ u & v & w \end{bmatrix}$;

$C + D = \begin{bmatrix} a+r & 0 & 0 \\ b+s & c+t & 0 \\ d+u & e+v & f+w \end{bmatrix}$,

which is another lower triangular matrix.

Problem Solving

1. $P = \begin{bmatrix} 52.2 & 45.4 \\ 38.2 & 33.0 \\ 30.4 & 25.9 \\ 23.4 & 18.9 \end{bmatrix}$

2. 4×2

3. $M = \dfrac{1}{12}P$

4. $M = \begin{bmatrix} 4.4 & 3.8 \\ 3.2 & 2.8 \\ 2.5 & 2.2 \\ 2.0 & 1.6 \end{bmatrix}$

5. C

6. D

Reading Strategies

1. The matrix shows the same data as the table. Each row shows the length of each jump by each contestant. The columns show the length of each jump by each trial.

2. Matrix B shows the length of all three of Rafael's jumps, and matrix C shows the length of all three of Morgan's jumps.

3. Matrix D shows the length of all three jumps in trial 2.

4. A is 3×3, B and C are 1×3, D is 3×1.

5. No; because they have different dimensions

6. Yes; because they have the same dimensions

LESSON 4-2

Practice A

1. 3×6 2. 4×1

3. No

4. $= \begin{bmatrix} 2(2)+0(1) & 2(\underline{0})+0(\underline{3}) \\ 1(\underline{2})+3(\underline{1}) & 1(\underline{0})+3(\underline{3}) \end{bmatrix}$;

$\begin{bmatrix} 4 & 0 \\ 5 & 9 \end{bmatrix}$

5. $\begin{bmatrix} 3 & 41 \\ 5 & 11 \end{bmatrix}$

6. $\begin{bmatrix} 5 & 15 \\ 5 & 3 \\ 3 & 9 \\ 2 & 0 \end{bmatrix}$

7. $\begin{bmatrix} 37 & 41 & 4 & 20 \\ 8 & 8 & 10 & 10 \end{bmatrix}$

8. a. $\begin{bmatrix} 15 & 6 & 2 \\ 17 & 3 & 4 \end{bmatrix}, \begin{bmatrix} 5 \\ 10 \\ 25 \end{bmatrix}$

Holt Algebra 2

b. $\begin{bmatrix} 185 \\ 215 \end{bmatrix}$

c. Julie 185, Steve 215

Practice B

1. 3×4 2. 4×8

3. No

4. $\begin{bmatrix} 17 & -2 & -12 & -20 \\ 10 & -4 & -6 & -10 \end{bmatrix}$

5. $\begin{bmatrix} -8 & 15 \\ -5 & 19 \\ 25 & -17 \\ -3 & 3 \end{bmatrix}$

6. $\begin{bmatrix} -4 & 0 & 3 & 5 \\ -19 & 6 & 12 & 20 \\ 14 & -12 & -6 & -10 \\ 9 & -10 & -3 & -5 \end{bmatrix}$

7. $\begin{bmatrix} 14 & -2 \\ 4 & 2 \end{bmatrix}$

8. a. $\begin{bmatrix} 3 & 2 & 0 & 1 \\ 2 & 4 & 0 & 0 \\ 0 & 1 & 3 & 1 \end{bmatrix}, \begin{bmatrix} 1 \\ 2 \\ 3 \\ 4 \end{bmatrix}$

b. $\begin{bmatrix} 11 \\ 10 \\ 15 \end{bmatrix}$

c. Jamal 11, Ken 10, Barry 15

Practice C

1. No   2. $\begin{bmatrix} 13 & -23 & 16 \\ -7 & 1 & -3 \end{bmatrix}$

3. $\begin{bmatrix} 11 & 3 & -16 \\ 13 & -4 & -18 \\ -3 & 31 & 4 \end{bmatrix}$ 4. $\begin{bmatrix} 1 & 48 & -2 \\ -4 & -11 & 6 \end{bmatrix}$

5. No   6. $\begin{bmatrix} 37 & -32 \\ -24 & 21 \end{bmatrix}$

7. $\begin{bmatrix} 48 & -4 & 9 \\ -30 & 3 & -6 \end{bmatrix}$ 8. $\begin{bmatrix} 0 & -24 & 6 \\ 17 & 9 & -5 \\ -9 & -5 & 2 \end{bmatrix}$

9. $\begin{bmatrix} -18 & 6 & 24 \\ 1 & -17 & -4 \\ -2 & 6 & 4 \end{bmatrix}$

10. a. $[1.65 \quad 2.1 \quad 3.2]$

$\begin{bmatrix} 18 & 21 & 20 & 25 & 12 \\ 12 & 50 & 10 & 5 & 10 \\ 60 & 55 & 40 & 60 & 25 \end{bmatrix}$

b. [246.9 315.65 182 243.75 120.8]

c. Tue, Mon, Thu, Wed, Fri

Reteach

1. Yes; 2×1

2. 2×1; 1×2; yes; 2×2

3. 2×2; 1×2; no

4. $\begin{bmatrix} 3 \\ 1 \end{bmatrix} [4 \quad 3] = \begin{bmatrix} 3(4) & 3(3) \\ 1(4) & 1(3) \end{bmatrix} = \begin{bmatrix} 12 & 9 \\ 4 & 3 \end{bmatrix}$

5.

$\begin{bmatrix} -1 & 0 \\ 3 & -2 \end{bmatrix} \begin{bmatrix} 1 & 2 \\ -4 & 0 \end{bmatrix} = \begin{bmatrix} -1(1)+0(-4) & -1(2)+0(0) \\ 3(1)+-2(-4) & 3(2)+(-2)(0) \end{bmatrix} = $

$\begin{bmatrix} -1 & -2 \\ 11 & 6 \end{bmatrix}$

6. $\begin{bmatrix} -2 & -16 \\ 3 & -6 \end{bmatrix}$

Challenge

1. V KA.QHNT

2. CAN I HAVE CAR

Problem Solving

1. $S = \begin{bmatrix} 25 & 38 & 28 \\ 35 & 29 & 37 \\ 20 & 31 & 39 \\ 40 & 32 & 36 \end{bmatrix};$

$D = \begin{bmatrix} 3.1 & 2.0 & 3.5 & 1.5 \\ 2.1 & 1.8 & 3.7 & 2.8 \\ 2.3 & 2.4 & 3.0 & 3.5 \end{bmatrix}$

2. $S \times D = P$

3. Possible answer: because matrix S has the same number of columns (3) as matrix D has rows (3); the result will be a 4×4 matrix.

Holt Algebra 2

$$4.\ P = \begin{bmatrix} 221.7 & 185.6 & 312.1 & 241.9 \\ 254.5 & 211.0 & 340.8 & 263.2 \\ 216.8 & 189.4 & 301.7 & 253.3 \\ 274.0 & 224.0 & 366.4 & 275.6 \end{bmatrix}$$

5. The numbers along the main diagonal of the product matrix give the final scores.

6. Lupe: 301.7; Amy: 275.6; Beth: 221.7; Jon: 211

Reading Strategies

1. *DE* is not possible because matrix *D* has 2 columns and matrix *E* has 3 rows; *ED* is possible because matrix *E* has 2 columns and matrix *D* has 2 rows.

2. *DF* is possible because matrix *D* has 2 columns and matrix *F* has 2 rows; *FD* is not possible because matrix *F* has 3 columns and matrix *D* has 2 rows.

3. Possible answer: Matrix multiplication is not commutative because the products are not the same when the order of multiplication is reversed. Matrix *DF* is not the same as matrix *FD*.

4. Yes; both *EF* and *FE* are possible. Matrix *EF* is 3 × 3 and matrix *FE* is 2 × 2.

LESSON 4-3

Practice A

1. $= \begin{bmatrix} -7+2 & 4+(\underline{\ 2\ }) \\ (\underline{\ 2\ })+(\underline{-8}) & (\underline{\ 6\ })+(\underline{-8}) \end{bmatrix}$

   G′(−5, −6), H′(6, −2)

2. G′(−2, 3), H′(9, 7)

3. G′(−13, −1), H′(−2, 3)

4. $= \begin{bmatrix} 8(\underline{-7}) & 8(\underline{\ 4\ }) \\ 8\ (\underline{\ 2\ }) & 8\ (\underline{\ 6\ }) \end{bmatrix}$

   G′(−56, 16), H′(32, 48)

5. G′(−35, 10), H′(20, 30)

6. G′(−3.5, 1), H′(2, 3)

7. $\begin{bmatrix} -1(\underline{\ 2\ })+0(\underline{-3}) \\ 0\ (\underline{\ 2\ })+\ 1\ (\underline{-3}) \end{bmatrix}$

   (−2, −3); y-axis

8. (−10, −1); x-axis   9. (−5, 4); y-axis

Practice B

1. J′(2, −5), K′(7, −4), L′(6, −8)

2. J′(−5, 5), K′(0, 6), L′(−1, 2)

3. J′(−21, 7), K′(14, 14), L′(7, −14)

4. J′(−0.75, 0.25), K′(0.5, 0.5), L′(0.25, −0.5)

5. A′(2, 1), B′(1, 4), C′(−2, 2); reflection across the y-axis

6. A′(1, 2), B′(4, 1), C′(2, −2); 90° clockwise rotation

7. A′(−1, −2), B′(−4, −1), C′(−2, 2); 90° counterclockwise rotation

8. A′(−2, −1), B′(−1, −4), C′(2, −2); reflection across the x-axis

9. a. $\begin{bmatrix} -3 & -3 & 0 & 3 & 3 \\ -2 & 3 & 5 & 3 & -2 \end{bmatrix}$

   b. Multiply each entry in the matrix by 5.

   c. H′ (−15, −10) O′ (−15, 15) U′ (0, 25) S′ (15, 15) E′ (15, −10)

Practice C

1. $\begin{bmatrix} -9 & -9 & -9 & -9 & -9 \\ 4 & 4 & 4 & 4 & 4 \end{bmatrix}$

   D′(−8, 7), E′(−6, 6), F′(−8, 3), G′(−12, 2), H′(−11, 6)

2. scalar 0.1; D′(0.1, 0.3), E′(0.3, 0.2), F′(0.1, −0.1), G′(−0.3, −0.2), H′(−0.2, 0.2)

3. $\begin{bmatrix} 0 & 1 \\ -1 & 0 \end{bmatrix}$; D′(3, −1), E′(2, −3), F′(−1, −1), G′(−2, 3), H′(2, 2)

4. $\begin{bmatrix} 0 & -1 \\ 1 & 0 \end{bmatrix}$; D′(−3, 1), E′(−2, 3), F′(1, 1), G′(2, −3), H′(−2, −2)

5. $\begin{bmatrix} 1 & 0 \\ 0 & -1 \end{bmatrix}$; D′(1, −3), E′(3, −2), F′(1, 1), G′(−3, 2), H′(−2, −2)

6. $\begin{bmatrix} -1 & 0 \\ 0 & 1 \end{bmatrix}$; D′(−1, 3), E′(−3, 2), F′(−1, −1), G′(3, −2), H′(2, 2)

Holt Algebra 2

7. $\begin{bmatrix} 0 & 1 \\ 1 & 0 \end{bmatrix}$; D′(3, 1), E′(2, 3), F′(−1, 1),

G′(−2, −3), H′(2, −2)

8. a.

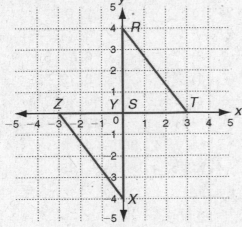

b. $\begin{bmatrix} 0 & 0 & 3 \\ 4 & 0 & 0 \end{bmatrix}$; $\begin{bmatrix} 0 & 0 & -3 \\ -4 & 0 & 0 \end{bmatrix}$

c. $\begin{bmatrix} -1 & 0 \\ 0 & -1 \end{bmatrix} \cdot \begin{bmatrix} 0 & 0 & 3 \\ 4 & 0 & 0 \end{bmatrix} = \begin{bmatrix} 0 & 0 & -3 \\ -4 & 0 & 0 \end{bmatrix}$

Reteach

1. $\begin{bmatrix} 0 & -2 & 1 \\ 3 & 0 & -2 \end{bmatrix}$ 2. $\begin{bmatrix} 3 & 3 & 3 \\ -2 & -2 & -2 \end{bmatrix}$

3. $\begin{bmatrix} 3 & 1 & 4 \\ 1 & -2 & -4 \end{bmatrix}$

D′(3, 1), E′(1, −2), F′(4, −4);

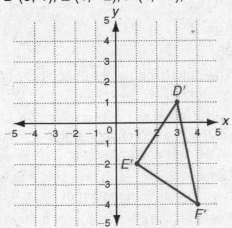

4. $\begin{bmatrix} 2 & 1 & 4 \\ 1 & 4 & 3 \end{bmatrix}$

A′(2, 1), B′(1, 4), C′(4, 3)

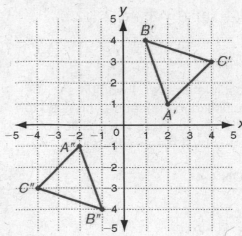

5. $\begin{bmatrix} -2 & -1 & -4 \\ -1 & -4 & -3 \end{bmatrix}$

A″(−2, −1), B″(−1, −4), C″(−4, −3)

Challenge

1. (−6, 5), (−3, 1), (−1, 4)
2. (4, −4), (−2, 4), (−6, −2)
3. (−1, 2), (3, 5), (0, 7)
4. $(1, -4), \left(-1, -5\frac{1}{2}\right), \left(\frac{1}{2}, -6\frac{1}{2}\right)$
5. (−5, 4), (−1, 1), (−4, −1)
6. (2, −11), (14, −2), (5, 4)

Problem Solving

1. Draw a triangle with vertices at (0, 0), (−3, 0), and (−3, 3).
2. a. Rotate 90° clockwise

   b. $\begin{bmatrix} 0 & 1 \\ -1 & 0 \end{bmatrix}$
3. a. Rotate 180°

   b. $\begin{bmatrix} -1 & 0 \\ 0 & -1 \end{bmatrix}$
4. a. Rotate 90° counterclockwise

   b. $\begin{bmatrix} 0 & -1 \\ 1 & 0 \end{bmatrix}$
5. B   6. D

Reading Strategies

1. The matrix describes the coordinates of the triangle after it has been translated 2 units left and 3 units up.

Holt Algebra 2

2. $A'(-1, 8)$, $B'(-8, -1)$, $C'(2, 0)$

3. $\begin{bmatrix} 1 & 1 & 1 \\ -4 & -4 & -4 \end{bmatrix}$

4. Possible answer: I would use multiplication because you need to reduce or enlarge the position of each vertex by the same factor.

LESSON 4-4

Practice A

1. 10; 1; -2
$= 60 - (-2) = 62$

2. -1 3. -15

4. 107

5. a. $\begin{bmatrix} 1 & -2 \\ 3 & 1 \end{bmatrix}$

b. 7

c. $x = \dfrac{\begin{vmatrix} c_1 & b_1 \\ c_2 & b_2 \end{vmatrix}}{D} = \dfrac{\begin{vmatrix} -9 & -2 \\ 1 & 1 \end{vmatrix}}{7}$

$y = \dfrac{\begin{vmatrix} a_1 & c_1 \\ a_2 & c_2 \end{vmatrix}}{D} = \dfrac{\begin{vmatrix} 1 & -9 \\ 3 & 1 \end{vmatrix}}{7}$

d. $x = -1$; $y = 4$

6. $x = 5$; $y = -2$ 7. $x = 3$; $y = -4$

8. $x = 6$; $y = 1$

Practice B

1. -16 2. 3

3. 10 4. -36

5. -30 6. -31

7. $(10, -7)$ 8. $(6, 5)$

9. $(1, -4)$ 10. $(5, 2)$

11. $(-3, -9)$ 12. $(2, 3)$

13. a. $\begin{cases} 4x + 2y = 41 \\ 5x + 3y = 55 \end{cases}$

b. $\begin{bmatrix} 4 & 2 \\ 5 & 3 \end{bmatrix}$; $\det = \begin{vmatrix} 4 & 2 \\ 5 & 3 \end{vmatrix} = 2$

c. $x = 6.5$; $y = 7.5$

d. Babysitting: $6.50, yard work: $7.50

Practice C

1. 34 2. 0

3. 27 4. $(-3, -5)$

5. $(2, -3)$ 6. $(4, 5)$

7. $(7, -1)$ 8. $(9, -2)$

9. $(8, 7)$ 10. $(0, 2, 1)$

11. $(1, 3, -4)$ 12. $(2, -3, 4)$

13. a. $\begin{cases} x + y = 20{,}000 \\ 0.045x + 0.035y = 785 \end{cases}$

b. -0.01

c. $\dfrac{\begin{vmatrix} 20{,}000 & 1 \\ 785 & .035 \end{vmatrix}}{-.01}$

d. $8500

Reteach

1. 6 2. $\dfrac{1}{2}$

3. -6; -4; 14 4. -5.4

5. -8 6. 12

7. -2; -2; 3 8. 1; 2; 1

9. -1; 5; 8 10. $\dfrac{1}{2}$; 3

Challenge

1. a. 36

b. The determinants are opposites of one another.

c. Possible answer: If two rows of a matrix are interchanged, the determinant changes sign.

2. a. Determinant is -108, which is 3 times the original determinant of R.

b. Possible answer: If a row of a matrix is multiplied by a constant, the value of the determinant is multiplied by that same constant.

3. a. -972

b. The determinant of T is $27 (3^3)$ times the determinant of R. The determinant

Holt Algebra 2

of the second matrix will be $16(4)^2$ times greater. Possible answer: If an $n \times n$ matrix is multiplied by a constant k, the determinant will be multiplied by k^n.

4. a. $U = \begin{bmatrix} 1 & 0 & 4 \\ -1 & 2 & 13 \\ 0 & 2 & -1 \end{bmatrix}$;

   the determinant of U is -36.

   b. Possible answer: This is an invariant operation. Adding a multiple of one row to another row does not change the determinant.

Problem Solving

1. $\begin{cases} 1.5s + 2c + 0.5r = 2450 \\ 2.5s + 3c + 1.5r = 4310 \\ 2s + 1.5c + 1.6r = 3150 \end{cases}$

2. $D = \begin{vmatrix} 1.5 & 2.0 & 0.5 \\ 2.5 & 3.0 & 1.5 \\ 2.0 & 1.5 & 1.6 \end{vmatrix}$ 3. $D = 0.7$

4. $s = 590$; $c = 620$; $r = 650$

5. A   6. B

Reading Strategies

1. a. $\begin{bmatrix} 6 & 9 \\ 5 & 8 \end{bmatrix}$

   b. $\begin{bmatrix} -3 & -5 \\ -2 & -8 \end{bmatrix}$

2. a. $\begin{bmatrix} -4 & 3 \\ -5 & 7 \end{bmatrix}$

   b. $\begin{bmatrix} \dfrac{1}{4} & -\dfrac{1}{2} \\ -10 & 8 \end{bmatrix}$

3. a. $\begin{bmatrix} -5 & 7 \\ -5 & 7 \end{bmatrix}$

   b. $\begin{bmatrix} -6 & 3 \\ 6 & -3 \end{bmatrix}$

4. a. $\begin{bmatrix} 3 & -4 \\ -4 & 5 \end{bmatrix}$

b. $\begin{bmatrix} 5 & 11 \\ -4 & -9 \end{bmatrix}$

5. It must be a square matrix and the products of the diagonals are equal.

LESSON 4-5

Practice A

1. Yes   2. Yes

3. $D = -2$; $\begin{bmatrix} -2 & \dfrac{5}{2} \\ 1 & -1 \end{bmatrix}$

4. $D = -10$; $\begin{bmatrix} -0.2 & 0.3 \\ 0.4 & -0.1 \end{bmatrix}$

5. $D = -2$; $\begin{bmatrix} 0 & \dfrac{1}{2} \\ 1 & \dfrac{3}{2} \end{bmatrix}$

6. $D = -4$; $\begin{bmatrix} \dfrac{1}{4} & \dfrac{1}{4} \\ \dfrac{1}{4} & -\dfrac{3}{4} \end{bmatrix}$

7. a. $\begin{bmatrix} 5 & 3 \\ 2 & 2 \end{bmatrix} \begin{bmatrix} x \\ y \end{bmatrix} = \begin{bmatrix} -12 \\ 4 \end{bmatrix}$

   b. $\begin{bmatrix} \dfrac{1}{2} & -\dfrac{3}{4} \\ -\dfrac{1}{2} & \dfrac{5}{4} \end{bmatrix}$

   c. $(-3, 1)$

8. $\begin{bmatrix} 3 & -2 \\ 2 & -3 \end{bmatrix} \begin{bmatrix} x \\ y \end{bmatrix} = \begin{bmatrix} 4 \\ 11 \end{bmatrix}$; $(-2, -5)$

9. $\begin{bmatrix} 3 & 1 \\ 2 & 3 \end{bmatrix} \begin{bmatrix} x \\ y \end{bmatrix} = \begin{bmatrix} 3 \\ 9 \end{bmatrix}$; $(0, 3)$

10. $\begin{bmatrix} 2 & 3 \\ 1 & 4 \end{bmatrix} \begin{bmatrix} x \\ y \end{bmatrix} = \begin{bmatrix} -1 \\ -8 \end{bmatrix}$; $(4, -3)$

Practice B

1. Yes   2. Yes

3. Yes   4. $\begin{bmatrix} 1 & 0 \\ 4 & -1 \end{bmatrix}$

Holt Algebra 2

5. $\begin{bmatrix} 3 & -2 \\ -7 & 5 \end{bmatrix}$

6. $\begin{bmatrix} \dfrac{3}{4} & 1 \\ -\dfrac{5}{4} & -2 \end{bmatrix}$

7. $\begin{bmatrix} -\dfrac{1}{3} & -1 \\ -\dfrac{2}{3} & -1 \end{bmatrix}$

8. $\begin{bmatrix} 1 & 1 \\ \dfrac{5}{4} & 1 \end{bmatrix}$

9. The inverse does not exist.

10. $\begin{bmatrix} 3 & 2 \\ 4 & 3 \end{bmatrix} \begin{bmatrix} x \\ y \end{bmatrix} = \begin{bmatrix} -5 \\ -9 \end{bmatrix}$; (3, −7)

11. $\begin{bmatrix} -6 & 4 \\ 5 & -3 \end{bmatrix} \begin{bmatrix} x \\ y \end{bmatrix} = \begin{bmatrix} 8 \\ -5 \end{bmatrix}$; (2, 5)

12. $\begin{bmatrix} 4 & 5 \\ 5 & 3 \end{bmatrix} \begin{bmatrix} x \\ y \end{bmatrix} = \begin{bmatrix} 0 \\ 13 \end{bmatrix}$; (5, −4)

13. $\begin{bmatrix} 5 & -3 \\ 6 & -5 \end{bmatrix} \begin{bmatrix} x \\ y \end{bmatrix} = \begin{bmatrix} 8 \\ 4 \end{bmatrix}$; (4, 4)

14. a. $\begin{cases} 3x + 2y = 39 \\ 2x + y = 23 \end{cases}$

b. $\begin{bmatrix} 3 & 2 \\ 2 & 1 \end{bmatrix} \begin{bmatrix} x \\ y \end{bmatrix} = \begin{bmatrix} 29 \\ 23 \end{bmatrix}$; pistachios: $7 per pound, cashews: $9 per pound

Practice C

1. $\begin{bmatrix} \dfrac{5}{6} & -\dfrac{7}{6} \\ -\dfrac{1}{3} & \dfrac{2}{3} \end{bmatrix}$; (8, −3)

2. $\begin{bmatrix} -\dfrac{3}{2} & \dfrac{5}{2} \\ -\dfrac{13}{2} & \dfrac{21}{2} \end{bmatrix}$; (0, −1)

3. $\begin{bmatrix} 11 & 7 \\ 3 & 2 \end{bmatrix}$; (−2, 0)

4. $\begin{bmatrix} \dfrac{7}{5} & -\dfrac{8}{5} \\ -\dfrac{2}{5} & \dfrac{3}{5} \end{bmatrix}$; (6, −1)

5. $\begin{bmatrix} -\dfrac{5}{7} & \dfrac{3}{7} \\ \dfrac{9}{7} & -\dfrac{4}{7} \end{bmatrix}$; (−3, 5)

6. $\begin{bmatrix} -\dfrac{5}{11} & \dfrac{7}{11} \\ \dfrac{3}{11} & -\dfrac{2}{11} \end{bmatrix}$; (8, −3)

7. Possible answer: $\begin{bmatrix} 3 & -4 \\ -6 & 8 \end{bmatrix}$

8. Possible answer: $\begin{bmatrix} 3 & 8 \\ -6 & -4 \end{bmatrix}$

9. $e = 2$, $f = 8$, $g = -1$, $h = -5$

10. $\begin{bmatrix} 12 & 4 \\ 8 & 3 \end{bmatrix} \begin{bmatrix} x \\ y \end{bmatrix} = \begin{bmatrix} 70 \\ 50 \end{bmatrix}$; a single ticket costs $2.50 and a book of tickets costs $10.00.

Reteach

1. 3; $\dfrac{1}{3}$; $\dfrac{1}{3}$; $\begin{bmatrix} -\dfrac{2}{3} & -\dfrac{7}{3} \\ \dfrac{1}{3} & \dfrac{2}{3} \end{bmatrix}$

2. 4; $\dfrac{1}{4}$; $\begin{bmatrix} \dfrac{1}{2} & -\dfrac{1}{4} \\ -2 & \dfrac{3}{2} \end{bmatrix}$; $\begin{bmatrix} -1 & -3 \\ -\dfrac{1}{2} & -2 \end{bmatrix}$ 3. 2

4. a. $\begin{bmatrix} 1 & 1 \\ 1 & 2 \end{bmatrix} \begin{bmatrix} x \\ y \end{bmatrix} = \begin{bmatrix} 2 \\ 6 \end{bmatrix}$

b. 1

c. $\begin{bmatrix} 2 & -1 \\ -1 & 1 \end{bmatrix}$

d. (−2, 4)

5. a. $\begin{bmatrix} 2 & 3 \\ 1 & 2 \end{bmatrix} \begin{bmatrix} x \\ y \end{bmatrix} = \begin{bmatrix} -1 \\ 1 \end{bmatrix}$

b. 1

c. $\begin{bmatrix} 2 & -3 \\ -1 & 2 \end{bmatrix}$

d. (−5, 3)

Challenge

1. a. $\begin{bmatrix} 3 & -3 \\ -6 & 7 \end{bmatrix}\begin{bmatrix} a & b \\ c & d \end{bmatrix} = \begin{bmatrix} 1 & 0 \\ 0 & 1 \end{bmatrix}$

   b. $3a - 3c = 1$, $3b - 3d = 0$, $-6a + 7c = 0$, $-6b + 7d = 1$

   c. $A^{-1} = \begin{bmatrix} \dfrac{7}{3} & 1 \\ 2 & 1 \end{bmatrix}$

   d. $\begin{bmatrix} 3 & -3 \\ -6 & 7 \end{bmatrix}\begin{bmatrix} \dfrac{7}{3} & 1 \\ 2 & 1 \end{bmatrix} = \begin{bmatrix} 1 & 0 \\ 0 & 1 \end{bmatrix}$ and

   $\begin{bmatrix} \dfrac{7}{3} & 1 \\ 2 & 1 \end{bmatrix}\begin{bmatrix} 3 & -3 \\ -6 & 7 \end{bmatrix} = \begin{bmatrix} 1 & 0 \\ 0 & 1 \end{bmatrix}$

2. $\begin{bmatrix} -\dfrac{3}{40} & \dfrac{1}{20} \\ -\dfrac{11}{40} & -\dfrac{3}{20} \end{bmatrix}$

3. The inverse is not defined.

4. $\begin{bmatrix} -2 & 6 & -1 \\ -4 & 9 & -1 \\ 3 & -7 & 1 \end{bmatrix}$ 5. $x = \dfrac{1}{2}$, $y = 3$

6. $x = -5$, $y = -3$, $z = 6$

7. $x = 0$, $y = 3$, $z = 2$, $w = 1$

Problem Solving

1. $\begin{cases} 3p + 3t + f = 5.52 \\ p + 2t + 3f = 4.59 \\ 2p + 2t + 2f = 4.68 \end{cases}$

2. $\begin{bmatrix} 3 & 3 & 1 \\ 1 & 2 & 3 \\ 2 & 2 & 2 \end{bmatrix}\begin{bmatrix} p \\ t \\ f \end{bmatrix} = \begin{bmatrix} 5.52 \\ 4.59 \\ 4.68 \end{bmatrix}$

3. 4

4. $A^{-1} = \begin{bmatrix} -0.5 & -1 & 1.75 \\ 1 & 1 & -2 \\ -0.5 & 0 & 0.75 \end{bmatrix}$

5. $\begin{bmatrix} p \\ t \\ f \end{bmatrix} = \begin{bmatrix} 0.84 \\ 0.75 \\ 0.75 \end{bmatrix}$

6. Pasta salad: $.84 per oz tuna salad: $.75 per oz fruit salad: $.75 per oz

7. D   8. B

Reading Strategies

1. Yes; Possible answer: Because matrix H is a square matrix and its determinant is not 0.

2. The identity matrix

3. Because the formula involves multiplying by $\dfrac{1}{\det A}$ and $\dfrac{1}{0}$ is undefined

4. F is a square matrix and its determinant is not 0.

LESSON 4-6

Practice A

1. a. $\begin{cases} 3x + 2y = 2 \\ x - 4y = 24 \end{cases}$

   b. $\left[\begin{array}{cc|c} 3 & 2 & 2 \\ 1 & -4 & 24 \end{array}\right]$

2. $\left[\begin{array}{cc|c} 2 & 5 & 1 \\ 1 & -1 & 4 \end{array}\right]$ 3. $\left[\begin{array}{cc|c} 5 & -2 & 0 \\ 3 & -4 & 14 \end{array}\right]$

4. $\left[\begin{array}{cc|c} 4 & -9 & 1 \\ -2 & 1 & 1 \end{array}\right]$

5. a. $\left[\begin{array}{cc|c} 6 & 4 & 4 \\ 1 & -4 & 24 \end{array}\right]$

   b. $\left[\begin{array}{cc|c} 7 & 0 & 28 \\ 1 & -4 & 24 \end{array}\right]$

   c. $\left[\begin{array}{cc|c} 1 & 0 & 4 \\ 1 & -4 & 24 \end{array}\right]$

   d. $\left[\begin{array}{cc|c} 1 & 0 & 4 \\ 0 & 4 & -20 \end{array}\right]$

   e. $\left[\begin{array}{cc|c} 1 & 0 & 4 \\ 0 & 1 & -5 \end{array}\right]$

   f. $x = 4$, $y = -5$

6. $(3, -1)$ 7. $(-2, -5)$

8. $(7, 3)$

Holt Algebra 2

Practice B

1. $\begin{bmatrix} 2 & -1 & 0 & | & -1 \\ 1 & 1 & 1 & | & 1 \\ 0 & 4 & 5 & | & 3 \end{bmatrix}$

2. $\begin{bmatrix} 3 & -2 & 0 & | & 4 \\ 1 & -1 & -3 & | & 0 \\ -1 & 2 & 8 & | & 0 \end{bmatrix}$

3. $\begin{bmatrix} 1 & 0 & 1 & | & 1 \\ 3 & -5 & 0 & | & 12 \\ 0 & 2 & -3 & | & 9 \end{bmatrix}$

4. $\begin{bmatrix} 4 & 3 & | & -11 \\ 2 & -3 & | & 17 \end{bmatrix}$; $(1, -5)$

5. $\begin{bmatrix} 3 & 7 & | & -1 \\ 6 & 11 & | & 10 \end{bmatrix}$; $(9, -4)$

6. $\begin{bmatrix} 2 & -3 & | & -1 \\ 5 & -12 & | & 2 \end{bmatrix}$; $(-2, -1)$

7. $\begin{bmatrix} 1 & 6 & | & 0 \\ 2 & 9 & | & -3 \end{bmatrix}$; $(-6, 1)$

8. a. $\begin{cases} 10d + 25q = 495 \\ d = q - 3 \end{cases}$

   b. $\begin{bmatrix} 10 & 25 & | & 495 \\ 1 & -1 & | & -3 \end{bmatrix}$

   c. 12 dimes and 15 quarters

10. 35 nickels and 25 pennies

Practice C

1. $\begin{bmatrix} 5 & -3 & | & 14 \\ 3 & 4 & | & -9 \end{bmatrix}$; $(1, -3)$

2. $\begin{bmatrix} 9 & 11 & | & -19 \\ 15 & 22 & | & -17 \end{bmatrix}$; $(-7, 4)$

3. $\begin{bmatrix} 7 & 2 & | & -4 \\ 5 & -3 & | & 37 \end{bmatrix}$; $(2, -9)$

4. $\begin{bmatrix} 6 & -5 & | & -5 \\ -8 & 3 & | & -19 \end{bmatrix}$; $(5, 7)$

5. $\begin{bmatrix} 1 & -1 & 1 & | & -1 \\ 0 & -1 & 4 & | & 0 \\ 2 & 0 & -1 & | & 8 \end{bmatrix}$; $(5, 8, 2)$

6. $\begin{bmatrix} 0 & 3 & 1 & | & -1 \\ -3 & 5 & 2 & | & 0 \\ 1 & 1 & 0 & | & 0 \end{bmatrix}$; $(-1, 1, -4)$

7. a. 640 minutes

   b. Plan B

8. 4 dimes

Reteach

1. $\begin{bmatrix} 5 & -7 & | & 1 \\ 2 & -1 & | & -3 \end{bmatrix}$

2. $\begin{bmatrix} 8 & -1 & | & -9 \\ -1 & -4 & | & 7 \end{bmatrix}$

3. $\begin{bmatrix} 1 & 1 & -1 & | & 5 \\ -1 & 0 & 2 & | & 3 \\ 0 & 1 & -4 & | & -1 \end{bmatrix}$

4. $\begin{bmatrix} 1 & -1 & 1 & | & 1 \\ 3 & 0 & -5 & | & 2 \\ 0 & -6 & 1 & | & -8 \end{bmatrix}$

5. $\begin{bmatrix} -1 & 3 & 1 & | & 0 \\ 2 & -1 & 8 & | & 0 \\ -1 & 1 & -1 & | & -4 \end{bmatrix}$

6. a. $\begin{bmatrix} 1 & 1 & | & -2 \\ 1 & -2 & | & 7 \end{bmatrix}$

   b. $\begin{bmatrix} 1 & 1 & | & -2 \\ 0 & -3 & | & 9 \end{bmatrix}$

   c. -3; $\begin{bmatrix} 1 & 1 & | & -2 \\ 0 & 1 & | & -3 \end{bmatrix}$

   d. $\begin{bmatrix} 1 & 0 & | & 1 \\ 0 & 1 & | & -3 \end{bmatrix}$

   e. 1; -3

Challenge

1. $\begin{bmatrix} 0 & 1 \\ -1 & 0 \end{bmatrix}$

2. $\begin{bmatrix} \dfrac{2}{11} & \dfrac{3}{11} \\ -\dfrac{1}{11} & \dfrac{4}{11} \end{bmatrix}$

3. The inverse is not defined.

4. $\begin{bmatrix} 1 & 0 & 0 \\ 0 & 2 & -7 \\ 0 & -1 & 4 \end{bmatrix}$

5. $\begin{bmatrix} -\dfrac{4}{3} & -\dfrac{5}{3} & 1 \\ -\dfrac{4}{3} & -\dfrac{8}{3} & 1 \\ \dfrac{1}{3} & \dfrac{2}{3} & 0 \end{bmatrix}$

6. The inverse is not defined.

Holt Algebra 2

Problem Solving

1. $\begin{cases} b = p + 1 \\ m = 3p \\ 6m + 5.5b + 9.5p = 236.5 \end{cases}$

2. $\begin{bmatrix} 0 & 1 & -1 & | & 1 \\ 1 & 0 & -3 & | & 0 \\ 6 & 5.5 & 9.5 & | & 236.5 \end{bmatrix}$

3. $\begin{bmatrix} 1 & 0 & 0 & | & 21 \\ 0 & 1 & 0 & | & 8 \\ 0 & 0 & 1 & | & 7 \end{bmatrix}$

4. 21 mugs, 8 bowls, 7 plates

5. C   6. A

Reading Strategies

1. Possible answer: An augmented matrix shows the coefficients and the constants of the linear equations in the order they appear in the equations.

2. $\begin{cases} -5x + 10y = 3 \\ 2x - 4y = 1 \end{cases}$

3. Possible answer: Multiplying the equation by 3 gives an equation equivalent to the original equation. In the same way, multiplying one row of the augmented matrix by 3 gives a matrix equivalent to the original matrix.

LESSON 5-1

Practice A

1. a.

x	$f(x) = x^2 - 3$	$(x, f(x))$
-2	$f(-2) = (-2)^2 - 3$	(-2, 1)
-1	-2	(-1, -2)
0	-3	(0, -3)
1	-2	(1, -2)
2	1	(2, 1)

b.

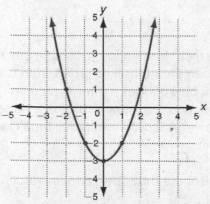

2. Reflected across the x-axis

3. Translated 1 unit right

4. Translated 7 units up

5. Horizontal stretch by a factor of 3

6. Translated 3 units left

7. Vertical stretch by a factor of 5

8. a. $g(x) = (x + 2)^2 + 3$

   b.

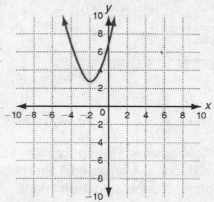

Practice B

1.

x	$f(x) = x^2 + 2x - 1$	$(x, f(x))$
-2	-1	(-2, -1)
-1	-2	(-1, -2)
0	-1	(0, -1)
1	2	(1, 2)
2	7	(2, 7)

2. Translated 2 units right, 2 units up

3. Reflected across the x-axis and horizontal compression by a factor of 3

4. Horizontal stretch by a factor of 2

5. $g(x) = -\left(\dfrac{1}{3}x\right)^2 - 2$

6. Vertical translation; possible answer: at a given time a ball dropped from tower A will be 200 feet higher than a ball dropped from tower B at the same time. Tower A is 200 feet taller than tower B.

Practice C

1. Parabola that opens downward

2. The ball rises.

3. Reflected across x-axis, translated 1.5 units right and 36 units up, vertically stretched by a factor of 16

4.

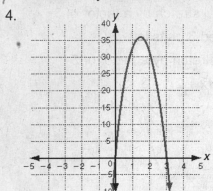

5. $g(x) = -\dfrac{1}{5}x^2 + 2$ 6. $m(x) = -3x^2$

7. Possible answer: Both parabolas open upward; one is translated 1 unit down and the other is translated 1 unit right.

8. Translation 2 units right

Reteach

1.

x	$f(x) = x^2 - 6x + 7$	$(x, f(x))$
1	$f(1) = 1^2 - 6(1) + 7 = 2$	$(1, 2)$
2	$f(2) = -1$	$(2, -1)$
3	$f(3) = -2$	$(3, -2)$
4	$f(4) = -1$	$(4, -1)$
5	$f(5) = 2$	$(5, 2)$

2. -3

Graph is shifted 1 unit left and 3 units down.

3. $(3, 2)$

Graph is shifted 3 units right and 2 units up.

Challenge

1. $y = -5(x + 1)^2 + 4$

2. $y = \dfrac{1}{2}(x - 2)^2 - 3$ 3. $y = 7(x + 3)^2 - 4$

4. $y = -\dfrac{1}{4}(x - 2)^2 + 3$

Problem Solving

1.

Time (t)	$f(t) = -16t^2 + 185$	$(t, f(t))$
0	$f(0) = -16(0)^2 + 185$	$(0, 185)$
1	$f(1) = -16(1)^2 + 185$	$(1, 169)$
2	$f(2) = -16(2)^2 + 185$	$(2, 121)$
3	$f(3) = -16(3)^2 + 185$	$(3, 41)$
4	$f(4) = -16(4)^2 + 185$	$(4, -71)$

2.

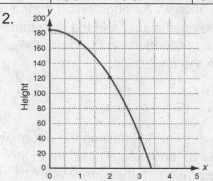

3. $f(x) = x^2$ 4. Parabola

5. The graph is translated up 185 units. Since a is negative, it is reflected across the x-axis. Since $|a| = 16$, it is stretched vertically by a factor of 16.

6. D 7. B

Reading Strategies

1. a. Line

   b. Parabola

   c. Parabola

   d. Line

2. Domain = set of all real numbers; range = $[3, \infty)$

3. Slope $= \dfrac{1}{2}$; possible answer: since the slope is positive, the line slopes from the lower left to the upper right.

Holt Algebra 2

4. (−6, −3); since *a* is positive, the parabola opens upward.

LESSON 5-2

Practice A

1. $x = 4$

2. $x = 2$

3. $x = -6$

4. $x = -1$

5. True

6. False

7. False

8. a. Upward

   b. $x = -\dfrac{1}{3}$

   c. $\left(-\dfrac{1}{3}, \dfrac{2}{3}\right)$

   d. 1

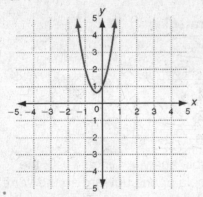

   e. Minimum

   f. $\dfrac{2}{3}$

9. a. Downward

   b. $x = -1$

   c. (−1, 0)

   d. −2

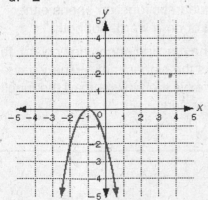

e. Maximum

f. 0

Practice B

1. $x = 2$

2. $x = \dfrac{3}{4}$

3. $x = -3$

4. a. Downward

   b. $x = 1.5$

   c. (1.5, 3.25)

   d. 1

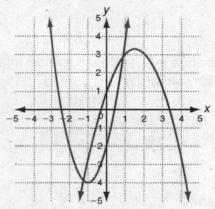

5. a. Upward

   b. $x = -1$

   c. (−1, −4)

   d. −2

6. Minimum: 0; domain: all real numbers; range: $\{y \mid y \geq 0\}$

7. Maximum: 8.25; domain: all real numbers; range: $\{y \mid y \leq 8.25\}$

8. Day 45; 182,250 records

Practice C

1. a. Upward

   b. $x = -2$

   c. (−2, 2)

   d. 4

2. a. Downward

   b. $x = -3$

   c. (−3, 1)

   d. −17

Holt Algebra 2

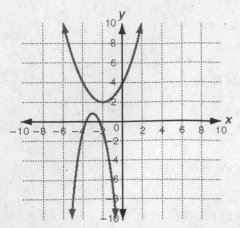

3. Possible answer: $f(x) = (x - 2)^2 - 1$

4. $b = -16$ 5. $k = -20$

6. $400   7. $6,400,000

8. The revenue is 0, because no packages would be sold at $800.

Reteach

1. 1; –4; 3   2. Upward

3. $x = 2$ 4. $f(2) = -1$

5. (2, –1)   6. 3

7. Minimum; 2; 1; $\{y \mid y \geq 1\}$

8. Maximum; 1; –1; $\{y \mid y \leq -1\}$

Challenge

1. Possible answer: The house is 60 feet long plus the additional x length of fence on each side of the house.

2. Possible answer: The perimeter of the fence can be a maximum of 260 feet. Subtract 60 feet for the house length and the 4x lengths to get $260 - (60 + 4x)$, and then divide by 2 for the two equal sides.

3. Exactly at the ends of the backside of the house

4. $f(x) = -4x^2 + 80x + 6000$

5. 6400; 6400 square feet is the maximum area of the backyard that can be fenced.

6. 80 feet by 80 feet

Problem Solving

1. $a < 0$, so the graph opens downward.

2. $x = 40$ 3. –30

4. (40, 18)

5.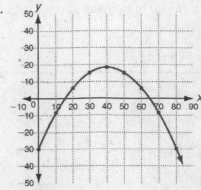

6. a. Maximum

   b. 18

   c. Possible answer: 18 miles per gallon is the highest gas mileage that this car will achieve. That occurs at a speed of 40 miles per hour.

7. D   8. C

Reading Strategies

1. $f(x) = 2x^2 - 3$

   $g(x) = -x^2 + x + 1$

   $h(x) = \frac{1}{2}x^2 + x + 3$

   $k(x) = -6x^2 - x - 5$

2. a. Possible answer: Since $a > 0$, the parabola opens upward so the vertex is at the lowest point. Therefore, the function has a minimum.

   b. Possible answer: Use the formula $x = -\frac{b}{2a}$ to find the x-value of the vertex. Then substitute the x-value in the function to find the y-value, which is the minimum.

3. No; a quadratic function opens either upward or downward, not both.

4. Since the function opens downward, the vertex is the highest point. The y-value of the vertex is the maximum of the function. The maximum is –5.

LESSON 5-3

Practice A

1. False   2. True

Holt Algebra 2

3. False   4. Upward

5. –6   6. (0.5, –6.25)

7.

x	–2	–1	0	2	4
f(x)	0	–4	–6	–4	6

8. –2 and 3

9. a. 0

   b. 2; 5; 0

   c. 2; 0; 5; 0

   d. –2; 5

10. 1, –1

11. a. $(x - 1)(x - 2)$

   b. $x^2 - 3x + 2$

Practice B

1.

x	–4	–3	–2	–1	0
f(x)	2	0	0	2	5

   –2 and –3

2.

x	–2	0	2	4	6
f(x)	–7	5	9	5	–7

   –1 and 5

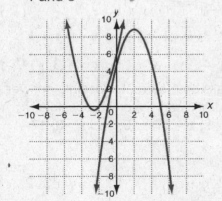

3. –3   4. –0.5, –4

5. –5, 4   6. $\dfrac{2}{3}$

7. –0.75, 0.75   8. $f(x) = x^2 - 5x - 14$

9. $f(x) = x^2 + 7x - 8$ 10. About 7.5 s

Practice C

1. –6, –5   2. 0.5, 12

3. $-\dfrac{1}{3}, \dfrac{1}{3}$ 4. 3.5

5. $-2, \dfrac{2}{3}$

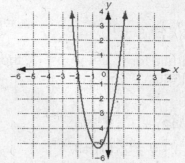

6. $f(x) = x^2 - 5x - 6$

7. $f(x) = x^3 - 6x^2 - x + 30$

8. For roots 2 and 1: $f(x) = x^2 - 3x + 2$

9. $f(x) = x^2 - 4x$

10. a. $h(t) = -16t^2 + 100t$

   b. 6.25 s

Reteach

1. 6; 4x; 6; $x = 0$ or $x = 6$

2. 3; 1; 3; 1; $x = -3$ or $x = -1$

3. $x^2 - 5x + 4 = 0$

   $(x - 4)(x - 1) = 0$

   $x - 4 = 0$ or $x - 1 = 0$

   $x - 4$ or $x = 1$

4. $3x^2 + 12x = 0$

   $3x(x + 4) = 0$

   $3x = 0$ or $x + 4 = 0$

   $x = 0$ or $x = -4$

5. 0

   $(2x)^2 - (7)^2 = 0$

   $(2x + 7)(2x - 7) = 0$

   $2x + 7 = 0$ or $2x - 7 = 0$

   $x = -\dfrac{7}{2}$ or $x = \dfrac{7}{2}$

6. 0

   $x^2 - 2(4)(x) + (4)^2 = 0$

   $(x - 4)^2 = 0$

   $(x - 4) = 0$

   $x = 4$

     Holt Algebra 2

Challenge

1. $(x^2)^2 + 4(x^2) - 5 = 0$ 2. No

3. $(x^4)^2 - 17(x^4) + 16 = 0$

4. No

5. $\left(\sqrt{x}\right)^2 - 2\left(\sqrt{x}\right) - 8 = 0$

6. It is in quadratic form. Let $y = x - 3$, then $y^2 - 4y - 21 = 0$.

7. $x(x^2 - 9) = 0$

8. $x^3(x^2 - 4x - 12) = 0$ 9. No

10. $(x^2)^2 - 10(x^2) + 9 = 0; \pm 1, \pm 3$

11. $9\left(x^2\right)^2 - 18\left(x^2\right) + 8 = 0; \pm\sqrt{\dfrac{2}{3}}, \pm\sqrt{\dfrac{4}{3}}$

12. $\left(\sqrt{x}\right)^2 - 3\left(\sqrt{x}\right) - 4 = 0; 16$

Problem Solving

1. a. $a = -16, b = 80, c = 0$

   b. $t = \dfrac{-80}{2(-16)} = 2.5$ seconds

   c. 100 feet

   d. 5 seconds

2. a. $h(t) = -16t^2 + 80t + 21$

   b. $(4t + 1)(-4t + 21) = 0$

   c. Possible answer: Erin has the roots correct. Set each factor equal to 0 and solve for t. But the rocket will stay in the air 5.25 seconds. (The negative root represents the time before launch since the rocket is starting at 21 feet, not at ground level.)

3. A   4. C

Reading Strategies

1. Possible answer: The points where the function crosses the x-axis are the zeros of the function.

2. No; possible answer: a parabola can cross the x-axis at most at two points.

3. a. 1 and –1

   b. Factoring; possible answer: since the function was already factored, I just set each factor equal to 0 and solved for x.

4. No zeros exist for this function. Possible answer: Since the parabola opens down and its vertex is below the x-axis, the graph will not cross the x-axis.

5. Possible answer: I would check some factors of c to see if I could easily factor the equation. If not, then I would make a graph.

LESSON 5-4

Practice A

1. $\sqrt{9}$

   $x + 1 = \pm 3, x = -4$ or 2

2. $\sqrt{16}$

   $x - 2 = \pm 4, x = -2$ or 6

3. $\sqrt{25}$

   $x + 3 = \pm 5, x = -8$ or 2

4. $\left(\dfrac{4}{2}\right)^2 = 4$ 5. $\left(\dfrac{2}{2}\right)^2 = 1$

6. $\left(\dfrac{-8}{2}\right)^2 = 16$ 7. a. $\left(\dfrac{10}{2}\right)^2; \left(\dfrac{10}{2}\right)^2$

   b. 25; 25

   c. 5; 5; 45

   d. 5; $\sqrt{45}$

   e. $-5 \pm 3\sqrt{5}$

8. $x = 3 \pm 4\sqrt{2}$ 9. $x = -13, -1$

10. They are both correct. Possible answer: A quadratic can have two possible solutions; $x - 7 = \pm 10$, so $x = -3, 17$.

Practice B

1. $x = \pm 2\sqrt{6}$ 2. $x = 7 \pm 3\sqrt{2}$

3. $4; (x - 2)^2$ 4. $36; (x + 6)^2$

5. $d = \dfrac{5}{2} \pm \dfrac{\sqrt{41}}{2}$ 6. $x = -3, 1$

7. $x = 3 \pm \sqrt{19}$ 8. $x = -\dfrac{3}{2} \pm \dfrac{\sqrt{13}}{2}$

9. $f(x) = (x - 3)^2 - 11; (3, -11)$

10. $g(x) = (x - 2)^2 - 3; (2, -3)$

Holt Algebra 2

11. $h(x) = 3(x - 1)^2 - 18$; $(1, -18)$

12. $f(x) = -2(x + 4)^2 + 36$; $(-4, 36)$

13. a. Base = 8 ft, height = 20 ft

    b. Base = 10 ft, height = 16 ft

Practice C

1. 121; $(x - 11)^2$

2. $\dfrac{81}{4}$; $\left(x + \dfrac{9}{2}\right)^2$

3. $x = -7 \pm \sqrt{73}$

4. $x = 2 \pm \sqrt{3}$

5. $x = -1, 4$

6. $x = -4 \pm 2\sqrt{3}$

7. $f(x) = (x - 2)^2 - 21$, $(2, -21)$

8. $g(x) = \left(x - \dfrac{1}{4}\right)^2 + \dfrac{15}{16}$; $\left(\dfrac{1}{4}, \dfrac{15}{16}\right)$

9. $h(x) = 3(x - 4)^2 - 33$; $(4, -33)$

10. $f(x) = -\left(x + \dfrac{3}{2}\right)^2 + \dfrac{57}{4}$; $\left(-\dfrac{3}{2}, \dfrac{57}{4}\right)$

11. $f(x) = x^2 - 6x + 10$ 12. y-intercept = 17

13. a. $S(t) = (t - 3)^2 + 4$

    b. 13; $t = 6$

    c. $(3, 4)$; the minimum price

Reteach

1. 24; $x^2 = 8$; $x = \pm 2\sqrt{2}$

2. $(x - 4)^2 = 18$; $x - 4 = \pm\sqrt{18}$; $x = 4 \pm 3\sqrt{2}$

3. $6x^2 = 42$; $x^2 = 7$; $x = \pm\sqrt{7}$

4. $(x - 1)^2 = 10$; $x - 1 = \pm\sqrt{10}$; $x = 1 \pm \sqrt{10}$

5. $\dfrac{81}{4}$; $\dfrac{81}{4}$; $\left(x + \dfrac{9}{2}\right)^2$

6. -4; -2; 4; 4; $(x - 2)^2$

7. $x^2 - 10x + 25$

    $(x - 5)^2$

8. $x^2 + 3x + \dfrac{9}{4}$

    $\left(x + \dfrac{3}{2}\right)^2$

Challenge

1. a. $l^2 = wl + w^2$, $l^2 - wl - w^2 = 0$

    b.

$$l^2 - wl = w^2, l^2 - wl + \left(\dfrac{w}{2}\right)^2 = w^2 + \left(\dfrac{w}{2}\right)^2,$$

$$\left(l - \dfrac{w}{2}\right)^2 = \dfrac{5w^2}{4}, l - \dfrac{w}{2} = \dfrac{\sqrt{5}w}{2}, l = \dfrac{1 + \sqrt{5}}{2}w, l \cong 1.618w$$

2. Possible answer: The ratio of length to width is about 1.588, a little less than the golden ratio.

3. a. $1, 2, \dfrac{3}{2}, \dfrac{5}{3}, \dfrac{8}{5}, \dfrac{13}{8}, \dfrac{21}{13}, \dfrac{34}{21}, \dfrac{55}{34}, \ldots$

    b. The golden ratio, 1.618

4. 2, 1.5, 1.667, 1.6, 1.625, 1.615, 1.619, 1.618; they seem to approach the golden ratio.

Problem Solving

1. a. $15 = -5t^2 + 30t$

    b. $t^2 - 6t = -3$

    c. $t = 0.6, 5.4$

    d. Possible answer: He is partially correct. The flare will first reach 15 meters at 0.6 second after firing and then again at 5.4 seconds. (The function has two solutions.)

    e. Possible answer: He is correct. The flare will first reach 15 meters at 0.6 second after firing. Also, the difference between 5.4 and 0.6 seconds (the two solutions) is 4.8 seconds, which is about 5 seconds.

2. a. $h(t) = -5(t^2 - 6t + 9) + 45$

    b. $h(t) = -5(t - 3)^2 + 45$

    c. The constant term; 45 meters

3. A   4. B

Reading Strategy

1. $(x - 1)^2$ 2. a. 4

   $(4x - 5)^2$ b. $(x - 2)^2$

   $x^2 + 6x + 9$

   x^2

3. $(x + 1)^2$; the side of the model square is $x + 1$.

LESSON 5-5

Practice A

1. $3i; 7i - 1; -2i$
2. i
3. -1
4. a
5. bi
6. $2i$
7. $9i$
8. $-9i$
9. $8i$
10. $5i$
11. $21i$
12. $1 - 2i$
13. $-5i$
14. $2 + 3i$
15. a. $x = \sqrt{-25}$, so $x = 5i$ and $-5i$.

   b. Possible answer: You could multiply $(x + 5i)(x - 5i)$ to get the original expression.

16. a. $x = \sqrt{-16}$, so $x = 4i$ and $-4i$.

   b. Possible answer: You could multiply $(x + 4i)(x - 4i)$ to get the original expression.

Practice B

1. $4i\sqrt{2}$
2. $6i\sqrt{2}$
3. $\frac{1}{3}i$
4. $x = \pm 3i\sqrt{3}$
5. $x = \pm i\sqrt{7}$
6. $x = \pm 4i\sqrt{3}$
7. $x = \pm i\sqrt{21}$
8. $x = 4, y = 5$
9. $x = -\frac{1}{3}, y = \frac{1}{2}$
10. $x = 1 \pm i\sqrt{3}$
11. $x = -3 \pm i\sqrt{5}$
12. $-3 - i$
13. $-4 - 3i$
14. $-11i$
15. $3 \pm i\sqrt{11}$

Practice C

1. $x = \pm 2i\sqrt{14}$
2. $x = \pm i\sqrt{11}$
3. $x = 3 \pm i\sqrt{11}$
4. $x = 2 \pm 2i$
5. $x = 1 \pm i\sqrt{2}$
6. $x = \frac{5}{3}, y = 1$
7. $x = -6, y = -8$
8. $x = 2, y = 0.25$
9. $-25 - i\sqrt{3}$
10. $\frac{12}{5} + 5i$
11. $-2 + 1.5i$

12. Imaginary; possible answer: since a is positive, the parabola opens upward and the vertex is at the minimum. Since the function is in vertex form, you can tell that the vertex is at $(1, 5)$. With a minimum at 5, the function never crosses the x-axis, so the zeros have to be imaginary.

13. a. The beginning and end of the flight when the speed of the rocket is 0

   b. $t = -3 \pm 5i$

   c. No; possible answer: the zeros are imaginary because the graph never crosses the x-axis so the function never equals 0. The speed of the rocket must be 0 before takeoff and after landing.

Reteach

1. $6i\sqrt{2}$
2. $12i\sqrt{2}$
3. $10i$
4. $15i\sqrt{6}$
5. $16i$
6. $-7i\sqrt{2}$
7. $9i$
8. $1 - 4i$
9. $12 + i$
10. $x = \pm 3i\sqrt{2}$
11. $x = \pm\sqrt{-4}$

   $x = \pm 2i$
12. $x^2 = -49$

   $x = \pm\sqrt{-49}$

   $x = \pm 7i$
13. $x^2 = -100$

   $x = \pm\sqrt{-100}$

   $x = \pm 10i$
14. $x^2 = -36$

   $x = \pm\sqrt{-36}$

   $x = \pm 6i$
15. $x^2 = -12$

   $x = \pm\sqrt{(4)(3)(-1)}$

   $x = \pm 2i\sqrt{3}$

Challenge

1. $2i, -7i$
2. $-6i, -8i$
3. $9i, -12i$
4. $5i, 49i$

5. $-16i, -36i$

6. $-\dfrac{4}{3}i, -i$

7. $\dfrac{1}{5}i, 2i$

8. $-3i, -5i$

9. $-\dfrac{13}{4}i, 5i$

10. $\dfrac{5}{6}i, \dfrac{3}{2}i$

Problem Solving

1. a. $t = 1 \pm \dfrac{i}{2}$

b. No; possible answer: the roots are imaginary numbers.

2. a.

b	Function	Roots
24	$d(t) = 16t^2 - 24t + 20$	$\dfrac{1}{4}\left(3 \pm i\sqrt{11}\right)$
32	$d(t) = 16t^2 - \_\_\,t + 20$	$1 \pm \dfrac{i}{2}$
40	$d(t) = 16t^2 - \_\_\,t + 20$	$\dfrac{1}{4}\left(5 \pm \sqrt{5}\right)$
48	$d(t) = 16t^2 - \_\_\,t + 20$	$\dfrac{3}{2} \pm \sqrt{1}$

b. $b = 40$ and 48

c. Possible answer: Real roots mean that ringing the bell is possible.

3. About 36 feet per second

4. C

5. D

Reading Strategies

1. $i\sqrt{9}$; $3i$; $\sqrt{-8}$

2. $3i$ or $-3i$

3. a. $x^2 = -1$, so $x = \pm\sqrt{-1}$, $x = i$ and $-i$

b. Because the square of a real number cannot be a negative number

4. $\left(\sqrt{5}i\right)^2 = \left(\sqrt{5}\right)^2 (i)^2 = 5(-1) = -5; \left(-\sqrt{5}i\right)^2$
$= \left(-\sqrt{5}\right)^2 (i)^2 = 5(-1) = -5$

5. Real number; $(3i)(5i) = 15i^2 = 15(-1) = -15$

LESSON 5-6

Practice A

1. $x = \dfrac{\pm\sqrt{-16}}{2}$

$x = \pm 2i$

2. $x = \dfrac{-(-5) \pm \sqrt{(-5)^2 + 4 \cdot (2) \cdot (3)}}{2 \cdot 2}$

$x = \dfrac{5 \pm \sqrt{25 - 24}}{4}$

$x = 1, 1.5$

3. $x = -1 \pm i\sqrt{3}$

4. $x = 0, -2$

5. -15

6. 1

7. 0

8. One real solution

9. Two real solutions

10. Two nonreal complex solutions

11. Two real solutions

12. a. 15 ft

b. 11 ft

Practice B

1. $x = -9, -1$

2. $x = -1 \pm \sqrt{7}$

3. $x = 0.5$

4. $x = -3, 1$

5. $x = -1, -0.5$

6. $x = \dfrac{-5 \pm \sqrt{37}}{2}$

7. Two nonreal solutions

8. Two real solutions

9. One real solution

10. a. 0.5 s

b. 15 ft

c. 1 s

Practice C

1. $x = -4 \pm \sqrt{19}$

2. $x = \dfrac{3 \pm \sqrt{11}}{2}$

3. $x = \dfrac{1 \pm i\sqrt{47}}{2}$

4. $x = -\dfrac{5 \pm \sqrt{185}}{4}$

5. $x = \dfrac{3 \pm \sqrt{5}}{2}$

6. $x = \dfrac{5 \pm \sqrt{13}}{3}$

7. Two nonreal solutions

8. Two real solutions

9. One real solution

Holt Algebra 2

10. About 1.49 s   11. 2.9 s

12. 37.7 ft   13. 3.5 m

Reteach

1. $a = 1$, $b = 1$, $c = -1$

$$x = \frac{-(1) \pm \sqrt{(1)^2 - 4(1)(-1)}}{2(1)}$$

$$x = \frac{-1 \pm \sqrt{1 + 4}}{2}$$

$$x = \frac{-1 \pm \sqrt{5}}{2}$$

2. $x^2 - 6x + 6 = 0$

$a = 1$, $b = -6$, $c = 6$

$$x = \frac{-(-6) \pm \sqrt{(-6)^2 - 4(1)(6)}}{2(1)}$$

$$x = \frac{6 \pm \sqrt{36 - 24}}{2}$$

$$x = 3 \pm \sqrt{3}$$

3. $a = 1$, $b = -12$, $c = 36$

0

1 real solution

4. $x^2 - 4x + 7 = 0$

$a = 1$, $b = -4$, $c = 7$

-12

2 complex solutions

5. $x^2 - 7x + 3 = 0$

$a = 1$, $b = -7$, $c = 3$

37

2 real solutions

Challenge

1.

Equation	Roots	Sum of the Roots	Product of the Roots
a. $x^2 - 6x + 8 = 0$	4, 2	6	8
b. $x^2 - 7x + 12 = 0$	4, 3	7	12
c. $x^2 + 2x - $	5, −7	−2	−35

	Equation	Roots	Sum of the Roots	Product of the Roots
	$35 = 0$			
d.	$4x^2 - 8x + 3 = 0$	$\frac{1}{2}, \frac{3}{2}$	2	$\frac{3}{4}$
e.	$9x^2 + 3x - 2 = 0$	$\frac{1}{3}, -\frac{2}{3}$	$-\frac{1}{3}$	$-\frac{2}{9}$

2. a. $r_1 + r_2 = -\dfrac{b}{a}$

b. $r_1 r_2 = \dfrac{c}{a}$

3. $x^2 - 4x - 1 = 0$ 4. $k = -3$

5. C   6. A

Problem Solving

1. a. $t = -0.25$, 1.5

b. 30 ft

2. a. $t = -0.23$, 1.61; 35.4 ft

b. $t = -0.21$, 1.77; 44.3 ft

c. $t = -0.19$, 1.94; 54.3 ft

3. C   4. C

Reading Strategies

1. $a = 2$, $b = -6$, $c = -9$

2. $(-6)^2 - 4(2)(-9) = 108$

3. Since the discriminant is positive, the equation has two real roots.

4. Yes; since the equation has two real roots, the related function has two zeros.

5. $x = \dfrac{-(-6) \pm \sqrt{108}}{2(2)} = \dfrac{3 \pm 3\sqrt{3}}{2}$

LESSON 5-7

Practice A

1.

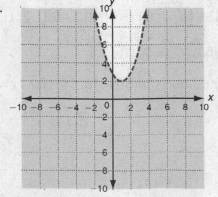

Holt Algebra 2

c. $(0, 0); 0 < 3$ ✓

2. a. -5

   b. $(2, -1)$

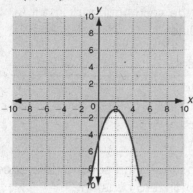

   c. $(0, 0); 0 \geq -5$ ✓

3. a. $x^2 + x - 8 = -6$

   b. $x = -2, 1$

   c. $x = -3, -2 \leq -6$ X; $x = 0, -8 \leq -6$ ✓;
      $x = 2, -2 \leq -6$ X

   d. $-2 \leq x \leq 1$

4. $x < -8$ or $x > -2$

5. $-3 < x < 4$

6. $x \leq -6$ or $x \geq 4$

7. Between 40 and 70 employees

Practice B

1.

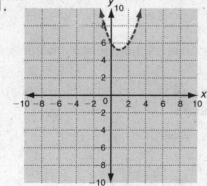

2.

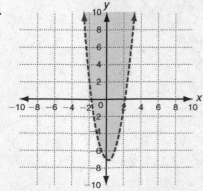

3. $-7 \leq x \leq 4$

4. $x < 3$ or $x > 6$

5. $x < -1$ or $x > 3$

6. $-5 < x < -1$

7. $x \leq 2$ or $x \geq 6$

8. $-\dfrac{4}{3} \leq x \leq 1$

9. More than 30 but fewer than 60

Practice C

1.

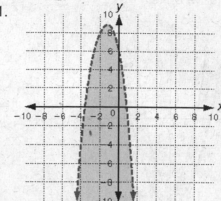

2.

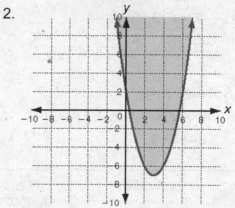

3. $x \leq 3$ or $x \geq 7$

4. $-\dfrac{1}{2} < x < 4$

5. $-4 \leq x \leq 4$

6. $x < -6$ or $x > 12$

7. $x = \dfrac{3 \pm i\sqrt{31}}{2}$

8. a. 13.6 s

   b. More than 10.4 s but less than 13.6 s into the race

   c. Less than 10.4 s into the race

Reteach

1. $(2, -1); 3$; solid boundary; $1 \geq 0$

2. $(-2, 3); -1$; dashed boundary; $0 < 2$

3. 3; 0; $-1, 3$; $-2, 0, 4$; $x \leq -1$ or $x \geq 3$

4. $x^2 + x - 2 = 0$; $-2, 1$; $-3, 0, 2$; $-2 < x < 1$

Holt Algebra 2

Challenge

1. (–2, 1), (2, 1)   2. 4 units

3. The area enclosed between the segment and each parabola is $\frac{32}{3}$ square units so the area bounded by both parabolas is $\frac{64}{3}$ square units.

4.

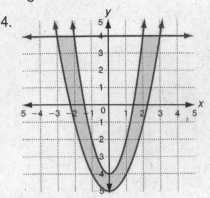

5. (–3, 4), (–2, 4), (2, 4), (3, 4)

6. Area $= \frac{108}{3} - \frac{64}{3} = \frac{44}{3}$ square units

Problem Solving

1. a. $-28x^2 + 1400x - 3496 \geq 10{,}000$

   b. $x = 13.04,\ 36.96$

   c.

x-value	Evaluate	$P \geq$ 10,000?
10	$-28(10)^2 + 1400(10) -$ 3496	no
30	13,304	yes
40	7704	no

   d. From 14 to 36 people

2. Possible answer: The range is narrower. There must be between 17 and 33 people to take the tour.

3. B   4. B

Reading Strategies

1. $y \geq x^2 + 1$ and $y \leq x^2 + 1$

2. $y < x^2 + 1$; (0, 1) is not a solution of this inequality because that point lies on the boundary line, which is not part of the solution.

3. The region inside the curve not including the boundary line

4. $y \geq x^2 + 1$; possible answer: (4, 20)

5. Change the solid boundary line to a dashed line

LESSON 5-8

Practice A

1. a. –12, –9, –6, –3

   b. 3, 3, 3

   c. Yes, because the second differences are a nonzero constant

2. a. –6, –5, –4, –3

   b. 1, 1, 1

   c. Yes, because the second differences are a nonzero constant

3. a. $c = -12$; $36a + 6b + c = 12$; $4a + 2b + c = -8$

   b. $a = \frac{1}{2}$, $b = 1$, $c = -12$

   c. $f(x) = \frac{1}{2}x^2 + x - 12$

4. $f(x) = x^2 - 12x + 22$ 5. $f(x) = -2x^2 + 20$

Practice B

1. Yes, because all the second differences are 2

2. No, because the second differences are not constant

3. $f(x) = x^2 + 2x - 8$

4. $f(x) = -x^2 + 8x - 7$

5. $f(x) = x^2 - 4x - 6$ 6. $f(x) = 2x^2 - x + 3$

7. a. $E = 2v^2$

   b. 50 joules

   c. 8 m/s

Practice C

1. –5; –12   2. 0; 2

3. $f(x) = 2x^2 + x - 3$

4. $f(x) = -x^2 + 11x - 28$

5. $f(x) = x^2 - 8x + 15$ 6. $f(x) = x^2 - 5x - 6$

Holt Algebra 2

7. No; possible answer: a quadratic function can be defined by 3 noncollinear points, but these 3 points lie on the same line so the points define a linear function.

8. a. $f(x) = -2x^2 + 18x + 20$

   b. 10 minutes

Reteach

1. 14, 0, 14; not a quadratic function
2. 2, 2, 2; quadratic function
3. 0, 3, 3; not a quadratic function
4. 5, 5, 5; quadratic function
5. a. $(0, 1)1 = a(0)^2 + b(0) + c$

   $c = 1$

   b. $(1, -2)-2 = a(1)^2 + b(1) + c$

   $a + b + c = -2$

   c. $(2, -3)-3 = a(2)^2 + b(2) + c$

   $4a + 2b + c = -3$

   d. $a = 1, b = -4, c = 1$

   e. $f(x) = x^2 - 4x + 1$

Challenge

1. 4; 4; 4; 4; 0; 0; 0
2. Yes; 2nd degree; $y = ax^2 + bx + c$
3. a. $a = 2$

   b. $b = -1$

   c. $c = 5$

   d. $y = 2x^2 - x + 5$;

Problem Solving

1. a. Yes; possible answer: the first differences of the y-values in the table are not constant. The second differences are constant (3). So this data represents a quadratic function.

   b. $\begin{cases} 25a + 5b + c = 7 \\ 100a + 10b + c = 17 \\ 400a + 20b + c = 46 \end{cases}$

   c. $a = 0.06, b = 1.1, c = 0$

   d. $f(x) = 0.06x^2 + 1.1x$

   e. 282 ft

2. B   3. C

Reading Strategies

1. Yes. The second differences are constant and nonzero.
2. No. The second differences are not constant.
3. Yes. The second differences are 9; they are constant and nonzero.

LESSON 5-9

Practice A

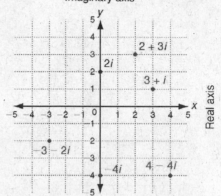

7. $2\sqrt{10}$ 8. $\sqrt{10}$
9. 5   10. $10i$
11. $-4i$ 12. $2 + 12i$
13. $4 + 6i$ 14. $-3 - 4i$
15. $10 - 5i$ 16. $6i$
17. $-20i$ 18. $12 + 16i$
19. $-10 + 6i$ 20. $7 - 11i$
21. $-8 + 9i$ 22. $-i$
23. $\dfrac{5}{3} - \dfrac{2}{3}i$ 24. $\dfrac{1}{5} + \dfrac{13}{5}i$

Practice B

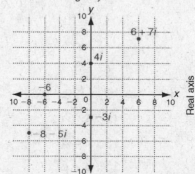

6. $2\sqrt{5}$ 7. $\sqrt{26}$

Holt Algebra 2

8. 3

9. $5 - 7i$

10. $-1 - 10i$

11. $-7 + 10i$

12. $9 + 6i$

13. $3 + 14i$

14. $9 + 20i$

15. $\dfrac{4}{3} - \dfrac{2}{3}i$

16. $\dfrac{14}{17} + \dfrac{5}{17}i$

17. $-2i$

18. $8 + 2i$

Practice C

1. $6\sqrt{5}$

2. $\sqrt{65}$

3. $\dfrac{\sqrt{2}}{2}$

4. $13 + 3i$

5. $-8 - 17i$

6. $\dfrac{1}{4} - \dfrac{1}{2}i$

7. $-5 + 2i$

8. $6 - 8i$

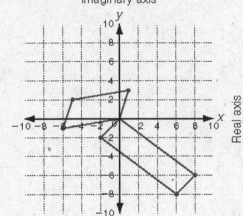

9. $\dfrac{53}{65} + \dfrac{31i}{65}$

10. $-14 - 80i$

11. $\dfrac{9}{5} + \dfrac{7i}{5}$

12. $2 - i$

13. $-4i$

14. 10

15. $14 + 5i$

Reteach

6. 8

7. $\sqrt{5}$

8. 3

9. $\sqrt{29}$

10. 9

11. 5

12. $9 - i$

13. $7 - 4i$

14. $4 + 8i$

15. $3 - 8i$

16. $-2i$

17. $-15 + 20i$

18. $10i$

19. $7 + 4i$

20. $-12 + 16i$

Challenge

1. Square roots should be simplified first.

2. 6; 6

3. The answers are the same. Yes; this will always be true in the system of real numbers. The order of operations can be reversed in this case; yes

4. $\sqrt{3}i \cdot \sqrt{12}i = \sqrt{3} \cdot \sqrt{12} \cdot i^2 = \sqrt{36}i^2$
$= 6 \cdot -1 = -6; \sqrt{36} = 6$

5. The answers are different. The order of operations cannot be changed in this case.

6. Possible answer: When multiplying radicals that have negative radicands, first simplify the radical using the imaginary number i, and then find the product.

7. -32

8. 12

9. -5

10. $-30i$

11. $6i$

12. $4i\sqrt{2}$

Problem Solving

1.

n	$Z_{n+1} = (Z_n)^2 + c$	Z_n
1	$Z_1 = 1 + 2i$	$Z_1 = 1 + 2i$
2	$Z_2 = (1 + 2i)^2 + 1$	$Z_2 = -2 + 4i$
3	$Z_3 = (-2 + 4i)^2 + 1$	$Z_3 = -11 - 16i$
4	$Z_4 = (-11 - 16i)^2 + 1$	$Z_4 = -134 + 352i$

2. $(-13, -35i)$; possible answer: this point cannot be generated using the given formula.

3. D

4. B

5. A

6. C

Reading Strategies

1. a. $-3i$

b. $3 - 4i$

c. $-1 - i$

Holt Algebra 2

d. $-3 + 4i$

e. $3i$

f. $2 + i$

g. -4

2. $5 + \sqrt{-4} = 5 + 2i = 5 + 2i$; located 5 units to the right and two units up

3. $\sqrt{2}$; the point $(-1 + i)$ is one vertex of a right triangle with vertices at the origin and $(-1 + 0i)$. Each leg of the triangle equals 1. Using the Pythagorean Theorem, $1^2 + 1^2 = c^2$, $c^2 = 2$, $c = \sqrt{2}$.

4. The real value is the same for both, and $3i$ and $-3i$ are the same distance from the real number axis. So the distances to the origin are corresponding sides on congruent triangles.

LESSON 6-1

Practice A

1. 2

2. 0

3. 4

4. 1

5. 3

6. 5

7. a. $x^3 + 2x^2 - 7x + 1$

b. 1

c. 3

d. 4

e. Cubic polynomial with 4 terms

8. a. $4x^2 - 3x + 5$

b. 4

c. 2

d. 3

e. Quadratic trinomial

9. $9x + 15$

10. $2x - 12$

11. $x^2 + 2x + 2$

12. $-x^2 + 3x - 5$

13. $7c + 17$

Practice B

1. 2

2. 7

3. 11

4. $-4x^3 + x^2 + 7x + 6$; -4; 3; 4; cubic polynomial with 4 terms

5. $2x^5 + 7x^4 + x^2 - 12x - 3$; 2; 5; 5; quintic polynomial with 5 terms

6. $11x^3 + x^2 + 3x + 4$

7. $-3x^3 - 8x^2 - 6x - 4$

8. $3x^4 + x^3 + 10x^2 + 7$

9. $-x^7 + 21x^2 + 9x - 6$

10. From left to right, the graph increases, decreases slightly, and then increases again. It crosses the x-axis once, so there is 1 real zero.

11. From left to right, the graph alternately decreases and increases, changing direction 3 times. It crosses the x-axis 4 times, so there are 4 real zeros.

12. a. 161 ft and 105 ft

b. The height of the baseball 3 s after being hit by the bat and the height of the baseball 5 s after being hit by the bat

Practice C

1. $9x^5 - 3x^4 + 5x^3 - 10x^2 + 2x - 1$; 9; 5; 6 terms; quintic polynomial with 6 terms

2. $6x^3 + 8x^2 + 4x - 7$

3. $-x^5 - 4x^4 - 2x^3 - 19x + 13$

4. $x^6 - 7x^5 - 2x^4 + 6x^2 - x - 19$

5. $x^4 + 8x^3 - 2x^2 + 4x - 4$

6. $7x^5 + 2x^4 - 3x^3 + x^2 + 6x - 10$

7. From left to right, the graph increases, decreases substantially, and then increases again. It crosses the x-axis 3 times, so there are 3 real zeros.

8. From left to right, the graph decreases and then increases. It crosses the x-axis twice, so there are 2 real zeros.

9. Profits increased from 1994 to 1995

Reteach

1. 3; 4

2. $5x^2 - x$; 3; 4; 3

3. $7x^5 + 6x^3$; 7; 5; 2

4. $x^4 - 2x^3 - 3x^2 - x + 8$; 1; 4; 5

5. $2x^3 + 5x^2 + 5x + 1$

Holt Algebra 2

6. $4x^3 \qquad + x - 5$
   $\underline{+2x^3 + 4x^2 - x}$
   $6x^3 + 4x^2 - 5$

7. $x^3 + 6x^2 + 2x - 2$

8. $(4x^3 + 6) + (-3x^2 + x^3)$
   $\quad 4x^3 \qquad\qquad + 6$
   $\underline{+ \quad x^3 - 3x^2}$
   $5x^3 - 3x^2 + 6$

Challenge

1. $Q_6(x) = x^6 + x^5 + x^4 + x^3 + x^2 + x + 1$

2. a. positive
   b. positive
   c. positive

3. a. always positive
   b. The graph is always above the x-axis.

4. $Q_3(x) = x^3 + x^2 + x + 1$

5. a. $x = -10$
   b. $x = 10$
   c. $x = -1$

6. a.

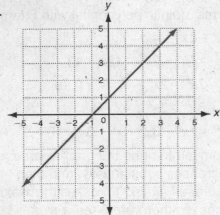

b. When $x < -1$ the graphs are below the x-axis; when $x = -1$ the graphs cross x-axis; when $x > -1$ the graphs are above the x-axis.

c. The sum consists of only 1 and -1. When n is odd, the sum has the same number of (-1)s as it has (1)s, so the sum is 0.

7. 1

Problem Solving

1. a. $SA = \pi\left(\dfrac{d}{2}\right)^2 + \pi\left(\dfrac{d}{2}\right)s$

b. Possible answer: πrs because it gives the surface area of the curved part of the cone, not the circular base; the base is against the cylinder so it isn't part of the surface area of the castle.

2. a. $SA = \dfrac{\pi d^2}{2} + dh\pi$

b. Possible answer: just the curved part and one base; the top of the cylinder is hidden because the cone sits on it.

3. $SA = \pi\left(\dfrac{d}{2}\right)(d - 0.6) + \pi d(d + 4) + \pi\left(\dfrac{d}{2}\right)^2$

4. B   5. C
6. C   7. B

Reading Strategies

1. A monomial has only one term, whereas a polynomial has one or more terms.

2. $\boxed{4x^2 - x}$; $|2n^2 + 1|$; $\boxed{3x\sqrt{17}}$; $\boxed{6z^2}$; $\dfrac{x^2}{z^2} + 1$

3. a. $-x^5 + x + 1$; quintic
   b. $x^3 + x^2 - 2x + 6$; cubic

4. 4; 4; 2   5. 5; 3; -6

LESSON 6-2

Practice A

1. x^2; 4; $2x^3 + 8x$ 2. 2; m^3; $6m - 3m^4$
3. $6p^2 + 42p$ 4. $x^3 + 3x^2 - x$
5. $4x^3 - 10x^2 + 12x$
6. a. $-3x^2$
   b. $-6x$
   c. 3
   d. $-3x^2 - 6x + 3$
   e. $x^3 - x^2 - 7x + 3$
7. x^2; $3x$; -2; x^2; $3x$; -2
   $x^3 + 2x^2 - 5x + 2$
8. $x + 3$; $x + 3$; $x^2 + 6x + 9$
   $x^3 + 9x^2 + 27x + 27$
9. $x - 5$; $x - 5$; $x^2 - 10x + 25$
   $x^3 - 15x^2 + 75x - 125$
10. $3wd - 4d$

Holt Algebra 2

Practice B

1. $12x^4 + 4x^2$
2. $-9x^3 - 18x^2 - 36x$
3. $-6x^5 - 42x^4 + 24x^3 - 18x^2$
4. $-4x^6 + 10x^5 - 7x^4 + 2x^3$
5. $-35m^3n^4 + 10m^4n^3 - 30m^3$
6. $xy^2 + 2xy - 12x + 2y^2 + 4y - 24$
7. $4p^3 - p^2 + 4p^2q - 2pq - 8pq^2 - q^2 - 8q^3$
8. $2x^2y^2 + 6x^3 + xy^3 + 3x^2y - y^3 - 3xy$
9. $27x^3 - 27x^2 + 9x - 1$
10. $x^4 - 16x^3 + 96x^2 - 256x + 256$
11. $3a^2 - 24ab + 48b^2$
12. $5x^6 - 30x^4y + 60x^2y^2 - 40y^3$
13. $8y^5 + 14y^4 + 7y^3 + y^2$

Practice C

1. $n + 1$ 2. n
3. 0 4. n
5. $-10x^2y^3 - 4xy^4 + y^5$
6. $8a^3 - 12a^2b + 6ab^2 - b^3$
7. $5h^4 - 40h^3 + 120h^2 - 160h + 80$
8. $-2m^4 + 12m^3n + 6m^2n^2 - m^2n + 6mn^2 + 3n^3$
9. $\dfrac{1}{27}x^3 + \dfrac{4}{3}x^2 + 16x + 64$
10. $8x^6 - 10x^5 + 4x^4 - 5x^3 - 4x + 5$
11. $a^5 + a^4b^2 + a^3b^4 + a^2b^6$
12. $k^6 - 10k^4 - 9k^3 + 12k^2 - 12k - 108$
13. $-0.0001t^5 - 0.004t^4 + 2.999t^3 - 0.04t^2 + 30t$

Reteach

1. $4x^4 + 8x^3 - 12x^2$
2. $3c^4d^2 - c^3d^3 + 7c^2d^4$
3. $5\left(x \cdot x^3\right)y^2 + 5(4)\left(x \cdot x^2\right)y^2 + 5(2)xy^2$

$5x^4y^2 + 20x^3y^2 + 10xy^2$
4. $3(8)\left(a^2 \cdot a^2\right)b^2 + 3(-2)\left(a^2 \cdot a\right)\left(b^2 \cdot b\right) + 3(-1)a^2\left(b^2 \cdot b^2\right)$

$24a^4b^2 - 6a^3b^3 - 3a^2b^4$

5. $2y^3\left(y^2\right) + 2y^3(-9y) + 2y^3(4)$

$2\left(y^3 \cdot y^2\right) + 2(-9)\left(y^3 \cdot y\right) + 2(4)y^3$

$2y^5 - 18y^4 + 8y^3$
6. $x^2y^2(4x^2) + x^2y^2(7y);\ 4\left(x^2 \cdot x^2\right)y^2 + 7x^2\left(y^2 \cdot y\right)\ 4x^4y^2 + 7x^2y^3$
7. $x^3 - 2x^2 + 2x - 3x^2 + 6x - 6$

$x^3 - 5x^2 + 8x - 6$
8. $a\left(a^2\right) + a(ab) + a(-4b) + b\left(a^2\right) + b(ab) + b(-4b)$

$a^3 + a^2b - 4ab + a^2b + ab^2 - 4b^2$

$a^3 + 2a^2b - 4ab + ab^2 - 4b^2$
9. $x^3 + 6x^2 + 2x - 12$
10. $y^3 - 4y^2 + 4y - 1$

Challenge

1. a. 1, 4, 10, 16, 19, 16, 10, 4, 1
   b. $x^8 + 4x^7 + 10x^6 + 16x^5 + 19x^4 + 16x^3 + 10x^2 + 4x + 1$
2. a. 1, 5, 15, 30, 45, 51, 45, 30, 15, 5, 1
   b. $x^{10} + 5x^9 + 15x^8 + 30x^7 + 45x^6 + 51x^5 + 45x^4 + 30x^3 + 15x^2 + 5x + 1$
3. $126x^5$
4.
```
                    1
                1  1  1  1
            1  2  3  4  3  2  1
         1  3  6  10 12 12 10 6  3  1
       1 4 10 20 31 40 44 40 31 20 10 4 1
```
5. $12x^4$ 6. $31x^8$

Problem Solving

1.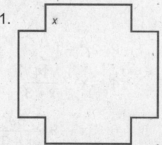

2. $24 - 2x$
3. $V = (x)(24 - 2x)(24 - 2x)$
4. $V = 4x^3 - 96x^2 + 576x$
5. Possible answer: The side length of the finished box is $24 - 2x$, and $24 - 2(12) = 0$.

Holt Algebra 2

6. 800; 972; 1024; 980; 864

7. a. 4

   b. Possible answer: The volume increases up to $x = 4$ and then decreases after that.

   c. 4 by 16 by 16 inches

Reading Strategies

1. Yes; $3x^2$
2. No; $2x^2 + x - 3$
3. a. $6x^4 + 3x^3 - 9x^2$

   b. 3

   c. 4
4. $x^n x^m = x^{n+m}$

LESSON 6-3

Practice A

1. $x + 5 + \dfrac{21}{x - 3}$
2. $3x - 3 - \dfrac{6}{x + 2}$
3. $2x^2 + 2x + \dfrac{x}{2x + 1}$
4. $2x^2 - 4x + 5$

5. a. 1

   b. 9

   c. 46

   d. 46

   e. $x + 9 + \dfrac{46}{x - 5}$

6. $x - 10 + \dfrac{26}{x + 2}$
7. $x + 7 + \dfrac{19}{x - 3}$

8. $P(4) = 5$
9. $P(-3) = -4$

Practice B

1. $x + 2$
2. $2x^2 + 1$
3. $-3x + 2$
4. $3x^2 - \dfrac{14}{x + 3}$
5. $3x - 2$
6. $5x - 19 + \dfrac{69}{x + 3}$
7. $9x + 2 + \dfrac{5}{x - 1}$
8. $-6x + 47 - \dfrac{339}{x + 7}$
9. $P(3) = 11$
10. $P(-2) = -36$
11. $2t + 10$

Practice C

1. $x^2 + 5x - 12$
2. $x^2 + 15x + 45 + \dfrac{131}{x - 3}$
3. $4x^3 + 9x^2 + 5 + \dfrac{9}{3x - 1}$
4. $-x^2 + 6x - 7$
5. $9x + 51 + \dfrac{317}{x - 6}$
6. $3x^3 - 6x^2 + 10x - 20 + \dfrac{41}{x + 2}$
7. $6x^4 + 6x^3 + 6x^2 + 3x + 4 + \dfrac{2}{x - 1}$
8. $-x^3 - 10x^2 - 24x - 72 - \dfrac{217}{x - 3}$
9. $P(5) = 438$
10. $P(-2) = -79$
11. $2t^2 + 100$

Reteach

1. $4x - 1 + \dfrac{8}{x + 2}$
2. $2x + 1 + \dfrac{5}{x + 4}$
3. $3x + 10$
4. $2x + 1 - \dfrac{8}{3x + 2}$
5. $4x - 1 + \dfrac{12}{x + 2}$
6. $a = 5$

   $2x + 4 + \dfrac{8}{x - 5}$

Challenge

1. $2x - 2 + \dfrac{1}{x + 3}$
2. $x^2 + 7x + 16 + \dfrac{53}{x - 3}$
3. $5x^2 - 10x + 26 - \dfrac{44}{x + 2}$
4. $\dfrac{1}{2}x^3 + \dfrac{1}{4}x^2 + \dfrac{1}{8}x + \dfrac{1}{16}$

Holt Algebra 2

5. $x - 2 + \dfrac{5}{2x - 1}$ 6. $x + \dfrac{2}{3} - \dfrac{16\frac{1}{3}}{3x + 5}$

7. $x^4 + 2x^3 + 4x^2 + 8x + 16 - \dfrac{1}{4x - 8}$

8. $x^4 + 9x^2 + 81$

Problem Solving

1. $\dfrac{\sqrt{3}}{4} x^2$

2. B   3. C

4. A   5. D

Reading Strategies

1. Multiply divisor and quotient and add remainder, and see if it equals the dividend. $x(3x + 6) + 2 = 3x^2 + 6x + 2$

2. a. $x + 3 + \dfrac{1}{x + 1}$

    b. $(x + 3)$ R1

    c. $x + 1 \overline{)x^2 + 4x + 4}$ R1   with $x + 3$ above

    d. $(x + 1)(x + 3) + 1$

3. No; the degree of the divisor has to be less than the degree of the dividend.

4. The product of the divisor and the quotient equals the dividend.

LESSON 6-4

Practice A

1. False   2. True

3. False   4. True

5. Yes   6. No

7. $2(x + 4)(x + 1)$

8. $(x + 2)(x + 1)(x - 1)$ 9. $(x^2 + 7)(x + 1)$

10. $(x + 2)(x - 2)(x - 2)$

11. $(g + 2)(g^2 - 2g + 4)$

12. $2m(4 - m)(16 + 4m + m^2)$

13. No; possible answer: the polynomial is the difference of two cubes; she used the formula for the sum of two cubes.

Practice B

1. Yes   2. No

3. Yes   4. No

5. $x(2x - 1)(x + 1)$ 6. $(4x + 1)(x^2 - 2)$

7. $(5x^3 + 1)(x^2 - 1)$

8. $2x(x + 3)(x^2 - 3x + 9)$

9. $(4x - 1)(16x^2 + 4x + 1)$

10. $3x(x + 2)(x^2 - 2x + 4)$

11. 2016; $-(x - 10)(x^2 - 6x + 14)$

Practice C

1. $(x + 5)(2x - 4)$

2. $(x - 1)(x^3 - 5x^2 - x - 1)$

3. $(x + 2)(3x^2 + 6x + 5)$

4. $(x - 8)(x^3 - 4x + 1)$ 5. $(4x - 3)(4x^2 + 5)$

6. $3x^2(x^2 + 9)(x^2 + 9)$ 7. $x^4(x - 5)^2$

8. $2(3x^2 + 2)(x + 2)$

9. $2x(5x + 3)(25x^2 - 15x + 9)$

10. $-3x^2(x - 2)(x^2 + 2x + 4)$

11. $(t - 4)(t - 5)(t + 5)$; the voltage is equal to zero at 4 s and 5 s.

Reteach

1. $(x - 3)(x^2 - 4)$

    $(x - 3)(x + 2)(x - 2)$

2. $x^2(x + 6) - 1(x + 6)$

    $(x + 6)(x^2 - 1)$

    $(x + 6)(x + 1)(x - 1)$

3. $(x^3 + x^2) + (-9x - 9)$

    $x^2(x + 1) - 9(x + 1)$

    $(x + 1)(x^2 - 9)$

    $(x + 1)(x + 3)(x - 3)$

4. $(x^3 + 2x^2) + (-16x - 32)$

    $x^2(x + 2) - 16(x + 2)$

    $(x + 2)(x^2 - 16)$

    $(x + 2)(x + 4)(x - 4)$

5. $(3x + 2)(9x^2 - 6x + 4)$

6. $(y - 6)(y^2 + 6y + 36)$

7. $y^3 + 3^3$

    $(y + 3)(y^2 - 3y + 9)$

8. $x^3 - 1^3$

$(x-1)(x^2 + x + 1)$

Challenge

1. $\{[(6)x + 8]x - 5\}x + 1$

2. $(\{[(-2)x + 5]x - 1\}x + 3)x - 4$

3. $N(3) = 128$ 4. $N(3) = 128$

5. $N(x) = 5x^3 - 3x^2 + 7x - 1$

6. $N(3) = 5 \cdot 3^3 - 3 \cdot 3^2 + 7 \cdot 3 - 1 = 128$

7. $P(x) = \{[(2)x - 6]x - 2\}x - 30$, $P(4) = \{[(2)4 - 6]4 - 2\}4 - 30 = [(2)4 - 2]4 - 30 = (6)4 - 30 = -6$; The numbers in the innermost nests are the coefficients of the quotient, and the last number is the remainder. So the quotient is $2x^2 + 2x + 6$ and the remainder is -6.

8. The quotient is $2x^2 + 2x + 6$ and the remainder is -6.

Problem Solving

1. a. $-2, 4, 6$

   b. $(x + 2)(x - 4)(x - 6)$

2. a. $-4, -1, 0$

   b. $(2x + 2)(x + 4)(x)$

3. a. $5, 8, 9$

   b. $(x - 5)(x - 8)(x - 9)$

4.

Basket	Dimensions (in terms of x)	Actual Dimensions	Volume
A	$(x - 5)$, $(x - 8)$, $(x - 9)$	7 by 4 by 3	84 cubic units
B	$(x + 2)$, $(x - 4)$, $(x - 6)$	14 by 8 by 6	672 cubic units
C	$(2x + 2)$, $(x + 4)$, (x)	26 by 16 by 12	4992 cubic units

5. No; the dimensions of each basket are doubled from one size to the next except for 14 to 26.

6. No; $\dfrac{84}{672} \neq \dfrac{672}{4992}$

Reading Strategies

1. Multiply $(x + 3)$ and $(x^2 + 2)$.

2. No; there are no two factors that have $x^2 + 2$ as their product.

3. 5

4. a. $(x^3 - 8x^2) + (-x + 8)$

   b. x^2

   c. -1

   d. $x^2(x - 8) - 1(x - 8) = (x - 8)(x^2 - 1)$

   e. $x^2 - 1$; $(x + 1)(x - 1)$

   f. $(x - 8)(x + 1)(x - 1)$

LESSON 6-5

Practice A

1. $x^2 + 2x + 1$; $-1, 0$

2. $2x^2 - 18$; $-3, -2, 3$

3. $-5, 0$ 4. $-1, 0, 7$

5. $x = -3$ with multiplicity 1; $x = 0$ with multiplicity 1; $x = 1$ with multiplicity 1

6. $x = 0$ with multiplicity 1; $x = 1$ with multiplicity 2

7. $x = 1$ with multiplicity 2; $x = 5$ with multiplicity 1

8. $x = -6$ with multiplicity 2; $x = 0$ with multiplicity 1

9. $\pm\dfrac{1}{3}, \pm 1$

10. $\pm 1, \pm 2, \pm 3, \pm 4, \pm 6, \pm 12$

11. $\pm\dfrac{1}{2}, \pm 1, \pm 2, \pm\dfrac{5}{2}, \pm 5, \pm 10$

12. $\pm 1, \pm 3, \pm 9$

13. Stefan is correct. The roots of the expression are 2 and -2, both of which have multiplicity 1.

Practice B

1. $\dfrac{1}{3}, \dfrac{\sqrt{3}}{3}, -\dfrac{\sqrt{3}}{3}$ 2. $-4, 0, 6$

3. $-7, 0, 1$ 4. $-2, 0, 4$

5. $x = -1$ with multiplicity 3

6. $x = 3$ with multiplicity 1; $x = -4$ with multiplicity 2

7. $-4, 1, -7$ 8. $-5, -\dfrac{1}{3}, 2$

9. a. $x^3 + x^2 - 2x - 8 = 0$

            Holt Algebra 2

b. ±1, ±2, ±4, ±8

c. $2, \dfrac{-3 \pm i\sqrt{7}}{2}$; no, 2 of the roots are irrational numbers.

d. 2 m wide, 4 m long, and 1 m deep

Practice C

1. −5, 0, 7   2. 0, 3, 4

3. $x = 2$ with multiplicity 3

4. $x = -4$ with multiplicity 2; $x = -2$ with multiplicity 1

5. −8, 0, 6   6. $3, 6, 2 \pm \sqrt{3}$

7. −3, 0, 1   8. $-3, 1, -3 \pm \sqrt{11}$

9. a. $2x^3 - 4x^2 - 64 = 0$

   b. ±1, ±2, ±4, ±8, ±16, ±32, ±64

   c. $4, -1 \pm i\sqrt{7}$; no, 2 of the roots are irrational numbers.

   d. 4 in. wide, 8 in. long, and 2 in. deep

Reteach

1. $3x^4(x - 5)(x + 2)$; −2, 0, 5

2. $x^2(x^2 - 5x + 6)$; $x^2(x - 2)(x - 3)$; 0, 2, 3

3. $2x(x^2 - 3x - 18)$; $2x(x - 6)(x + 3)$; −3, 0, 6

4. $2x^4(x^2 - 16)$; $2x^4(x + 4)(x - 4)$; −4, 0, 4

5. a. ±1, ±3, ±5, ±15

   b. 3 or 5

$\dfrac{p}{q}$	Coefficients of the Equation			
	1	−7	7	15
1	1	6	13	28
3	1	−4	−5	0
5	1	−2	−3	0

   c. $(x - 3)(x^2 - 4x - 5) = 0$; $(x - 3)(x - 5)(x + 1) = 0$

   d. $x = 3$ or $x = 5$ or $x = -1$

Challenge

1. $y = (x + 3)(x)(x - 4)$

2. $y = -(x + 1)^2(x - 1)(x - 3)$

3. $y = (x + 5)(x + 2)^2\left(x - \dfrac{1}{2}\right)(x - 3)$

4. $y = (x + 6)^2(x)(x - 1)(x - 3)^2(x - 4)^2$

5. $y = (x + 3i)(x - 3i)(x - 1)^2\left(x - \left(1 + \sqrt{3}\right)\right)$
$\left(x + \left(1 + \sqrt{3}\right)\right)$

Problem Solving

1. $V = w(w + 10)(w - 14)$

2. $w^3 - 4w^2 - 140w - 76{,}725 = 0$

3. No; yes; no

The constant term is 76,725, which is not a multiple or 4 or 10, but is a multiple of 5.

4. Students should test possible roots that are multiples of 5 but not multiples of 10, such as 35, 45, and 55.

5. C   6. A

Reading Strategies

1. Substitute the value of the root in the function and see if it equals 0.

2. $(x - 3)$ and $(x + 2)$

3. a. $(x + 4)$

   b. 3 times

4. $4x$, $(x - 3)$, $(x + 3)$; −3, 0, 3

5. $-x$, $(x - 5)$, $(x - 1)$; 0, 1, 5

6. $(x + 2)$, $(x + 2)$, $(x - 2)$; −2, 2

LESSON 6-6

Practice A

1. 3   2. 5

3. 4

4. a. $P(x) = x(x + 1)(x - 2)$

   b. $P(x) = (x^2 + x)(x - 2)$

   c. $P(x) = x^3 - 2x^2 + x^2 - 2x$

   d. $P(x) = x^3 - x^2 - 2x$

5. $P(x) = x^3 - 3x^2 - 13x + 15$

6. $P(x) = x^3 + 4x^2 - x - 4$

7. a. 2

   b. $2i, -2i$

         Holt Algebra 2

c. $P(x) = (x + 2i)(x - 2i)$

d. $P(x) = x^2 + 4$

8. $P(x) = x^3 + 2x^2 - 3x - 6$

9. $P(x) = x^3 - 7x^2 + 17x - 15$

10. $x = 6, \pm\sqrt{2}$

Practice B

1. $P(x) = x^3 - 2x^2 - 11x + 12$

2. $P(x) = x^3 - \dfrac{7}{2}x^2 - \dfrac{17}{2}x + 5$

3. $P(x) = x^5 - 4x^4 + x^3 - 4x^2 - 12x + 48$

4. $P(x) = x^5 + 5x^4 + 7x^3 + 35x^2 - 18x - 90$

5. $x = i, -i, -3$, and 5

6. $x = 2, -2, 2i$, and $-2i$

7. $x = -4i, 4i, 2$, and -6

8. $x = -3i, 3i$, and -3

9. $V(t) = t^3 - 10t^2 + 23t - 14$

Practice C

1. $P(x) = x^3 - \dfrac{17}{4}x^2 - \dfrac{39}{4}x - \dfrac{9}{2}$

2. $P(x) = x^4 - 9x^3 + 39x^2 - 225x + 350$

3. $P(x) = x^4 + 4x^3 + 4x^2 + 4x + 3$

4. $P(x) = x^5 - 4x^4 - 2x^3 + 8x^2 - 24x + 96$

5. $x = -\dfrac{3}{2}i, \dfrac{3}{2}i$, 3, and -1

6. $x = i\sqrt{3}$, $-i\sqrt{3}$, 1, and -4

7. $x = 1 + i, 1 - i, -3$, and 4

8. $x = 2i, -2i$, and -6 9. 3 inches

Reteach

1. $x^2 + 4x - 5$

   $x^3 + 4x^2 - 5x - 2x^2 - 8x + 10$

   $x^3 + 2x^2 + 13x + 10$

2. $(x^2 + 3x)(x + 1)$

   $x^3 + 3x^2 + x^2 + 3x$

   $x^3 + 4x^2 + 3x$

3. $(x - 1)(x - 4)(x - 5)$

   $(x^2 - 5x + 4)(x - 5)$

   $x^3 - 10x^2 + 29x - 20$

4. $(x + 2)(x - 3)(x - 6)$

$(x^2 - x - 6)(x - 6)$

$x^3 - 7x^2 + 36$

5. $(x - 2)(x - 4)(x - 6)$

   $(x^2 - 6x + 8)(x - 6)$

   $x^3 - 12x^2 + 44x - 48$

6. $(x + 5)(x)(x - 5)$

   $x(x^2 - 25)$

   $x^3 - 25x$

7. 1; 2; 1; 2; $x^2 + 4$; 2i; –2i

Challenge

1. $-5 + 3 = -2$; $(-5)(3) = -15$

2. $-2 + 1 + 4 = -(-3) = 3$; $(-2)(1) + (-2)(4) + (1)(4) = -6$; $(-2)(1)(4) = -8$

3. $z_1z_2z_3 = -84 = (7)(-3)(z_3)$; $z_3 = 4$

4. $-2 + 5 + z_3 + z_4 = 1$; $(-2)(5) + (-2)(z_3) + (-2)(z_4) + (5)(z_3) + (5)(z_4) + (z_3)(z_4) = -19$; $z_3 = 1$; $z_4 = -3$

5. $(x - z_1)(x - z_2)(x - z_3) = x^3 - (z_1 + z_2 + z_3)x^2 + (z_1z_2 + z_1z_3 + z_2z_3)x - z_1z_2z_3$

Problem Solving

1. a. $V = 4\pi r^2$

   b. $V = \dfrac{1}{2}\left(\dfrac{4}{3}\pi r^3\right)$

2. $\dfrac{13}{12}\pi = 4\pi r^2 + \dfrac{2}{3}\pi r^3$

3. $8r^3 + 48r^2 - 13 = 0$

4.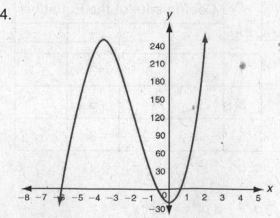

5. $\dfrac{1}{2}$

6. $x = \dfrac{-26 \pm 21.6}{8}$; both these roots are negative, so they cannot be the radius.

Holt Algebra 2

7. 0.5 inch

Reading Strategies

1. Find the factors corresponding to the roots and multiply the factors.

2. x

3. a. $(x + 2)(x + 2)(x + 2) = 0$, or $x^3 + 6x^2 + 12x + 8$.

   b. because multiplying the equation by a nonzero number will not change its roots

4. a. $(x)(x)(x)(x + 2) = x^4 + 2x^3 = 0$

   b. 4

LESSON 6-7

Practice A

1. 1; 2   2. −3; 3

3. 2; 4; $x \to -\infty$, $P(x) \to +\infty$; $x \to +\infty$, $P(x) \to +\infty$

4. −6; 5; $x \to -\infty$, $P(x) \to +\infty$; $x \to +\infty$, $P(x) \to -\infty$

5. ±1, ±2, ±4

6. $(x - 1)(x^2 + 5x + 4)$

7. $(x - 1)(x + 4)(x + 1)$

8. y-intercept = −4; $P(-2) = 6$; $P(-3) = 8$

9. As $x \to -\infty$, $P(x) \to -\infty$, as $x \to +\infty$, $P(x) \to +\infty$

10.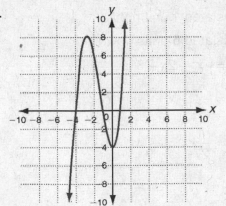

Practice B

1. 2; 5; as $x \to +\infty$, $P(x) \to +\infty$; and as $x \to -\infty$, $P(x) \to -\infty$

2. −4; 2; as $x \to -\infty$, $Q(x) \to -\infty$; and as $x \to +\infty$, $Q(x) \to -\infty$

3. Even; negative   4. Even; positive

5. Odd; positive

6. ±1, ±2, ±3, ±4, ±6, ±12

7. −4, −3, and 1

8. As $x \to +\infty$, $P(x) \to +\infty$, and as $x \to -\infty$, $P(x) \to -\infty$

9.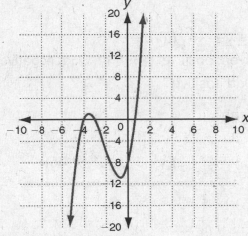

10. About 5400 in year 20

Practice C

1. −6; 4; as $x \to -\infty$, $R(x) \to -\infty$: and as $x \to +\infty$, $R(x) \to -\infty$

2. −16; 3; as $x \to -\infty$, $Q(x) \to +\infty$: and as $x \to +\infty$, $Q(x) \to -\infty$

3. Odd; negative   4. Even; positive

5. Odd; positive

6.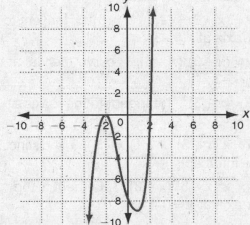

7. Minima: 4.5; maxima: 5.1 and 13.5

8. Minima: −8.68; maxima: 0

9. a. 3.03 m^3

   b. 1.9 m by 2.9 m by 0.55 m

Holt Algebra 2

Reteach

1. Positive, 3, odd

    as $x \to -\infty$, $P(x) \to -\infty$

    as $x \to +\infty$, $P(x) \to +\infty$

2. $-9x^6$

    negative, 6, even

    as $x \to -\infty$, $P(x) \to -\infty$

    as $x \to +\infty$, $P(x) \to -\infty$

3. Even; positive   4. Odd; negative

5. Odd positive

Challenge

1. a. 3

    b. $y = (x + 3)(x + 1)(x - 1)(x - 5)$

    c.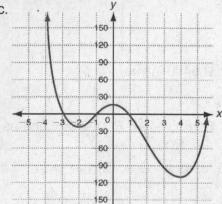

2. $y = (x + 3)(x + 1)(x - 1)(x - 5)$; 3; 4 distinct x- intercepts

3. $y = (x + 3)^2(x - 1)(x - 5)$; 3; tangent to the x-axis at $x = -3$

4. $y = (x + 3)^3(x - 5)$; 1; curve "bends" at $x = -3$

5. $y = (x + 3)^4$; 1; tangent to the x-axis at $x = -3$

6. $y = x(x + 3)(x - 1)(x - 5)$; 3; 4 distinct x- intercepts

7. $y = x^2(x + 3)(x - 3)$; 3; tangent to the x-axis at $x = 0$

8. $y = x^3(x - 3)$; 1; curve "bends" at $x = 0$

9. $y = x^4$; 1; looks like a parabola

Problem Solving

1. $V(x) = x(11 - 2x)(17 - 2x)$

2. a. $4x^3 - 56x^2 + 187x = 0$

b. Positive

c. Odd

d. As $x \to +\infty$, $V \to +\infty$, and as $x \to -\infty$, $V \to -\infty$.

3. a. 2

   b. About 183 and −64

4. Values of x greater than 5.5 or less than 0

5. About 2.3 and 183   6. 183 cubic inches

7. 2.3 in. by 6.4 in. by 12.4 in.

8. A   9. D

Reading Strategies

1. a. Its degree is even and the leading coefficient is less than zero.

   b. The function approaches $-\infty$ as $x \to +\infty$.

   c. The function approaches $-\infty$ as $x \to -\infty$.

2. As $x \to +\infty$, $P(x) \to +\infty$; As $x \to -\infty$, $P(x) \to -\infty$

3. Odd   4. It is positive.

LESSON 6-8

Practice A

1. Translated 5 units up

2. Translated 10 units left

3. Translated 1 unit right

4. Translated 6 units down

5. $g(x) = -x^3 - 2x - 3$

6. $g(x) = -x^3 + x + 1$ 7. $g(x) = \frac{1}{2}x^4 + 1$

8. $g(x) = \frac{1}{27}x^3 + \frac{1}{9}x^2 - 6$

            Holt Algebra 2

9. $x^3 - 3x + 3$

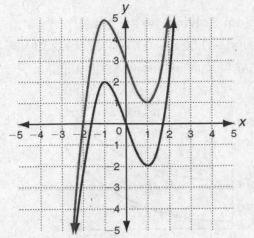

10. $2x^3 - 6x$

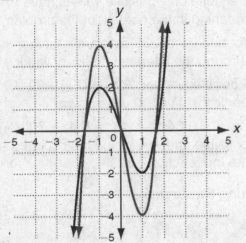

11. $-x^3 + 3x$

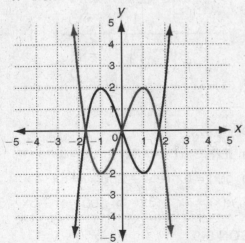

12. The profits decreased by \$100,000.

Practice B

1. $g(x) = (x + 4)^3 + 1$ 2. $g(x) = 3x^3 + 3$

3. $g(x) = \left(\dfrac{1}{2}x\right)^3 + 1$

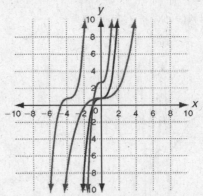

4. $g(x) = x^3 + 4x^2 + 5x + 12$

5. $g(x) = x^3 - 4x^2 + 5x - 12$

6. Vertically compressed by a factor of 4

7. Translated 3 units down

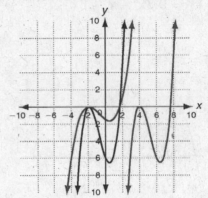

8. $-x^3 + 4x^2 + x + 11$

9. $\dfrac{1}{4}(x - 3)^3 + (x - 3)^2 - \dfrac{1}{4}(x - 3) + \dfrac{5}{4}$

10. $N(t) = 8t^2 - 2t + 4000$

Practice C

1. a. $g(x) = -2(x - 5)^4 + 7(x - 5)^2 - 4$

   b. $g(x) = \dfrac{1}{4}\,(-2x^4 + 7x^2 - 4)$

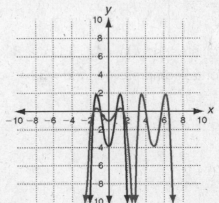

2. a. $g(x) = -2(0.25x)^4 + 7(0.25x)^2 - 4$

Holt Algebra 2

b. $g(x) = 4(-2x^4 + 7x^2 - 4)$

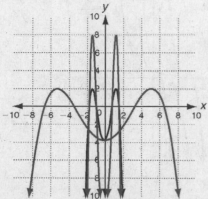

3. $g(x) = -4(x + 2)^3 + 5$ 4. $g(x) = 20x^3 - 4$

5. $g(x) = 12(x - 3)^3 - 15$

6. $6\sin(x) + 1 \approx 0.3x^5 - x^3 + 6x + 1$

Reteach

1. Up; $g(x) = x^3 + 3$

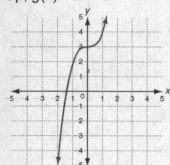

2. Right; $g(x) = (x - 3)^3 + 2$

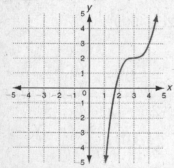

3. Vertical stretch; $g(x) = 4x^4 - 12x^2 + 8$

4. Horizontal compression; $g(x) = 32x^4 - 24x^2 + 4$

Challenge

1. $f(x) + 11$

   $f(x - 2) + 27$

   $-f(x) - 7$

2. $0.5f(x)$ 3. $-f(x) - 9$

4. $f(x - 2) + 8$ 5. $-f(x + 4) - 3$

6. $-f(x - 5) - 5$ 7. $f(x + 3) + 4$

Problem Solving

1. $N(x) = 0.02x^3 + 0.4x^2 + 0.2x + 235$

2. Vertical translation of 200 units up

3.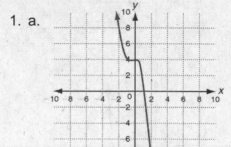

4. Because only positive values have meaning in the context of the problem

5. An additional 200 cars are passing through the intersection every week.

6. Possible answer: $R(x) = C(x) - 30$; vertical shift of 30 units down

7. $2C(x) = 0.04x^3 + 0.8x^2 + 0.4x + 70$; possible answer: a new mall opened at the intersection.

Reading Strategies

1. a.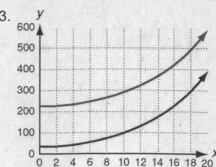

   b. $(1, -2)$

2. a. $f(x) = -x^3 - 4$; $f(x) = -x^3 + 4$

   b. $g(x) = 6x^5 + x^3 - 2$; $g(x) = 6x^5 + x^3 + 2$

   c. $h(x) = -x^2 + 3x - 5$; $h(x) = x^2 + 3x + 5$

LESSON 6-9

Practice A

1. First   2. Third

3. Second   4. Second

5. First   6. Third

Holt Algebra 2

7. a. Third

   b. Cubic

8. a. Fourth

   b. Quartic

9. a. Third

   b. Cubic

10. $f(x) \approx 0.167x^3 + 2x^2 + 3.833x - 5$

11. $f(x) \approx 0.625x^3 - 2.438x^2 + 29.438x -$
   68.063

Practice B

1. Quartic   2. Cubic

3. Quadratic   4. Cubic

5. a. $f(x) = 7y^4 - 180y^3 + 1200y^2 + 1000$

   b. $11,000

Practice C

1. Quartic   2. Quadratic

3. Cubic   4. Quartic

5. a. $f(t) = -1t^3 + 35t^2 - 190t + 1000$

   b. 2010

Reteach

1. 7; 1; 1; 7

   6; 0; 6

   6; 6

2. Cubic

3. −3; 53; 152; 256; 327

   56; 99; 104; 71

   43; 5; −33

   −38; −38

4. $f(x) \approx -0.099x^4 + 2.88x^3 - 17.6x^2 + 35.5x - 34$

Challenge

1. $y = -\dfrac{1}{25}x^2 + \dfrac{7}{5}x + 24$

2. Possible answer: $y = 3x^2 - 24x + 45$

3. $y = x^3 - 3x^2 - 10x + 24$

4. $y = \dfrac{1}{4}x^4 - 2x^3 - \dfrac{11}{2}x^2 + 14x + \dfrac{69}{4}$

Problem Solving

1. a. 5, 10, 18, 29, 43

   b. 5, 8, 11, 14

   c. 3, 3, 3

   d. 0, 0

   e. Cubic

2. a. $R^2 \approx 0.8945$

   b. $R^2 \approx 0.9458$

   c. 1

3. $f(x) = 0.5x^3 - 0.5x^2 + 3x$

4. 168   5. B

6. D

Reading Strategies

1. Cubic function   2. 13

3. a. 7, 1, 1, 7, 19

   b. Yes; −6, 0, 6, 12

   c. Yes; 6, 6, 6

   d. Cubic function

LESSON 7-1

Practice A

1. Growth   2. Decay

3. a. 2.5

   b. Growth

   c.

x	−2	−1	0	1	2	3
f(x)	0.48	1.2	3	7.5	18.75	46.875

   d.

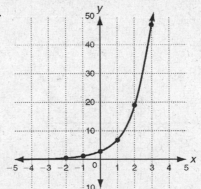

4. Decay

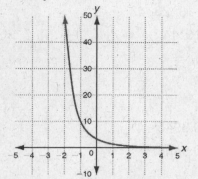

5. Growth

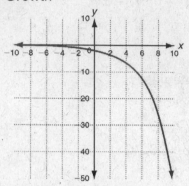

6. a. $y = 100,000(1.04)^x$

b.

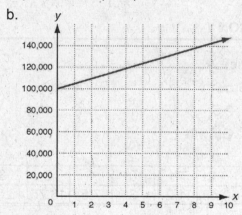

c. 2012

Practice B

1. Growth

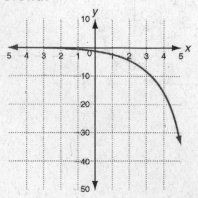

2. Decay

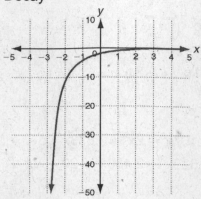

3. Decay

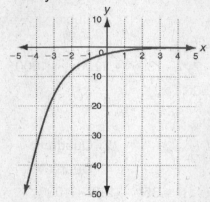

4. Growth

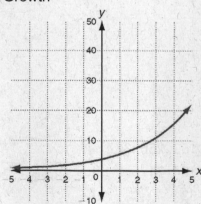

5. a. $y = 20,000(0.85)^x$

b.

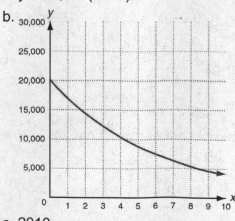

c. 2010

Holt Algebra 2

Practice C

1. Decay

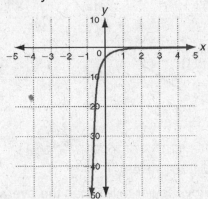

2. Growth

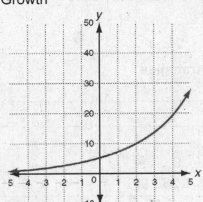

3. Growth

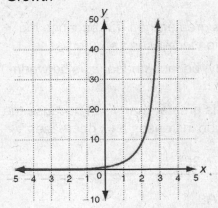

4. No   5. Yes

6. Yes   7. $13,900

8. $85,500

9. a. $y = 100,000(1.04)^x$

b.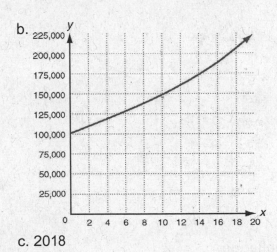

c. 2018

Reteach

1. 0.8; 1.6

$h(x)$ shows exponential growth.

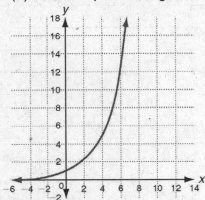

2. 12; 0.7

$p(x)$ shows exponential decay.

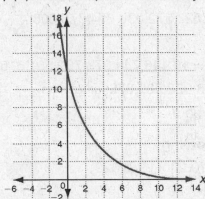

3. a. 40,000

b. 0.08

c. $f(t) = 40,000(1.08)^t$

d. 5.25 yr

Holt Algebra 2

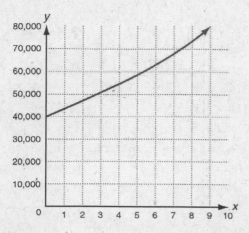

Challenge

1.

Square n	Grains of Wheat on Square n	Total Grains of Wheat on Board
1	1	1
2	2	3
3	4	7
4	8	15
5	16	31
6	32	63
7	64	127
8	128	255
9	256	511
10	512	1023

2. 2^{n-1}

3. $2^{63} = 9,223,372,036,854,775,808$

4. $2^{n} - 1$

5. $2^{64} - 1 = 18,446,744,073,709,551,615$

6. 147,573,952,589,676 kilograms

7. 254.4 years

Problem Solving

1. $m(t) = 10,200(1 + 0.029)^{t}$

2. 8; 12; 16; 20

   11,436; 12,821; 14,374; 16,116; 18,068

3. He drove more miles; about 5,900 miles more.

4. a. $n(t) = 10,200(1 + 0.078)^{t}$

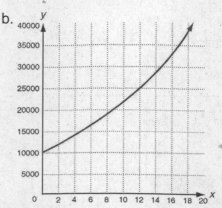

b.

About 34,000 miles

c. He drove fewer miles than the average light truck driver by about 12,000 miles.

5. D   6. G

Reading Strategies

1.

x	−2	−1	0	1	2	3
$f(x) = 3^{x}$	$\frac{1}{9}$	$\frac{1}{3}$	1	3	9	27
$f(x) = 0.4^{x}$	6.25	2.5	1	0.4	0.16	0.064

2. Growth; because base, b, is greater than 1

3. $f(4)$ is greater than $f(3)$ because the function increases as x increases.

4. Decay; because base, b, is between 0 and 1

5. $f(-3)$ is greater than $f(-2)$ because the function increases as x decreases.

LESSON 7-2

Practice A

1. a. c.

Holt Algebra 2

b. Domain: $\{x \mid 0 \le x \le 6\}$; range:

$\{y \mid 3 \le y \le 7\}$

d. Domain: $\{x \mid 3 \le x \le 7\}$; range:

$\{y \mid 0 \le y \le 6\}$

2. a. Adding 9

b. Dividing by 2

c. $\frac{1}{2}(x+9)$

3. $f^{-1}(x) = -\frac{x}{4}$ 4. $f^{-1}(x) = x - 6$

5. $f^{-1}(x) = \frac{x}{3} + 4$ 6. $f^{-1}(x) = -\frac{x-6}{10}$

7. $f^{-1}(x) = \frac{x-1}{7}$ 8. $f^{-1}(x) = \frac{x}{22}$

9. a. $c = x + 0.15x$, or $c = 1.15x$

b. $x = \frac{c}{1.15}$

c. $x = 8.60$

Practice B

1. $f^{-1}(x) = \frac{x+10}{15}$ 2. $f^{-1}(x) = -\frac{x-10}{4}$

3. $f^{-1}(x) = -\frac{x-12}{9}$ 4. $f^{-1}(x) = \frac{x-2}{5}$

5. $f^{-1}(x) = x - 6$ 6. $f^{-1}(x) = x - \frac{1}{2}$

7. $f^{-1}(x) = -12x$ 8. $f^{-1}(x) = 4x + 12$

9. $f^{-1}(x) = \frac{6x-1}{3}$, or $f^{-1}(x) = 2x - \frac{1}{3}$

10. $f^{-1}(x) = \frac{1}{2}x + 2$

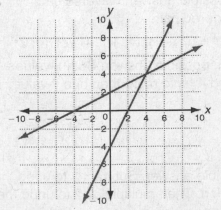

11. $f^{-1}(x) = \frac{2}{5}(x+2)$

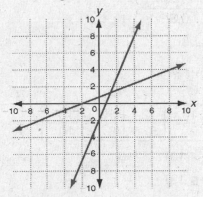

12. a. $c = \frac{d + 1.5}{0.15}$

b. $c = 130$

c. $\$112$

Practice C

1. $f^{-1}(x) = 5x - 5$ 2. $f^{-1}(x) = \pm\sqrt{x-9}$

3. $f^{-1}(x) = -\frac{x-7}{4}$ 4. $f^{-1}(x) = -8x - 2$

5. $f^{-1}(x) = \pm 4\sqrt{x}$ 6. $f^{-1}(x) = \frac{6x+2}{5}$

7. $f^{-1}(x) = 3x + 4$

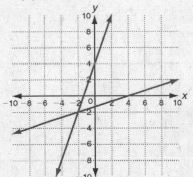

8. $f^{-1}(x) = \frac{x-3}{0.3}$

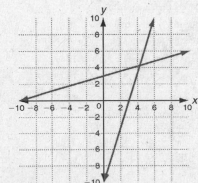

Holt Algebra 2

9. a. $c = 0.8(v - m)$

   b. $v = \dfrac{c + 0.8m}{0.8}$

   c. $240,000

Reteach

1.

x	6	10	12	13	13
y	0	2	5	8	10

$\{x | 0 \le x \le 10\}$

$\{y | 6 \le y \le 13\}$

$\{x | 6 \le x \le 13\}$

$\{y | 0 \le y \le 10\}$

2. $f^{-1}(x) = x + 4$

   $f(5) = 1;\ f^{-1}(1) = 5$

3. $f^{-1}(x) = 6x$

   $f(12) = 2;\ f^{-1}(2) = 12$

4. $f^{-1}(x) = x - 3$

5. $f^{-1}(x) = \dfrac{x}{14}$

Challenge

1. Possible answer: For every value of y, except 0, there are 2 values of x.

2. Yes; $y = \dfrac{x + 4}{3}$; yes

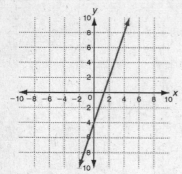

3. Yes; $y = \dfrac{1}{x}$; yes

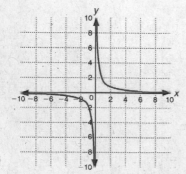

4. Yes; $y = \sqrt[3]{x}$; yes

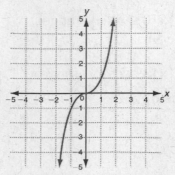

5. No; function is not one-to-one;

$y = -3 \pm \dfrac{\sqrt{1 - 4x}}{2}$; inverse is not a function.

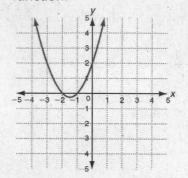

Problem Solving

1. a. $p = 1.09(3n + 5)$

   b. $\dfrac{p - 5.45}{3.27} = n$

   c. $n = \dfrac{42.51}{3.27} = 13$

   d. The price has increased by $1.

2. a. $76.30

   b. $2.00

3. C   4. B

Reading Strategies

1. a. Possible answer: Reverse each ordered pair.

   b. $R^{-1} = \{(1, -1), (1, 1), (4, -2), (4, 2)\}$

   c. No; possible answer: Both x-values 1 and 4 have more than one y-value.

2. a. 3

   b. 2

   c. 8

3. Possible answer: Subtract 1 to undo the addition. Then multiply by 2 to undo the division.

Holt Algebra 2

Practice A

1. 3   2. 6

3. 2   4. $\log_2 8 = 3$

5. $\log_{17} 1 = 0$ 6. $\log_1 1 = 12$

7. $\log_4 1024 = 5$ 8. $\log_3 729 = 6$

9. $\log_5 625 = 4$ 10. 4^3

11. 8^3 12. 6^2

13. $10^2 = 100$ 14. $5^3 = 125$

15. $9^0 = 1$ 16. $2^7 = 128$

17. $3^5 = 243$ 18. $100^3 = 1,000,000$

19. 4   20. 5

21. 0   22. 4

23. 0   24. 2

25. 4   26. 9

27. 4   28. 3

29. 2   30. 3

Practice B

1. $\log_3 2187 = 7$ 2. $\log_{12} 144 = 2$

3. $\log_5 125 = 3$ 4. $10^5 = 100,000$

5. $4^5 = 1024$ 6. $9^3 = 729$

7. 6   8. 1

9. 0   10. 2

11. 0   12. 4

13. Domain: $\{x | x > 0\}$; range: all real numbers

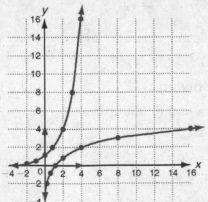

14. Domain: $\{x | x > 0\}$; range: all real numbers

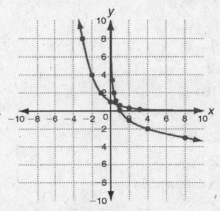

15. a. pH = $-\log(0.000316)$

b. 3.5

Practice C

1. $\log_{20} 8000 = 3$ 2. $\log_{11} 14,641 = 4$

3. $\log_a c = b$ 4. $10^7 = 10,000,000$

5. $6^3 = 216$ 6. $p^r = q$

7. 0   8. 4

9. 3   10. 5

11. 0   12. 4

13. Domain: $\{x | x > 0\}$; range: all real numbers

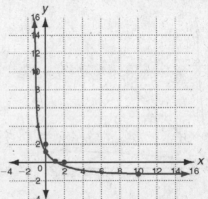

14. Domain: $\{x | x > 0\}$; range: all real numbers

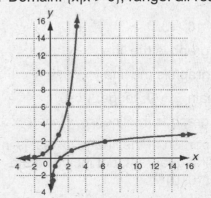

15. a. pH = $-\log(0.00794)$

b. 2.1

Holt Algebra 2

Reteach

1. $\log_7 49 = 2$

2. $b = 6$, $x = 3$, $a = 216$

   $\log_6 216 = 3$

3. $b = 2$, $x = 5$, $a = 32$

   $\log_2 32 = 5$

4. $9^3 = 729$

5. $b = 2$, $x = 6$, $a = 64$

   $2^6 = 64$

6. $b = 10$, $x = 3$, $a = 1000$

   $10^3 = 1000$

7.

x	-2	-1	0	1	2
$f(x)$	$\dfrac{1}{16}$	$\dfrac{1}{4}$	1	4	16

x	$\dfrac{1}{16}$	$\dfrac{1}{4}$	1	4	16
$f^{-1}(x)$	-2	-1	0	1	2

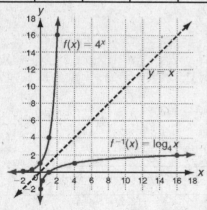

Challenge

1. a. $\log_{10} 10^x = x$

   b. The graph is the line $y = x$.

   c. The graph is the line $y = x$.

2. a. Domain: $x > 0$; range: $y > 0$

   b. The graph is the line $y = x$ where $x > 0$.

   c. The portion of the line $y = x$ that is in the first quadrant, not including the point $(0, 0)$

3. Domain: $x \neq 0$; range: all real numbers

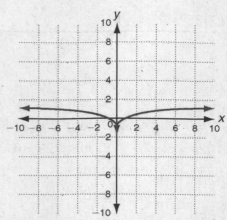

4. Domain: $x > 0$; range: $y > 0$

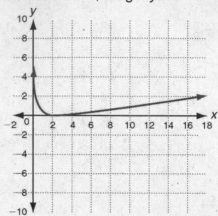

5. Domain: $x \neq 0$; range: all real numbers

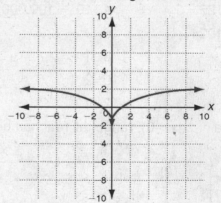

Problem Solving

1. a. pH = $-\log$ (0.0000629)

   b. pH = 4.2

2. a. pH = $-\log$ (0.0000032)

   b. pH = 5.5

   c. Rainwater in eastern Ohio has a lower pH than that in central California by 1.3 units.

3. D   4. J

5. A   6. H

Reading Strategies

1. $4^2 = 16$; $\log_5 0.2 = -1$; $\log_6 1 = 0$

2. $\log_b 1 = 0$ is the same as $b^0 = 1$ and any number to the 0 power is 1.

3. $f^{-1}(x) = \log_4 x$

4. a. $g^{-1}(x) = \log_{\frac{1}{2}} x$

   b. Domain of $g(x)$ is all real numbers
      range of $g(x)$ is $y > 0$
      domain of $g^{-1}(x)$ is $x > 0$
      range of $g^{-1}(x)$ is all real numbers.

LESSON 7-4

Practice A

1. 4
2. 64; 64; 6
3. 3125; 3125; 5
4. $\log_{10} 10,000 = 4$
5. $\log_6 6 = 1$
6. $\log_8 64 = 2$
7. $\log_5 25 = 2$
8. $\log_3 3 = 1$
9. $\log_2 32 = 5$
10. $\log_4 16 = 2$
11. $\log_6 36 = 2$
12. $\log_5 125 = 3$
13. 4
14. 4
15. 9
16. 4
17. 12
18. 2
19. 1.59
20. 1.77
21. 1.46
22. 10^{22} ergs

Practice B

1. $\log_3 243 = 5$
2. $\log_2 128 = 7$
3. $\log_{10} 10,000 = 4$
4. $\log_6 216 = 3$
5. $\log_3 81 = 4$
6. $\log_4 4096 = 6$
7. $\log_2 8 = 3$
8. $\log_{10} 100 = 2$
9. $\log_4 64 = 3$
10. $\log_2 64 = 6$
11. $\log_3 243 = 5$
12. $\log_6 36 = 2$
13. 6
14. $x - 5$
15. 30
16. 1
17. 5
18. 8
19. 0
20. 3.10
21. 1.43
22. $1.26 \times 10^{18.1}$ ergs

Practice C

1. $\log_6 216 = 3$
2. $\log_3 3 = 1$
3. $\log_4 16 = 2$
4. $\log_6 1296 = 4$
5. $\log_5 125 = 3$
6. $\log_8 32,768 = 5$
7. $\log_5 625 = 4$
8. $\log_2 4 = 2$
9. $\log_3 81 = 4$
10. $\log_8 4096 = 4$
11. $\log_7 7 = 1$
12. $\log_{10} 10,000 = 4$
13. 6
14. 8^x
15. 20
16. $2x + 1$
17. $2x - 2$
18. 17
19. 2.93
20. -6
21. -12
22. 4.32
23. 6
24. 3.32
25. a. $\log_{1.06} 1.6$

    b. 8 years

Reteach

1. 3
2. $\log_2 16$; 4
3. $\log_9 (3 \cdot 27)$; $\log_9 81$; 2
4. $2 \cdot 3 = 6$
5. $4 \cdot 4 = 16$
6. $3 \log_9 81$; $3 \cdot 2 = 6$
7. $5y$
8. 75
9. $3x$

Challenge

1. Both expressions equal $\dfrac{3}{2}$.

2. Result is $\dfrac{3}{2}$; formula is easier to compute.

3. Result is $\dfrac{6}{5}$; formula is easier to compute.

4. $\log_a b \cdot \log_b c = \log_a c$

   $\log_a b \cdot \log_b c = \dfrac{\log b}{\log a} \cdot \dfrac{\log c}{\log b}$

   $= \dfrac{\log c}{\log a} \cdot \dfrac{\log b}{\log b} = \dfrac{\log c}{\log a} = \log_a c$

5. $\log_2 13 = \dfrac{\log 13}{\log 2} \approx 3.7$

6. $\log_2 32 = 5$; possible answer: using the Chain Rule is much easier.

Holt Algebra 2

Problem Solving

1. a. $7.8 = \dfrac{2}{3}\log\left(\dfrac{E}{10^{11.8}}\right)$

   b. $23.5 = \log E$

   c. Yes; by the definition of logarithm; $E = 10^{23.5}$

   d. They are both correct; $10^{23.5} = 3.16 \times 10^{23}$.

2. A

3. G

4. C

5. F

Reading Strategies

1. True; Product Property
2. True; Quotient Property
3. False; Power Property
4. False: Inverse Property
5. $5 \log x$; Power Property
6. $\log x$; Quotient Property
7. 1; Product Property
8. $x \log x$; Power Property
9. $2 \log xy$; Quotient Property and Power Property
10. 7; Product Property and Inverse Property
11. $x = 1$

LESSON 7-5

Practice A

1. 129; $x \approx 0.645$
2. $x \approx 3.43$
3. $x \approx 0.161$
4. $x = -3$
5. $x = 2$
6. $x \approx 1.686$
7. $x = 9$
8. $x = -10$
9. $x = -2$
10. $x = 8$
11. $x = 3125$
12. $x = 10$ (or $x = -2$)
13. $x = 9000$
14. $x = 2.5$
15. $x = 2$
16. 19 years

Practice B

1. $x \approx 0.9307$
2. $x \approx 4.5449$
3. $x = -4$
4. $x = 3$
5. $x \approx -6.67$
6. $x = 6$
7. $x = -8$
8. $x = -0.6$

9. $x = 5$
10. $x = 256$
11. $x = 9$
12. $x = 22$
13. $x = 10^{15}$
14. $x = 20$
15. $x = 16$
16. $x = 56$
17. $x = \pm 2$
18. $x = -1, -2$
19. $x < 11$
20. $x = 10,000$
21. $x = 4$
22. 2009

Practice C

1. $x = 2$
2. $x \approx 1.414$
3. $x \approx 3.4$
4. $x = 12$
5. $x = -3.75$
6. $x = -2$
7. $x = -0.5$
8. $x = -6.5$
9. $x = -0.5$
10. $x = 32.5$
11. $x = 20$
12. $x = 1$
13. $x = 8000$
14. $x = 10^9$
15. $x = 7$ or $x = -2$
16. $x = \pm 11$
17. $x = 5$
18. $x = -0.1, 1$
19. $x = \pm 20$
20. $x = -3$, or $x = \dfrac{1}{2}$
21. $x \le 1$ or $x \ge 3$
22. a. $A = 9000(1.0425)^t$

    b. 20 years

    c. $72,118.34

Reteach

1. $x = -2.5$; $4^{-(-2.5)} = 32$
2. $x \approx 1.024$; $3^{4(1.024)} \approx 90.01$
3. $\log 5^{x-3} = \log 600$

   $(x - 3) \log 5 = \log 600$

   $x \approx 6.975$

   $5^{6.975 - 3} \approx 600.352$

4. $3^{2} = x$

   $x = 9$

5. $4x + 8 = 100$

   $4x = 92$

   $x = 23$

6. $\log\left(\dfrac{75x}{3}\right) = 1$; $\log 25x = 1$; $10^1 = 25x$;

   $10 = 25x$; $x = \dfrac{2}{5}$

Challenge

1. $T(t) - T_A = [T_0 - T_A] b^t$

$$\frac{T(t) - T_A}{T_o - T_A} = b^t$$

$$\log\left(\frac{T(t) - T_A}{T_o - T_A}\right) = t \log b$$

$$= \frac{\log\left(\dfrac{T(t) - T_A}{T_o - T_A}\right)}{t} = \log b$$

$$= 10^{\left(\dfrac{\log\left(\frac{T(t)-T_A}{T_o-T_A}\right)}{t}\right)} = b$$

2. $b \approx 0.97854$

3. First 3 steps same as #1;

4. $\log\dfrac{\left(\dfrac{T(t) - T_A}{T_o - T_A}\right)}{\log b} = t$; About 37 min

5. $b \approx 0.98362$　　　　6. About 55 min

7. About 30 min

Problem Solving

1. a. 437 mg

   b. $C(t) = C_0(1 - 0.15)^t$

   c. 2.3 h

2. a. He can graph the equation $102 = 437(0.85)^t$ and find the value of t where $C(t)$ is 102.

   b. $y = 102$ and $y = 437(0.85)^t$

   c.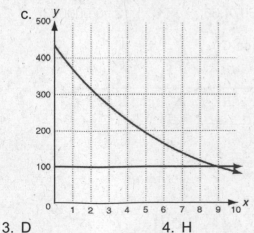

3. D　　　　　　　　4. H

Reading Strategies

1. a. 2^4

   b. $2^x = 2^4$; $x = 4$

   c. Letting $x = 4$, $2^4 = 16$

2. a. $10^2 = x$

   b. $x = 100$

   c. $\log_{10} 100 = \log_{10} 10^2 = 2$

3. a. $3^5 = 3^x \cdot (3^2)^2 = 3^5 = 3^x \cdot 3^4$

   b. $3^5 = 3^{x+4}$

   c. $5 = x + 4$; $x = 1$.

4. a.

$4x + 2\log 10x - 2\log x = 10$	Use of the Power Property
$2(2x + \log 10x - \log x) = 10$	Factor left side
$2x + \log 10x - \log x = 5$	divide both sides by 2
$2x + \log\left(\dfrac{10x}{x}\right) = 5$	use of the Quotient Property

   b. $2x + 1 = 5$; $x = 2$

LESSON 7-6

Practice A

1. a.

x	−2	−1	0	1	2	3
$f(x)$	7.4	2.7	1	0.37	0.14	0.05

   b.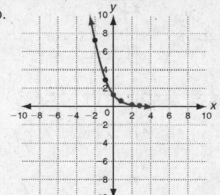

2.

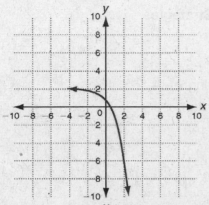

3.

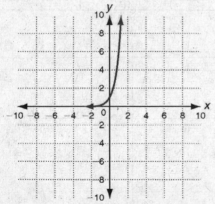

4. $7x$

5. $x + 4$

6. x

7. x^3

8. $(x + 1)^5$

9. $x - 1$

10. $3x$

11. $(5x)^{-1}$, or $\dfrac{1}{5x}$

12. $2x$

13. $8080.37

Practice B

1.

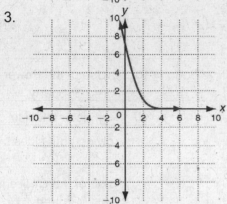

2.

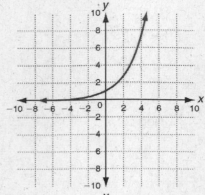

3.

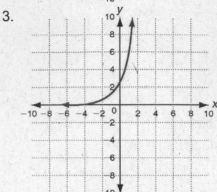

4.

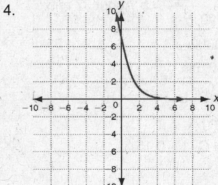

5. $x + 2$

6. $2x$

7. x^7

8. $3x + 1$

9. 1

10. $2x + y$

11. $6074.36

12. 0.000693

Practice C

1.

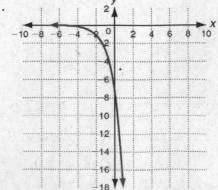

Holt Algebra 2

2.

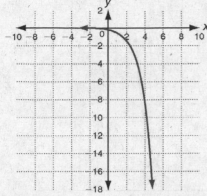

3. $5x - 3$

4. $(8x)^2$

5. $(x - 2)^4$

6. $(4 - x)^{-1}$, or $\dfrac{1}{4 - x}$

7. $\sqrt{x}$

8. $\dfrac{4}{x}$

9. The investment of $12,000 will earn $5901.90 in interest; the investment of $9000 will earn $5185.56 in interest. The first investment will earn more interest.

10. a. 0.000283

   b. 3710 years

Reteach

1. $-6x$

2. $t - 3$

3. x^2

4. $1.8 \ln e$; 1.8

5. $(x + 1) \ln e$; $x + 1$

6. $e^{\ln x^2}$; x^7

7. 500; 0.045; 10; $784.16

8. $1182.94

9. a. $6201.23

   b. $61.70

Challenge

1. $\dfrac{1}{8 \cdot 7 \cdot 6 \cdot 5 \cdot 4 \cdot 3 \cdot 2 \cdot 1}$

2. a. 2.7083

   b. 2.718055556

   c. 2.718281526

3. $e = 1 + \dfrac{1}{1} + \dfrac{1}{2 \cdot 1} + \dfrac{1}{3 \cdot 2 \cdot 1} + \cdots$

4. $5 + \dfrac{5}{6}$; $\dfrac{5760}{2119} \approx 2.718263332$

5. $18 + \dfrac{1}{22}$; $\dfrac{1,084,483}{398,959} \approx 2.718281828$

6. Possible answer: Both of the given continued fractions can be used to determine the value of e.

Problem Solving

1. 194

2. $k = 0.0934$

3.

Year	2006	2007	2008	2009	2010
t	3	4	5	6	7
Population, P_t	257	282	309	340	373

4. C

5. C

6. C

7. D

Reading Strategies

1. a. $e^{3 \ln x} = e^{\ln x^3}$

   b. x^3

2. a.

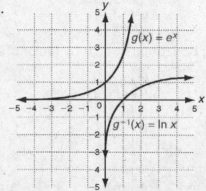

   b. Reflection over the line $y = x$

   c. Possible answer: The x- and y-values of each point in one graph are reversed in the other graph.

3. a. P

   b. t

   c. r

LESSON 7-7

Practice A

1. a.

x	-3	-2	-1	0	1
$f(x)$	0.0625	0.25	1	4	16

Holt Algebra 2

b.

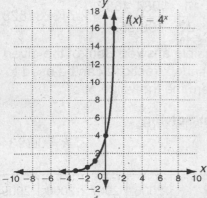

$f(x) = 4^x$

c. $y = 0$

d. Translated 1 unit left

2. $y = 0$; reflected across the x-axis

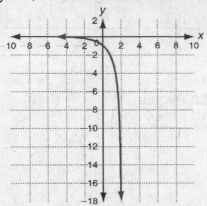

3. $y = 0$; horizontal stretch by factor of 2

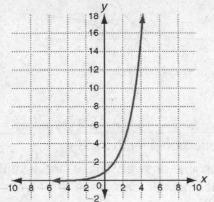

4. $g(x) = \ln(-x)$ 5. $g(x) = 8^{2x}$

6. $g(x) = 4(3^x)$

7. a. $g(x) = \log(x + 3)$

   b. $g(x) = -\log(x + 3)$

Practice B

1.

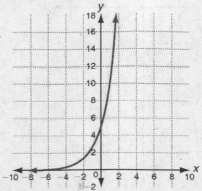

$y = 0$; it is the graph of $f(x) = 2^x$ stretched vertically by a factor of 5.

2.

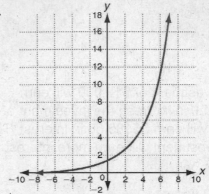

$y = 0$; it is the graph of $f(x) = 5^x$ stretched horizontally by a factor of 4.

3.

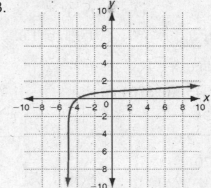

$x = -5$; it is the graph of $f(x) = \log x$ translated 5 units left.

4.

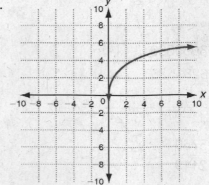

Holt Algebra 2

x = 0; it is the graph of f(x) = ln x translated 3 units up.

5. g(x) = log (−x + 1)−4

6. g(x) = 2 · 8^{5x − 3}   7. 8.7%

Practice C

1. y = 0; it is the graph of f(x) = 3^x horizontally compressed by a factor of 0.5.

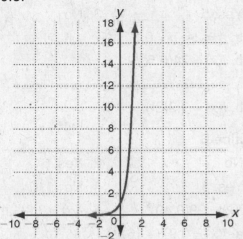

2. x = 0; it is the graph of f(x) = ln x reflected across the x-axis.

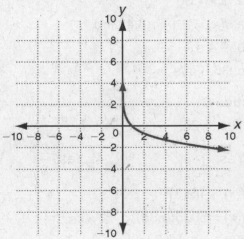

3. g(x) = −7 · 9^x − 1

4. $g(x) = -3\ln\left(\frac{2}{3}x + 8\right) + 7$

5. f(x) = −log(3x + 11) − 2

6. f(x) = −4 · 7^{x − 1} + 5

7. Translate 2 units up and 2 units right and then reflect across the x-axis

8. $27,647.16

Reteach

1. 3

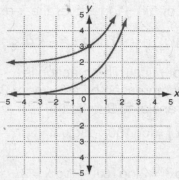

2. 4; y = 0

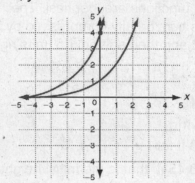

3. x = 0

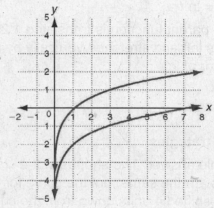

4. x = 1

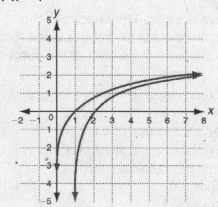

Holt Algebra 2

Challenge

1. They are identical. The graphs are reflections of $f(x) = \log x$ over the x-axis.

2. $\log \dfrac{1}{x} = \log(x^{-1}) = -1 \cdot \log x = -\log x$

3. They are identical. The function is vertically compressed by a factor of 0.5 and then translated 2 units up.

4. $\log(100\sqrt{x}) = \log 100 + \log \sqrt{x}$

$= \log 10^2 + \log x^{\frac{1}{2}} = 2\log 10 + \dfrac{1}{2}\log x = 2 + \dfrac{\log x}{2}$

5. The three functions are identical. The function is horizontally compressed by a factor of 2 and then shifted 1.5 units right.

6. $2^{2x-3} = 2^{2(x-1.5)} = 4^{x-1.5} = \dfrac{4^x}{4^{1.5}} = \dfrac{4^x}{8}$

Problem Solving

1. a. About 3 ft tall

   b. About 0.45 ft; that is the initial height of the plant.

2. a. $g(t) = \ln t$

   b. The parent function is translated 1.25 units left and stretched vertically by a factor of 2.

   c. B

3. A   4. H

Reading Strategies

1. Possible answer: The shapes of the curves are the same, but the curve for $g(x)$ is shifted 4 units down from the curve for $f(x)$.

2. Possible answer: The shapes of the curves are the same, but the curve for $g(x)$ is shifted 5 units right of the curve for $f(x)$.

3. Possible answer: The curve for $g(x)$ is a vertical stretch of the parent function by a factor of 8.

4. Possible answer: The curve for $g(x)$ is the curve for $f(x)$ reflected across the x-axis.

5. $g(x) = \ln(x+7)$ 6. $g(x) = e^{-x}$

7. $g(x) = \log 6x$

LESSON 7-8

Practice A

1. a. 0.25, 1, 4, 16, 64

   b. $\dfrac{64}{16} = 4,\ \dfrac{16}{4} = 4,\ \dfrac{4}{1} = 4,\ \dfrac{1}{0.25} = 4$

   c. Yes, 4

   d. Yes

2. Yes; 5   3. No

4. a. $a = 24,\ b = 0.5$

   b. $f(x) = 24(0.5^x)$

5. a. $a = 3.3,\ b = 2$

   b. $f(x) = 3.2(2^x)$

Practice B

1. No   2. Yes; 6

3. Yes; 3   4. No

5. $f(x) = 29(0.49)^x$ 6. $f(x) = 3.8(1.15)^x$

7. a. $f(x) = 0.97(1.16)^x$

   b. 15 cm

   c. $367.36

8. a. $f(x) = 1.14 + 8.42 \ln x$

   b. 9.4 s

   c. 35.6 m/s

Practice C

1. Yes; 1.25   2. No

3. Yes; $\dfrac{3}{2}$ 4. Yes; $\dfrac{2}{3}$

5. $f(x) = 4(2.3)^x$

6. $f(x) = 3035(0.35)^x$

7. $f(x) = -4 + 0.5 \ln x$

8. $f(x) = 1.97 - 0.7 \ln x$

9. a. $350(1.18)^x$

   b. 11.9 min

   c. 7,194,299

Reteach

1. 18, 72

   $\dfrac{4.5}{1.125} = 4,\ \dfrac{18}{4.5} = 4,\ \dfrac{72}{18} = 4$; data set is exponential with a constant ratio of 4.

Holt Algebra 2

2. 8, 24, 72, 216

$\dfrac{24}{8} = 3, \dfrac{72}{24} = 3, \dfrac{216}{72} = 3$; data set is exponential with a constant ratio of 3.

3. a. $B(t) \approx 251.9(1.4)^t$

   b. About 5.8 min

Challenge

1. Independent variable, years; dependent variable, number of subscribers; exponential model

2. $y \approx 0.67(1.39)^x$; yes, because $r^2 = 0.9767$

3. Predicted value is about 67,341,000, which is close to the estimated number.

4. Possible answer: Predicted value is about 130,110,000, which is slightly higher than the estimated number.

5. Possible answer: Predicted value is 485,703,000, which is more than twice the estimated number.

6. Looking at the curve, as you move to the right, the graph of the model rises very sharply and grossly overestimates the number of subscribers.

Problem Solving

1. a. $W(t) = 47.34(1.13)^t$

   b. 2016

2. a. $T(t) = 1809.17 - 510.69 \ln t$

   b. 2009

3. C   4. G

5. D   6. F

Reading Strategies

1. a. First differences are all 2.

   b. Possible answer: because all the first differences are the same

2. a. 0.5, 1, 2, 4, 8

   b. All ratios are 2.

   c. Possible answer: because all the ratios of first differences are the same

3. Possible answer: The graph of $f(x)$ is a straight line, and the graph of $g(x)$ is a curve; the range of $f(x)$ is all real numbers, but the range of $g(x)$ is $y > 0$; $g(x)$ has an asymptote at $y = 0$.

4. Exponential function; ratios of the first differences are the same, $\dfrac{3}{4}$